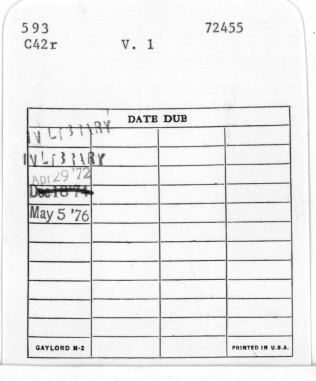

| DATE DUE | | |
|---|---|---|
| IN LIBRARY | | |
| IN LIBRARY | | |
| Apr 29 '72 | | |
| Dec 18 '74 | | |
| May 5 '76 | | |
| | | |
| | | |
| | | |
| | | |
| | | |
| GAYLORD M-2 | | PRINTED IN U.S.A. |

# RESEARCH IN PROTOZOOLOGY

# RESEARCH IN PROTOZOOLOGY

In Four Volumes

EDITED BY

## TZE-TUAN CHEN

*Professor of Zoology*
*University of Southern California*
*Los Angeles, California*

## VOLUME 1

PERGAMON PRESS

OXFORD · LONDON · EDINBURGH · NEW YORK
TORONTO · SYDNEY · PARIS · BRAUNSCHWEIG

Pergamon Press Ltd., Headington Hill Hall, Oxford
4 & 5 Fitzroy Square, London W.1

Pergamon Press (Scotland) Ltd., 2 & 3 Teviot Place, Edinburgh 1

Pergamon Press Inc., 44–01 21st Street, Long Island City, New York 11101

Pergamon of Canada, Ltd., 6 Adelaide Street East, Toronto, Ontario

Pergamon Press (Aust.) Pty. Ltd., 20–22 Margaret Street, Sydney, N.S.W.

Pergamon Press S.A.R.L., 24 rue des Écoles, Paris 5ᵉ

Vieweg & Sohn GmbH, Burgplatz 1, Braunschweig

First edition 1967

Library of Congress Catalog Card No. 66–22364

2817/67

# CONTENTS

# PREFACE

IT HAS been a quarter of a century since the publication of *Protozoa in Biological Research* by Calkins & Summers. Some indication of the extent of the progress made during that period is given by a comparison of the chapter on cytoplasmic inclusions in the 1941 review with the chapter on cytoplasmic organelles and inclusions in the first volume of this review; this extent indicates a need for a contemporaneous review.

We hope that this four-volume work will serve as a source of reference for students, protozoologists, and biologists in general. It covers the entire field of protozoology, including morphology, physiology, genetics, reproduction, movement, respiration, morphogenesis, nutrition and growth, immunology, ecology, effects of radiation, parasitology, taxonomy, and others.

Knowledge of protozoa is more important than is generally realized. Developments in this field are important because they contribute to developments in medicine, public health, physiology, experimental biology, biochemistry, etc.

The authors tried to avoid overlapping; the little that does occur appears valuable for its presentation of diverse points of view.

The editor wishes to express his deep gratitude for the unfailing cooperation of the many eminent protozoologists who have contributed to this review. He is especially grateful to Dr. D. H. Wenrich for his valuable suggestions, and to Dr. Ruth S. Lynch for her great help in editing the manuscripts. He is also indebted to the Board of Consultants, consisting of Drs. William Balamuth, A. C. Giese, R. F. Kimball, Norman D. Levine, William Trager, and D. H. Wenrich, who have helped the editor in making certain decisions on matters of importance.

*Los Angeles, California*                                           T. T. CHEN

# CYTOPLASMIC ORGANELLES
# AND INCLUSIONS OF PROTOZOA

Everett Anderson

*Department of Zoology, University of Massachusetts, Amherst, Massachusetts*

# CONTENTS

# I. INTRODUCTION†

This chapter is concerned with the heterogeneous complex of organelle systems and inclusion bodies which are suspended in the cytoplasmic matrix. Their study commenced in Delft, Holland when Anton van Leeuwenhoek (1632–1723) used his simple light microscope to discover unicellular organisms[207] which von Siebold later named Protozoa.[317] Refinement of the microscope and development of cytological techniques was closely followed by knowledge of the detailed structure of all cells. The abundance and variety of the cytoplasmic inclusions in the Protozoa indicated their unique value for the study of cytoplasmic organization. The structure of organelles has been stressed; comparatively little is known of the related physiology. An attempt, however, will be made, wherever possible, to correlate the two. The guiding principle of dynamic morphology is to understand that "What we are dealing with from the molecule all the way up—is not what is present but what structure does it have that gives it opportunity to operate, to act."[345]

## II. LAMELLAR SYSTEMS

One of the most impressive features of the organelles of both unicellular and multicellular organisms is the frequent occurrence of membranous elements. Presumably the function of these membranes is to increase the active surface area.[108, 283]

### A. Mitochondria

When the common presence of mitochondria in metazoan cells was established, a search commenced for these organelles in unicellular forms. In 1910 Fauré-Frémiet[92] published his monograph on mitochondria in Protozoa. He believed mitochondria to be universal, self-perpetuating entities of cytoplasm. He noted that they were usually randomly distributed but at times showed a tendency to aggregate next to the plasma membrane. ([93], see also [172]) Their variety in both size and shape was revealed by light microscopy.[2]

In sectioned material Palade[247] found a limiting membrane and an internal sometimes granular matrix, and a unique internal structure: ". . . a system

† Some of the work reported here was supported by Research Grant GM 08776 from the U.S. Public Health Service.

of internal ridges (*cristae mitochondriales*) that protude from the inside surface of the membrane toward the interior of the organelle; these ridges are disposed in series, within which they appear to be parallel to one another and more or less regularly spaced."[246] Following Palade's description, Sjöstrand (cf.[321]) proposed that their internal structure is comprised of double membranes not necessarily continuous with the limiting membrane of the organelle. Wolken and Palade [363, 364] were among the first to deal with the fine structure of protozoan mitochondria. Later investigations have identified mitochondria in almost all major groups of Protista.[34, 56, 84, 97, 148, 180, 240, 269, 313, 342, 355] Elements comparable to the "cristae mitochondriales" or "double membranes" have often been described as finger-like projections (microvilli) protruding into the interior of the mitochondrion from the inner limiting membrane. In *Paramecium multimicronucleatum* and *Tetrahymena pyriformis*, the microvilli, which are sometimes branched, pursue a sinuous course (Figs. 1 and 2, M) within the organelle and terminate in the mitochondrial matrix without making a second contact with the inner membrane.[85, 312] In other organisms, the microvilli may open directly in the cytoplasmic matrix. (cf. [292]) In the ciliate, *Opalina ranarum*,† the mitochondria have a more or less tubular internal structure and correspond to what have been called Zeller bodies.[238, 239] In certain forms the internal structure resembles that found in metazoan cells,[8, 9] (compare Fig. 9, M, with Fig. 3, M'). The fairly numerous mitochondria of *Chilomonas* show considerable variation in shape; some are highly branched.[9] In *Spirostomum* along with more typical forms are some atypical ones, their interiors consisting of stacks of parallel membranes.[276] In the heliozoan *Actinosphaerium nucleofilum*[13] and in *Toxoplasma*,[116, 342] mitochondria sometimes display a tubular internal structure although typically the interiors are filled with vesicular units. These vesicular mitochondria bear some structural resemblance to multivesicular bodies.

In certain Protozoa the microvilli of the mitochondria are more complex. In *Pelomyxa carolinensis* they form a zigzag pattern[256] and show bulbous enlargements at the inflection points on the undulation and in addition a densely packed fibrillar material in the stroma.

In many protozoan groups differences in organelle fine structure occur in relation to physiological diversity. Of special significance is the complete absence of typical mitochondria in *Plasmodium berghei*.[295] Instead, a concentric double membrane, derived from an invagination of the plasma membrane, is located near the periphery of the organism (Fig. 3, CM). This system shares certain morphological features with mitochondria of the spermatocytes of *Helix promatia*[20] and Rudzinska and Trager[295] suggest that it may represent mitochondria. In some bacteria and certain members of

† Certain investigators classify the opalinids as flagellates. The reader is referred to Pitelka[262] for literature on this subject.

the genus *Bacillus*,[99, 109, 222, 344] a double membrane system exists which is also derived from the plasma membrane by invagination. Significantly, the entire cytochrome and succinic dehydrogenase systems of certain bacteria reside in the plasma membrane.[222, 314] These findings suggest that the plasma membrane in these forms, presumably enzymatically altered, is performing the function of mitochondria. Although the "dorsal cisternae" of *Giardi muris* at times appear to contain a homogeneous material (Fig. 4, DC), might it not be that they may harbor certain enzyme systems unique to this organism or comparable to those of others?

In certain parasitic flagellates,[6, 7, 12, 14, 147, 149] and ciliates,[234] mitochondria are either not well developed or entirely absent. Since these organisms are generally obligate anerobes, their energy is derived through fermentation.[175] In *Plasmodium cathermerium* mitochondria are present in oocysts and sporozoites[77] but are absent in merozoites.[225] While mitochondria are virtually absent in the trophic form of the gregarine *Gregarina rigida*,[23] mitochondria with tubular interiors are found at the periphery of the cephalont of the epimerite embedded in the host cell (Beams and Anderson, unpublished). There is pressing need for a systematic study of mitochondria in this group of organisms. Such a study should be rewarding especially in view of the complicated life cycle and the possibility of organelle differentiation and "dedifferentiation".

The literature on changes in mitochondrial morphology induced by certain physiological and pathological conditions has been reviewed by Rouiller;[292] a few examples will be cited here. It is well known that encystment occurs regularly in some unicellular forms either during reproduction or under adverse environmental conditions.[173] So far, Vickerman's work[337] is the only study to emphasize the change in mitochondrial structure in Sarcodina during encystment. In the active form of limax amoeba, *Acanthameba*, he found filamentous mitochondria showing tubular cristae enmeshed in a honeycomb-matrix and usually also a small, dense intracristal spherical body. At encystment the intracristal body decreases in size and becomes vesicular, the organelle assuming a spherical shape and decreasing in overall diameter. This altered structure is thought to represent a state of minimal metabolic activity. Beers[26] found, in *Didinum nasutum*, that mitochondria disappear in the later stages of encystment. To my knowledge no modern cytological techniques have been applied to an investigation of this group during encystment. Bak and Elliott[17] studied mitochondrial changes during the growth cycle of *Tetrahymena pyriformis* and during logarithmic growth found elongated mitochondria usually in close association with the inner plasma membrane. During the stationary growth phase many of the mitochondria moved deep into the endoplasm and became oval. Ten days later, dense intramitochondrial bodies appeared. As these bodies increased in size and filled the entire mitochondrial matrix the cristae were completely lost. The reaction of the dense intramitochondrial bodies to Sudan black B and oil red O led Bak and Elliott[17] to suggest that they were composed of lipid. In non-dividing *Tetrahymena* (strain W) Roth and Minick[289] found the tubules composing the mitochondria to be closely packed; in individuals in the early stages of macronuclear division, the tubules are loosly packed and usually contain a "central dense mass".

The origin of mitochondria is not yet settled; whether they are formed *de novo* or from pre-existing mitochondria is moot. Gey *et al.*[119] have proposed that they are derived from vesicles brought into the cytoplasm by pinocytosis. As previously noted, Rudzinska and Trager[295] suggested that in *Plasmodium berghei* the mitochondria may be derived from the plasma membrane. Such ideas are certainly worthy of further investigation, since there is some evidence that mitochondria may be derived from the plasma membrane in metazoan cells.[283] Wohlfarth-Botterman ([354], see also [356]) has suggested that mitochondria arise mainly from free vesicular units in the cytoplasm which enlarge and develop a tubular interior. Some years ago, Joyet-Lavergne[184] and Calkins[42] thought mitochondria were derived from the nucleus. (see also[162]) Ehret and Powers[81] suggested their origin from the macronucleus in *Paramecium* and Brandt and Pappas[34] presented evidence suggesting derivation from the nuclear envelope in *Amoeba*. Increase of mitochondria by division is an old concept; some investigators have presented pictorial evidence highly suggestive of such reproductive mechanisms. [171, 216, 354] But a convincing demonstration of the origin of mitochondria is still wanting.

Working with the yeast *Torulopisi utilis,* Linnane and his associates studied its cytology and enzymology under both aerobiasis and anaerobiasis.[210]

Under aerobiasis the mitochondria had the characteristic cristae; isolated mitochondria showed electron transport, oxidative phosphorylation, and participation in the Krebs cycle. Under anaerobiasis no mitochondria were found. But in the cytoplasm numerous membranes displayed two geometrical patterns: one a multimembrane system similar to that demonstrated by Rudzinska and Trager[295] for *P. berghei,* and the other showing characteristic features of an endoplasmic reticulum. Their particulate fraction showed both succinic and $NADH_2$ dehydrogenase activity, both known to be present in aerobic cells.[142] Particles derived from fractions of anaerobically grown cells, unlike those obtained from aerobically grown cells, contain no detectable cytochromes. However, when cultures of anaerobically grown *T. utilis* were aerated, the reticular membranes rearranged themselves in parallel arrays which subsequently "... fuse and infold to form primitive mitochondria containing few cristae." The authors further noted that during this rearranging process, cytochromes were synthesized.

A new morphological definition of mitochondria emerged with electron microscopy. The one so aptly constructed by Rouiller[292] is useful. He states, "A mitochondrion is morphologically defined as a cell organelle bounded by a double membrane within which are membranous structures either villous or vesicular, a ground substance or granular matrix and occasionally, very dense granulations." Mitochondria are also being defined biochemically. Many synonyms attached to this organelle in the past have been retired.

The establishment of the reality of mitochondria was followed by a lengthy controversy concerning their function. Most of their physiology and micro-chemistry derives from experiments on metazoan cells.[29, 163, 208] Their respiratory function has been known for many years;[192] today we casually speak of them as "the powerhouse of cells".[319] Only meager information has been derived from experiments on unicellular organisms. Protozoan mitochondria, like those of metazoan cells, can be stained with Janus green B, and give a positive reaction with tetrazolium.[98] Holter[165] demonstrated that certain large granules of centrifuged amoebae contain enzymes such as succinic dehydrogenase, acid phosphatase and protease. He suggested that this granular component was chemically similar to mitochondria of metazoan cells. Klein and Neff[195] isolated large volumes of mitochondria from *Acanthomoeba* by differential centrifuging and concluded that these organelles have many properties similar to those found in mammalian tissue.

Mitochondria may release their contents into the general cytoplasm through gaps in their limiting membrane.[354] Furthermore, Powers, *et al.*[270] and Rouiller[292] suggest that the mitochondrial tubules of *Paramecium* and *Stentor* appear to be directly connected with the cytoplasm. Chandra[53] has put forth the thesis (with evidence gathered from mammalian tissue) that the inner membrane of these organelles is not a distinct entity, but an integral part of what is essentially a single unit. The structure proposed by Chandra[53] would make the intramitochondrial substance accessible to the cytoplasm through intermembranous channels. Chandra suggests that such a structure facilitates the swelling of this organelle either by an "... unfolding of the cristae or sliding of the two membranes or by both these processes occurring simultaneously."

Precisely what the relationship is between the cristae, tubules, and microvilli in mitochondria is not known. Perhaps this inner framework is favorable for *in situ* functioning of the large number of enzymes involved in the many complex biochemical reactions of mitochondria.[319] Green and his associates[142, 143] have developed techniques expressly designed for reconstructing the finer details of mitochondrial structure and function and have obtained a small mitochondrial fragment to which they have applied the term electron transport particle. This unit of variable size can carry out the reactions of the citric acid cycle as long as it retains a well-defined double membrane; but when the outer membranous element is removed this capacity is lost. Under certain conditions an electron transport particle can be obtained which oxidizes both succinate and $NADH_2$. Accordingly, the authors suggest that a mitochondrion may be thought of as a polymer of repeating units of electron transport particles. Experimental designs such as those constructed by Green and his group[143] should be applicable to those unicellular forms in which mitochondria are one of the most noticeable components of the cytoplasm.

As one reads the literature concerning mitochondria one must agree with the statement made by E. V. Cowdry[62] at a symposium held in 1953 on the *Structure and Function of Mitochondria*: "... it is really surprising how much older workers learned about mitochondria: (a) that they were basic components of cells as characteristic of the cytoplasm as chromatin is of the nucleus; (b) that they provide a very extensive surface area of interaction with the cytoplasm; (c) that they are of lipoprotein composition and (d) that they are centers of constructive metabolism, veritable little manufacturing plants of numerous products essential to life."

## B. Kinetoplast

The kinetoplast, typically described as a rod-shaped body, is found in the cytoplasm of the Trypanosomidae and the Bodonidae.[19, 51, 69, 178, 196, 197, 198, 201, 206, 211, 214, 316, 348] It lies just anterior to the kinetosome of the flagellum and perpendicular to the long axis of the organism (Fig. 5, KP). Contrary to earlier opinion, it has no direct anatomical connection with the kinetosome of the flagellum (Fig. 5, KS). In preparations stained with Giemsa or iron hematoxylin it appears as a dense homogeneous and spherical or ovoid body (see insert, Fig. 5, KP). In 1924 Bresslau and Scremin[38] demonstrated that the kinetoplast was Feulgen positive, an observation many times confirmed. Under close examination, Feulgen preparations show the kinetoplast to consist of two components: (a) a Feulgen-positive central area and (b) a Feulgen-negative peripheral portion.[60] Cosgrove and Anderson[60] found that the stainability of the kinetoplast decreased but was not abolished after prolonged treatment of the organisms with deoxyribonuclease.

The mitochondrial nature of the kinetoplast has been repeatedly pointed out. In 1925 Causey[49] called attention to similarity in staining properties of the kinetoplast and mitochondria in *Leishmania braziliensis* and concluded that the kinetoplast was a mitochondrion. The observations made by him and others using light optics have been confirmed with electron optics. Both kinetoplast and mitochondrion present a submicroscopic structure of transversely oriented double membranes or cristae (Fig. 5, C).[54, 57, 170, 226, 261, 273, 274, 275, 280, 281, 326] In *Trypanosoma mega*[326] the double membranes show considerable variation, some being concentrically arranged as in *Plasmodium berghei* demonstrated by Rudzinska and Trager.[295] In addition to the finely granular kinetoplast matrix there are transversely oriented dense fibrils 25 Å in diameter, similar to macromolecular units of DNA in the nucleoplasm of bacteria (Fig. 5, DF). In *Trypanosoma lewisi* the fibrillar material appears as a bundle but in *Bodo* it is rather dispersed.[261,280]

Steinert *et al.*[323] and Steinert and Steinert[328] have used tritiated thymidine and autoradiographic methods to investigate the cyclic DNA synthesis in *T. mega*. These authors suggest a possible genetic function of the kinetoplast. (see also [324, 325]) They further suggest[326] that the close synchrony of DNA synthesis in the nucleus and kinetoplast provides evidence which supports the old binucleate theory of Hartmann.[155, 331] This suggestion has been challenged by Ris[281] who states: "Since the flagellate nucleus contains typical chromosomes with 100 Å thick fibrils and the kinetoplast bacteria-type nucleoplasm with 25 Å fibrils, it (the kinetoplast) cannot be a secondary nucleus."

Rudzinska, D'Alesandro and Trager[297, 298] have recorded some interesting changes in the kinetoplast of *Leishmania donovani*. D'Alesandro[64] found that *L. donovani*, freshly removed from hamster spleen, differed antigenically from leptomonads. This observation led the group to wonder if there were any detectable fine structural differences among the various stages. They made observations on the intracellular forms of *L. donovani*, freed from host cells, and leptomonads (Leishmania forms become leptomonads when incubated at 28°C. for up to 21 hours). They found that in Leishmanias the kinetoplast is a regularly shaped elongate organelle with one to several cristae and a dense fibrillar band within the matrix. After incubation for five and a half hours at 28°C. the kinetoplast was large, irregular in shape and the fibrillar band less dense. Frequently, the kinetoplast was extended into the typical mitochondrial structure observed by other investigators.

The kinetoplast may be altered in its fine structure or entirely lost from the organism. Occasionally this follows the use of certain drugs.[229, 260, 333, 336] Hoare[160] has presented evidence of the spontaneous occurrence of strains of *Trypanosoma evansi* devoid of the kinetoplast; such strains may be maintained for a considerable length of time. He envisions the perpetuation of akinetoplastic forms to be due to the failure of the kinetoplast to divide and regards the phenomenon as a mutation of plasmogenes. Once the organism loses its kinetoplast it does not arise *de novo*. Werbitzki[348] produced an akinetoplastic strain of a trypanosome with acridine dyes and suggested that this structure is apparently not essential to the life of the organism. Muehlpfordt[229] noted that akinetoplastic forms of trypanosomes can be obtained by treating the organisms with the drug trypaflavin. However, the kinetoplast reappears when the treatment is stopped. In *Schizotrypanum cruzi*, the kinetoplast is not removed by trypaflavin.[229, see also 336]

The function and origin of the kinetoplast is unknown. Ris[281] stated that, "Whether it is a mitochondrion-like endosymbiote in addition to the regular mitochondria of the flagellate or the 'mother mitochondrion' of the cell which buds off smaller mitochondria must be determined from a study of akinetoplastic strains of Trypanosomes."

## C. Chloroplast

Certain cytoplasmic organelles are unique to specific groups of Protozoa. One of these, the chloroplast, which contains chlorophyll, is a dominant cytoplasmic organelle in some unicellular organisms; among them are

certain members of the Euglenoidina.[181] Those organisms are readily
cultured and are prime experimental material for chloroplast studies.[36, 37, 70, 139, 140, 141, 150, 194, 235, 271, 304, 305] Even within a given species
chloroplasts vary greatly in size, shape, and number. From observations made
with polarization optics investigators were able to deduce that this organelle
has an orderly arranged lamellar pattern.(cf. [110]) These earlier findings were
substantiated and extended by the morphological work of Wolken and
Palade[363, 364] who were able to show, in light-adapted *Euglena gracilis* var.
*bacillaris*, that the interior of the chloroplast contains a regular pattern of
approximately twenty-one highly oriented dense lamellar layers. Each layer
has a thickness of 250 Å.(see also [360]) In 1957 Sager and Palade[303] investigated the normal green strain of *Chlamydomonas reinhardii* and suggested that the basic structural units of chloroplasts are discs, each of which is
constructed of a pair of membranes joined at their edges to form flat closed
vesicles. Gibbs[120] has presented a rather detailed analysis of the chloroplast of *E. gracilis* var. *bacillaris* and *E. gracilis* strain Z. She reported
that these chloroplasts consist of from ten to forty-five moderately dense
bands (Fig. 7), each band varying in width from 25 $\mu$ to 210 $\mu$. A band
(lamella of other authors) is defined by Gibbs as consisting "... of a variable
number of closely appressed discs.... In a section perpendicular to the plane
of the discs, a band which is interpreted as three appressed discs appears as
a thin dark lamella, a light space, a thick dark lamella, a light space, a thick
dark lamella, a light space and finally another thin dark lamella." It has been
suggested that chlorophyll is a component of the lamellae.[301, 365] The
entire organelle complex is surrounded by a double membrane envelope
which is sometimes continuous with the outer nuclear envelope.[123]

The previous anatomical studies concerned themselves with chloroplasts
of flagellates grown in light. If similar organisms are grown in a dark environment, interesting changes are observable in the substructure of the organelle which presumably are concomitant with dark adaptation. Wolken and
Palade[364] showed that in dark adapted Euglena, there is a disorganization
of the bands along with a disappearance of chlorophyll. This effect is reversible, for when organisms are returned to light the original substructure
is restored. There is good evidence to suggest that at the time the internal
structure is being reorganized, chlorophyll is resynthesized.[301, 362] In the
yellow strain of *Chlamydomonas* where chlorophyll is absent, there is no
indication of any band organization.[302] In addition to the lamellar structures there are other components within the matrix of the organelle, namely
granules and lipid bodies.[120, 302]

Non-green forms of *Euglena* can also be obtained by the treatment of the
culture with certain drugs. It has been found that furadantin[221] and
streptomycin[1, 272] can produce chlorosis of certain green euglenids.(see
also [177]) Apparently a phenomenon similar to that which occurs when dark-
adapted animals are returned to light occurs here, i.e., the animals regain

their green pigment when the drugs are withheld from the culture. One drug, the antihistamine pyribenzamine, has been found to produce a permanently colorless culture of *E. gracilis* var. *bacillaris*.[150] Permanently colorless organisms have also been obtained by ultraviolet irradiation.[305]

It has long been known that within the chloroplast of *E. gracilis* there exists another structure known as the pyrenoid which exhibits staining properties different from other portions of the organelle.[121, 178, 201] Gibbs[120] has shown that the pyrenoid is a differentiated region of the chloroplast matrix (Fig. 7, P), appearing as laminae separated from each other by fine lamellae directly continuous with the lamellae of the chloroplast. Each pyrenoid is rimmed on each side by a hemispherical shell of paramylon which appears structureless in electron micrographs (Fig. 7, PA). The pyrenoid of chloroplasts found in *Chlorogonium elongatum* consists of a dense finely granular substance.[154] Sager and Palade[303] found that the pyrenoid in *Chlamydomonas* is distinguished by "... a network of tubules embedded in a matrix of dense, finely granular material." These authors further noted that the matrix of the pyrenoid is continuous with that of the chloroplast and the tubules are connected with the discs of the surrounding chloroplast.

Epstein and Schiff[88] have studied the development of chloroplasts in *Euglena gracilis* by means of fluorescent and electron microscopy.(see also [87]) They suggest two methods of chloroplast formation: (a) by lamellae developing within the chloroplast and (b) by coalescence of proplastids. They further noted that under light conditions lamellae appear in the chloroplast at the rate of one about every six hours. Gibbs[122] presented evidence that chloroplast development in *Ochromonas danica* begins as a series of vesicles. These vesicles subsequently enlarge, arrange themselves linearly and finally fuse into discs. Some of the developmental patterns of chloroplasts in unicellular forms parallel those suggested by others for this organelle in higher plants.[161, 349]

Many studies have attempted to chemically characterize the chloroplast. It has been found that chlorophyll constitutes five to eight per cent of the organelle. Carotenoids, cytochromes $f$ and $b_3$, lipids, proteins, and ribo- and deoxy-ribonucleic acids are also present.(cf. [362])

The replication of chloroplasts is apparently dependent upon synthesis of a specific DNA located within the organelle. Scher and Sagan[305] compared the incorporation of $H^{-3}$ thymidine into normal green *E. gracilis* with that into temporary and permanent colorless organisms; the temporary colorless organisms are produced by dark adaptation and the permanent ones by ultraviolet irradiation. They found that only the permanently colorless *Euglena* failed to incorporate $H^{-3}$ thymidine into cytoplasmic structures and suggested that this, "... presumably reflects the inability of these cytoplasmic structures to synthesize DNA as a consequence of ultraviolet irradiation." Excellent studies dealing with the presence of DNA in the chloroplast of *Chlamydomonas moewusii* have been published by Ris[280] and Ris and

Plaut.[282] These authors found that the chloroplast of *C. moewusii* contain
one or more bodies of irregular shape which give a Feulgen-positive reaction
of the same intensity as the nucleus. After deoxyribonuclease digestion the
Feulgen reaction is either abolished or reduced markedly. When cells are
stained with acridine orange, the chloroplasts show a bright yellowish-green
fluorescence, indicative of the presence of DNA. When such cells are subjected to ribonuclease digestion followed by DNase digestion, the fluorescence of the organelle as well as of the nucleus disappears. Utilizing the
fixative developed for bacteria by Ryter *et al.*[299] to preserve the 25 Å
microfibrils which correspond to DNA macromolecules, Ris and Plaut were
able to demonstrate areas within the chloroplast composed of these microfibrils. The areas containing DNA are surrounded by lamellae of the chloroplast. These findings would substantiate the claim that the chloroplast
behaves as a genetic unit and need not be primarily under the control of the
nucleus. From the results of their study, Ris and Plaut[282] drew attention to
the striking structural and chemical similarity of a chloroplast and a blue-
green alga, thereby recalling the old hypothesis of Famintzin[91] and Mere-
schowski[224] who suggested that chloroplasts originated from endosymbiotic
blue-green algae.(see also [40, 318]) Ris and Plaut concluded: "This hypothesis
also explains why the photosynthetic apparatus is associated with membrane
systems which traverse freely the cytoplasm in blue-green algae but which in
higher plants are incorporated into complex cell organelles, having a high
degree of genetic individuality and containing just about every classified
organelle found in free-living blue-green algae."

## D. Golgi Complex

It was some years after the discovery of the Golgi material (1898) in
metazoan cells[129] that cytologists attempted to demonstrate this system in
unicellular organisms. In 1914 Hirschler[159] employing Golgi's technique,
demonstrated osmiophilic rings and crescents in the cytoplasm of the
gregarine, *Monocystis ascidae*. Some years later, Golgi bodies were found in
other sporozoans by King and Gatenby[191] and Joyet-Lavergne.[185] The
osmiophilic material demonstrated by these authors was found, often in a
juxtanuclear position, in the early stages of the life cycle of these sporozoans.
This osmiophilic substance was thought to be Golgi material since it was
isomorphic with a material which gave a similar chemical reaction in ectoder-
mal cells of developing embryos.[41] In the later stages of the life cycle of
this group, the Golgi material is found dispersed throughout the cytoplasm.
Duboscq and Grassé[74] presented evidence which suggested to them that
the parabasal bodies of flagellates are homologous to the Golgi material
found in germ cells of metazoans. (see also[3, 21, 39, 94, 130, 181, 190, 215, 322])
Reviews by Palay,[253] Pollister and Pollister[263] and Dalton[65] bring

together the numerous publications concerning the widely divergent views of the Golgi complex.

In 1953 Dalton and Felix[66] published an important paper showing that the phase and electron microscopes clearly demonstrated Golgi material in cells of the epididymis of the mouse. At the electron microscope level this material shows two components: (a) a parallel array of double membrane lamellae and (b) a multitude of vesicles of various diameters. This dual system is often referred to as the Golgi complex.[232] It is not clear what functional relationship, if any, exists between the Golgi complex in metazoan cells and that of Protozoa. In many ciliates the Golgi complex is conspicuously absent. (cf. [76, 189, 277, 285]) In most flagellates the Golgi complex is very well developed.[7, 8, 9, 12, 52, 58, 131, 133, 136, 138, 149, 174, 287, 293] Here, as in other Protista, the membranes are usually joined at their edges, enclosing slit-like areas; with this arrangement they resemble flattened sacs which in many instances have dilated extremities (Figs. 8, 9, and 10, GC). In glutaraldehyde fixed specimens, many of the flattened sacs of the Golgi complex contain an electron opaque substance (Fig. 10, GC). Usually associated with these flattened sacs is a vast assemblage of smooth, membraned and/or fuzzy, coated vesicles. (cf. [31, 237, 254])

Commonly associated with the Golgi material in many polymastigotes as well as in other flagellates is a slender striated filament.[12, 58, 149, 212] This filament (Fig. 8, PF) gives structural polarity to the Golgi complex.[134] Using this striated filament as a marker in *Trichonympha*, Grimstone[149] found the Golgi sacs proximal to the filament to be greatly inflated and closely embracing the filament; the distal sacs are swollen and inflated at their edges, and those occupying an intermediate position are only slightly swollen over most of their width.

Almost all parabasal bodies of flagellates present an organization which permits them to be referred to as Golgi complexes. However the so-called parabasal body of the flagellate *Lophomonas blattarum* is an exception. Under the light microscope this structure appears to completely surround the nucleus, and as early as 1926 Kudo[200] questioned its nature. The electron microscope reveals it as a portion of the nuclear envelope.[25] The Golgi complex of *Lophomonas* is found in the cytoplasm.

Gatenby, Dalton and Felix[115] found membranous material surrounding the contractile vacuole of *Chlamydomonas eugametos* and agreed with early investigators that this material was the Golgi complex. ([233], see also[114]) As techniques of electron microscopy improved, the question of the nature of this osmiophilic associate (cf. [187]) of the contractile vacuole was raised again. Schneider[306] showed that the osmiophilic material (nephridial plasma) of the contractile vacuole of *Paramecium* has no morphological relation to the Golgi complex. (cf. [85, 117, 118, 135]) (For a discussion of the contractile vacuole see the chapter on this subject in the present volume.)

The origin of the Golgi complex is not known. Grassé and Carasso[136] suggested that in *Joenia* the complex may divide. In other organisms this organelle is thought to arise *de novo*. Grimstone[149] studied the effects of host (termite) starvation on the Golgi complex of the parasite *Trichonympha* and found that the normal number of sacs constituting the Golgi complex of organisms from non-starved hosts ranged from eleven to twenty- one with an average of fifteen. After two days of starvation the complex, instead of being constituted of un-inflated sacs, consisted of inflated sacs and vesicles and their average number fell to one. After three days of starvation all that remained of the well developed Golgi was its associated periodic filament. These effects on the complex after host starvation are reversible up to at least three days. If at the end of the third day the host was fed, it was noted that within twenty-four hours the average number of sacs increased to twenty-five. At the end of forty-eight hours all organelles appeared to have regained their normal appearance. Grimstone suggests that when these sacs are lost, they disappear from the distal side by conversion into cytoplasmic vesicles. He speculates that the loss of these flattened sacs distally is normally balanced by new ones appearing proximally. He further suggests that the granular membranes (endoplasmic reticulum) are responsible for the refor- mation of the flattened saccular component of the complex. (see also[89]) Grimstone[149] views the Golgi complex as a ". . . steady state system through which there is a constant flow of membranes." (see also[148]) From a study made on normally fed, dividing, starved and refed *Pelomyxa illinoisensis*, Daniels[67] proposed that vesicles formed as a result of pinocytosis and phagocytosis, "either flatten or invaginate and form the cisternae of the Golgi apparatus".

Very little is known about the chemical composition of the Golgi complex of Protozoa. Cytochemical investigations by Grimstone[149] indicate that the complex in certain flagellates consists of carbohydrates. El Mofty[86] demonstrated some alkaline phosphatase in the Golgi material in *Tricho- nympha*. Nath and Dutta[234] bring together an appreciable amount of literature dealing primarily with the cytochemistry of organelles and other components of Protozoa. (see also[83, 105, 106, 107, 165, 257, 258, 309, 310, 329]) With the newer methods now being worked out in this field, much work on organelle cytochemistry of unicellular forms needs to be initiated as well as reinvestigated. (see[46, 278])

No attempts have been made to isolate the Golgi material in Protozoa. In the interesting beginning with metazoan cells made by Kuff and Dalton[202] lipid phosphatase and acid phosphatase activity was found concentrated in the Golgi fraction. Undemonstrated were RNA, cytochrome oxidase, deoxyribonuclease, glucoronidase, esterase and ATPase. The authors state " . . . the rather negative picture that has emerged with regard to enzymatic activity might be significant in itself since the possibility must be kept in mind that the Golgi membranes may carry out their role in secretion and absorption in some chiefly non-enzymatic fashion".

The function of the Golgi complex is unknown; however, investigators have implicated a secretory function.[74, 132, 136, 347] Morphological data suggest that the Golgi material in *Chilomonas paramecium*[9] may function in the formation of the uniquely structured ejectisomes (Fig. 9, EJ). (These structures were formerly called trichocysts; cf.[164].) Other convincing morphological evidence from observations on both plant and animal cells indicate that the Golgi complex is concerned with the concentration of various substances.[46, 227, 278] There is at least one well known function of the Golgi complex in metazoan cells, the formation of the acrosome during spermatogenesis.[22, 102, 113] Cowdry[61] has stated: "It may be found that the activities of the Golgi apparatus may be bent in one direction during spermatogenesis and along entirely different lines in cells spezialized to perform other duties".

### E. Endoplasmic Reticulum

The first demonstration of the existence of basophilic regions in the cytoplasm of unicellular organisms came in the investigations of R. Hertwig.[158] Hertwig believed that the basophilic substance of the cytoplasm of certain species of rhizopods was given off by the nucleus and consequently referred to it as "chromidia". Hertwig's drawing illustrating this concept in the form of a "scattered chromidial net" is shown in Fig. 12. Figure 13 shows an arrangement of the basophilic material of *Tetrahymena pyriformis* not unlike that depicted by Hertwig. This chromidial concept of Hertwig was extended to include metazoan cells under the so-called "chromidial hypothesis" advanced by Goldschmidt and Popoff. ([128], see also [351]) Since these early times it has become evident that many of the cytoplasmic constituents included under the chromidial hypothesis do not show characteristics that would warrant their continued definition as chromidia.

In 1945, Porter, Claude and Fullam,[268] with the aid of the electron microscope, made a revolutionary observation on whole mounts of cells grown in tissue culture. They described a lace-like reticulum in the cytoplasm. Because of its location this system was later called the endoplasmic reticulum and was subsequently recognized as equivalent to the ergastoplasm of Garnier.[112] In certain cells this system shows a complicated geometrical configuration while in others it displays a simple topography. In many cells, cisternae of the system may be scattered at random through the cytoplasm. On the membrane surfaces there may be a host of 80–150 Å dense particles, called ribosomes or RNP particles because of their large content of ribonucleoprotein. Other membranes may be devoid of these particles. This condition has allowed investigators to speak of two varieties of endoplasmic reticuli: (a) a rough variety, which has ribosomes attached to the membrane and (b) a smooth variety which consists of membranes devoid of RNP particles. In some cells ribosomes fill the cytoplasmic matrix though there is little or no evidence of an associated membrane system.[152, 244, 245, 249, 250, 251, 265, 266, 321]

Investigations on a wide variety of Protozoa show that almost all groups possess some form of endoplasmic reticulum. Although less complex and less abundant than in metazoan cells, the endoplasmic reticulum of protozoa often exhibits such structural permutations as: (a) a membrane system studded with 50–180 Å dense particles (Fig. 9, ER); and (b) elongate tubular or oval structures with smooth membrane surfaces (Fig. 9, ES).[23, 149, 157, 203, 205, 223, 236, 256, 289, 307, 332, 357, 358, 359] Some authors have reported the absence of elements of the endoplasmic reticulum in several unicellular forms.[23, 285] These findings should be checked utilizing the advancements in fixation and embedding which are now available. (cf. [338])

In many unicellular forms the endoplasmic reticulum shows no special orientation. However, in some trichomonads certain light microscopists (e.g. Kofoid and Swezy,[199]) called attention to an area of basophilic material surrounding the nucleus ("nuclear cloud", see inset Fig. 18, NC) as well as the axostyle (chromatic ring). These areas are composed of cisternae of the endoplasmic reticulum (Fig. 8, and 11, ER). Similarly in *Entosiphon sulcatum* long slender units of the endoplasmic reticulum immediately surround the nucleus,[8] and in *E. sulcatum* the reticulum may be responsible for the unusual thickness of the nuclear envelope observed with the light microscope.[204] In a few organisms the endoplasmic reticulum may be closely associated with the inner plasma membrane (Fig. 1, ER) and along with certain fibrous protein structures (trichites).[8] Endoplasmic reticulum in great quantity is present in ciliates of the family Paraisotrichidae (Fig. 14 and 15, ER); spherical, membrane-bound bodies, are closely associated with slender elements of the reticulum (Fig. 14, ER). In *Campanella umbellaria* and *Ophrydium versatile*, Fauré-Fremiet and Rouiller[100] interpreted the cortical portion of the contractile vacuole as a specialized portion of the endoplasmic reticulum.

Continuity between the nuclear envelope and endoplasmic reticulum has been repeatedly demonstrated.[265, 267, 303, 343] Some of the best examples in Protozoa are in *Trypanosoma gambiense*[230] (Fig. 16, ER) and *Tetrahymena pyriformis*[85] (Fig. 1, ER). In view of this close association, Porter[265] has suggested: "For conceptual purposes . . . in a situation where valid simplications are welcome, it is reasonable to regard the nuclear envelope as *the constant part* of this system and to think of the cytoplasmic part as derivatives or extensions of the envelope. In other words the endoplasmic reticulum becomes a unit system of the cell based on the nuclear envelope".

The endoplasmic reticulum of *T. gambiense* is also connected with the vesicular component of the Golgi complex (Fig. 17, ER, GC), and a similar relationship has also been found in a number of other cells.[22, 267, 366] This helps to substantiate the concept that a direct channel for transport exists in the communication of nuclear envelope, endoplasmic reticulum and Golgi complex. Further support is given by the work of Novikoff and his associates who describe nucleoside diphosphatase activity in the nuclear envelope and endoplasmic reticulum which rapidly splits the diphosphates of uridine, gaunosine, and inosine and slowly splits thiaminopyrophatate.[89, 241, 242, 243]

The endoplasmic reticulum and the configuration it assumes at the time of cell division has not been investigated in Protozoa with the same precision as it has in other cells.[267] Roth and Minick[289] investigated nuclear and cytoplasmic events during the division of *Tetrahymena pyriformis* (strains W and HAM 3) and noted that during the interphase the endoplasmic reticulum consisted of a number of membranes of the rough variety. These usually lay near the macronuclear envelope; a few were scattered through the cytoplasm. In strain W the authors found that the amount and complexity of the endoplasmic reticulum increased as division approached. The same increase, however, was not found in strain HAM 3. In early phases of stomatogenesis of *T. pyriformis*, Williams *et al.*[352] noted that a highly developed endoplasmic reticulum of the smooth variety was localized around the stomatogenic kinetosomes at the time of active ciliary synthesis. It is interesting to note that the endoplasmic reticulum of the rough variety is usually found closely associated with the macronuclear envelope.

Also meager for unicellular organisms is the evidence concerning the chemical composition of the endoplasmic reticulum and its function.[311] However, by use of biochemical techniques the endoplasmic reticulum of the rough variety has been found to be involved in cytoplasmic protein synthesis.[32, 43, 47, 252, 320]

## III. STIGMA

The stigma, located at the anterior end of many Euglenids, attracted the attention of early investigators[341] and has long been a subject of interest and controversy among protozoologists.[96, 361] Because of its hematochrome pigment bodies, the stigma appears reddish or sometimes brownish. In *Euglena* the pigment bodies constituting the stigma lie outside the chloroplast.[120] They are discrete, dense, homogeneous, loosely packed structures disposed in a curvilinear fashion within one or two plates. In *Chlorogonium elongatum* and *Chlamydomonas reinhardii* the bodies comprising the stigma lie within the chloroplast.[154, 303] (Fig. 6, S). In *Chlamydomonas* the stigma consists of a series of plates made up of bodies with a dense core and a less dense peripheral portion. These bodies range from 100 to 140 mu in diameter. They are embedded within the chloroplast matrix in a definite spatial relationship to the surrounding membrane of the organelle and the lamellae. Immediately inside the limiting membrane lies one plate of stigma bodies, followed by a lamella, a second plate of bodies and another lamella.[303]

Earlier investigators advanced the thesis that the stigma was a light absorbing shield which prevented light from coming in contact with the true photoreceptor.[217] In this connection, Gibbs[120] has described the paraflagellar body originally recorded in *E. viridis* by Wager.[341] This body lies at the base of one of the flagella, enclosed within the flagellar membrane. Wager[341] says: "The presence of this enlargement of the flagellum in such a position at once suggests the simple explanation that the light rays which are absorbed by the eye-spot cause a stimulation of the enlargement in some way; this stimulation, reacting upon the flagellum, causes its movements to become modified and so results in a change in the direction of the movement of the cell." The paraflagellar body is oval or slightly plano-convex, moderately dense with a less dense core having a suggestion of a lamellate internal structure. This body has been found in *E. viridis* by de Haller[153] and is presumably the structure designated by Roth[286] as the intraflagellar swelling in his earlier work on *E. gracilis*. Whether or not this structure is a photoreceptor is unknown. Gibbs[120] compared her findings with those of other investigators and observed that the association between the paraflagellar body and the flagellum is much like the association between other known photoreceptors and cilia. In *Chromulina*[293] there is a specialized inward directed flagellum adjacent to the stigma. Rouiller and Fauré-Frémiet[292] draw a similar analogy to certain photoreceptors of metazoans. (see also [96, 103]) Gibbs[120] suggests that the best way to determine whether this body is a photoreceptor would be to isolate the structure and look for a photosensitive pigment. Her speculation that the paraflagellar body may be a photoreceptor may find some support in the work of Hartshorne[156] on *Chlamydomonas reinhardii*. Although this organism has not been shown to have a paraflagellar body, Hartshorne has shown that an a-stigmatic mutant of the organism is phototactic, but its response is much below that of the normal animals. He further suggests that all photoreceptor activity might not reside entirely within the stigma.

## IV. GASTRIOLES

All protozoa which ingest nutritive particulates form conspicuous vacuoles within their endoplasm.[186, 193, 201, 327, 350] Volkonsky[339, 340] suggested that these structures be called *gastrioles*, since they were analogous to the stomach and intestine of higher organisms. This terminology is adopted here. Mast[218] has stated that much of the information we have concerning the formation of gastrioles is gathered from a single group of organisms, the ciliates. (For a detailed discussion see Kitching[193] and Wichterman.[350]

To date, relatively little new information has been added to the understanding of the physiology involved in the formation of the gastriole. Mast[218] recorded physiological changes and anatomical modifications associated with the gastrioles in *Amoeba*. He provided evidence for several stages in the formation of this structure in this organism. Once the original gastriole is formed, its diameter becomes reduced. This, according to Mast, is accomplished by the removal of water from the gastriole, thus terminating the life of the ingested organism and causing gastriolar contents to become acid. The diameter of the gastriole then increases, presumably due to the accumulation of an alkaline fluid. This is followed by a second reduction in overall diameter. It is during this time that digestion products are introduced into the amoeba's cytoplasm. Mast's careful study laid the groundwork for the only detailed paper[288] thus far written on this group. The most comprehensive investigation to date made on ciliates has been done by Favard and Carasso[101] (Figs. 19 and 20). Roth[288] noted that the membrane bounding the newly formed gastriole in *Pelomyxa carolinensis* and *P. illinoisensis*, is a smooth, single layered structure. This observation, along with those of other investigators,[13, 44, 101, 186, 231] shows that the gastriole is not just an interface between the continuous phase of the cytoplasm and dispersed phase of the gastriole contents. Moreover, in 1937 King and Beams[188] demonstrated that the gastrioles of *Paramecium* maintain their relative shape for at least one half-hour after removal from the paramecium. Roth[288] further showed that while the ingested organism shows little or no degenerative changes during the second part of the cycle, the membrane of the gastriole becomes highly specialized; its surface area is greatly increased by being thrown into a number of short and long filamentous protrusions. Roth suggests that, ". . . since the morphology of the food organism is still relatively unaltered, it is possible that this is the time during which substances originating in the amoeba cytoplasm are being transferred to the vacuolar fluid to change the hydrogen ion concentration from acidic to basic values." He concluded that the products of digestion are distributed to the cytoplasm by a mechanism of pinocytosis. (see also [13, 44, 101]) In connection with this, Carasso *et al.*[44] have been able to demonstrate, at ultrastructural levels, ADPase, ATPase and acid phosphatase in pinocytotic vesicles which are produced during the second phase of the gastriole in the ciliate *Campanella umbellaria*. Carasso *et al.*[44] indicate that the presence of these enzymes may be involved in the digestive process as well as in active transport.

In other organisms where gastrioles have been investigated at substructural levels there is no evidence suggesting that specific organelles are closely associated with the initial gastrioles. But reports based on light microscopic observations indicate that mitochondria are closely associated with this structure.[172] Torch[334] found that mitochondria are never in intimate contact with the membrane of newly formed gastrioles. However, after digestion begins, they are found in close association with the smaller gastrioles. There is also a report by Causey[48] suggesting that mitochondria surrounding gastrioles of *Endamoeba gingivalis* show different shapes according to metabolic activity (i.e., they are rod-shaped if associated with gastrioles but become spherical when associated with pseudopodia).

Prior to the work of Rudzinska and Trager[294, 295, 296] it was generally thought that all intracellular parasites obtained their nutritive substance by diffusion. In three species of haemosporidians, *Plasmodium lophurae*, *P. berghei* and *Babesia redhaini*, Rudzinska and Trager described a mechanism for food-getting which they call phagotrophy—*the engulfment of a host cell cytoplasm followed by the formation of a gastriole* (Fig. 3, GA), and the digestion of the haemoglobin within the gastriole. In *P. berghei*, however, digestion of the haemoglobin does not take place inside the gastriole, a conclusion based on the fact that the gastriole never contains hematin. Hematin is found, instead, in many pinocytotic vesicles which surround the large gastriole, some of these vesicles showing direct continuity with the mother gastrioles (Fig. 3, P). It is in these smaller vesicles that the authors suggest that digestion processes are initiated.[295]

## V. PINOCYTOTIC VESICLES

The ingestion of fluids by cells was first observed by Edwards[80] while studying the feeding reactions of *Amoeba*. He found that food-cups could be formed not only in response to food-organisms but also in response to certain salt solutions. The ingestion of fluids by mammalian cells grown in tissue culture was documented in 1931 by Lewis[209] and the phenomenon was termed by him pinocytosis. At the time of this discovery, Lewis emphasized the general importance of the process and envisioned it to have unlimited application to cell physiology. Some years after, Mast and Doyle[219] presented evidence that *Amoeba* could also ingest fluid by pinocytosis, thus re-emphasizing and confirming the observations made earlier by Edwards.[80] It was Palade[248] who first observed a vesiculation of the plasma membrane of metazoan cells and suggested that pinocytosis may also occur at submicroscopic levels within the organism. From observations such as these Bennett[28] stated his well known hypothesis of membrane flow: ". . . membrane flow may be an important part of a type of active transport mechanism carrying particles, including ions, along, within, into, and out of cells. If membrane is being formed or synthesized in one region, and being broken down or enzymatically destroyed at another, it would be expected to flow from the membrane source to the membrane sink or site of breakdown." Much work has been presented to substantiate Bennett's hypothesis. The careful work of Brandt[33] and Schumaker[308] represent some of the initial, leading experimental data which verified Bennett's hypothesis. Brandt,[33] using fluorescent labeling techniques, found that proteins were adsorbed to the PAS-positive[255] plasma membrane of *Chaos chaos* (cf. [16]). The plasma membrane invaginates and the resulting concavities become pinocytotic vesicles. Schumaker[308] using protein labeled with iodine studied the uptake of ribonuclease and cytochrome *c* by *Amoeba proteus*. He suggested that proteins are bound to the plasma membrane and are subsequently carried into the organism by pinocytotic activity. The fate of the contents of these pinocytotic vacuoles is not known. (cf. [4, 5, 220]) The work of Chapman-Andersen and Holter[55] is noteworthy. From their experiments dealing with carbon 14-labeled glucose, they suggested that the contents of the vacuoles empty into the cytoplasm within forty-five minutes. A similar conclusion has been reached by Brandt and Pappas. ([35], also see[50]) Holter and Marshall[169] found that amoebae which have their protein labeled with flurocein, accumulate this substance in the mitochondria within three days. (cf. [166, 167]) It has been shown that acid phosphatase is closely associated with pinocytotic vesicles in some unicellular forms.([130, 284, 310], see also [329]) Only more experimentation will disclose whether or not all of these structures can be equated to hydrolase-rich lysosomes described by de Duve[78, 79] and Novikoff.[243]

Recently, investigators have shown that in a variety of metazoan cells small surface invaginations, which are destined to form micropinocytoitic vesicles, become altered by the development of a fuzzy coat on their cytoplasmic surfaces. (cf. [31]) Along the plasmalemma of *Trichonomonas muris*[11] are pit-like formations whose adjacent cytoplasmic areas also display the fuzzy coat. These invaginations of the plasmalemma are thought to be initial stages in the formation of coated vesicles seen in the peripheral cytoplasm. Roth and Porter[290, 291] and Anderson[10] have shown that vesicles of a similar architecture are found in oocytes during the stage of protein yolk deposition. That ferritin-labeled albumin is taken up by these coated vesicles led Roth and Porter[291] to offer the hypothesis that these vesicles may be involved in selective uptake of protein. (see also[104]) Micropinocytotic vesicles (smooth surfaced) of other cell types may be selective for the uptake of other classes of substances. (cf. [352a])

## VI. PARAMYLUM BODIES

Paramylum bodies, in euglenids commonly thought to represent reserve carbohydrates, may be found associated with the chloroplast[120] or free in the cytoplasm. In many species they are few in number while in others (*Chilomonas paramecium*) they are so abundant as to give to the cytoplasm an aveolar appearance.[9] In its chemistry, paramylum differs from starch in not showing a positive staining reaction with iodine.

In *Peranema trichophorum*, Roth[287] called attention to certain spindle shaped homogeneous bodies surrounded by a single membrane. He suggested that these structures may possibly be paramylum bodies. Anderson[9] describes the large paramylum bodies of *Chilomonas paramecium* as consisting of two parts: (a) a clear central area and (b) an outer usually relatively homogeneous area (Fig. 9, P), which sometimes contains a filamentous material. These paramylum bodies are surrounded by two membranes, an inner smooth membrane and an outer one which is sometimes studded with RNP particles. Others do not call these bodies paramylum in *C. paramecium*, but refer to them as leucosin bodies.[63, 176] Hutchens and his group[176] found that these structures give the starch-iodine reaction after boiling and consist of approximately equal portions of amylopectin and amylose.

## VII. CRYSTALS

In *Amoeba*, as in other forms, there are many structures of a crystalline nature.[5, 45] One of the most complete studies on crystals is that of Griffin.[146] He studies three amoebae gathered from mass cultures,[145] (*A. proteus, A. dubia* and *Chaos chaos*), and found two morphologically distinct crystals types. One of these is plate-like and often birefringent; the other is bipyrimidal and isotropic. This observation is contrary to the observation of Grunnbaum *et al.*,[151] who are of the opinion that only one type exists. When Griffin dissolved in water a mixture of the two types of crystals and then recrystallized them, the recovered product is in the form of birefringent plates. On the basis of physiochemical properties, elemental analysis, X-ray diffraction patterns, infra-red spectra, and optical properties, Griffin concluded that the recovered crystals were identical with synthesized carbonyl diurea. He further suggested that since carbonyl diurea is a nitrogen excretion product, it represents an end product of purine metabolism. Unfortunately the substance of the crystals is extracted when the organisms are subjected to procedures used in electron microscopy and it is therefore difficult, if not impossible, to discern their substructure. In some electron micrographs a membrane surrounds a clear area or negative image of some crystalline structure[68] but it is doubtful that all crystals are enclosed within a vacuole.

Also under discussion are the so-called Alpha bodies. Cohen[59] has suggested that they are seen in electron micrographs as dense particles within vesicles. Greider *et al.*[144] however, were not able to observe them.

## VIII. MINERAL CONCRETIONS

Some ciliates contain mineral concretions; a few of these are composed of calcium carbonate but the chemical nature of most is unknown.[95] Some of these concretions, for example in the families Loxodidae, Butschliidae and Paraisotrichidae, are organized into definite structures.[201] These concrement vacuoles, known as Muller's vesicles in species of the family Loxodidae, are simple,[259] those of the other two families are more complex. In organisms like *Blepharoprosthium*, the concrement vacuole consists of at least four parts: (a) a vacuolar wall which is permanent, (b) two systems of fibrils, (c) a vacuolar cap and (d) the concretions. These vacuoles have been considered sensory organs. Their detailed anatomy should be studied, especially since Dogiel's[73] pictures show that their structure is similar to that described for statocysts of certain invertebrates.

## IX. CHROMATOID BODIES

In the cytoplasm of the cyst as well as in the trophozoite of the parasitic amoeba, *Endamoeba invadens,* there are 10 $\mu$ structures which stain intensely with basic dyes and are commonly referred to as chromatoid bodies.[18] The chromatoid bodies are smaller and are more numerous in the trophozoites, often single units rather than conformations. Deutsch and Zaman[72] investigated their substructural and other properties. They found them composed of a considerable number of globular units with a diameter of 200 Å arranged in a crystalline pattern. When the living organism is subjected to ribonuclease for four hours and later prepared for electron microscopy, the globular units appear flattened and composed of linearly arranged sub-units. A similar picture was obtained when organisms were fixed in formalin without the ribonuclease treatment. Histochemical studies show that the chromatoid body is primarily composed of ribonucleic acid and some unspecified protein. The function of the chromatoid body is unknown.

## X. GRANULAR COMPONENT

Many studies have been made on organisms with a particularly rich granular endoplasm . (cf. [130]) One such organism is the thigmotrich, *Conchophthirus curtus.*[27] In this ciliate the main portion of its anterior region is filled with such an extensive array of granules that Beers[27] has called this region the granuloplasm. From cytochemical tests, Beers was able to show that these granules are Feulgen-negative; they contain neutral fat, fatty acid, phospholipid, glycogen and mucin. On the basis of these tests he recommended that these granules be referred to as "muciferous granules", and suggests that ". . . the granules and granuloplasm constitute a mucin-secreting organelle which supplies mucin to the underlying thigomotactic cilia."

## XI. PIGMENT BODIES

Located just beneath the pellicle and between the ciliary lines, in *Stentor coeruleus* and *Blepharisma undulans,* are uniformly arranged pigment bodies approximately 0.3–0.5 $\mu$ in diameter. In *Blepharisma,* these bodies contain the pigment zoopurpurin[15] and in *Stentor* they contain the pigment stentorin. (cf. [201]) Much of what we know about the pigment comes from a series of papers published by Giese[124, 125, 126, 127] on the pigment bodies of *Blepharisma undulans.* In 1949, Giese and Zeuten[127] found that when *Paramecium multimicronucleatum* was placed in a culture of *Blepharisma undulans,* the paramecia were irreversibly injured. The substance producing this effect, a photolabile cytotoxin, was liberated by *Blepharisma.* Later this substance was found to produce an injurious effect on a wide variety of other protozoans, rotifers, and blastulae and gastrulae of the sea urchin, *Strongylocentrotus purpuratus*. This photolabile toxin is produced by the pigment bodies within the cell. When organisms are grown in the dark a large number of pigment bodies accumulate in the cytoplasm. In dim light the organisms become bleached. On exposure to brilliant light in the presence of oxygen the heavily pigmented organisms usually die.[124] Because of this, Giese[124] suggested that the pigment is a photodynamic sensitizer.

As stated above, the pigment bodies of *Stentor coerulus* and *Blepharisma undulans* are located beneath the pellicle and between the ciliary lines. In 1929, Nadler[231a] noted that when *Blepharisma undulans* was exposed to 1/10,000 M strychnine, morphine sulphate and a variety of other chemicals, the pellicle of the cell could be discarded. Interestingly enough, the shedding of the pellicle is accomplished without interfering with the kinetosomes of the cilia. Impressed with the experiments of Nadler[231a] and Giese,[124] Kennedy[186a] investigated, with the aid of the electron microscope, the effect of strychnine and light on pigmentation in *Blepharisma undulans*. In appearance, the pigment bodies are of two types: (a) a spherical dense one encompassed by a smooth membrane (Fig. 22, $P_1$) and (b) one whose somewhat granular interior is less dense and encircled by a crinkled membrane (Fig. 22, $P_2$, see also [179]). Upon exposure to strychnine and light these granules are released from the cell. According to Kennedy[186a] ". . . the pigment granules become loosened from the surrounding membranes. Eventually these membranes break, simultaneously releasing the granules from the cell (Figs. 23, 24, P). Fusion occurs between adjacent membraneless granules with the simultaneous incorporation of membrane fragments. This fusion of granules and membranes results in the formation of the pigmented 'capsule' around the animal."

The chemistry of these bodies in *Stentor* and *Blepharisma* has been analyzed by Weisz.[346] He found them basophilic, Feulgen-negative, and reactive to Sudan black. This suggests the presence of lipids. They also gave a positive Nadi reaction and stained with Janus green as do mitochondria. Their origin is unknown.

In addition to containing chloroplasts some species of Euglena (*E. rubra, E. sanguinea*) are endowed with an abundant supply of red pigment bodies which contain hematochrome.[353] When organisms like *E. rubra* are centrifuged the pigment bodies accumulate in the center of the organism.[182, 183] In very bright light they readily disperse and it has been shown that the blue end of the visible spectrum is much more effective in stimulating dispersion than the red.[183] The fine structure of these bodies has not been investigated; a detailed morphligical study of organisms containing them should be rewarding. One would like to know the mechanism by which they are dispersed. Is there some special modification of the cell which accomplishes the scattering, similar to that alluded to for melanophores of *Libestes* in the form of ". . . contracting and relaxing fibrils in the zone between the two

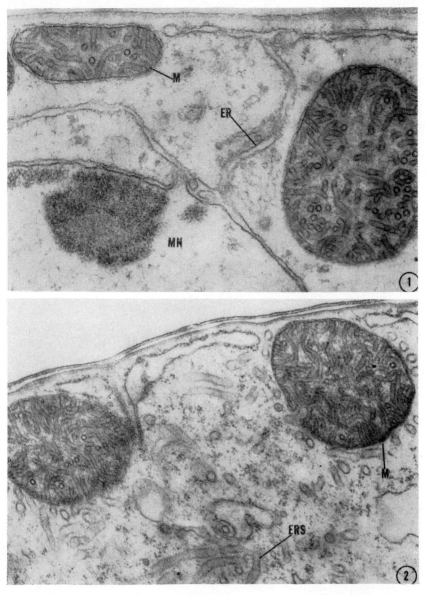

PLATE 1

FIGS. 1 and 2. Areas of the cytoplasm of *Tetrahymena pyriformis* showing
granular endoplasmic reticulum (ER) continuous with the outer envelope of
the macronucleus (MN), a smooth variety of the endoplasmic reticulum
(ERS) and mitochondria (M). Osmium fixation. × 27,000.
From A. M. ELLIOTT and I. J. BAK.[85]

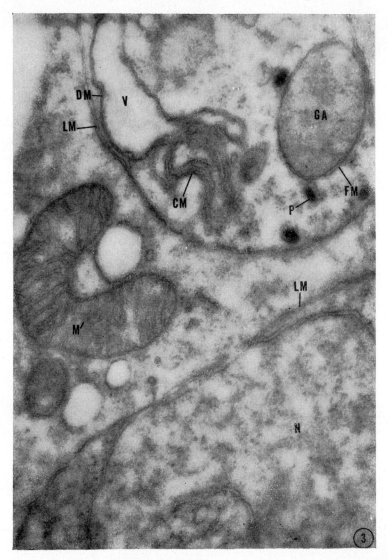

PLATE 2

FIG. 3. Sections through two plasmodia (*Plasmodium berghei*) parasitizing
the same reticulocyte. GA, gastriole encased in a double membrane (FM);
P. vesicles with pigment granules; DM, double membraned vacuole (V);
CM, double membraned organelle; N, nucleus; LM, limiting plasma
membrane; M′, mitochondrion of host cell. Osmium fixation. × 76,000.
From M. RUDZINSKA and W. TRAGER.[295]

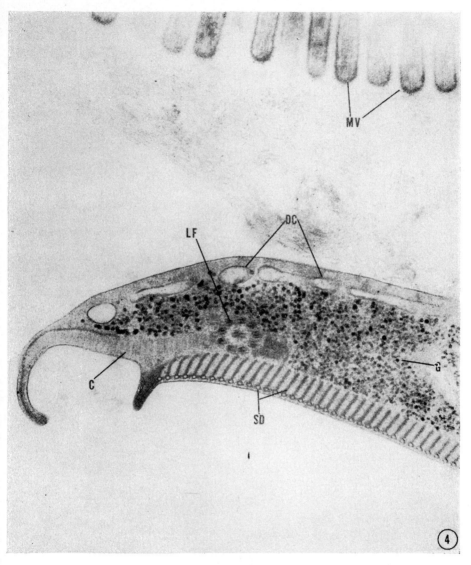

PLATE 3

FIG. 4. A section of *Giardia muris* illustrating elements of the "sucking disc" (SD), costa (C), a dense granular component (G), filaments of a lateral flagellum (LF) and dorsal cisternae (DC). Note also the intestinal microvilli (MV). Glutaraldehyde-osmium fixation. × 54,000.

Courtesy of Dr. D. FRIEND, Harvard Medical School.

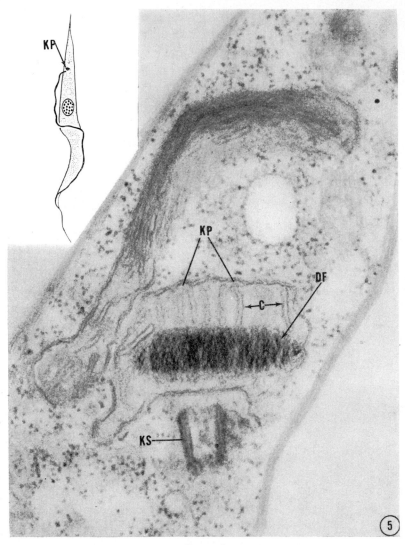

PLATE 4

FIG. 5. The inset is a line drawing of *Trypanosoma lewisi* stained with Giesma showing the location of the kinetoplast (KP) with respect to the entire organism. The electron micrograph shows a similar organism fixed in Ryter-Kellenberger buffered osmium solution (uranyl acetate post-treatment). Note kinetoplast (KP) showing a dense fibrillar (DF) component (DNA) and cristae (C) which are characteristic of mitochondria. The kinetosome (KS) of the flagellum is also illustrated. × 75,000.

From H. RIS.[281]

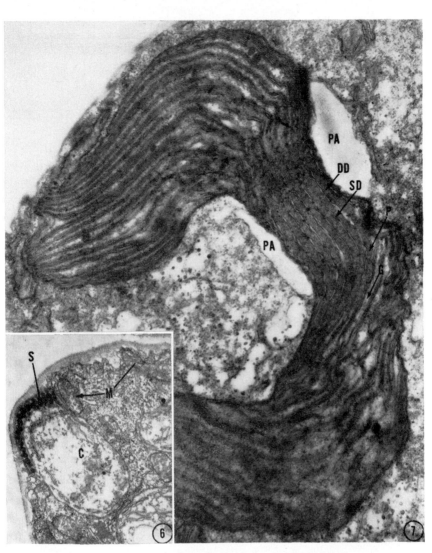

FIG. 6. An electron micrograph showing an intrachloroplastic stigma (S), and mitochondria (M) of *Chlorogonium elongatum*. Osmium fixation. × 30,000. From G. DE HALLER and CH. ROUILLER.[154]

FIG. 7. An electron micrograph of the chloroplast of *Euglena gracilis* var. *bacillaris*. (DD), double disc crossing pyrenoid; (G), granular chloroplast matrix; (P), dense pyrenoid matrix; (PA), paramylum; (SD), single disc crossing pyrenoid. Osmium fixation. × 41,000. From S. P. GIBBS.[120]

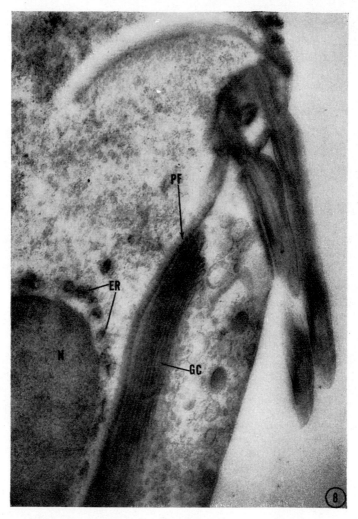

PLATE 6

FIG. 8. A tangential section of *Tritrichomonas muris* illustrating the well developed Golgi complex (GC) which is oriented parallel to the striated parabasal filament (flagellar rootlet) (PF). Cisternae of the endoplasmic reticulum (ER) surrounding the nucleus (N). Osmium fixation. × 65,000.
From E. ANDERSON and H. W. BEAMS.[9]

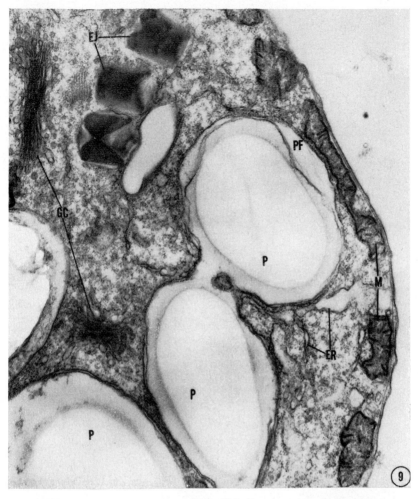

PLATE 7

FIG. 9. Micrograph showing a small portion of *Chilomonas paramecium*. The three paramylum bodies (P) show clear interiors with an outer homogeneous region limited by a double membrane. Sometimes a fine filamentous component (PF) is found in the outer homogeneous area. Other cytoplasmic components illustrated are Golgi complexes (GC), peripherally located mitochondria (M), endoplasmic reticulum (rough variety) (ER) and three ejectisomes (EJ). Osmium fixation. × 65,000. From E. ANDERSON.[12]

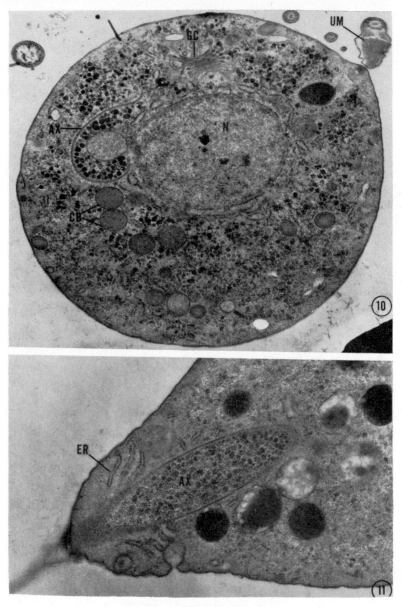

PLATE 8

FIG. 10. A tangential section through *Trichomonas muris* showing the Golgi complex (GC), undulating membrane (UM), tubular elements of the axostyle (AX) and chromatic bodies (CB). Glutaraldehyde-osmium fixation. × 30,000. From E. ANDERSON, unpublished.

FIG. 11. A section through the posterior end of *Trichomonas muris* depicting the axostyle (AX) and cisternae of the endoplasmic reticulum. (ER). Glutaraldehyde-osmium fixation. × 40,000. From E. ANDERSON, unpublished.

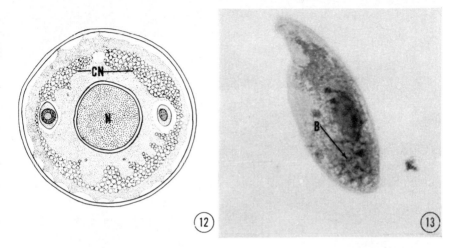

PLATE 9

FIG. 12. Diagram of the rhizopod *Arcella* showing nucleus (N) and scattered chromidial net (CN). (Redrawn from Hertwig. From *The Cell in Development and Heredity*, 3rd ed., 1947. Courtesy of the MacMillian Co.)

FIG. 13. A photomicrograph of *Tetrahymena pyriformis* stained with Korson's trichrome. Note the net-like appearance which the basophilic material (B) assumes in this organism. Picture taken from a slide prepared by Dr. NORMAN WILLIAMS.

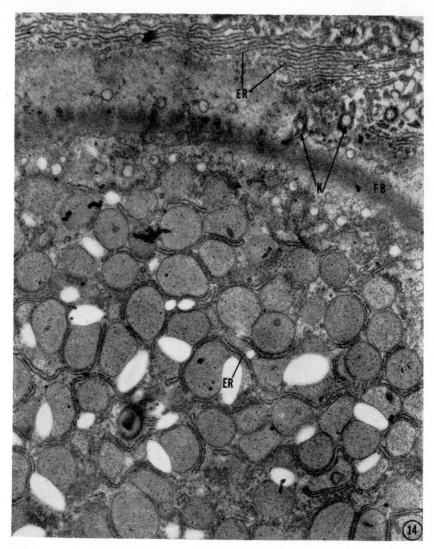

PLATE 10

FIG. 14. A small area of the cytoplasm of *Paraisotricha* sp. illustrating some finely granular bodies with rough-type enodplasmic reticulum (ER) closely associated with their periphery. In the upper portion of the figure are profiles of the endoplasmic reticulum arranged in parallel array. Note the kinetosomes (K) and the fibrillar band (FB) which divides the organism into ecto- and endoplasm. Glutaraldehydeosmium fixation. × 18,900.

From E. ANDERSON and J. N. DUMONT, unpublished.

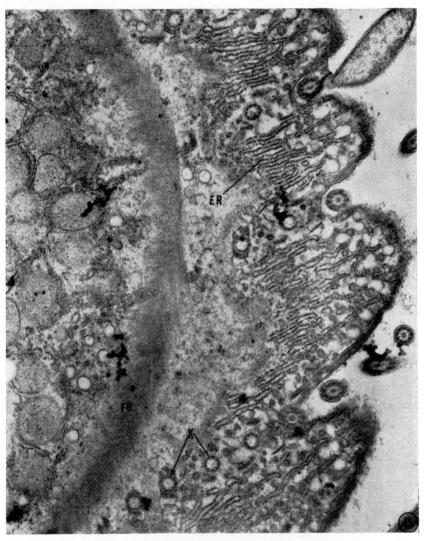

PLATE 11

FIG. 15. A tangential section through *Paraisotricha* sp. depicting the endoplasmic reticulum (ER) within the ectoplasmic ridges of the organism, profiles of kinetosomes (K) and the dense fibrillar band (FB). Glutaraldehydeosmium fixation. × 20,500.

From E. ANDERSON and J. N. DUMONT, unpublished.

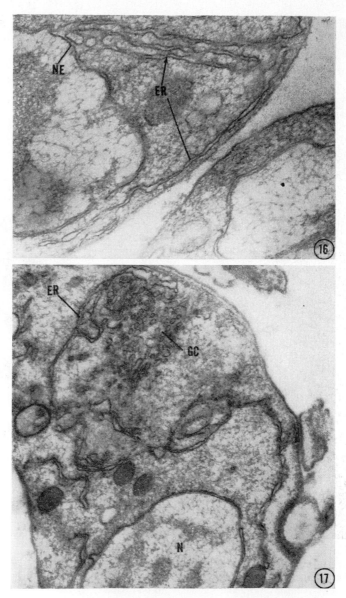

PLATE 12

FIGS. 16 and 17. These micrographs show sections of *Trypanosoma gambiense* after fixation in potassium permanganate. The endoplasmic reticulum (ER) in Fig. 16 is continuous with the outer nuclear envelope (NE) and the same component in Fig. 17 is continuous with the vesicular elements of the Golgi complex (GC). Fig. 16 × 75,000; Fig. 17 × 52,000.

From H. MUHLPFORDT and M. BAYER.[230]

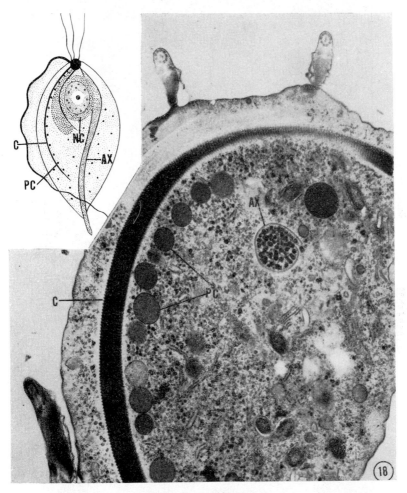

PLATE 13

FIG. 18. Inset is a diagram of *Trichomonas muris* showing the organelle systems of a typical trophic organism. Paracostal bodies are labeled *PC*, costa *C*, "nuclear cloud" *NC* and axostyle *AX*. The electron micrograph is a tangential section through the lateral portion of *T. muris* showing the curved costa (C), paracostal bodies (PC), and elements of the axostyle (AX). Glutaraldehyde-osmium fixation. × 40,000.

From E. ANDERSON, unpublished.

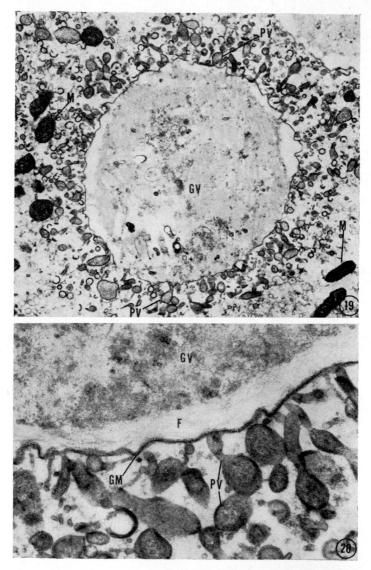

PLATE 14

FIGS. 19 and 20. Sections illustrating the second stage in the maturation of a gastriole (GV) of *Campanella*. This stage is distinguished by the formation of numerous pinocytotic vesicles (PV) of varying shapes. Note also mitochondria (M) in the vicinity of the gastriole. In the high magnification image featured as Fig. 20 the encompassing membrane of the gastriole is well delineated (GM) and has on its inner surface a layer of filamentous material (F). This filamentous material presumably facilitates the adsorption of substances during the process of pinocytosis. Fig. 19. × 8,000; Fig. 20 × 40,000. Osmium tetroxide fixation. From FAVARD and CARASSO.[101]

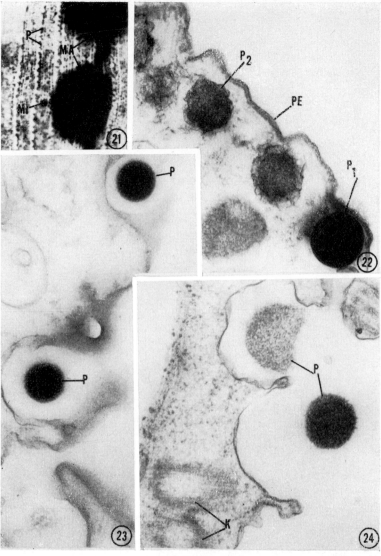

PLATE 15

FIG. 21. A portion of a whole mount of *Blepharisma undulans* stained with protargol. Note pigment bodies (P), macronuclei (MA) and a micronucleus (MI). × 1,500.

FIG. 22. A section through the surface of an untreated organism illustrating pigment bodies ($P_1$ and $P_2$) and the pellicle (PE). Osmium fixation × 80,000.

FIG. 23. A section through the surface of an organism treated with strychnine sulfate depicting pigment bodies (P) being discharged from the organism. Osmium fixation. × 56,000.

FIG. 24. A section through the surface of an organism after being exposed to light for 18 hours. Note discarded pigment bodies (P) and the undisturbed kinetosomes (K). Osmium fixation. × 81,800. All figures courtesy of Dr. J. R. KENNEDY, JR., Bowman Gray School of Medicine.

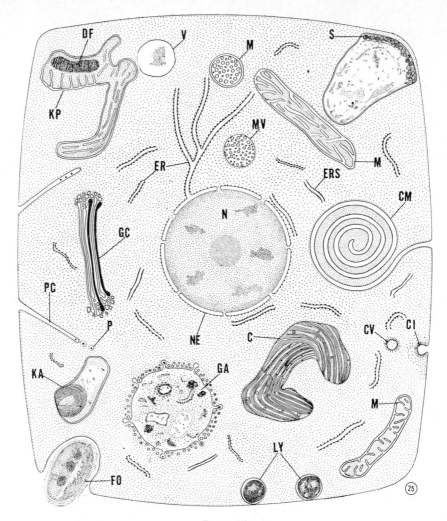

PLATE 16

FIG. 25. A diagram showing an array of cytoplasmic constituents which may be found in various groups of protozoa. DF, dense fibrillar DNA component of kinetoplast; V, vesicle with a dense interior; M, mitochondria; S, stigma within a chloroplast; MV, multivesicular body; ER, endoplasmic reticulum of the rough variety some of which is directly connected with the nuclear envelope (NE); ERS, endoplasmic reticulum of the smooth variety; CM, concentric membrane system; N, nucleus; C, chloroplast; GC, Golgi complex with coated vesicles; PC, pinocytotic channel; P, pinocytotic vesicle; KA, kappa with its contained DNA component; FO, food organism being engulfed; GA, gastriole showing attached and unattached pinocytotic vesicles; LY, lysosomes; CV, coated invagination; CV, coated vesicle.

cell membranes",[90] or is this phenomenon brought about solely by chemical means?

## XII. CHROMATIC BODIES

Peculiar cytoplasmic structures which stain densely with basic dyes are found in certain flagellates and in the past have been called chromatic granules.[111, 228, 300, 347] In some forms, these bodies occupy specific areas within the cytoplasm. Many are found parallel to the costa (a striated flagellar rootlet in certain organisms of the order Polymastigina, see C, Fig. 18) where they are called paracostal bodies (Fig. 18, PC); some are found along the axostyle and referred to as paraaxostylar bodies, and others are scattered in the cytoplasm. In *Trichomonas muris* each of these bodies is limited by a membrane and each is composed of vesicles and/or granules of varying size.[12] Anderson and Beams[12] have stated that "One may speculate that these organelles may be modified or specialized mitochondria carrying an array of enzyme systems directly or indirectly related to the general metabolism of the organism." In connection with this, Sharma and Bourne[315] have demonstrated succinic dehydrogenase and cytochrome oxidase in the chromatic bodies of *T. vaginalis*.

## XIII. CONCLUDING COMMENTS

The cytological investigation dealing with unicellular organisms during the past seven or eight years (cf. [82, 262, 335]) has helped to resolve some of the more outstanding controversial morphological problems and has paved the way for research aimed at discerning function. The more general regularly occurring cytoplasmic organelle systems of Protozoa have a substructure similar to that in cells of plants and higher animals. Particular organelle systems of a lamellar nature have been shown by the newer cytological techniques to be more pronounced within certain unicellular forms than in others. This kind of anatomical variation within the Protozoa presents an excellent opportunity to frame questions on comparative dynamic cytology.

Although it is difficult to draw a typical protistan cell, one can construct a picture which includes many of the general cytoplasmic constituents as well as a few of the variations encountered in particular groups. Such an effort is diagrammatically represented in Figure 25.

Notwithstanding the extent of our knowledge of the anatomy of most of the cytoplasmic constituents, we are still confronted with many unresolved questions. A few of these may be listed: What is the functional significance, if any, of tubular versus vesicular mitochondria; of the high development of the Golgi complex in some forms and its virtual absence in others? Does the absence of the Golgi complex in certain ciliates have some functional significance as the absence of mitochondria in certain parasitic or endocommensal forms? What is the physiological significance of the striated filament associated with the Golgi complex in certain flagellates? In Protistan cells does the endoplasmic reticulum perform functions similar to those which it performs in metazoan cells? What is the physiological significance of the location of dense bodies comprising the stigma within the chloroplast in some forms, outside in others? How are we to classify the myriad inclusions which periodically occur in the cytoplasm? What is the function and chemical composition of the many, apparantly physiologically different, vacuolar and granular components of the cytoplasm?

As data for these questions become available we will not only be able to construct a "typical" protistan cell in terms of anatomy but also construct a biochemical protistan cell similar to those which are emerging for bacteria, plant and metazoan cells.

## XIV. REFERENCES

1. AARONSON, S., and SCHER, S. (1960) Effect of aminotriazole and streptomycin on multiplication and pigment production of photosynthetic micro-organisms. *J. Protozool.* **7**, 156.
2. ALEXEIEFF, A. G. (1916) Mitochondries chez quelques protistes. *Compt. Rend. Soc. Biol.* **79**, 1072.
3. ALEXEIEFF, A. G. (1917) Mitochondries et corps parabasal chez les flagelles. *Compt. Rend. Soc. Biol.* **80**, 358.
4. ANDERSEN, C. C., and NILSSON, J. R. (1960) Electron micrographs of pinocytosis channels in *Amoeba proteus. Expt'l. Cell Res.* **19**, 631.
5. ANDERSEN, N. (1956) Cytological investigations on the giant amoeba *Chaos chaos.* L.C.R. Lab. Carlsberg (*Ser. Chim.*) **29**, 435.
6. ANDERSON, E. (1955) The electron microscopy of *Trichomonas muris. J. Protozool.* **2**, 114.
7. ANDERSON, E. (1957) Further observations on the fine structure of *Trichomonas. J. Protozool.* **4** (Suppl.), 9.
8. ANDERSON, E. (1962a) The cytoarchitecture of *Entosiphon sulcatum. Amer. Zool.* **2**, 386.
9. ANDERSON, E. (1962b) A cytological study of *Chilomonas paramecium* with particular reference to the so-called trichocysts. *J. Protozool.* **9**, 380.
10. ANDERSON, E. (1964a) Oocyte differentation and vitellogenesis in the roach *Periplaneta americana. J. Cell Biol.* **20**, 131.
11. ANDERSON, E. (1964b) Cytoplasmic microtubules and specialized micropinocytotic regions of the plasmalemma of *Trichomonas muris. J. Protozool.* **11** (Suppl.), 86.
12. ANDERSON, E., and BEAMS, H. W. (1959) The cytology of *Tritrichomonas* as revealed by the electron microscope. *J. Morph.* **104**, 205.
13. ANDERSON, E., and BEAMS, H. W. (1960) The fine structure of the heliozoan, *Actinosphaerium nucleofilum. J. Protozool.* **7**, 190.
14. ANDERSON, E., SAXE, L. H., and BEAMS, H. W. (1956) Electron microscope observation of *Trypanosoma equiperdum. J. Parasitol.* **42**, 11.
15. ARCIKOVSKIJ, V. (1905) Über das Zoopurpurin ein neues Pigment der Protozoa (*Blepharisma lateritinus* Ehrgb.) *Arch. Protistenk.* **6**, 227.
16. BAIRAT, A., and LEHMANN, F. E. (1953) Structural and chemical properties of the plasmalemma of *Amoeba proteus. Expt'l. Cell Res.* **5**, 220.
17. BAK, I. L., and ELLIOTT, A. M. (1962) Structural changes in the mitochondria of *Tetrahymena pyriformis* during the growth cycle, in *Electron Microscopy* (ed. S.S. Breese, Jr.) Academic Press, New York, p. UU-13.

18. BARKER, D. C., and DEUTSCH, K. (1958) The chromatoid body of *Entamoeba invadens*. *Expt'l. Cell Res.* **15**, 604.
19. BARROW, J. H. (1954) The biology of *Trypanosoma diemyctyli*, Tobey II. Cytology and morphology of *T. diemyctyli* in the vertebrate host, *Triturus viridescens*. *Trans. Amer. Micr. Soc.* **73**, 242.
20. BEAMS, H. W., and TAHMISIAN, T. N. (1954) Structure of the mitochondria in the male germ cells of *Helix* as revealed by the electron microscope. *Expt'l. Cell Res.* **6**, 87.
21. BEAMS, H. W., and ANDERSON, E. (1961) Fine structure of Protozoa. *Ann. Rev. Microbiol.* **15**, 47.
22. BEAMS, H. W., TAHMISIAN, T. N., DEVINE, R. L., and ANDERSON, E. (1956) Phase-contrast and electron microscope studies on the dictyosome and acroblast (Golgi bodies) in the male germ cells of the cricket. *J. Roy. Micro. Soc.* **76**, 98.
23. BEAMS, H. W., TAHMISIAN, T. N., DEVINE, R. L., and ANDERSON, E. (1959) Studies on the fine structure of a gregarine parasitic in the grasshopper, *Melanoplus differentialis*. *J. Protozool.* **6**, 136.
24. BEAMS, H. W., KING R. L., TAHMISIAN, T. N., and DEVINE, R. L. (1960) Electron microscope studies on *Lophomonas striata* with special reference to the nature and position of the striations. *J. Protozool.* **7**, 91.
25. BEAMS, H. W., TAHMISIAN, T. N., ANDERSON, E., and WRIGHT, B. (1961) Studies on the fine structure of *Lophomonas blattarum* with special reference to the so-called parabasal apparatus. *J. Ultrastructure Res.* **5**, 166.
26. BEERS, C. D. (1935) Structural changes during encystment and excystment in the ciliate *Didinium nasutum*. *Arch. Protistenk.* **84**, 133.
27. BEERS, C. D. (1962) The chemical nature and function of the endoplasmic granules of the ciliate *Conchophthrius curtus*. *J. Protozool.* **9**, 364.
28. BENNETT, H. S. (1956) The concepts of membrane flow and membrane vesiculation as a mechanism for active transport and ion pumping. *J. Biophys. Biochem. Cytol.* **2**, (Suppl.) 99.
29. BENSLEY, R. R., and HOERR, N. L. (1934) Studies on cell structure by the freezing-drying method. VI. The preparation and properties of mitochondria. *Anat. Rec.* **60**, 449.
30. BIRNS, M. (1960) The localization of acid phosphatase activity in the amoeba, *Chaos chaos. Expt'l. Cell Res.* **20**, 202.
31. BOWERS, B. (1964) Coated vesicles in the pericardial cells of the aphid (*Myzua persicae*). *Protoplasma* **59**, 351.
32. BRACHET, J. (1957) *Biochemical Cytology* (Academic Press, New York).
33. BRANDT, P. W. (1958) A study of the mechanism of pinocytosis. *Expt'l. Cell Res.* **15**, 300.
34. BRANDT, P. W., and PAPPAS, G. D. (1959) Mitochondria. II. The nuclear-mitochondrial relationship in *Pelomyxa carolinensis* Wilson (*Chaos chaos* L.) *J. Biophys. Biochem. Cytol.* **6**, 91.
35. BRANDT, P. W., and PAPPAS, G. D. (1962) An electron microscope study of pinocytosis in amoeba. II. The cytoplasmic uptake phase. *J. Cell Biol.* **15**, 55.
36. BRAWERMAN, G., and CHARGAFF, E. (1959) Factors involved in the development of chloroplasts in *Euglena gracilis*. *Biochem. Biophys. Acta* **31**, 178.
37. BRAWERMAN, G., and CHARGAFF, E. (1960) A self-reproducing system concerned with the formation of chloroplasts in *Euglena gracilis*. *Biochem. Biophys. Acta* **37**, 221.
38. BRESSLAU, E. L., and SCREMIN, L. (1924) Die Kerne der Trypanosomen und ihr Verhalten zur Nuclearreaction. *Arch. Protistenk.* **48**, 509.
39. BROWN, V. E. (1930) The Golgi apparatus of *Pyrsonympha* and *Dienympha*. *Arch. Protistenk.* **71**, 453.
40. BUCHNER, P. (1953) *Endosymbiose der Tiere mit pflanzlichen Mikroorganismen*. Bukhauser, Basel.

41. CAJAL, RAMON Y SANTIAGO. (1904) Variaciones morfologicas del reticulo mervioso de invertebrados sometidos a la accion de condiciones de naturales. *Trab. Lab. Invest. Biol. Univ. Madr.* **1**, 3.
42. CALKINS, G. N. (1930) *Uroleptus halseyi* n. sp. II. The origin and fate of the macronuclear chromatin. *Arch. Protistenk.* **69**, 151.
43. CAMPBELL, P. N. (1960) The synthesis of proteins by the cytoplasmic components of animal cell. *Biol. Rev.* **35**, 413.
44. CARASSO, N., FAVARD, P., and GOLDFISCHER, S. (1964) Localisation a l'échelle des ultrastructure d'activités de phosphatases en rapport avec les processus digestifs chez un cilie (*Campanella umbellaria*). *J. Microscopie* **3**, 297.
45. CARLSTROM, D., and MOLLER, K. M. (1961) Further observations on the native and recrystallized crystals of the amoeba *Amoeba proteus. Expt'l. Cell Res.* **24**, 393.
46. CARO, L. G. (1961) Electron microscopic radioautography of thin sections: The Golgi zone as a site of protein concentration in pancreatic acinar cells. *J. Biophys. Biochem. Cytol.* **10**, 37.
47. CASPERSSON, T. (1950) *Cell Growth and Cell Function.* Norton, New York.
48. CAUSEY, D. (1925a) Mitochondria and Golgi bodies in *Endamoeba gingivalis* (Gross) Brumpt. *Univ. Calif. Publs. Zool.* **28**, 1.
49. CAUSEY, D. (1925b) Mitochondria in *Leishmania brasiliensis. Univ. Calif. Publ. Zool.* **28**, 19.
50. CHADWICK, A. (1961) The fate of radioactively labelled glycine introduced into *Amoeba proteus* and *Stentor coeruleus. Expt'l. Cell Res.* **25**, 131.
51. CHAKROBORTY, J., GUHA, A., and DAS GUPTA, N. N. (1962) Cytology of the flagellate form of *Leishmania donovani* with consideration of the evidence for abnormal nuclear division. *J. Parasitol.* **48**, 131.
52. CHAKRABORTY, J., DAS GUPTA, N. N. and RAY, H. N. (1962) An electron microscope study of the *Trichomonas criceti. Cytologia* **26**, 320.
53. CHANDRA, S. (1962) The reversal of mitochondrial membrane. *J. Cell Biol.* **12**, 503.
54. CHANG, P. C. H. (1956) The ultrastructure of *Leishmania donovani. J. Parasit.* **42**, 126.
55. CHAPMAN-ANDERSEN, C. and HOLTER, H. (1955) Studies on the ingestion of 14C glucose by pinocytosis in the amoeba *Chaos chaos. Expt'l. Cell Res.* (Suppl.) **3**, 52.
56. CHEISSIN, E. M., and MOSEVICH, T. N. (1962) An electron microscope study of *Colpidium colpoda. Arch. Protistenk* **106**, 181.
57. CLARK, T. B., and WALLACE, F. G. (1960) A comparative study of kinetoplast ultrastructure in the Trypanosomatidae. *J. Protozool.* **7**, 115.
58. CLEVELAND, L. R., and GRIMSTONE, A. V. (1964) The fine structure of the flagellate *Mixotrichia paradoxa* and its associated micro-organisms. *Proc. Roy. Soc.* (Series B) **159**, 688.
59. COHEN, A. I. (1957) Electron microscopic observations of *Amoeba proteus* in growth and inanition. *J. Biophys. Biochem. Cytol.* **3**, 859.
60. COSGROVE, W. B., and ANDERSON, E. (1954) The kinetoplast of *Crithidia fasciculata. Anat. Rec.* **120**, 813.
61. COWDRY, E. V. (1924) *General cytology.* Univ. of Chicago Press, Chicago, Ill.
62. COWDRY, E. V. (1953) Historial background of research on mitochondria. *J. Histochem. Cytochem.* **1**, 183.
63. CUNNINGHAM, W. L., MANNERS, D. J., and RYLEY, J. F. (1961) Structure of a reserve polysaccharide (Paramylon) from *Peranema trichophorum. Proc. Biochem. Soc.* **82**, 12.
64. D'ALESANDRO, P. A. (1962) *In vitro* studies of ablastin, the reproduction inhibiting antibody to *Trypanosoma lewisi. J. Protozool.* **8**, 351.
65. DALTON, A. J. (1960) Golgi apparatus and secretion granules, in *The Cell* (ed., J. Brachet and A. E. Mirsky) Vol. II, Academic Press, New York.
66. DALTON, A. J., and FELIX, M. D. (1953) Studies on the Golgi substance of the epithelial cells of the epididymus and duodenum of the mouse. *Amer. Jour. Anat.* **92**, 277.

67. DANIELS, E. W. (1964) Origin of the Golgi system in amoebae. *Z. Zellforsch.* **64**, 38.
68. DANIELS, E. W., and ROTH, L. E. (1961) X-irradiation of the giant amoeba. *Pelomyxa illinoisensis*. Electron microscopy of centrifuged organisms. *Radiation Res.* **19**, 66.
69. DAS GUPTA, N. N., GUHA, A., and DE, M. L. (1954) Observations on the structure of *Leishmania donovani* the kala-azar parasite. *Expt'l. Cell Res.* **6**, 353.
70. DEKEN-GRENSON, M. DE, and MESSIN, S. (1958) La continuité génétique des chloroplasts chez les Euglènes. 1. Mécanisme de l'apparition des lignées blanches dans les cultures traitées par la streptomycine. *Biochem. Biophys. Acta* **27**, 145.
71. DEUTSCH, K., and DUNN, A. E. G. (1955) The effect of ribonuclease on *Hartmanella astronyxis*. *Expt'l. Cell Res.* **17**, 356.
72. DEUTSCH, K., and ZAMAN, V. (1959) An electron microscope study of *Entamoeba invadens* Rodhain 1934. *Expt'l. Cell Res.* **17**, 310.
73. DOGIEL, V. (1929) Die sog. "Konkrementen vakuole" der Infusorien als eine Statocyste betrachtet. *Arch. f. Protistenk.* **68**, 319.
74. DUBOSCQ, O., and GRASSÉ, P. P. (1933) L'appareil parabasal des Flagelles. *Arch. Zool. exp. gen.* **73**, 381.
75. DU BUY, H. G., MATTERN, C. F. T., and RILEY, F. L. (1965) Isolation and characterization of DNA from kinetoplast of *Leishmania enriettii*. *Sci.* **147**, 754.
76. DUMONT, J. N. (1961) Observations on the fine structure of the ciliate *Dileptus anser*. *J. Protozool.* **8**, 392.
77. DUNCAN, D., EADES, J., JUKINA, S. R., and MICKS, D. (1960) Electron microscope observations on malarial oocysts (*Plasmodium cathemerium*). *J. Protozool.* **7**, 18.
78. DUVE, C. DE (1957) Les lysosomes: un nouveau groupe de granules cytoplasmiques. *J. Physiol.* **49**, 113.
79. DUVE, C. DE (1959) Lysosomes, a new group of cytoplasmic particles, in *Subcellular Particles* ed. T. Hayashi, pp. 128. The Ronald Press Co., New York, New York.
80. EDWARDS, G. (1925) Formation of food-cups in amoeba induced by chemicals. *Biol. Bull.* **48**, 236.
81. EHRET, C. F., and POWERS, E. L. (1955) Macronuclear and nucleolar development in *Paramecium bursaria*. *Expt'l. Cell. Res.* **9**, 241.
82. EHRET, A. F., and HALLER, G. DE, (1963) Origin, development and maturation of organelles and organelle systems of the cell surface in *Paramecium*. *J. Ultrastructure Res.*, Suppl. **6**, 1.
83. ELLIOTT, A. M., and HUNTER, R. L. (1951) Phosphatase activity in *Tetrahymena*. *Biol. Bull.* **100**, 165.
84. ELLIOTT, A. M., and TREMOR, J. W. (1958) The fine structure of the pellicle in the contact area of conjugating *Tetrahymena pyriformis*. *J. Biophys. Biochem. Cytol.* **4**, 839.
85. ELLIOTT, A. M., and BAK, I. J. (1964) The contractile vacuole and related structures in *Tetrahymena pyriformis*. *J. Protozool.* **11**, 250.
86. EL MOFTY, M. M. (1957) Cytochemical localization of acid phosphatase in *Trichonympha turkestancia* Bernstein (*Trichonympha, Trichonymphidae*) *Nature*, Lond. **180**, 1367.
87. EPSTEIN, H. T., BOY DE LA TOUR, E., and SCHIFF, J. A. (1960) Fluorescense studies of chloroplast development in *Euglena*. *Nature*, London **185**, 825.
88. EPSTEIN, H. T., and SCHIFF, J. A. (1961) Studies of chloroplast development in *Euglena*. Electron and fluorescence microscopy of the proplastid and its development into a mature chloroplast. *J. Protozool.* **8**, 427.
89. ESSNER, E., and NOVIKOFF, A. B. (1962) Cytological studies on two functional hepatomas-interrelations of endoplasmic reticulum, Golgi apparatus and lysosomes. *J. Cell. Biol.* **15**, 289.
90. FALK, S., and RHODIN, J. (1956) Mechanism of pigment migration within teleost melanophores in Electron Microscopy. Proc. Stockholm. Conf., pp. 213., Academic Press, New York.

91. FAMINTZIN, A. (1907) Die Symbiose als Mittel der Synthese von Organismen. *Biol. Centralbl.* **27**, 353.
92. FAURÉ-FRÉMIET, E. (1910) La continuité des mitochondries à travers des générations cellulaires et le rôle de ces éléments. *Anat. Anz.* **36**, 186.
93. FAURÉ-FRÉMIET, E. (1910) Étude sur les mitochondries des protozoaires et des cellules sexuelles. *Arch. Anat. Micr.* **11**, 457.
94. FAURÉ-FRÉMIET, E. (1957a) Finer morphology of microorganisms. *Ann. Rev. Microbiol.* **11**, 6.
95. FAURÉ-FRÉMIET, E. (1957b) Concrétions minérales intracytoplasmiques chez les cilies. *J. Protozool.* **4**, 96.
96. FAURÉ-FRÉMIET, E. (1958a) The origin of the metazoa and stigma of the phyto-flagel-lates. *Quart. J. Micro. Sci.* **99**, 123.
97. FAURÉ-FRÉMIET, E. (1958b) Ultrastructures et différentiations protoplasmiques chez les ciliata (XV Intern. Congress Zool.) London, p. 475.
98. FAURÉ-FRÉMIET, E., and GAUCHERY, M. (1954) La reduction des sels de tetrarolium par les Infusories cilies. *Compt. Rend. Soc. Biol.*, **148**, 640.
99. FAURÉ-FRÉMIET, E. and ROUILLER, CH. (1958) Étude au microscope électronique d'une bacterie sulfureuse, *Thiouulum majus* Hinze. *Expt'l. Cell Res.* **14**, 29.
100. FAURÉ-FRÉMIET, E. and ROUILLER, CH. (1959) Le Cortex de la vacuol econtractile et son ultrastructure chez les cilies. *J. Protozool.* **6**, 29.
101. FAVARD, P., and CARASSO, N. (1964) Étude de la pinocytose au niveau des vacuoles digestives de cilies peritriches. *J. de Microscopie.* **3**, 671.
102. FAWCETT, D. W. (1958) The structure of the mammalian spermatozoon. *Internat'l. Rev. Cytol.* **7**, 195.
103. FAWCETT, D. W. (1961) *Cilia and Flagella, in the Cell* (eds. J. BRACHET and A. E. MIRSKY) Vol. II, Academic Press, New York, pp. 217.
104. FAWCETT, D. W. (1964) Local specializations of the plasmalemma in micropinocytosis vesicles of erythroblasts. *Anat. Rec.* **184**, 370.
105. FENNELL, R. A., and MARKE, F. O. (1954) The relation between vitamins, inorganic salts and the histochemical characteristics of *Tetrahymena gelei w. J. Morph.* **94**, 587.
106. FENNELL, R. A., and DEGENHARDT, E. F. (1957) Some factors affecting alkaline phosphatase activity in *Tetrahymena pyriformis w. J. Protozool.* **4**, 30.
107. FENNELL, R. A., and PASTOR, E. P. (1958) Some observations on the esterases of *Tetrahymena pyriformis w.* I. Evidence for the existence of aliesterases. *J. Morph.* **103**, 187.
108. FERNÁNDEZ-MORÁN, H. (1961) Lamellar systems in myelin and photoreceptors as revealed by high-resolution electron microscopy. In *Macromolecular complexes.* ed. M. V. EDDS, Jr. The Ronald Press Co., New York, New York, p. 113.
109. FITZ-JAMES, P. C. (1960) Participation of the cytoplasmic membrane in the growth and spore formation of bacilli. *J. Biophys. Biochem. Cytol.* **8**, 507.
110. FREY-WYSSLING, A. *Macromolecules in Cell Structure*, Harvard Univ. Press, Cambridge, Mass., 1957.
111. GABER, J. R. (1954) The morphology and taxonomy of the intestinal protozoa of the American woodchuck, *Marmota linnaeus. J. Morph.* **94**, 473.
112. GARNIER, CH. (1899) Contribution a l'étude de la structure des cellules glandulairse séreuses. Du rôle de L'ergastoplame dans la secrètion (Thèse, Nancy).
113. GATENBY, J. B., and BEAMS, H. W. (1935) The cytoplasmic inclusions in the spermatogenesis of man. *Quart. J. Micro. Sci.* **78**, 1.
114. GATENBY, J. B., and TAHMISIAN, T. N. (1959) The contractile vacuole and Golgi apparatus of *Ephydatia fluviatilis*: an electron microscope study. *J. Roy. Micr. Soc.* **77**, 107
115. GATENBY, J. B., DALTON, A. J., and FELIX, M. D. (1955) The contractile vacuole of parazoa and protozoa and the Golgi apparatus. *Nature*, Lond. **176**, 301.

116. GAVIN, M. A., WANKO, T., and JACOBS, L. (1962) Electron microscope studies of reproducing and interkinetic *Toxoplasma*. *J. Protozool.* **9**, 222.
117. GELEI, J. V. (1925) Nephridialapparat bei den Protozoen. *Biol. Zentralbl.* **45**, 676.
118. GELEI, J. VON (1928) Nochmals über den Nephredialapparat bei den Protozoen. *Arch. Protistenk.* **64**, 479.
119. GEY, G. O., SHAPRAS, P., BANG, B. F., and GEY, M. K. (1955) Some relations of inclusion droplets (Pinocytosis-Lewis) and mitochondria behaviour in normal and malignant cells, *Fine Structure of Cells*, Groningen, Noordhoff.
120. GIBBS, S. P. (1960) The fine structure of *Euglena gracilis* with special reference to the chloroplast and pyrenoids. *J. Ultrastructure Res.* **4**, 127.
121. GIBBS, S. P. (1962a) The ultrastructure of the pyrenoids of algae, exclusive of the grccn algae. *J. Ultrastructure Res.* **7**, 247.
122. GIBBS, S. P. (1962b)Chloroplast development in *Ochromonas danica. J. Cell Biol.* **15**,343.
123. GIBBS, S. P. (1962c) Nuclear envelope-chloroplast relationships in algae. *J. Cell Biol.* **14**, 433.
124. GIESE, A. C. (1946) An intracellular photodynamic sensitizer in *Blepharisma. J. Cell and Comp. Physiol.* **28**, 119.
125. GIESE, A. C. (1949) A cytotoxin from *Blepharisma. Biol. Bull.* **97**, 145.
126. GIESE, A. C. (1953) Some properties of a photodynamic pigment from *Blepharisma. J. Gen. Physiol.* **37**, 259.
127. GIESE, A. C., and ZEUTEN, E. (1949) Photooxidations in pigmented *Blepharisma. J. Gen. Physiol.* **32**, 525.
128. GOLDSCHMIDT, R., and POPOFF, M. (1907) Die Caryokinese der Protozoa und der Chromidialapparat der Protozoen und Metazoenzelle. *Arch. Protistenk.* **8**, 321.
129. GOLGI, C. (1898) Sur la structure des cellules nerveuses, ses ganglions spinaux. *Arch. Ital. Biol.* **30**, 60.
130. GRASSÉ, P. P. (1952) Generalities, in Grassé, P. P., *Traité de Zoologie* (1), Masson et Cie, Paris. **37**.
131. GRASSÉ, P. P. (1956a) L'ultrastructure de *Pyrsonympha vertens* (Zooflagellata Pyrsonymphina): les flagelles et leur coaption avec le corps, l'axostyle contractile, le paraxostyle, le cytoplasme. *Arch. Biol.*, Paris **67**, 595.
132. GRASSÉ, P. P. (1956b) L'appareil parabasal et l'appareil de Golgi sont un même organitè. Leur ultrastructure, leurs modes de secrètion. *Compt. Rend. Acad. Sci. Paris* **242**, 858.
133. GRASSÉ, P. P. (1956c) L'appareil de Golgi des Protozaires et son ultrastructure comparée à celle des Mètazoaires. Proc. of the Stockholm Conference on Electron Microscopy. Stockholm.
134. GRASSÉ, P. P. (1957) Ultrastructure, polarité et reproduction de l'appareil de Golgi. *Compt. Rend. Acad. Sci. Paris* **245**, 1278.
135. GRASSÉ, P. P., and HOLLANDE, A. (1941) Vacuoles pulsatiles et appareil de Golgi dans l'évolution de la cellule. *Arch Zool. Exp. Gen.* **82**, 301.
136. GRASSÉ, P. P., and CARASSO, N. (1957) Ultra-structure of the Golgi apparatus in Protozoa and Metazoa (somatic and germinal cells). *Nature*, Lond. **179**, 31.
137. GRASSÉ, P. P., and THEODORIDES, J. (1958) La présence de l'ergastoplasme chez les Protozoaires (cas des Grégarines). *Compt. Rend. Acad. Sci. Paris* **246**, 1352.
138. GRASSÉ, P. P., CARASSO, N., and FAVARD, P. (1955) Les dictyosomes appareil de Golgi et leur ultrastructure. *Compt. Rend. Acad. Sci. Paris* **241**, 1243.
139. GREENBLATT, C. L., and SHARPLESS, N. E. (1959a) Effects of some metabolic inhibitors on the pigments of *Euglena gracilis* in an acidic medium. *J. Protozool.* **6**, 241.
140. GREENBLATT, C. L., and SHARPLESS, N. E. (1959b) Addendum to: Effects of metabolic inhibitors on pigments of *Euglena. J. Protozool.* **6**, 319.
141. GREENBLATT, C. L., OLSON, R. A. and ENGEL, E. K. (1960) Absorption microscopy of enzymatically treated cell-free chloroplast. *J. Biophys. Biochem. Cytol.* **7**, 235.

142. GREEN, D. E. (1959) Mitochondrial structure and function, in *Subcellular Particles* ed. T. Hyashi, p. 84. The Ronald Press Co., New York.

143. GREEN, D. E., and HATEFI, Y. (1961) The mitochondrion and biochemical machines. *Science* **133**, 13.

144. GREIDER, M. H., KOSTER, W. J., and FRAJOLA, W. J. (1958) Electron microscopy of *Amoeba proteus*. *J. Protozool.* **5**, 139.

145. GRIFFIN, J. L. (1960a) An improved mass culture method for the large, free-living amoebae. *Expt'l. Cell Res.* **21**, 107.

146. GRIFFIN, J. L. (1960b) The isolation, characterization and identification of the crystalline inclusions of the large free-living amoebae. *J. Biophys. Biochem. Cytol.* **7**, 227.

147. GRIMSTONE, A. V. (1958) Aspects of cytoplasmic organization in *Trichonympha*. Proc. XV Int. Congr. Zool. Lond., p. 480.

148. GRIMSTONE, A. V. (1959a) Cytology, homology, and phylogeny—a note on 'organic design'. *Amer. Nat.* **93**, 273.

149. GRIMSTONE, A. V. (1959b) Cytoplasmic membranes and the nuclear membrane in the flagellate *Trichonympha*. *J. Biochem. Biophys. Cytol.* **6**, 369.

150. GROSS, J. A., JAHN, T. L., and BERNSTEIN, E. (1955) The effect of antihistamines on the pigments of green protista. *J. Protozool.* **2**, 71.

151. GRUNBAUM, B. W., MOLLER, M. K., and THOMAS, R. S. (1959) Cytoplasmic crystals of the amoebae: *Amoeba proteus* and *Chaos chaos*. *Expt'l. Cell Res.* **18**, 385.

152. HAGUENAU, F. (1958) The ergastoplasm: its history, ultrastructure and biochemistry. *Intern. Rev. Cytol.* **7**, 425.

153. HALLER, G. DE (1958) Contribution à la cytologie d'Euglena viridis, in 4th International Conf. on Electron Microscopy (ed. BARGMANN, W., PETERS, D., and WOLPERS, C.), Springer Verlag, Berlin, p. 517.

154. HALLER, G. DE, and ROUILLER, Ch. (1961) La structure fine de *Chlorogonium eleongatum*. 1. Étude systématique au microscope électronique. *J. Protozool.* **8**, 452.

155. HARTMANN, M. (1913) *Flagellata*, Fisher, Jena.

156. HARTSHORNE, J. N. (1953) The function of the eyespot in *Chlamydomonas*, *New Phytol.* **52**, 292.

157. HEDLEY, R. H., and BERTAUD, W. S. (1962) Electron microscopic observations of *Gromia oviformis* (Sarcodina). *J. Protozool.* **9**, 79.

158. HERTWIG, R. (1902) Die Protozoen und die Zelltheorie. *Arch. f. Protistenk.* **1**, 1.

159. HIRSCHLER, J. (1914) Über plasmastrukturen (Golgi'scher Apparat, Mitochondrien, u. a.) in den Tunicaten, Spongien und Protozoenzellen. *Anat. Anzeiger* **47**, 289.

160. HOARE, C. A. (1954) The loss of the kinetoplast in trypanosomes with special reference to *Trypanosoma evansi*. *J. Protozool.* **1**, 28.

161. HODGE, A. J., McLEAN, J. D., and MERCER, F. V. (1956) A possible mechanism for the morphogenesis of lamellar systems in plant cells. *J. Biophys. Biochem. Cytol.* **2**, 597.

162. HOFFMAN, H., and GRIG, G. W. (1958) An electron microscopic study of mitochondria formation. *Expt'l. Cell Res.* **15**, 118.

163. HOGEBOOM, G. (1955) Fractionation of cell components of animal tissues. *Methods Enzymol.* **1**, 16.

164. HOLLANDE, A. (1942) Étude cytologique et biologique de quelques flagelles libres. *Arch. Zool. Expt'l. Gen.* **83**, 24.

165. HOLTER, H. (1954) Enzymatic studies on mitochondria of amoeba, in Symposium on Fine Structure of Cells, 8th Congr. on Cell Biology, Leiden, Interscience Publishers, Inc., New York.

166. HOLTER, H. (1959a) Problems of pinocytosis, with special regard to amoeba. *Ann. N. Y. Acad. Sci.* **78**, 524.

167. HOLTER, H. (1959b) Pinocytosis. *Intern'l. Rev. Cytol.* **8**, 480.

168. HOLTER, H., and KOPAC, M. J. (1937) Studies in enzymatic histochemistry. XXIV. Localization of peptidase in the amoeba. *J. Cell. Comp. Physiol.* **10**, 423.

169. HOLTER, H., and MARSHALL, J. M. (1954) Studies on pinocytosis in the amoeba, *Chaos chaos. Comp. Rend. Trav. Lab. Carlsberg* **29**, 7.

170. HORNE, R. W., and NEWTON, B. A. (1958) Intracellular structures in *Strigomonas oncopelti*. II. Fine structure of the kinetoplast-blepharoplast complex. *Expt'l. Cell Res.* **15**, 103.

171. HORNING, E. S. (1926) Studies on the mitochondria of *Paramecium. Aust. J. Exp. Biol. Med. Sci.* **3**, 91.

172. HORNING, E. S. (1927) On the orientation of mitochondria in the surface cytoplasm of infusorians. *Aust. J. Exp. Biol. Med. Sci.* **4**, 187.

173. HORNING, E. S. (1929) Mitochondrial behavior during the life cycle of a sporozoon (*Monocystis*). *Quart. J. Micro. Sci.* **73**, 135.

174. HOVASSE, R. and JOYON, L. (1957) Sur l'ultrastructure de la Chrysomonadine *Hydrurus foetidus* Kirchner. *C. R. Acad. Sci. Paris.* **245**, 110.

175. HUNGATE, R. E. (1955) *Mutualistic intestinal Protozoa, in Biochemistry and Physiology of Protozoa*, vol. II. eds. S. H. HUNTER and A. LWOFF, Academic Press, New York.

176. HUTCHENS, J. O., PODOLSKY, B., and MORALES, M. F. (1948) Studies on the energetics and kinetics of carbon and nitrogen metabolism of *Chilomonas paramecium. J. Cellular Comp. Physiol.* **33**, 117.

177. HUTNER, S. H., and PROVASOLI, L. (1951) *The Phytoflagellates in Biochemistry and Physiology of Protozoa* (ed. A. LWOFF), Academic Press, New York, p. 27.

178. HYMAN, L. H. (1940) *The Invertebrates: Protozoa through Ctenophora*, McGraw-Hill Book Co., New York.

179. INABA, F., NAKAMURA, R., and YAMAGUCHI, S. (1958) An electron microscope study of the pigment granules of *Blepharisma. Cytologia* **23**, 72.

180. JACKSON, S. F., and RANDALL, J. T. (1958) Cytoplasmic fine structure. *Proc. Roy. Soc. B*, **148**, 290.

181. JAHN, T. L. (1946) The Euglenoid Flagellates. *Quart. Rev. Biol.* **21**, 246.

182. JOHNSON, L. P. (1939) A study of *Euglena rubra* Hardy. *Trans. Amer. Micro. Soc.* **58**, 42.

183. JOHNSON, L. P., and JAHN, T. L. (1942) Cause of the green-red color change in *Euglena rubra. Physiol. Zool.* **15**, 89.

184. JOYET-LAVERGNE, P. (1926a) Recherches sur les cytoplasmes des Sporozoaires. *Arch. Anat. Micr.* **22**, 1.

185. JOYET-LAVERGNE, P. (1926b) Sur la coloration vitale des éléments de Golgi des grégarines. *Compt. Rend. Soc. Biol. Paris* **94**, 830.

186. JURAND, A. (1961) An electron microscopic study of food vacuoles in *Paramecium aurelia. J. Protozool.* **8**, 125.

186a. KENNEDY Jr., J. R. (1964) The effect of strychnine and light on pigmentation in *Blepharisma undulans. J. Protozool.* (Suppl.) **11**, 22.

187. KING, R. L. (1935) The contractile vacuole of *Paramecium multimicronucleatum. J. Morphol.* **58**, 555.

188. KING, R. L., and BEAMS, H. W. (1937) The effect of ultracentrifuging on *Paramecium*, with special reference to recovery and macronuclear reorganization. *J. Morphol.* **61**, 27.

189. KING, R. L., BEAMS, H. W., TAHMISIAN, T. N., and DEVINE, R. (1958) The ciliature and infraciliature of *Nyctotherus ovalis* Leidy. *J. Protozool.* **8**, 98.

190. KING, S. D. (1927) The Golgi apparatus of Protozoa, *J. Roy. Micro. Soc.* **47**, 342.

191. KING, S. D., and GATENBY, J. B. (1923) The Golgi bodies of a coccidian. *Quart. J. Micro. Sci.* **67**, 381.

192. KINGSBURY, (1912) Cytoplasmic fixation. *Anat. Rec.* **6**, 39.

193. KITCHING, J. A. (1956) Food Vacuoles. *Protoplasmologia* **11** (D), 3b.

194. KLEIN, A. (1960) The effect of low temperature on the development of the lamellar system on chloroplast. *J. Biophys. Biochem. Cytol.* **8**, 529.

195. KLEIN, R. L., and NEFF, R. T. (1960) Osmotic properties of mitochondria isolated from *Acanthamoeba* sp. *Expt'l. Cell Res.* **19**, 133.

196. KLEINSCHMIDT, A., and KINDER, E. (1950a) Elektronenoptische Befunde an Ratten-trypanosomen. *Zbl. Bakt.* (1. Abt. Orig.), **156**, 219.

197. KLEINSCHMIDT, A., and KINDER, E. (1950b) Elektronenoptische Untersuchungen an Trypanosomen. *Optik* **7**, 322.

198. KRANEVELD, F. C., HOUWINK, A. L., and KEIDEL, H. J. W. (1951) Electron micro-scopical investigations on trypanosomes. I. Some preliminary data regarding the structure of *Trypanosoma evansi. Proc. Acad. Sci. Amst.* **54**, 393.

199. KOFOID, C. A., and SWEZY, O. (1915) Mitosis and multiple fission in trichomonad flagellates. *Proc. Amer. Acad. Arts. Sci.* **51**, 289.

200. KUDO, R. R. (1926) Observations on *Lophomonas blattarum*, a flagellate inhabiting the colon of the cockroach *Blatta orientalis. Arch. Protistenk.* **53**, 191.

201. KUDO, R. R. (1963) *Protozoology.* 4th ed. Charles C. Thomas, Springfield, Ill.

202. KUFF, E. L., and DALTON, A. J. (1959) Biochemical studies of isolated Golgi mem-branes. In *Subcellular Particles*, ed. T. HAYASHI, p. 114. The Ronald Press Co., New York, N.Y.

203. KUMMEL, G. (1958) Die Gleitbewegung der Gregarinen. Elektronen-mikroskopische und experimentelle Untersuchungen. *Arch. f. Protistenk.* **102**, 501.

204. LACKEY, J. B. (1929) Studies in the life histories of Euglenida 1. The cytology of *Entosiphon sulcatum* (Duj.) Stein. *Arch. Protist.* **66**, 176.

205. LACY, D. D., and MILES, H. B. (1959) Observations by electron microscopy on the structure of an acephaline gregarine (*Apolocystis elongata*, Phillips and Mackinnon.) *Nature*, London **183**, 1456.

206. LAVIER, G. (1927) Sur la structure du corps parabasal des trypanosomes. *Compt. Rend. Acad. Sci.*, Paris **186**, 106.

207. LEUWENHOEK, A. (1677) Letters translated in *Philosophical Transactions*, London **12**, 821.

208. LEHNINGER, A. L. (1962) Water uptake and extrusion by mitochondria in relation to oxidative phosphorylation. *Physiol. Rev.* **42**, 467.

209. LEWIS, W. H. (1931) Pinocytosis. *Bull. Johns Hopkins Hospital* **49**, 17.

210. LINNANE, A. W., VITOLS, E., and NOWLAND, P. G. (1962) Studies on the origin of yeast mitochondria. *J. Cell. Biol.* **13**, 345.

211. LOFGREN, R. (1950) The structure of *Leishmania tropica* as revealed by phase and electron microscopy. *J. Bact.* **60**, 617.

212. LUDVIC, J. (1954) Studium bunecne morfologie *Trichomonas foetus* (Reidmüller) elektronovym mikroskopen. *Mem. Soc. Zool. Tchecosl.* **18**, 189.

213. LUDVIC, J. (1960) The electron microscopy of *Sarcocystis miescheriana* Kuhn 1865. *J. Protozool.* **7**, 128.

214. LWOFF, A., and LWOFF, M. (1931) Recherches sur la morphologie de *Leptomonas faciculata* et de *L. oncopelti* (Flagelles trypanosomides). *Arch. Zool. Exp. Gen.* **71**, 21.

215. LWOFF, A., and LWOFF, M. (1931a) Recherches morphologiques sur *Leptomonas ctenocephali*. Remarques sur L'appareil parabasal. *Bull. Biol.* **65**, 170.

216. MANTON, I. (1959) Electron microscopical observations on a very small flagellate: The problem of *Chromulina pusilla* Butcher. *J. Mar. Biol. Assoc. U.K.* **38**, 319.

217. MAST, S. O. (1938) Factors involved in the process of orientation of lower organisms in light. *Biol. Rev.* **13**, 186.

218. MAST, S. O. (1942) The hydrogen ion concentration of the content of the food vacuoles and the cyptoplasm in amoeba and other phenomena concerning food vacuoles. *Biol. Bull.* **83**, 173.

219. MAST, S. O., and DOYLE, W. L. (1934) Ingestion of fluid by amoeba. *Protoplasma* **20**, 255.

220. MARSHALL, J. M., SCHUMAKER, V. N., and BRANDT, P. W. (1959) Pinocytosis in amoebae. *Ann. N.Y. Acad. Sci.* **78**, 515.

221. McCALLA, D. R. (1962) Chloroplast of *Euglena gracilis* affected by furadantin. *Science* **137**, 225.

222. McQUILLEN, K. (1956) Capabilities of bacterial protoplasts, in *Bacterial Anatomy*, (E. T. C. SPOONER and B. A. D. STOCKER, Eds.) Cambridge University Press, 127.

223. MERCER, E. H. (1959) An electron microscopic study of *Amoeba proteus*. *Proc. Roy. Soc. B*, **150**, 216.

224. MERESCHKOWSKI, C. (1905) Über Natur und Ursprung der Chromatophoren im Pflanzenreiche. *Biol. Centralbl.* **25**, 593.

225. MYER, H., and OLIVERA MUSACCHIO, M. DE (1960) Electron microscope study of the exoerthrocytic form of *Plasmodium gallinaceum* in thin sections of infected tissue cultures. *J. Protozool.* **7**, 222.

226. MEYER, H., and QUEIROGA, L. T. (1960) Submicroscopical aspects of *Schizotrypanum cruzi* in thin sections. *J. Protozool.* **7**, 124.

227. MOLLENHAUER, H. H., WHALEY, W. G., and LEECH, J. H. (1961) A function of the Golgi apparatus in outer rootcap cells. *J. Ultrastructure Res.* **5**, 193.

228. MOSKOWITZ, N. (1951) Observation on some intestinal flagellates from reptilian host (Squamata). *J. Morph.* **89**, 257.

229. MUEHLPFORDT, H. (1959) Vergleichende Untersuchung über die Wirkung des Trypaflavins auf den Blepharoplast verschiedener Trypanosomen. *Zeit. Tropenmed. Parasit.* **19**, 19.

230. MUEHLPFORDT, H. VON, and BAYER, M. (1961) Elektronenmikroskopische Untersuchungen an Protozoen (*Trypanosoma ganbiense*) *Z.F. Tropenmedizin und Parasitologie* **12**, 334.

231. MÜLLER, M., and ROHLICH, P. (1961) Studies on feeding and digestion in protozoa. II. Food vacuole cycle in *Tetrahymena Corlissi*. Acta Morphologica. *Acad. Sci. Hungaricae* **10**, 297.

231 a. NADLER, J. E. (1929) Notes on the loss and regeneration of the pellicle in *Blepharisma undulans*. *Biol. Bull.* **56**, 327.

232. NAHM, L. J. (1940) The problem of Golgi material in plant cells. *Bot. Rev.* **6**, 49.

233. NASSONOV, D. (1924) Der Excretionapparat (Kontraktile Vacuole) der Protozoa als Homologon des Golgischen Apparats der Meteozoazellen. *Arch. f. Mik. Anat. u. Entruick. Mech.* **103**, 437.

234. NATH, V., and DUTTA, G. P. (1962) Cytochemistry of protozoa, with particular reference to the Golgi apparatus and the mitochondria. *Internat'l. Rev. of Cytol.* **13**, 323.

235. NEFF, R. H. (1960) Volume, nucleic acid and nitrogen contents of strains of green and colorless *Euglena gracilis* and of *Astasia longa*. *J. Protozool.* **7**, 69.

236. NEWTON, B. A., and HORNE, R. W. (1957) Intracellular structures in *Strigomonas oncopelti*. Cytoplasmic structures containing ribo-nucleoprotein. *Expt'l. Cell Res.* **13**, 563.

237. NOIROT-TIMOTHÉE, C. (1957) L'ultrastructure de l'appareil de Golgi des Infusoires Ophryoscolecidae. *Compt. Rend. Acad. Sci. Paris* **244**, 2847.

238. NOIROT-TIMOTHÉE, C. (1958) Quelques particularités de l'ultrastructure *d'Opalina ranarum* (Protozoa, Flagellate). *Compt. Rend. Acad. Sci. Paris* **247**, 2445.

239. NOIROT-TIMOTHÉE, C. (1959) Recherches sur l'ultrastructure *d'Opalina ranarum*. *Ann. Sci. Nat. Zool. et Biol. Animale* **12**, 265.

240. NOIROT-TIMOTHÉE, C. (1960) Étude d'une familie de cilies: Les "Ophryoscolecidae", Structure et ultrastructure. Theses Paris, Masson et Cie., Editures. Libraires de l'Academie de Medicine.

241. NOVIKOFF, A. B. (1960) Biochemical and staining reactions of cytoplasmic constituents. In *Developing Cell Systems and Their Control*. The Ronald Press Co., New York, p. 167.

2a*

242. NOVIKOFF, A. B., HEUS, M., ESSNER, E., and IACIOFANO, P. (1961) Nucleosidedi-phosphatase activity in the endoplasmic reticulum and nuclear membrane of liver and other cells. First Ann. Meeting of the Amer. Soc. for Cell Biol., p. 155.
243. NOVIKOFF, A. B., ESSNER, E., GOLDFISHER, S., and HEUS, M. (1962) Nucleosidi-phosphatase activities of cytomembranes. Sym. Internat'l. Soc. Cell *Biol.* **1**, 149.
244. OBERLING, C. (1959) The structure of cytoplasm. *Int'l. Rev. Cytol.* **2**, 1.
245. PALADE, G. E. (1952) A study of fixation for electron microscopy, *J. Expt'l. Med.* **95**, 285.
246. PALADE, G. E. (1952a) The fine structure of mitochondria. *Anat. Rec.* **114**, 427.
247. PALADE, G. E. (1953a) An electron microscope study of the mitochondrial structure. *J. Histochem. Cytochem.* **1**, 188.
248. PALADE, G. E. (1953b) Fine structure of blood capillaries. *J. Appl. Physics* **24**, 1424.
249. PALADE, G. E. (1955a) A small particulate component of the cytoplasm. *J. Biophys. Biochem. Cytol.* **1**, 59.
250. PALADE, G. E. (1955b) Studies on the endoplasmic reticulum II. Simple disposition in cells *in situ. J. Biophys. Biochem. Cytol.* **1**, 567.
251. PALADE, G. E. (1956) The endoplasmic reticulum. *J. Biophys. Biochem. Cytol.* **2**, (Suppl.) 85.
252. PALADE, G. E. (1958) Microsomes and ribonucleoprotein particles. In *Microsomal particles and protein synthesis*, ed. R. B. Roberts, Pergamon Press, New York.
253. PALAY, S. L. (1958) The morphology of secretion, in *Frontiers in Cytology*, p. 305. Yale Univ. Press, New Haven.
254. PALAY, S. L. (1963) Alveolate vesicles in Purkinje cells of the rat's cerebellum. *J. Cell Biol.* **19**, 89A.
255. PAPPAS, G. D. (1954) Structural and cytochemical studies of the cytoplasm in the family Amoebidae. *Ohio J. Sci.* **54**, 195.
256. PAPPAS, G. D. and BRANDT, P. W. (1959) Mitochondria. I. Fine structure of the complex patterns in the mitochondria of *Pelomyxa carolinensis* Wilson (*Chaos chaos* L.) *J. Biophysic. Biochem. Cytol.* **6**, 85.
257. PASTOR, E. P., and FENNELL, R. A. (1959) Some observations on the esterases of *Tetrahymena pyriformis W.* II. Some factors affecting aliesterase and cholinesterase activity. *J. Morph.* **104**, 143.
258. PATTIELO, W. H., and BECKER, E. R. (1955) Cytochemistry of *Emeria brunette* and *E. acervulina* of the chicken. *J. Morph.* **96**, 1.
259. PENARD, E. (1922) Le genre Loxodes. *Revue Suisse de Zool.* **25**, 1.
260. PIEKARSIK, G. (1949) Blepharoplast und Trypaflavinwirkung bei *Trypanosoma brucei. Zbl. Bakt.* (1. Abt. Orig.) **153**, 109.
261. PITELKA, D. R. (1961) Observations on the kinetoplast-mitochondrion and the cyto-stome of *Bodo. Expt'l. Cell. Res.* **25**, 87.
262. PITELKA, D. R. (1963) *Electron Microscopic Structure of Protozoa.* Pergamon Press, New York.
263. POLLISTER, A. W., and POLLISTER, P. F. (1957) The structure of the Golgi apparatus. *Intn'l. Rev. Cytol.* **6**, 85.
264. PORTER, K. R. (1956) The submicroscopic morphology of protoplasm. *Harvey Lect.* **51**, 175.
265. PORTER, K. R. (1961) The endoplasmic reticulum: Some current interpretations of its form and function. In *Biological Structure and Function* (eds., T. W. GOODWIN and O. LINDBERG). Academic Press, New York, p. 128.
266. PORTER, K. R., and PALADE, G. E. (1957) Studies on the endoplasmic reticulum III. Its form and distribution in striated muscle cells. *J. Biophys. Biochem. Cytol.* **3**, 269.
267. PORTER, K. R., and MACHADO, R. D. (1960) Studies on the endoplasmic reticulum. IV. Its form and distribution during mitosis in cells of onion root tip. *J. Biophys. Biochem. Cytol.* **7**, 167.

268. PORTER, K. R. CLAUDE, A., and FULLAM, E. (1945) A study of tissue culture cells by electron microscopy. *J. Expt'l. Med.* **81**, 233.

269. POWERS, E. L., EHRET, C. F., and ROTH, L. E. (1955) Mitochondrial structure in Paramecium as revealed by electron microscopy. *Biol. Bull.* **108**, 182.

270. POWERS, E. L., EHRET, C. F., ROTH, L. E., and MINICK, O. T. (1956) The internal organization of mitochondria. *J. Biophys. Biochem. Cytol.* **2**, 341.

271. PRINGSHEIM, E. G., and HOVASSE, R. (1948) The loss of chromatophores in *Euglena gracilis. New Phytol.* **47**, 52.

272. PROVASOLI, L., and PRINGSHEIM, E. G. (1951) Destruction of chloroplast by streptomycin. *Cold. Spr. Symp. Quart. Biol.* **16**, 113.

273. PYNE, C. K. (1958) Electron microscopic investigations of the leptomonad form of *Leishmania donovani. Expt'l. Cell Res.* **14**, 388.

274. PYNE, C. K. (1959) L'ultrastructure de *Cryptobia helicis* (Fam. Bodonidae). *Compt. Rend. Sci. Paris* **248**, 1410.

275. PYNE, C. K. and CHAKROBORTZ, J. (1958) Electron microscopic studies on the basal apparatus of the flagellum in the protozoan, *Leishmania donovani. J. Protozool.* **5**, 264.

276. RANDALL, J. T. (1957) The fine structure of the protozoan *Spirostomum ambiguum. Symp. Soc. Exptl. Biol.* **10**, 185.

277. RANDALL, J. T., and JACKSON, F. S. (1958) Fine structure and function in *Stentor polymorphus. J. Biophys. Biochem. Cytol.* **4**, 807.

278. REVEL, J. P., and HAY, E. D. (1963) An autoradiographic and electron microscopic study of collagen synthesis in differentiating cartilage. *Z. Zellforsch.* **61**, 110.

279. RIS, H. (1960) The structure of the kinetoplast in trypanosomes. 10ème Congrès. Int. Biol. Cellulaire, Paris. Resumé des communications, 232. Paris: L'Expansion Scient. Franc.

280. RIS, H. (1961) Ultrastructure and molecular organization of genetic systems. *Canadian J. Genet. and Cytol.* **3**, 95.

281. RIS, H. (1962) Ultrastructure of certain self dependent cytoplasmic organelles. In Electron Microscopy (5th International Congress for Electron Microscopy) ed. S.S. Breese, Jr. 2: XX-1. Academic Press, New York.

282. RIS, H., and PLAUT, W. (1962) Ultrastructure of DNA-containing areas in chloroplast of *Chlamydomonas. J. Cell Biol.* **13**, 383.

283. ROBERTSON, J. D. (1959) The ultrastructure of cell membranes and their derivatives. *Biochemical Soc. Symposia* **16**, 3.

284. ROSENBAUM, R. M., and WITTNER, M. (1962) The activity of intracytoplasmic enzymes associated with feeding and digestion in *Paramecium caudatum.* The possible relationship to neutral red granules. *Arch. Protistenk.* **106**, 223.

285. ROTH, L. E. (1957) An electron microscope study of the cytology of the protozoan *Euplotes patella J. Biophys. Biochem. Cytol.* **3**, 985.

286. ROTH, L. E. (1959a) A filamentous component of protozoan fibrillar systems. *J. Ultrastructure Res.* **1**, 223.

287. ROTH, L. E. (1959b) An electron microscope study of the cytology of the protozoan *Peranema trichophorum. J. Protozool.* **6**, 197.

288. ROTH, L. E. (1960) Electron microscopy of pinocytosis and food vacuoles in *Pelomyxa. J. Protozool.* **7**, 176.

289. ROTH, L. E., and MINICK, O. T. (1961) Electron microscopy of nuclear and cytoplasmic events during division in *Tetrahymena pyriformis* strains W and HAM 3. *J. Protozool.* **8**, 12.

290. ROTH, T. F., and PORTER, K. R. (1964) Yolk protein uptake in the oocyte of the mosquito *Ades aegypti. J. Cell Biol.* **20**, 313.

291. ROTH, T. F., and PORTER, K. R. (1963) Membrane differentiation for protein uptake. *Fed. Proc.* **22**, No. 2.

292. ROUILLER, CH. (1960) Physiological and pathological changes in mitochondrial morphology. *Internat'l. Rev. Cytol.* (eds. G. H. BOURNE and J. F. DANIELLI) Academic Press **9**, 227.

293. ROUILLER, CH., and FAURÉ-FRÉMIET, E. (1958) Structure fine d'une flagelle Chrysomonadien: *Chromulina psammobia. Expt'l. Cell. Res.* **14**, 47.

294. RUDZINSKA, M. A., and TRAGER, W. (1957) Intracellular phagotrophy by malaria parasites: an electron microscope study of *Plasmodium lophurae. J. Protozool.* **4**. 190.

295. RUDZINSKA, M. A., and TRAGER, W. (1959) Phagotrophy and two new structures in the malaria parasite *Plasmodium berghei. J. Biophys. Biochem. Cytol.* **6**, 103.

296. RUDZINSKA, M. A., and TRAGER, W. (1962) Intracellular phagotrophy in *Babesia rodhaini* as revealed by electron microscopy. *J. Protozool.* **9**, 279.

297. RUDZINSKA, M. A., D'ALESANDRO, P. A., TRAGER, W. (1962) The fine structure of the intracellular and leptomonad stages of *Leishmania donovani. J. Protozool.* (Suppl.) **9**,8.

298. RUDZINSKA, M. A., D'ALESANDRO, P., and TRAGER, W. (1964) The fine structure of *Leishmania donovani* and the role of the kinetoplast in the leishmania-leptomonad transformation. *J. Protozool.* **11**, 160.

299. RYTER, A., KELLENBERGER, E., BIRCH-ANDERSEN, A., and MAALOE, O. (1958) Étude au microscope électronique de plasmas contenant de l'acid désoxyribonucléique. *Z. Naturforsch.* **13**, 597.

300. SAMUELS, R. (1941) The morphology and division of *Trichomonas augusta* Alexeieff. *Trans. Amer. Micr. Soc.* **60**, 421.

301. SAGER, R. (1959) The architecture of the chloroplast in relation to its photosynthesis activities. *Brookhaven Symp. Biol.*, **11**, 101.

302. SAGER, R., and PALADE, G. E. (1954) Chloroplast structure in green and yellow strains of *Chlamydomonas. Expt'l. Cell Res.* **7**, 584.

303. SAGER, R., and PALADE, G. E. (1957) Structure and development of the chloroplast in *Chlamydomonas.* I. The normal green cell. *J. Biophys. Biochem. Cytol.* **3**, 463.

304. SAGER, R., and ZALOKAR, M. (1958) Pigments and photosynthesis in a carotenoid deficient mutant of *Chlamydomonas. Nature,* London **182**, 98.

305. SCHER, S., and SAGAN, L. (1962) Comparative studies of chloroplast replication: Ultraviolet inactivation and photoreactivation of cytoplasmic DNA synthesis associated with chloroplast replication in *Euglena gracilis. J. Protozool.* (Suppl.) **9**, 13.

306. SCHNEIDER, L. (1960) Elektronenmikroskopische Untersuchungen über das Nephridialsystem von Paramecium. *J. Protozool.* **7**, 75.

307. SCHOLTYSECK, E. O. (1962) Electron microscope studies on *Eimeria perforans* (Sporozoa). *J. Protozool.* **9**, 407.

308. SCHUMAKER, V. N. (1958) Uptake of protein from solution by *Amoeba proteus. Expt'l. Cell Res.* **15**, 314.

309. SEAMAN, G. R. (1959) Cytochemical evidence for urease activity in *Tetrahymena. J. Protozool.* **6**, 331.

310. SEAMAN, G. R. (1961) Acid phosphatase activity associated with phagotrophy in the ciliate, *Tetrahymena. J. Biophys. Biochem. Cytol.* **11**, 243.

311. SEAMAN, G. R., and GOTTLIEB, S. (1957) Protein synthesis by subcellular particles of *Tetrahymena pyriformis. J. Protozool.* **4**, (Suppl.), 11.

312. SEDAR, A. W., and PORTER, K. R. (1955) The fine structure of cortical components of *Paramecium multimicronucleatum. J. Biophys. Biochem. Cytol.* **1**, 583.

313. SEDAR, A. W., and RUDZINSKA, M. A. (1956) Mitochondria of Protozoa. *J. Biophys. Biochem. Cytol.* **2**, 331.

314. SEDAR, A. W., and BURDE, R. M. (1965) Localization of the succinic dehydrogenase system in *Escherichia coli* using combined techniques of cytochemistry and electron microscopy. *J. Cell. Biol.* **24**, 285.

315. SHARMA, N. N., and BOURNE, G. H. (1963) Studies on the histochemical distribution of oxidative enzymes in *Trichomonas vaginalis. J. Histochem. Cytochem.* **11**, 628.

316. SHIPLEY, P. G. (1916) The vital staining in *Trypanosoma lewisi* with Janus green. *Anat. Rec.* **10**, 439.
317. VON SIEBOLD, C. T. (1848) Lehrbuch der vergleichende Anatomie der Wirbellosen.
318. SIEGEL, R. W. (1960) Hereditary endosymbiosis, *Paramecium bursaria. Expt'l. Cell Res.* **19**, 239.
319. SIEKEVITZ, P. (1957) Powerhouse of the cell. *Scientific American* **191**, 131.
320. SIEKEVITZ, P. (1961) The effects of spermine on the nucleoprotein particles of guinea-pig pancreas. In *Biological Structure and Function*. Ed. T. W. GOODWIN and O. LINDBERG. Academic Press, New York, p. 239.
321. SJÖSTRAND, F. S. (1956) The ultrastructure of cells as revealed by the electron microscope. *Int. Rev. Cytol.* **5**, 455.
322. SMYTH, J. D. (1943) Golgi apparatus of Protozoa. *Biol. Rev.* **19**, 94.
323. STEINERT, G., FIRKET, H., and STEINERT, M. (1958). Synthèse d'acid désoxyribonucléique dans le corps parabasal de *Trypanosoma mega. Expt'l. Cell Res.* **15**, 632.
324. STEINERT, M. (1958a) Études sur le déterminisme de la morphogénèses Trypanosome. *Expt'l. Cell Res.* **15**, 560.
325. STEINERT, M. (1958b) Action morphogénétique de l'urée sur le Trypanosome. *Expt'l. Cell Res.* **15**, 431.
326. STEINERT, M. (1960) Mitochondria associated with the kinetonucleus of *Trypanosoma mega. J. Biophys. Biochem. Cytol.* **8**, 542.
327. STEINERT, M., and NOVIKOFF, A. B. (1960) The existence of a cytostome and the occurrence of pinocytosis in the trypanosome, *Trypanosoma mega. J. Biophys. Biochem. Cytol.* **8**, 542.
328. STEINERT, M., and STEINERT, G. (1962) La synthèse de l'acide désoxyribonucléique au cours du cycle de division de *Trypanosoma mega. J. Protozool.* **9**, 203.
329. SULLIVAN, W. D. (1950) Distribution of alkaline phosphatase in *Colpidium campylum. Trans. Amer. Micro. Soc.* **69**, 267.
330. SULLIVAN, W. R., and J. J. SPARKS. (1961) The effect of ultraviolet radiation on succinic dehydrogenase activity during different stages of cell division. *Expt'l. Cell Res.* **23**, 436.
331. SWEZY, O. (1916) The kinetonucleus of flagellates and the binuclear theory of Hartmann. Univ. Calif. Publ. *Zool.* **16**, 185.
332. THEODORIDES, J. (1959) Étude des Eugrégarines au microscope électronique. Proc. XV. Int. Congr. Zool. Lond., pp. 477.
333. TOBIE, E. J. (1951) Loss of the kinetoplast in a strain of *Trypanosoma equiperdum. Trans. Amer. Micr. Soc.* **70**, 251.
334. TORCH, R. (1955) Cytological studies on *Pelomyxa carolinensis* with special references to the mitochondria. *J. Protozool.* **2**, 167.
335. TRAGER, W. (1964) The cytoplasm of Protozoa in *The Cell* (eds. J. BRACHET and A. E. MIRSKY). Vol. **6**, p. 81. Academic Press, New York.
336. TRAGER, W. and RUDZINSKA, M. A. (1964) The riboflavin requirement and the effects of acriflavin on the fine structure of the kinetoplast of *Leishmania tarentolae. J. Protozool.* **11**, 133.
337. VICKERMAN, K. (1962) Patterns of cellular organization of *Limax amoebae*. An electron microscope study. *Expt'l. Cell Res.* **26**, 497.
338. VIVIER, E., and SCHREVEL, J. (1964) Étude, au microscope électronique, d'une grégarine du genre *Selenidium* parasite de *Sabellaria alveolata. J. Microscopie* **3**, 651.
339. VOLKONSKY, M. (1929) Les phénomènes cytologiques au cours de la digestion intracellulaire de quelques cilies. *Compt. Rend. Soc. Biol.* **101**, 133.
340. VOLKONSKY, M. (1934) L'aspect cytologique de la digestion intracellulaire, *Arch. Exp. Zellforsch.* **15**, 355.
341. WAGER, H. (1899) On the eye-spot and flagellum in *Euglena viridia. J. Linn. Soc. (Zool.).* **27**, 463.

342. WANKO, T., JACOBS, L., and GAVIN ,M. A. (1962) Electron microscope study of *Toxoplasma* cysts in mouse brain. *J. Protozool.* **9**, 235.

343. WATSON, M. L. (1955) The nuclear envelope. Its structure and relation to the cytoplasmic membranes. *J. Biophys. Biochem. Cytol* **1**, 257.

344. WEIBULL, C., Bacterial protoplasts, their formation and characteristics, in *Bacterial Anatomy* (E. T. C. SPOONER, and B. A. D. STOCKER, editors). Cambridge Univ. Press. 1956, p. 111.

345. WEISS, P. A. (1961) Fine structure and pattern of living things, in *Promise of the Life Sciences*, U.S. Dept. of Agriculture Grad. Sch. Wash., D. C., p. 53.

346. WEISZ, P. B. (1950) On the mitochondrial nature of the pigment granules in *Stentor* and *Blepharisma*. *J. Morph.* and *Physiol.* **86**, 177.

347. WENRICH, D. H. (1921) The structure and division of *Trichomonas muris* Hartman *J. Morphol.* **36**, 119.

348. WERBITZKI, F. W. (1910) Ueber blepharoplastlose Trypanosomen. *Centr. Bakt. u. Parasitenk. Abt.* 1 *Orig.* **53**, 303.

349. WETTSTEIN, D. VON (1959) Developmental changes in chloroplast and their genet control, in *Developmental Cytology* (ed. D. RUDNICK), The Ronald Press Co., New York, p. 123.

350. WICHTERMAN, R. (1953) *The Biology of Paramecium*. Blakiston Co., New York.

351. WILSON, E. B. (1947) *The cell in Development and Heredity.* 3rd ed. The Macmillan Co., New York.

352. WILLIAMS, N., ANDERSON, E., KESSEL, R., and BEAMS, H. W. (1960) Electron microscope observations on synchronously dividing *Tetrahymena*. *J. Protozool.* (Suppl.) **7**, 27.

352a. WILLIAMSON, J. R. (1964) Adipose tissue: Morphological changes associated with lipid mobilization. *J. Cell Biol.* **20**, 57.

353. WITTICH, G. H. VON (1863) Ueber den Farbstoff der *Euglena sanguinea*. *Virchows Arch.* **27**, 573.

354. WOHLFARTH-BOTTERMANN, K. E. (1956a) Die Entstehung, die Vermehrung und die Abscheidung geformter Sekrete der Mitochondrien von *Paramecium*. Proceedings of the Stockholm Conference on Electron Microscopy. Stockholm.

355. WOHLFARTH-BOTTERMANN, K. E. (1956b) Protistenstudien. VII. Die Feinstruktur der Mitochondrien von *Paramecium caudatum*. *Z. Naturf.* **11**b, 578.

356. WOHLFARTH-BOTTERMANN, K. E. (1957) Cytologische Studien. IV. Die Entstehung, Vermehrung und Sekretabgabe der Mitochondrien von *Paramecium*. *Z. Naturf.* **12**b, 164.

357. WOHLFARTH-BOTTERMANN, K. E. (1960) Licht- und elektronenmikroskopische Untersuchungen an der Amoebe *Hyalodiscus simplex* n. sp. *Protoplasma* **52**, 58.

358. WOHLFARTH-BOTTERMANN, K. E. (1961a) Die elektronenmikroskopische Finestruktur des Grundcytoplasmas nach "wasserloscher Einbettung". *Protoplasma* **54**, 20.

359. WOHLFARTH-BOTTERMANN, K. E. (1961b) Zum Mechanismus der Cytoplasmaströmung in dünnen Faden. *Protoplasma* **54**, 1.

360. WOLKEN, J. J. (1956) A molecular morphology of *Euglena gracilis* var. *bacillaris*. *J. Protozool.* **3**, 211.

361. WOLKEN, J. J. (1958) Studies of photoreceptor structures. *Ann. N. Y. Acad. Sci.* **74**, 164.

362. WOLKEN, J. J. 1961. The chloroplast: Its lamellar structure and molecular organization. In *Macromolecular Complexes* ed. M. V. EDDS, JR. The Ronald Press Co., New York, p, 85.

363. WOLKEN, J. J., and PALADE, G. E. (1952) Fine structure of chloroplast in two flagellates. *Nature*, Lond. **170**, 114.

364. WOLKEN, J. J., and PALADE, G. E. (1953) An electron microscope study of two flagellates. Chloroplast structure and variation. *Ann. N.Y. Acad. Sci.* **56**, 873.

365. WOLKEN, J. J., and SCHWERTZ, F. A. (1953) Chlorophyll monolayers in chloroplasts, *J. Gen. Physiol.* **37**, 111.

366. ZEIGEL, R. F. and DALTON, A. J. (1962) Speculations based on the morphology of the Golgi systems in several types of protein secreting cells. *J. Cell Biol.* **15**, 45.

# MOTILE BEHAVIOR OF PROTOZOA

THEODORE L. JAHN AND EUGENE C. BOVEE

*Department of Zoology, University of California, Los Angeles*

# CONTENTS

# I. MOVEMENT AS BEHAVIOR †

## A. As Evidence of Response to Stimuli

Movement is often the only readily detected protozoan response to stimuli.[657] Sollberger[856] considers "incessant movement in time and space" to be perhaps the principal characteristic of all life; and Carlson[150] suggests a fundamental calculable survival value for cell motility. It is, therefore, no surprise that for over 200 years the movements of protozoa have been considered the main indicators of their nature. Woodruff and Bunzel[986] among many others, use cessation of ciliary movement as a death criterion.

The site where behavior begins may be of submolecular size,[437, 872] and the resulting processes may be functional at the molecular level,[178, 473, 474, 475] but the gross results are usually changes in movement characteristic of each protozoan species.[89, 94, 140, 790, 791, 815]

## B. Absence of Neural Complications

The claims that protozoan fibrillar systems, especially in ciliates, work as "neuroid" systems[148, 356, 763, 806, 811, 849, 880, 881] have not been structurally nor functionally substantiated (cf. Section IV Ge and also reviews by Wichterman,[953] Pitelka,[715, 716] Jahn and Bovee,[443, 444] Taylor[882]). Protozoan responses are closely and cooperatively interrelated through the changing states of polymers in intracellular processes and dynamic properties of their surface membranes,[983] and protozoan movements must be considered in relation to hydrodynamics and thermodynamics and other applications of biophysics to cellular function.

## II. GENERAL EFFECTS OF PHYSICAL AND CHEMICAL FACTORS ON MOVEMENT

For over a century protozoa have been bludgeoned experimentally by various physical sources of energy, and treated with an imposing array of both inorganic and organic chemicals. Much human effort has been expended in thus observing and recording protozoan reactions, but the basic mechanisms of the reactions are only beginning to appear. The early and generally

† Based partly on experimental work financed by NIH Grants GM 6462 and GM 8611, NSF Grant GB 1589, and ONR Task NR-304-502, Contract Nonr 233.[65]

assumed "simplicity" of protozoan form and function, and later an alternative assumption of complex acellular evolutionary diversion[219, 417] are perhaps under- and over-estimates of protozoan organization. Protozoa are undeniably complex, not simple. Nevertheless, protozoa respond to gross changes in the physical environment as most other living things do, i.e., they move, or alter their movements. They accelerate or decelerate, turn or reverse, stop and start up again, and lose or gain coordination as they respond.

## A. The Shock Reaction

Perhaps Engelmann[251] first described the "shock" stoppage of protoplasmic movement in cells, including protozoa. He noted that electric current, passed through the water, abruptly stopped protoplasmic flow, movement and locomotion of unicellular organisms. This reaction to a suddenly applied environmental stimulus of shock strength is now known to be a generalized response of protozoa (and other single cells) whether the stimulus is white light,[268, 631] ultraviolet rays,[105, 106, 301, 379] X-rays,[199, 954] radium or other very short $(\alpha, \beta, \gamma)$ radiations,[397, 595, 819, 962] electricity,[236, 252, 349] ultrasonic vibration,[366, 804] mechanical agitation,[44, 81, 84, 529] mechanical injury,[681, 880] high hydrostatic pressure,[130, 532, 571] temperature change,[332] osmotic pressure,[378] pH,[378] gas tensions,[306, 409] metallic cation concentrations,[638, 691, 740] anesthetics and other fat solvents,[205] "tranquilizers," e.g., chlorpromazine,[672] and animal and plant toxins.[585, 825]

If the shock stimulus is severe enough, movement not only stops, but peripheral protoplasm contracts, and solation, disintegration and death follow.[39, 375, 376, 557] If movement is resumed after the possibly lethal stress has been removed, the movement may be abnormal.[955, 820]

When the change of conditions is initially of shock-strength, but sub-lethal, the protozoon usually resumes movement and locomotion after a time, often quickly, and even while the formerly shock-strength conditions continue or are repeatedly applied; i.e., the protozoon "adapts". Usually the resumed locomotion is neodirectional, often reversed (review Mast, [638]).

## B. A Classification of Responses

Organisms are assumed to have a *primary orientation* in space and time. This is altered by movements of the organisms in response to changes in environmental conditions, the alterations being termed *secondary orientations*.[271] The *secondary orientations* of protozoa are achieved without the functioning of a central nervous system as in higher organisms and at least in most cases also without even a neuromotor system. This secondary orientation directs the long axis of the body of the organism toward or away from the source of stimulation, or in some instances at an oblique angle to the source. Any movement directed in relation to the stimulus is referred to as a *taxis*. *Taxes* have been sub-divided into: 1) *tropotaxis*, a bilaterally-equated, smooth straight movement toward or away from stimulus; 2) *telotaxis*, a similar response without bilateral equating; 3) *klinotaxis*, movements directed toward or away from stimulus, plus bending, and comparative movements.[271] If the response is a non-directed velocity change it is termed a *kinesis*. That category has also been split into *orthokinesis*, or alterations of linear motile rate, and *klinokinesis*, or changes in the direction and rate of turning. Both taxes and kineses occur.

## C. Reactions to Radiation

### 1. VISIBLE LIGHT†

Protozoa usually respond to visible light below shock intensity. Where a spectral sensitivity has been determined it is principally to the shorter wave lengths, i.e., blue-greens, blues and blue violets (see Table 1), and the response is mainly evoked by a specific wave-length. In *Euglena gracilis*, for example, monochromatic light of the critical wavelength causes response at lesser intensities than does "white light" and at still lower intensities if the monochromatic rays are polarized.[979]

Two important but generally ignored facts concerning the reactions of *Euglena* to light are: 1) the photosensitive pigment probably is in the flagellar swelling rather than in the eyespot,[932] and 2) the action spectra of the organism may not be directly correlated with absorption peaks of the organism; and the errors in the latter are caused by light scattering.[573, 574, 842] On these bases some of the published data and speculation should be reevaluated.

What role the stigma plays is not clear, but it probably is a screening pigment.[932] Wolken[981] says that the effective wavelengths of light are those at which photosynthetic peaks also occur[134]. Apochlorotic *Euglena* are insensitive to light if they have lost both the stigma and the photoreceptor (i.e., swelling at the root of the flagellum adjacent to the stigma, [932]) but are photonegative if they have lost only the stigma and retain the photoreceptor; periodic shading of the photoreceptor by the stigma is assumed to be necessary for the photopositive response.[316, 918] It seems probable that continuation of experiments of the type by Vavra and Aaronson[918] may eventually solve the problem.

Although flagellates and amebas generally show a particular spectral sensitivity, ciliates, other than *Stentor* spp., do not.[48, 638, 953] Intensity of light, however, is a factor in the rate and direction of movement by ciliates as well as by amebas and flagellates. Adaptations to very high intensities have been demonstrated, e.g., a dark adapted *Amoeba* is stimulated by as

† See also reviews, Mast[638]; Giese[298].

little as 0.05 meter candles of light[645] and may be shock-stopped for one second by a brief flash of light at 500 meter candles intensity, delivering 7000 meter-candle-seconds of light energy. It then resumes locomotion and continues to move in light gradually increased to 40,000 meter candles.[268] This adaptation to intense light is partly retained for 24 hours by *Amoeba proteus*.[270]

Other protozoa which may show shock intensity stoppage and subsequent adaptation to brighter light include *Paramecium caudatum*,[953] *Stentor niger*,[907] and *Peranema trichophorum*.[841] Most other protozoa studied behave similarly to a greater or lesser degree.

The response of protozoa to light seems to be less amenable to analysis than the response of simple eyes or of plant cells which respond by nerve impulses or by photosynthesis. The difficulties of analysis and the resulting apparent greater complexity appears to be related to the directness of the action of the environment on the responding organelle.

The fundamental chemical basis of the visual mechanism in the primary sensory cells of metazoa was elucidated by studies of the absorption curves of the sensitive visual pigments, e.g., rhodopsin, by the determination of the validity of the Roscoe-Bunsen law, namely, that $I$ (intensity) times $t$ (duration of stimulus) is constant for any given set of conditions, and by the discovery that both the visibility curve and the action spectrum correspond closely to the absorption curve of the visual pigment.

These advances showed that for a given visual response a given minimal amount of some unstable photoproduct must be formed from the sensitive visual pigment and that this unstable photoproduct initiates the response. In this way the fundamental mechanism for the response to light by animal eyes was determined. Furthermore, the amount of the sensitive visual pigment was found to vary with the immediate past history of the organism (i.e., whether it was light or dark adapted). Accordingly, we have now developed a helpful but still incomplete description of the visual process.[433, 452] Somewhat similar studies definitely linked the process of photosynthesis to chlorophyll.

However, for the protozoa these methods have failed in many cases. The Roscoe-Bunsen law often is not followed; the laws of light adaptation and dark adaptation as worked out for the animal eye are not followed; and no pigment can be isolated which corresponds to the action spectrum of the response. Either the mechanisms involved are very different from the simple photochemical relationship known for the eye, or the presence of this relationship is hidden by another set of intermediate phenomena much more complex than ordinarily supposed. In *Amoeba* the first possibility apparently applies.

Engelmann[252] observed that when an ameba is suddenly subjected to a bright light, movement abruptly stops ("shock reaction") and then is gradually resumed. If the light intensity is increased slowly no shock reaction occurs. The exact nature of the shock reaction is highly variable and may consist of almost any gradation between momentary retardation and complete stoppage, even with reversal in the direction of streaming after recovery. There is no fixed threshold, and the "all or none" law does not apply.[636]

A key to understanding this and related phenomena was provided by Mast[637] who found that application of a very small but bright beam of light to the anterior end of a moving ameba is followed by the conversion of anterior plasmasol to plasmagel, that this effect occurs independently in any given pseudopodium in a multipodal specimen, and that this effect is not transmitted to other regions of the organism. Light has no effect on the hyaloplasm. In monopodal amebas illumination of all portions except the anterior end, if maintained by moving the light, produced an increase of 100 per cent in the gel/sol ratio, a decrease in external diameter of the gel tube, a greater decrease in the diameters of the contained flowing sol, an increase in length of the organism, and an increase in the rate of movement. The decreased external diameter of the gel tube was described as an elastic contraction caused by increased gel strength.[637]

If we consider these observations in relation to an equation (Section IVB 2b, below) which describes the forces involved in locomotion, we see that if the whole *Amoeba* is illuminated the values of at least seven and probably nine factors are changed. For these reasons one should not expect to find a simple type of response such as that of the primary sense cell of an animal eye; therefore there is no reason to expect the Roscoe-Bunsen law to be followed. In view of the lack of quantitative data on these changes the only prediction possible is that the result should be complex.

The above observations indicate why Folger[268] found that the procedures of psycho-physics did not apply to the response of *Amoeba*. He determined the reaction time (RT) of the shock reaction in response to light. The minimal duration of the stimulus (SP) was determined, and the latent period (LP) of the response was obtained by subtracting SP from RT. He found that when the intensity of the stimulating light was varied, the intensity $I$ times the duration of the stimulus (SP) also varied, i.e., the Roscoe-Bunsen law was not followed. Therefore, Folger[268] concluded, correctly, that the reactions of *Amoeba* do not depend upon the presence of a photochemical system as postulated by Mast[628] for *Volvox* and by Hecht[372, 373] for *Ciona* and *Mya*, and as now well recognized in visual physiology.[433]

The results of Mast and Stahler[645] on the rate of ameboid movement at various light intensities are also complex and, in this sense at least, are in accordance with the above observations and ideas. The rate of movement in very dim red light was about 134 μ/sec, and intensities above about 200 meter candles (mc) produced a "shock reaction." The animals became accommodated in ten or more minutes. After thirty minutes of exposure to 15,000 mc the ameba travelled 50 per cent faster than in dim red light. The velocity when plotted against intensity rose from 134 μ/sec, passed through a maximum of 219 μ/sec at 15,000 mc, and decreased to 128 μ/sec at 40,000 mc. These results demonstrate that in spite of the sol to gel changes produced by light an ameba is capable of moving rapidly in fairly bright light. Therefore, the changes in the variables of the equation (Section IVB2b) produced by light and listed above must change not only with intensity but also with time. This makes behavior of the animal even more unpredictable. *A. proteus* is usually photonegative (i.e., negatively phototactic),[206, 630] but at times may be photopositive.[789, 636] This is consistent with the above mentioned results.

Light intensity affects both rate of protoplasmic movement and locomotion (Table 2). This may, in the wild, be related to a daily activity cycle, involving growth and division as well as movement (cf. page 54). Certain amebas become more and less active, approximating a diurnal cycle, as light intensity rises and falls.[81, 84, 469, 561]

High intensity of light at 60,000 meter candles is followed by rapid loco-motion in gradually adapted *Amoeba proteus*.[638] This may be a photo-negative response, since some amebas e.g., *Flamella citrensis*,[85] are so photonegative that their continuous rapid locomotion is lethal.

Sporulation is triggered by light in starved dark-adapted myce-tozoa,[193, 348] but not in well fed ones,[502] and in pigmented but not colorless ones.[327] Migrating slug-aggregates of acrasid amebas are sensitive to and move toward light of as low an intensity as that produced by a luminescent bacterial colony, and their sporulation is light stimulated.[74, 75] In complete darkness these activities are delayed.[551]

For reasons stated above the facts concerning the effect of light on *Amoeba* and on green flagellates make obvious the difference between the mechanisms involved and those found in vertebrates. Furthermore, the mechanisms probably differ in the various groups of protozoa. In *Amoeba* light may directly affect the contractile mechanism (the protoplasm) whereas in flagellates it may directly affect whatever mechanism controls the flagellar beat (possibly the flagellar swelling) or even the flagellum itself. Any such direct effects probably involve photochemical processes for which there may or may not be a specialized photosensitive pigment. However, regardless of the existence of a specialized pigment, the primary effect will involve an electronic mechanism.

The mechanism by which light starts the reactive mechanism in protozoa or the visual process in vertebrates is incompletely known. One of the un-solved problems of vertebrate physiology is how a single quantum can initiate a nerve impulse in a retinal rod. For the protozoa we do not have adequate data concerning either the minimal number of quanta necessary or how any adequate number of quanta brings about the observed reactions. Some possibilities are that light converts a proenzyme into an enzyme,[933] or that it converts carotenoids or other substances from being electrical insulators into virtual electron conductors,[439] and that the chemical events are thereby started. The importance of electron mobility at submolecular levels is gradually being recognized,[184, 283, 594, 750, 872, 873] and it is now known[761, 762] that electron conduction can involve proteins as well as conjugated systems (alternating single and double bonds). The implications of some of our new knowledge of intramolecular electron movements for phototaxis, energy transfer, and the reactions at membrane surfaces (increased by the triplet state) are discussed by Reid,[750] and the relationship of electron conduction to bioelectromotive force by Cope.[184] Future studies of biological mechanisms must be pursued not only to the molecular level, but to the submolecular level. The ultimate analyses of biological phenomena will come from a study of the behavior of electrons at the submolecular level.

## 2. HEAT AND INFRA-RED RADIATION

Very little is known of the reactions of protozoa to infra-red rays, except as expressed in terms of temperature. What effects any specific wavelengths longer than the visible spectrum may have are apparently unknown. Wells[946] says that near infra-red radiation is followed by morphological responses similar to those following other types of radiation, but does not elucidate.

The rate of locomotion of protozoa varies with temperature,[577] with maximal rates developing at temperatures near but somewhat above the temperatures in which the organisms are usually found in the wild; e.g., *Amoeba proteus*, with a maximal rate at 26°C,[469] is more often found wild in Florida in sites where the temperature is 18–23°C.[87] Table 2 shows the temperatures for maximal locomotive rates of some other protozoa compared with their optimal growth temperatures. Hull[407] found that the suctorian *Podophrya collini* most rapidly ingested prey-cytoplasm at 18°C, the same temperature at which he regularly grew it in his laboratory. The rates of movement and locomotion in free-living protozoa begin to decrease at about 30°C, ceasing, usually, between 35–40°C (Table 2). Some are found active in the wild at temperatures up to 55°C.[560] For parasites of mammals and birds the temperature for maximal rate may be higher, but movement lessens rapidly and ceases at or near 40°C.

Certain locomotor organelles and mechanisms of protozoa become more active as temperature is increased to a critical figure and then less active with further increases, e.g., ciliary beat[849] increases up to 28°C in *Stentor niger*, then decreases; speed of contraction of *Carchesium* spasmonemes increases, but the degree of contraction is less as temperature increases;[910] frequency of avoiding reaction increases in *Paramecium* but becomes oscillating and ineffective above 30°C,[997] and the rate of shuttle-flow increases in *Physarum polycephalum* up to 25°C with decrease in amplitude of the oscillatory change, but only negligible change in the strength of the motive force.[501]

Exposure to low temperatures is followed by a decrease in the rate of locomotion by most protozoa. With slow cooling to temperatures below 5°C locomotion usually stops, or is very slow, and movements of locomotor organelles are slow. The membranelles of *Stentor coeruleus* still beat slowly for 1–3 hours at 0°C,[332] but with a frequency less than 1/4 that of the maximal rate at 28°C.[849] Super-cooled *Paramecium* may continue to swim at temperatures below 0°C so long as the water is not frozen, and may swim *backward*, ceasing to swim at − 14.2°C, although the cilia still continue to beat slowly for a time.[980] Metachronal wavelengths increase, but wave velocity decreases in *Stentor* as temperature decreases.[849] In amebas pinocytotic activity decreases at lower temperatures.[776, 892] A recent report indicates that *Paramecium caudatum* can adapt to 0°C, but its ciliary, feeding and cyclotic rates are greatly reduced.[725]

### 3. SHORT WAVE RADIATION†

#### a. "*Near*" or "*Long*" *Ultra-violet*

Protozoan motile mechanisms respond more obviously to near (longer) ultra-violet (i.e., those adjacent to short visible wavelengths) than to shorter wavelengths, and are injured by lower intensities of the former. Lethal "long" UV shock-stops movement, with coagulation, liquefaction, blistering, loss of pellicle and cilia, then disintegration.[297, 659] Microspot punctures start local reactions of a similar sort, the damaged cytoplasm[342] or ciliary organelles[967] being sloughed, with blockage of regeneration of the latter.[967]

Sublethal long UV, if of low intensity, briefly accelerates ameboid movement[956] and ciliary movement.[295, 1005] If of higher intensity, exposure to long UV is followed by violent contractions in long ciliates, e.g., *Spirostomum* and *Condylostoma*,[885] "frantic" swimming by *Stylonychia*,[293] or "flight" by other protozoa,[885, 886] and modifies duration of reversal response.[295] Nearly lethal intensities produce longer broader pseudopods and slower movement, sometimes oscillatory, in amebas[714, 961] and loss of motility in phytoflagellates[353] and ciliates.[649] The specific UV wavelengths which most critically affect ciliary activity of *Paramecium* are 245 mμ and 280.4 mμ,[297] and for the green flagellate *Platymonas subcordiformis*, 265 mμ. These imply effects on cytoplasmic protein or RNA rather than on DNA mechanisms.[298, 775]

#### b. "*Short*" *UV, X-ray, α, β, γ Radiation*

Schaudinn[796] first noted that X-rays slow and stop protozoan motility. Protozoan movements are affected much the same by all kinds of very short wavelength radiations. X-ray effects are like those of lethal intensities of long

† See reviews, Blum;[72] Duggar;[238] Giese;[297, 298] Kimball;[523] Wichterman;[956] and Zirkle.[1004]

UV, but require higher intensities (see Table 3). Low intensities cause initial acceleration, but effects are cumulative as radiation continues, with erratic swimming, circling, slowing, loss of coordination and stoppage of movement in amebas, ciliates and flagellates (see reviews, [522, 523, 956, 958]). If accumulated radiation is sublethal, *Paramecium* may recover, after 48 hours, with feeble ciliary beat, then gliding and then − much later − normal spiral swimming.[956]

Quartz ("short") UV,[105, 106, 107] and $\alpha$, $\beta$ and $\gamma$ rays from fission neutrons[201] have effects on motility of protozoa similar to those of X-rays except that they appear to act at local sites, like a UV micropuncture,[885, 886, 887, 888, 889] so that weak doses have little effect on motility. Subsequently, lethal doses may only temporarily affect visible motility, e.g., *Euglena gracilis*,[307] or only partly disrupt it, e.g., *Polytoma uvella*, due perhaps to damage to one basal granule[397, 398] or may cause local gelation followed by spreading of damage from irradiated areas of mycetozoa, e.g., *Physarum polycephalum*[819, 820] or *Fuligo* sp.[595]

## 4. POTENTIATION AND ALLEVIATION OF RADIATION DAMAGE

### a. Potentiation by chemicals (Blum;[72] Giese[297, 298])

Certain chemicals, called photodynamic, render the protozoa more sensitive to radiation damage, but have little or no effect in darkness.[72] Dyes which fluoresce in ultra-violet light, such as rose bengal and eosin, are very effective,[27, 28, 367, 368] but fluorescense is not directly related to the photodynamic effect, since some non-fluorescent dyes are more effective than some fluorescent ones.[367] The dyes sensitize the protozoan motile machinery to an intensity of radiation energy of one wavelength or another, visible or non-visible, which the protozoon would normally tolerate with impunity. Rose bengal (1/10,000) and eosin (1/2,000) have no effect in darkness, but partially solate and liquefy the protoplasm of *Amoeba proteus* and *Amoeba dubia* in light.[28] Neutral red more strongly gelates already established ectoplasmic gel of *Amoeba proteus*, delaying its solation at the rear during locomotion.[314, 440, 684] The shock reaction of *Peranema trichophorum* to light is accelerated up to 12 times by $5 \times 10^{-4}$ M solutions of certain photodynamic dyes, but slowed by others as much as one-third.[367]

Trypanosomes treated with acriflavine and irradiated with a 12 $\mu$ microbeam of light at 430–65 m$\mu$ at first accelerate their flagellar movements, but the irradiated part of the flagellum quickly stops, e.g., the basal fourth of the flagellum neither starts nor accepts waves of movement after one minute of irradiation, but the remainder still undulates; and if the midpart or tip is irradiated, it stops, but the remainder beats.[934]

The ciliate, *Blepharisma*, produces a photo-labile pigment, the alcohol extract of which is photodynamic to other ciliates, and sensitizes them to ultra-violet rays.[296] Acriflavine-treated *Stentor coeruleus* slow down and their cilia stop; then the organisms contract and shed the pellicle, and regeneration is blocked.[945] *Paramecium aurelia* is sensitized by photo-dynamic dyes to light of 440–510 m$\mu$, and even more to long ultra-violet (350–400 m$\mu$) but not to heat, nor to heat applied before light.[300]

Certain carcinogenic polycyclic hydrocarbons have such pronounced photodynamic effects on motility and survival of *Paramecium*[221, 255, 408] and *Tetrahymena* and other holotrichous ciliates[408] that these ciliates may be used for biological assay of such materials in air pollution[408] or toxicity of chemicals used in medical radiology.[621]

### b. Potentiation and Alleviation by Radiation

Some wavelengths of radiation potentiate protozoa to other wavelengths; and, conversely, some wavelengths alleviate damage by other wavelengths. For example, ultraviolet rays may render protozoa more susceptible to damage by heat, but the converse does not hold.[105, 106, 107, 300] However, near infra-red, which itself does not affect *Tetrahymena*, renders that proto-zoon more susceptible to immobilization by X-ray.[946]

Damage to protozoan motility caused by ultra-violet may be alleviated by visible light,[302] either white, or monochrome at 435 m$\mu$ (blue) or 405 m$\mu$ (violet); longer wavelengths are not effective, e.g., for *Astasia longa*,[805] *Chaos illinoisensis*,[201] *Paramecium aurelia*,[524] *Paramecium caudatum*,[113] and *Colpidium colpoda*.[297] There remains some residual damage to ciliary motility, however, due mainly to ultra-violet of 238.3 m$\mu$ and 245 m$\mu$, less if light be applied in intermittent flashes rather than as continuous light equivalent in time.[168, 297]

Potentially lethal radiation damage by UV, X-ray or fission neutrons which also affect the motile mechanism of a large ameba is alleviated by microinfusion of whole cytoplasm from an undamaged ameba of the same species and strain[199, 200, 201, 202, 203, 693] or from a previously severed uninjured part of the same ameba, or from other strains of the same species.[202] Cross-specific fusions are ineffective or only temporarily so, and are followed by death.[202] This work demonstrates that the lethal damage is inflicted on the cytoplasm rather than on the nucleus of the cell, a fact which is disturbing to those who insist that the genetic effects of radiation are far greater than the direct damage. Since the nucleus has important (but unresolved) functions in locomotion [Section IVB2c (3)] the locomotor effects of any major damage to the nucleus should be easily detectable. Regardless of what may be true of other groups of organisms, death of irradiated *Amoeba* follows damage to the cytoplasm and occurs long before any genetic effect could become evident.

### 5. RADIATION AND ACTIVITY CYCLES

There are some casual references to and assumptions of cyclic activity sequences in protozoa, usually as "diurnal cycles", but critical studies are few. Protozoa may have primary, intrinsic, diurnally-functional (i.e., "circadian") mechanisms that are only secondarily affected by environmental factors. They are not independent "biological clocks". However, evidence is accumulating that they have biochemical servomechanisms which sensitively respond to extrinsic energy, usually light or heat, and also to long ultra-violet and the near ("short") infra-red. In *Euglena gracilis*, the "clock" may be reset by visible light applied for a sufficiently long period of time, (more than 30 minutes) during a "dark" period of its normal cycle.[135, 136, 137, 138, 718]

Heat, either steady or cyclic, has been used for over a decade to hold in abeyance and to trigger the mitotic movements of cells, which are perhaps related to -SH bonding,[793] resulting in synchronous division of whole clones of various species of protozoa (see review, Scherbaum and Loefer,[797] for detailed discussion).

Normal daily cycles of movement and locomotion show correlation with diurnal changes of light and heat intensities, and also with mitotic activities. Dividing amebas,[154] flagellates,[135] or ciliates[952] are ordinarily less motile than non-dividing ones. *Amoeba proteus* on adequate food[733] at a constant temperature (23°C) in darkness, feeds and grows for about 20 hours, prepares for division for 3-1/2 hours, and completes division in 1/2 hour. Young clones of *Amoeba proteus* at a constant temperature of 24°C are actively motile and feeding only during that part of the day when light is greater than 200 ft. candles, suggesting a critical-intensity factor for activity, as also noted by Kavanau[518] for mice. Division can regularly be triggered in a culture of *Amoeba proteus* in the dark, if it is kept at 26°C half the day (i.e., 12 hours), and at 16°C the other half; feeding and growth occur during the warm period, and division during the cool period.[469] Numerous other amebas have shown daily activity cycles approximating a diurnal pattern,[81, 84, 85, 86, 89, 94] with division of some probably occurring during cooler dark hours.[85]

The activities of green *Euglena* may be light correlated,[136, 137, 138] but those without chlorophyll are not.[579] Green *Euglena gracilis* is non-motile in darkness, and begins division after one-half hour in darkness, completing division within two hours in the dark following previous exposure to continuous light. However, it does not divide in continuous light; neither will it divide in continuous darkness. Cook and James[183] synchronized the division of clonal colonies of *Euglena gracilis* on a 24 hour cycle of 16 hours of light (300 ft candles) and 8 hours of darkness, achieving repetitive nearly perfect synchrony so long as methionine and cysteine were present in the growth medium.

Motility, and locomotion in *Gonyaulax* are also rhythmically influenced by light, although the individual biochemical processes involved are not.[369]

There is some evidence, then, that both light and heat are involved in the apparent rhythmic functions of some protozoa, but no intrinsic "clock" is present to "time" the events in the life of the protozoon. Rather, as Sollberger[856] points out, the whole organism *is* the "clock," and its rhythms may be "tolerance tests" of its environment. These probably involve interactions of internal biochemical oscillator mechanisms which are thermodynamically influenced and biophysically oriented.

## D. Reactions to Electricity

### 1. GALVANOTAXIS

In some studies of the movement of protozoa in electric fields, it is assumed that the organisms have greater positive charge anteriorly than posteriorly, e.g., *Paramecium*,[73, 144] and therefore that they must move toward the cathode. This explanation is possible, but has not been shown to be correct for any known case of protozoan galvanotaxis, and galvanotaxis is better explained in other ways.[434, 436]

The membranes of all animal cells are polarized electrically so that the external surface is positive to the internal. The external surface has a zeta potential positive to the external medium, and by ordinary electrophoresis the unattached organism should move toward the cathode, small end foremost; but the effect of ciliary reversal would be superimposed on this electrophoretic effect and also should be greater. However, if the cilia of *Tetrahymena* are removed by treatment with chloral hydrate, the electrophoretic effect is great enough to be measured.[220]

### 2. GROSS EFFECTS OF ELECTRIC CURRENT †

All protozoa which have been tested show a pronounced shock reaction to application of either direct or alternating galvanic fields, with neodirectional movement or adaptation upon recovery. In weak direct current (i.e., sub-shock strength) *Amoeba proteus* moves somewhat more rapidly toward the cathode if already homodromically oriented (i.e., already moving toward the cathode), or turns or reverses to move cathodally if otherwise oriented. If the current is left on, however, it slows and stops in a few minutes.[349] *Chaos carolinensis*[191] and also the plasmodium of the mycetozoon *Physarum polycephalum* act similarly.[37]

Effects on the flow mechanism of a homodromically oriented ameba are: 1) failure at the anterior end to reform the plasmagel sheet, 2) failure to add new gel at the anterior end of the plasmagel tube, 3) accumulation of sol as a broad anterior expansion under the plasmalemma, 4) syneretic contraction of rear gel with a hyaline area between that gel and the plasmalemma, 5) yellow discoloration of the gel at the rear end, which disintegrates, and 6) death. All of these events can be summed up as due to increased gelation, gel contraction at the rear, and inhibition of gel formation at the advancing

---

† See also reviews, Hahnert,[349] Mast,[638] Kamiya,[502] Jahn and Bovee,[443, 444] Umrath.[913]

end, thereby disrupting the locomotor mechanism. Similar events occur in alternating current fields except that gel yellowing, contraction, and eventual dissolution occur at both polar surfaces, with lobate bulging of sol under plasmalemma in both perpendicular directions from the axis of the current, resulting in elongate pseudopods completely devoid of gel.[349, 645]

The galvanic responses of flagellates are not well known, and their cathodal responses appear to be so interrelated with reactions to other conditions that only statements of observed results, without conclusions, are possible.[354, 355, 638, 913] Mast[638] attributes most of the changes of flagellar beating he observed in *Volvox* and other phytoflagellates to slight, temporary polarity and permeability shifts, but offers no evidence.

In ciliates the classic "avoidance response", e.g., stopping, and reversal of cilia followed by backward swimming in *Paramecium,* is a response to nearly shock-strength current, strong enough to reverse more than half the body cilia. This is one of the few examples where a tactic orientation can be explained. At lower direct currents, only the cilia of the cathodal end or side reverse so that the protozoon gradually turns toward and finally swims toward the cathode. With various current strengths *Paramecium* and other ciliates may be induced to move toward cathode or toward anode,[638] and other species to move tranversely to the current (*Spirostomum,* Verworn,[922, 923] Grębecki,[328] *Homalozoon,* Flick[267]). Microelectrodal applications of current cause local reversals of cilia of *Opalina,* with variation of the metachronal wave pattern,[687] and cause reversal of *Paramecium* cilia as the current ($10^{-9}$ amp) passes inward through the cell surface, and an augmented normal ciliary beat occurs as the current moves outward through the cell surface.[667] Presman[735, 736] deduces mathematically from his data on the response of *Paramecium* to electricity that some sort of conductile system analagous to vertebrate nerve, with an all or none response, is present.

An often observed phenomenon, first noted by Ludloff[609] is that a ciliate (*Paramecium*) lying obliquely across a galvanic field reverses all cilia on the body on the cathodal side of a plane through the body at a right angle to the direction of current; and the stronger the current, the greater the portion of the body affected, up to 60 per cent. Mast[638] concluded that altered permeability of the surface was involved in these electrical phenomena, particularly since they resembled reversals of ciliary movements due to cation changes,[690, 691] but believed that the assumption of a neuromotor system was necessary. Recent reinterpretations of both electrical and ion studies[434, 435, 436] and newer galvanic studies[235, 237, 329, 330, 331] indicate that proportional surface concentrations of metallic cations are involved. These will be discussed in more detail later [Section IVG2b (1) (a)].

Contraction begins at the anodal end of a cell exposed to strong direct current.[561a, 922] This was observed before 1900 in *Actinosphaerium* and *Spirostomum* by Verworn,[922, 926] and since then by others in *Amoeba proteus,*[333, 349, 608, 635] *Noctiluca*[614] and *Paramecium.*[495, 499, 993] Re-

3*

cently this anodal contraction has been cinephotomicrographed in *Spiro-stomum* with high speed cameras[488] showing that the contraction is apparently related to proportional concentrations of cations, especially $Ca^{++}$, and their migrations in the cell following current flow, probably in accord with the principle of the Gibbs-Donnan equilibrium.[488]

### E. Reactions to Chemicals†

#### 1. CHEMOTAXIS

It is often tacitly assumed that responses of protozoa to chemicals are important in food getting, in pairing or aggregation during reproduction, avoidance of danger, attraction to optimal conditions and, for parasitic protozoa, attraction to a specific host.[560]

Responses to most chemicals show similarities to generalized shock and avoidance reactions and to reactions to radiation and galvanic fields; only a few are specific, and those are related mainly to pairing and aggregating.

Amebulas of the cellular slime molds apparently secrete a discrete substance, called *acrasin*, which attracts other amebulas so that they move together and aggregate to form the motile pseudoplasmodial slug from which the sorus is developed.[75] The chemical nature of acrasin is unknown, but its action is mimicked by vertebrate 17-keto-steroid sex hormones.[989] A wide range of other chemicals tested have no effect on the aggregative process, except for adenine, which inhibits, and histidine, which accelerates it.[110]

Microconjugant ("male") vorticellid telotrochs are apparently attracted to the macroconjugant by an exudate of the latter,[261] and the amino-acid spectrum of the macroconjugant differs from that of the morphologically identical trophic vorticellid.[262, 263]

The claim that a sex-attractant, assumed to be derived from crocin,[658] is present in *Chlamydomonas eugametos*, has not been substantiated.[737] However, more recent work indicates a substance *is* secreted by *C. moewusii* var. *rotunda* which attracts *both* mating types of *C. moewusii* and of *C. m.* var. *tenuichloris*, but neither mating type of *C. reinhardi*.[906] The chemo-kinesis is separate from the agglutination reaction of + and − strains. The chemo-attractant is volatile, and its effect is mimicked by $C_2H_4$, $C_2H_2$ and (weakly) by $CO$ and $CO_2$.

Chemotaxis toward food has also been reported for protozoa (amebas, Schaeffer,[788] Bovee;[90] *Paramecium*, Jennings,[478] Losina-Losinsky;[603] *Dileptus* and *Peranema*, Chen;[165] *Tetrahymena*, Corliss,[185]) but the chemical attractants in the food are unknown.

Although it appears that specific chemotaxis may exist, the chemistry of the attractants is obscure, as is also the mechanism of the taxis, especially with respect to the manner in which the chemicals affect the locomotor mechanisms.

† See reviews, Jennings,[477, 479] Mast,[638] Harris,[361] Tartar,[877] Sleigh.[852]

## 2. GASES

The role of gases in the behavior of protozoa will be limited here to the effects on motile behavior. For other roles of gases in the metabolism of protozoan cells the reader is referred to other reviews [see Jahn;[431] Danforth, this volume].

The usual method is to supply to the chamber above the culture medium a monogaseous or heterogaseous atmosphere unlike the normal atmospheric mixture, vary the partial pressures, and observe the effects; or to add one or another gas to the culture medium and observe the effects. Recent work has sought the intracellular sites of gaseous action by means of biochemical studies on whole cells, or homogenates, and by cytochemical reactions at various sites in the cell.

Continuous exposure to hydrogen, nitrogen, carbon dioxide, or oxygen results in slowing and cessation of movement, and ultimately in death of most of the protozoa tested.[409, 531, 562, 601] Shock-stoppage of movement may also occur with the sudden increase of oxygen tension[969, 971] or $CO_2$ tension (Kuhne[562] and others). In nitrogen, if some $CO_2$ is present, even the slight amount self produced, the motion of *Physarum polycephalum* increases initially, and may continue as long as 24 hours,[601] but if no oxygen is available movement ultimately slows and ceases.[26, 540] Few free-living protozoa are able to survive without both $O_2$ and $CO_2$ available at least in small amounts. Lowered $O_2$ slows *Amoeba proteus*.[409] At $O_2$ concentrations of less than 0.5 mg/l *Paramecium caudatum* and *Vorticella convallaria* are active only a short time. Swimming and ciliary beat are slowed and then stopped in less than 1 hour. The organisms die in about 12 hours.[531] However, *Metopus es* thrives and grows anaerobically.[48] Other protozoa active in apparently completely anaerobic conditions are the sewage organisms *Metopus sigmoides, Trimyema compressa* and *Saprodinium putrinum*,[565] a variety of the large ameba *Pelomyxa palustris*,[860] an ameba of anaerobic citrus-waste processing lagoons, *Flamella citrensis*,[85] and perhaps *Coleps hirtus* and *Frontonia leucas*.[593] Complete removal of $CO_2$ results in the gradual immobilization and death of *Physarum polycephalum*[601] and *Paramecium*.[306, 815] Excesses of $O_2$ and $CO_2$ also impair locomotion of protozoa, stopping and killing termite flagellates,[176] causing *Paramecium*[969, 971] and *Tetrahymena pyriformis*[249] to swim in slow motion at elevated $O_2$ pressures, with ultimate death, and markedly retarding swimming of *Paramecium* in excess $CO_2$ pressures under 1 atm.[306] $H_2S$ is generally poisonous to protozoa,[116] but may be required in the activity of some anaerobic species.[567]

Bovee[95] has observed that activity and survival of amebas and other protozoa in polluted streams is adversely affected by the high oxygen demand of normally derived and of industrial organic substances. The protozoa ceased moving and died after heavy pollution by plant organic detritus when a land-moving operation altered the pH of the stream from alkaline to acid (i.e., below pH 7.0) and lowered the free oxygen to less than 1/ppm. Bovee and Wilson[102] have noted the similar effect on activity and growth of the high oxygen demand of growth media employed in the culture of *Entamoeba moshkovskii*, growth and activity being greater when supplementary oxygen is provided by aeration.

The ratio of gases, especially $CO_2$ and $O_2$, may also be important in the motility of some protozoa. Kostir[554] found that under air having 1 per cent $CO_2$, few euglenas in the culture swam, but 95 per cent swam with 16 per cent $CO_2$. At 4 per cent $CO_2$ and 0 per cent $O_2$, 90 per cent of the euglenas swam, but slowly, and at 21 per cent $O_2$ only 5 per cent swam, but normally. Kostir concluded that an $O_2/CO_2$ ratio of about 4/1, is required for swimming and that either high $CO_2$ or low $O_2$ induced swimming.

Studies on the effects of inert gases are rare. Sears and Gittleson[817, 818] found that helium, nitrogen and argon at 1,000 lbs/sq. in. scarcely affect the movements of *Paramecium*, but xenon at less than 250 lbs/sq. in. alters movements and intracellular protoplasmic structure, causing narcosis and expansion of the cell surface.

Highly active gases, such as $H_2O_2$, are also highly toxic, quickly immobilizing and killing the cell.[956, 957, 959]

## 3. WATER

The importance of water in protozoan behavior and motility has long been underemphasized, despite the well known absolute necessity of water within and about the body of the protozoon. The motility mechanisms, and all metabolic events, involve the physical chemistry of the water which performs not only mediating but active roles in many of the metabolic processes. Szent-Györgyi[873] expresses this in straightforward language by stating that "structural water . . . is half the living machinery, and not merely a medium or space-filler," and that "half the contractile material of muscle is water, contraction is the collapse of its structure, induced by actomyosin."

Jahn and his co-workers (see citations below) have recently utilized hydrodynamic mechanics to describe the propulsion of various flagellates, ciliates and spirochaetes, and Gray,[324, 326] Hancock,[358] Machin[615, 616] and Lowndes[605, 606] have also recently discussed the role of hydrodynamics in flagellar movements (Section IVI8).

Allen and Roslansky[22] have indicated that water may have much to do with internal viscosity and organization of ameboid sol; interference microscopy reveals that the more aqueous sol of least protein density which is just behind the hyaline cap, is also the more viscous sol, and may have a birefringence (of as yet undetermined origin), indicating structure.[13, 17]

The sudden increase of the proportion of water in the medium[192, 791] or injected into the protozoon[153] is followed by a shock-reaction and stoppage of movement, with reversal of swimming in ciliates,[192] and anesthesia.[696]

Survivors of a stringent change (e.g., immersion in pure distilled water) adapt after some hours, during which movement may have slowed and stopped. They move normally on recovery.[192, 634]

Sudden withdrawal of water by immersion in hypertonic non-electrolyte solutions (e.g., glycerin, sucrose) also causes an initial stoppage of movement, but recovery and resumption of movement take place, though the protozoon decreases in volume, e.g., *Amoeba proteus*,[153] and various species of *Paramecium*.[953]

A number of marine amebas easily tolerate transfer to 50 per cent sea water, with little change in their activities, but slow down in their movements in 25 per cent sea water, and stop and round up if transferred to 10 per cent sea water.[791] Some freshwater ciliates tolerate direct transfer to as much as 40–50 per cent sea water, shrinking and usually for a time slowing in their movements, but eventually recovering full movement. Some ciliates and amebas adapt, in gradual stages, to 100 per cent sea water[261] and certain amebas to concentrated sea water.[791] Apparently, within the protozoon, a water balance related to its internal machinery is required before it can be fully motile, and this balance must be maintained with relation to an ion flux to and from the external medium.

In some protozoa a contractile vacuole is present which regularly maintains the necessary osmotic balance (see reviews, Kitching[530, 532, 535] and this volume for detailed discussion of the protozoan contractile vacuoles and their functions).

Experiments with heavy water clearly indicate an important role of water in the motile behavior and metabolism of protozoa. Deuterium water amounting to 50 per cent or more of the medium surrounding a protozoon gradually slows and stops its movement. Sudden exposure to 90 per cent and higher $D_2O$ is followed by shock-stoppage of ameboid movement, and the avoidance reaction of ciliates and flagellates.[282, 364] The effects are said *not* to be due to $H_2O_2$ accumulation.[364] The heavy hydrogen of $D_2O$ may change the physical nature of the water molecule so that it cannot substitute completely for the normal one; exactly how is unknown. *Euglena gracilis* may be adapted, slowly, over a six-month's period, to 99.4 per cent $D_2O$, but it becomes round, loses its eyespot and motility on each transfer to a new medium of higher $D_2O$ content. Most die. The few survivors slowly adapt, regaining normality at reduced levels of activity. The flagellum is reported to be morphologically unaffected.[618] Somehow, $D_2O$ also disturbs the circadian rhythm of *Euglena*.[138]

## 4. CATIONS

### a. Hydrogen (Hydronium) Ions

It has long been known[155, 986] that positively charged ions affect behavior and motility of protozoa. The concentration of hydrogen ions certainly affects movement and behavior, and these effects may be caused partly by the instability and apparent rapid transit of the hydronium ion ($H_3O^+$) by way of proton charge transfer.[50, 245] However, exactly how these effects are produced is still obscure, as Wiercinski (review, [960]) points out (also Bittar, [70]).

Determinations of the effect on locomotion of changes in external pH have been numerous, but in general rather unsatisfactory because of lack of knowledge of the concentrations of weak electrolytes in the medium and also lack of knowledge of the past history of the organisms. Estimates of the internal pH indicate that it is about 6.7−6.9 for most protozoa;[960] but these values are only approximate.

Hopkins[401] reported that *Amoeba proteus* moves most rapidly at an external pH of 6.6 (which is also its own approximate internal pH) *but only if already adapted to that pH externally*; if grown in media at pH 7.6 its maximal locomotion develops at pH 7.6. Amebas exchanged between those two pH levels become sluggish in their movements initially but later recover full motility.[402] J. W. Lee[576] gives an optimal pH of 7.0 for the rate of forward swimming for *Euglena gracilis*, and of pH 7.1, for *Chilomonas paramecium*, but he does not indicate the pH of the tryptone medium in which they grew. He also[578] reports maximal swimming velocity for 3 species of *Paramecium* in the alkaline range (pH 7.5), but again fails to indicate the pH of the growth medium. Dryl[234] also fails to give the pH of the growth medium, but did adapt *Paramecium caudatum* for 24 hours in a phosphate-buffered salt solution at pH 7.1, before testing. He gives pH 5.63 as that at which maximal forward velocity is attained. Chase and Glaser[162] earlier demonstrated that the chemical nature of the acids used in establishing the pH affect the rate of swimming; and Dryl[234] suggests that both temperature and the chemical composition of buffer systems are also involved. Pitts and Mast[719, 720, 721] and Mast and Prosser[642] found that *Amoeba proteus* moves faster in acid solutions of single cations, or in mixtures of monovalent cations, but if $Ca^{++}$ is added, a drop in rate of movement occurs at pH 7.0, and a second peak of rate occurs on the alkaline side. They could not correlate these results with other data, but perhaps the Gibbs-Donnan equilibrium is involved (cf. Section IV G 2b (2) (a), page 120).

Gunn and Walshe[345] have demonstrated that klinokinetic aggregation of *Paramecium* at neutral pHs is possible, because the number of random changes of direction is greater above and below the range of 7.0−8.2 pH. They used acetic acid and sodium bicarbonate to change the pH.

Borgers and Kitching[79] studied the effect of $CO_2$ on the aggregation of *Astasia* and found that the "preferred" tension of $CO_2$ depended upon the alkali reserve and that the organisms tended to accumulate at pH 5.3 to 6.3 regardless of the concentrations of bicarbonate, carbonate, carbonic acid, or carbon dioxide. It seems possible that this pH effect also could depend upon the internal pH, especially as determined by the bicarbonate equilibrium outside in accordance with the Jacobs[427] equation (Section IIE4b, below).

Obviously, then, the role of pH in protozoan behavior and motility is complexly interwoven with the roles of other factors, is part of a larger picture, and should not be considered alone.

## b. Weak Electrolytes

One subject that has been neglected in the study of pH effects on protozoa is the effect of pH on the dissociation, penetration, and accumulation of weak acids and alkalis, including acetate and other organic acids in which protozoa often are grown. The undissociated electrolyte penetrates very rapidly compared with the dissociated form. This difference in penetration was discussed by Jahn[429] in relation to growth experiments on ciliates by Elliott[247, 248] and on flagellates by Loefer[597, 598] and later[430] in relation to experiments on the effect of lack of carbon dioxide. The effect is much greater than indicated in these early papers. Not only does the external pH influence the penetration of the acid, but the difference between internal and external pH influences the amount accumulated inside, or excluded. Equations predicting accumulation or exclusion of monobasic acids were reviewed by Jacobs[427] and Höber[387].

The basic equation given by Jacobs[427] is:

$$C_i = \frac{1 + 10^{pH_i} - pK}{1 + 10^{pH_o} - pK} C_o$$

where $C_i$ and $C_o$ represent the total concentrations of the acid inside and outside, where $pH_i$ and $pH_o$ represent the pH values inside and outside, and pK is the pK value for the weak acid under consideration. This equation was extended to include dibasic acids by Wilson et al.[964] who found that theoretical accumulation factors could be as high as 160,000 times that of the external fluid. Another equation for monobasic acids was developed independently by Kotyk.[555] The Jacobs equation also has been used by Shilo and Shilo[843] to explain osmotic lysis in Prymnesium.

The possible effects of weak acids and alkalis on locomotion have not been studied in detail, but the results of Chase and Glaser[162] demonstrate that at the same pH weak and strong acids and alkalis have different effects on locomotion of Paramecium. This conclusion is supported by the results of Jahn et al.[455] on Tetrahymena.

Another possible application of the Jacobs equation that has never been used for the protozoa, but seems to offer great possibilities is the determination of the internal pH by comparison of the concentrations of a weak electrolyte inside and outside at a known pH outside.[131, 931] For example, it is generally assumed that the internal pH is constant in the absence of high concentrations of weak electrolytes either externally or internally,[843, 964] but this has never been demonstrated experimentally.

## c. Metallic Cations

Other cations besides the hydrogen ion, particularly those of metals, also have been long known to affect protozoan behavior and motility. An "ion antagonism" early discovered between certain monovalent ions (e.g., $Li^+$, $K^+$, $Na^+$) and certain divalent cations (e.g., $Ca^{++}$, $Sr^{++}$, $Mg^{++}$) affects the viscosity of protoplasm and the movements of amebas.[115, 378] $Ca^{++}$ and $Mg^{++}$ are said to be sometimes in opposition to one another and sometimes supplemental, depending on their concentrations and on the concentrations of $Na^+$ and $K^+$.[378] Excesses of cations have long been known to stop organellar movements of protozoa, with death following.[564, 746, 986] Absence of $Ca^{++}$ paralyzes the tentacle of *Noctiluca*; and replacement of $Ca^{++}$ restores tentacular movement.[241]

In amebas an excess of $K^+$ not only promotes solation of cytoplasm ([115] and others); it also weakens the elasticity of the ectoplasmic gel of the tube wall[509] and reduces the intensity of spontaneous spike potentials at the membrane.[879] A $K^+/Ca^{++}$ ratio of $1/40$ is required to prevent cytolysis of *Amoeba proteus*.[512] All of these effects are reversed by raising $Ca^{++}$ to normal levels, and gel strength is increased by raising $Ca^{++}$ somewhat above normal levels.[509] Other chemicals, such as citrate, EDTA, or other agents which bind or displace $Ca^{++}$, reduce viscosity and gel strength,[509, 1001, 1002] particularly if they interfere with $SH \rightleftharpoons SS$ links.[1001]

Oliphant[690, 691] thoroughly reinvestigated and extended earlier studies by Jennings,[476] Merton,[650] and Mast and Nadler[641] on the roles of cations and anions in relationship to the reversal of ciliary movements of *Paramecium*. He found that of 91 salts tested, ciliary reversal was induced by monovalent cations, but was not induced by most divalent or trivalent cations (exceptions being $Ba^{++}$ and $Mn^{++}$), nor by mineral or organic acids except carbonic and oxalic acids, or by non-electrolytes (sugars and urea), or by anions. Careful work by Kamada and Kinosita[498] on the principal antagonistic ions of the reversal phenomenon led Kamada[497] to the conclusion that reversal of the cilia is related to the removal of $Ca^{++}$ from the surface membrane of *Paramecium*, a point of view later adopted also by Ueda[910] for *Opalina*.

Dryl[237] reports that equal amounts of $Ba^{++}$ and $Ca^{++}$, or of $Sr^{++}$ and $Ca^{++}$ (1 mM of each) in the medium promote periodic ciliary reversals in *Paramecium*; these reversals are halted by addition of $Ca^{++}$, $K^+$, or $Mg^{++}$, but not by $Na^+$.

The data of Kamada and Kinosita[498] for a constant physiological state exactly fit the assumption of a constant ratio of monovalent/divalent cations, particularly $K^+/Ca^{++}$, *on* the surface membrane.[436] The most illuminating portion of this demonstration is existence of a Gibbs-Donnan equilibrium between the surface of the cell and the bulk of the solution; the $K^+/Ca^{++}$ ratio on the membrane therefore depends upon the $K^+/\sqrt{Ca^{++}}$

.ratio in the bulk of the solution, *regardless of dilution*. This means that *simple dilution of any mixture of K⁺ and Ca⁺⁺ used as an external medium will decrease the K⁺/Ca⁺⁺ ratio on the membrane, and will increase the absolute amount of calcium on the membrane.* Any ion increments which critically increase the proportion of monovalent cations at the surface will be followed by ciliary reversal, regardless of the means (chemical or electrical) by which these are increased. This principle should be applicable to all biological material, i.e., to all cell surfaces.

Cations of heavy metals which cause no reversal do, however, alter the ciliary beat, ultimately slowing and stopping it. According to Puytorac *et al.*[740] this is due to competition of $Ni^{++}$ (or other heavy) ions for the sites normally occupied by $Ca^{++}$ (which is antagonistic to the anesthesial effects of the $Ni^{++}$). Grębecki and Kusznicki[331] note that these effects and the $LD_{50}$ seem to be related to adsorption of cations at the surface, especially at alkaline pH values.

Andrejewa[40, 41] described experiments on the rate of swimming of *Paramecium* as a function of the concentration of mono-, di-, and trivalent salts in the medium. The salts used were $KCl$, $K_2SO_4$, $K_3FeCy_6$, $K_4FeCy_6$, $NaCl$, $Na_2NO_3$, $Na_2C_2H_2O_2$, $Na_2SO_4$, $Na_3C_6H_5O_7$, $LiCl$, $Li_2SO_4$, $Li_3C_6H_5O_7$, $MgCl_2$, $MgSO_4$, $CaCl_2$, and $AlCl_3$. She found that $AlCl_3$ depressed the rate about 50 percent in concentrations of 0.011 mM, and less in lower concentrations. However, the mono- and divalent salts caused as much as a hundred percent increase at low concentrations (0.001 mM to 0.007 mM) and no effect at 0.011 mM. These results are surprising for two reasons: 1) they were obtained at extremely low concentrations, and 2) the curves follow exactly the contours obtained by Loeb[596] for the zeta potential of colloids, but at very different (by more than four decimal places) concentrations. They also indicate that the rate of swimming (not the rate of electrophoresis, which was not investigated) varies with the assumed zeta potential of the cilia. If these results are confirmed they might be useful as an entering wedge in elucidating the mechanism by which ions control the ciliary beat.

According to Grębecki and Kuznicki[331] the zeta potential of the cell surface may be important in determining the toxicity of cations for *Paramecium*. As the pH is reduced to near the isoelectric point, the toxicity of several cations ($Ba^{++}$, $Co^{++}$, and $Ni^{++}$) is also reduced. This effect is to be expected since at low pH values $H^+$ will adsorb on the anionic sites of the cell surface and thereby compete with the toxic cations (either monovalently or divalently bound) which must be adsorbed in order to be toxic. This may also apply to the action of cilia. For example, a mere decrease in pH changes the Gibbs-Donnan ratio of monovalent to divalent ions in a solution; this may change the ratio of monovalently to divalently bound ions on the membrane in such a way that calcium is removed and cilia are reversed as by the addition of any other monovalent ion. The zeta potential is an expression

3a*

of the state of adsorption at the surface, and of the association energies of the various ions involved. The theory of the latter is explained by Ling.[594]

An "avoiding reaction" has been described for *Paramecium* as it approaches an area of high concentration of "toxic" chemicals, including monovalent cations.[477] Since these cations cause reversal of cilia, and backward swimming, it is possible to explain these "avoiding reactions" as a direct effect of cations (or other substances) on the cilia, without assuming any neural complications. It does not even seem necessary to assume that the cytoplasm or any of its formed elements is involved.

### d. Other Chemicals

Many papers have been published about the reactions of protozoa to chemicals. Wichterman[953] lists over 300 papers devoted only to *Paramecium*. *Physarum polycephalum* also has been treated with many chemicals (review, Kamiya [502]), as have ciliates other than *Paramecium*, various amebas, and flagellates (texts, Heilbrunn[375, 376, 377]), but little analysis of these observations exists, either for *Paramecium* or for other protozoa.

Chemotaxis of the protozoa has been studied more extensively than intensively, and some of the data are very difficult to interpret. Intensive studies might well be undertaken, and some of the methods used for fern and bracken spermatozoids could be used. For example, Brokaw[119, 120, 121] by varying the pH, has been able to demonstrate that in a malate solution bracken spermatozoids are attracted by the bimalate rather than by the malate ions; the spermatozoids are galvanotactic (to the anode) only in the presence of bimalate ions, a cis-configuration. No similar analyses have been made for protozoa.

The phenomenal development of biochemistry and physical chemistry has opened doorways which are beginning to show how certain chemicals slow and stop protozoan movements, and others speed them, involving the total biochemistry of the cell. The directions taken in the past two decades by chemical research on protozoa will be discussed further in relationship to the fundamental motile machinery (cf. pages 72–74).

## F. Mechanical Force

### 1. THIGMOTAXIS

If there is in protozoa an identifiable and specific response to contact it is yet to be demonstrated. The contact response is almost identical with those given to other mechanical stimuli discussed below.

### 2. LOCAL PRESSURE

Protozoa react to physical contact with stationary or moving objects in the water, and are plainly sensitive to mechanical pressure. This is evident to anyone who has seen *Paramecium* bump into an obstacle, back off, and resume forward movement at an angle of 20–30° to its original course.

Numerous reports also indicate that protozoa are more sensitive to contact at the anterior end than they are at the rear (an observation also true for most other stimuli locally applied, e.g., light, electricity, ultraviolet radiation, heat, and chemicals of various kinds). In ciliates this differential sensitivity has often been attributed to a supposed neuroid function of subpellicular fibrils, a "pacemaker",[481] or hypersensitive "motorium"[612] However, a similarly greater anterior sensitivity is also found in a locomoting ameba[638] where no subpellicular network can be visibly demonstrated. In flagellates also (e.g., *Peranema*[165]) the anterior flagellar end is more sensitive to stimuli than other parts.

If *Paramecium* is touched lightly anteriorly, it gives the "avoidance" response; but touched there forcibly, it swims some distance backwards. Touched posteriorly it swims more rapidly forward.[140, 479] This is exactly the same response elicited by the micro-beam of a mercury arc lamp with a strong UV band at 260 mμ.[359, 481] Similar gradients of anterior-posterior sensitivity have been observed in *Spirostomum*,[527, 528] *Dileptus*,[225] and *Stentor*.[877] For the latter, the higher anterior sensitivity is lessened if the mouth region is excised.[945] However, despite the numerous observations of anterior to posterior gradients of sensitivity in protozoa, no generally acceptable analysis is available.

Thigmotactic responses are not always negative. Sand-dwelling ciliates are positively responsive to contact with sand grains, and move about in the moist sandy channels on the bottom of the littoral zones of marine and fresh waters.[230, 231] The posterior cilia which form the holdfast organelle of *Stentor* appear to be involved in a positive thigmotaxis,[42] as are probably also those of *Urocentrum turbo*, adherence being perhaps related to a mucoid secretion of or from sacs at the bases of the cilia.[467]

Feeding pseudopods of amebas are sometimes positively thigmotactic,[90] other times not,[479] and the feeding tentacles of suctoria are positively thigmotactic to ciliates, but not to flagellates.[406]

Local pressures with a microneedle cause local gelations of ameboid and mycetozoan cytoplasm with movement away from the area of contact.[966, 502]

## 3. AGITATION

Brief agitation of the water by shaking lightly or with a needle usually briefly accelerates the swimming of ciliates,[854] but when the shaking is continued locomotion and then ciliary movement slow and stop, and internal viscosity is lessened.[529] Similar results are obtained with *Amoeba proteus*,[44] the ameba speeding up, then slowing, becoming spherical as it stops movement and withdraws its pseudopods. Brief vigorous agitation causes any of a variety of amebas to detach from the substrate and to assume a pelagic state with radiating pseudopods, motile in some species, not in others.[94] *Arcella vulgaris* when thus agitated will leave its shell, become spherical, and float, eventually settling and forming a new shell if not further disturbed

(Bovee, unpublished). Similar radiate states of amebas also follow sudden exposure to a new higher concentration of a chemical entering the water near the ameba or on transfer of the ameba to the more concentrated solution[634, 925] or to distilled water.[634]

## 4. MECHANICAL SHOCK

Jennings'[477] classic report on behavior of *Stentor roeseli* is often cited. He states that if the coverglass is tapped lightly and repeatedly the ciliate at first contracts into its tube, but eventually fails to contract. The phenomenon has been hailed as an "adaptation" phenomenon, but remains otherwise unanalyzed. Other ciliates, e.g. *Vorticella campanula*, *Metacystis lagenula*, and sarcodines *Heterophrys glabrescens*, *Hyalosphenia cuneata*[709, 893] and *Amoeba proteus*[269] at first halt and contract in response to continued tapping on the coverslip but ultimately "adapt" and fail to respond.

Water droplets of known mass, velocity and frequency of striking were used by Seifriz and Epstein[824] on the motile plasmodium of the mycetozoon *Physarum polycephalum*. They demonstrated gelation and cessation of movement at the rear where the drop struck, with duration of standstill increasing with the momentum of the drop. Similar studies with the ciliate *Spirostomum ambiguum* also indicate a relationship between myonemal contractions and the force and frequency of water droplets striking the organism, with greater force causing more prolonged contraction; "fatigue" and lysis occurred at higher frequencies.[525]

## 5. HIGH FREQUENCY SOUND

Ultra-sound causes responses similar to repeated mechanical shock or agitation. *Euglena* stops and may shed its flagellum;[365, 366] so also does *Trypanosoma equiperdum*, after initial uncoordinated movements.[920] *Paramecium* stops, contracts at 19 megacycles[984] and is ultimately torn apart, [985], but the infraciliature remains intact up to the point of bursting and disruption.[661] *Amoeba proteus* and *Amoeba dubia* at first speed up, then change direction, finally solate and disrupt,[365, 366] but if the ultra-sound is applied by way of a quartz microneedle inserted into the gelated rear end of the ameba there is local solation about the needle, but no other response.[804] *Plasmodium berghei* contracts and disintegrates.[919]

## 6. HYDROSTATIC PRESSURE

The effects of higher levels of hydrostatic pressure applied in a pressure chamber or by centrifugation superficially resemble those of high frequency sound, with rounding up and solation of cytoplasm as pressure is gradually increased, in flagellates, ciliates, suctoria and amebas.[130, 534, 533, 537, 569, 570, 571, 626, 627] When pressure is rapidly applied solation occurs so rapidly that a clavate ameba or a long ciliate or a helizoan axopod breaks up into globules.[533, 537, 539] Release of the high pressure is followed by instantaneous gelation and contraction of ameboid cytoplasm, and *Stentor* and *Spirostomum* contract. Most of the organisms tested can briefly withstand 10,000 to 14,000 $lb/in^2$ and recover, regenerating any lost organelles.[533, 537] These reactions are temperature dependent; in amebas 2000 $lb/in^2$ is offset by a drop from 25° to 15°C.[571] The significance of these reactions in relation to the mechanism of ameboid movement is discussed by Jahn.[440]

## G. Water Currents

Very little is known about the responses of protozoa to the currents of their watery medium. Most texts and reviews cite Jennings'[477] contention that *Paramecium* orients by positive *rheotaxis*, but there is no evidence for such a taxis, or even a kinesis. What seems like a response to current can be explained simply on the basis of the known hydrodynamic principles of swimming.

A free-swimming ciliate in an absolutely *uniform* rectilinear current of water would have no means of detecting the movement any more than we can sense the rotation of the earth. However, if the velocity of the current were different on two sides of the cell, or if the current were accelerating or decelerating, or nonrectilinear, then detection might be possible. In Jennings'[477] experiment the current was produced by squirting water through a pipette and obviously was not uniform, and therefore the data cannot be interpreted as a true rheotaxis. When the field of flow is non-uniform several types of response are possible. For example, a ciliate headed upstream in a non-uniform current would veer toward the higher velocity, and if headed downstream it would veer toward the lower velocity. An elongate ciliate crosswise of the stream would be passively turned either upstream or downstream, depending upon body geometry and the difference between the reduced weights of the two ends. These effects as described are purely physical, are determined by the hydrodynamics of the fluid, and do not require any response on the part of the organism. Therefore, they should not be considered as taxes but merely as a reorientation of the organism by the external environment. Any taxis, if present, would be superimposed on these effects. Details of these effects will be analyzed elsewhere by Jahn. Fish, for example, are often considered to be rheotactic, but they are completely unable to detect uniform rectilinear motion[322] and therefore are not truly rheotactic.

The response of flagellated protozoa to currents in the suspending medium has not been investigated. Rothschild's[769] discussion of rheotaxis in bull sperm reveals the existence of an enigma. He demonstrates that dead sperm are moved with "head" pointed downstream in the top half of a parabolic velocity gradient, but are moved with head pointed upstream in the bottom half of the gradient. Live sperm, however, swim actively upstream in both halves of the velocity gradient. In Rothschild's words: "Suggestions as to how a spermatozoon does it, would, therefore, be appreciated."

## H. Geotaxis

Here again little is known for protozoa. Dembowski[214, 215] describes the negative geotaxis of *Paramecium* as purely phsyical, caused by the fact that the posterior end of the body is heavier than the anterior end. By centrifugation he oriented the organisms centripetally, and they moved centripetally until the centrifugal force reached 9 G. If *Paramecium* stops briefly, its rear end sinks, pointing the anterior end up. On resuming normal ciliary beat it swims up. A very similar idea was proposed by Verworn.[922, 923] However, it was too simple to be accepted by investigators who were intent on looking for complex sensory structures in microorganisms,[546] and a rather bulky literature was published by Verworn's critics. Most and probably all of the "contradictory" evidence really is not contradictory. This subject will be reviewed elsewhere by Jahn.

Amebas can crawl vertically upward along the side of a vessel or object, but ordinarily do not, being usually found on the bottom of a vessel.[560] Mycetozoan plasmodia tend to climb upwards along the wall of the vessel,[37, 38] especially before sporulation.[147]

## I. Magnetic Fields

Brown[132] has recently attempted an assay of the effects of weak magnetic fields on movement of *Paramecium*. He suggests that the H-component of magnetism is related to the long axis of the body, and that an east-west placed magnet induces significantly more clockwise and counterclockwise turns by test ciliates than those made by controls. He also postulates a lunar cycle of effect such that a north-directed *Paramecium* tends more often to turn right (clockwise) during the first 4 days after new moon, and left (counter-clockwise) for the first 4 days after full moon. Kogan and Tikhonova[548a] say that *Paramecium* in a capillary tube stays longer in that end of the tube near the south pole; and that the magnetic effect lingers after removal of the magnetic field, lasting longer when the field is stronger. They also say that varying the nature of the solution in the capillary alters the duration of the effects of the magnetic field. There are as yet no other studies to confirm or deny any of these proposals. There are few, if any, other studies of protozoa in magnetic fields.

## J. Interactions of Physico-Chemical Factors

### LIMITATIONS OF KINESES OR TAXES AS EXPLANATION OF PROTOZOAN MOTILE RESPONSE

It is an over-complication to assume that a protozoon must have a conductile system analogous to a vertebrate nervous system, and it is an oversimplification to assume that the protozoon has specific immutable responses, and therefore is always positively or negatively taxic to this or that energy source. Studies of all cells, metazoan and protozoan, show that they have a high degree of biochemical and biophysical complexity, and also sometimes have narrow and sometimes broad areas of operation and margins of safety. On the basis of organization we may regard the cell as a huge computer on a molecular scale, with a very broad and complicated program, so that at any moment the overall reaction would be predictable if we knew the program. However, the program is continually being modified by feedback from its own operation, and in this sense a certain degree of surprise, and at times even apparent unpredictability may occur. Most of the macromolecules responsible for the organization and energy transfer are protein high polymers hooked to resonant chains.[7] Consequently, whatever alters the flow of energy or materials alters the motile reactions; whatever chemicals alter or interfere with the enzyme reactions of the cell change or halt its motile reactions; etc.

Although positively phototactic organisms may become photonegative (e.g., *Volvox*, review,[638]) and vice versa, geotaxis may be reversed (ciliates and flagellates may accumulate at either the top or the bottom of cultures), and paramecia which are normally cathodally galvanotaxic will become anodally galvanotaxic in the presence of barium chloride, we do not know enough about the chemical or physical mechanisms for these and many other reversals. We need more knowledge of where in the cell, and on what structural parts of molecules the chemical and physical forces act, as well as more about the organization of the submicroscopic molecular units and their normal and abnormal roles.

Fortunately, almost all of the biochemistry and biophysics already documented for metazoan cells has been found to apply to protozoan cells. Development of cell membranes, mitochondria, cilia (and flagella), ribosomes, nuclear membranes, chromosomes, centrioles, enzymes, energy sources (e.g., ATP), and cycles (e.g., Krebs' tricarboxylicacid), vitamins and their roles, basic amino-acid requirements, and even certain metabolic losses apparently antedated the evolution of protozoan and metazoan bodies. The fundamental processes of protozoan or metazoan cells are largely the same, often identical. It is unlikely to be either a biological or evolutionary accident that metazoan and protozoan cilia are morphologically the same, (see review, Pitelka,[715]) or that their actomyosins and ATP-systems can cross-react,[669, 670] or that their mitochondria are morphologically similar (review, Novikoff,[685]) and contain similar functionally-identifiable enzyme systems.[410, 411]

Many of the older observations of effects of chemicals on protozoa now need to be reinterpreted in more precise biophysical and biochemical terms. For example, Brinley's[116] observation that complete $O_2$ depletion and KCN poisoning slow and stop ameboid movement in a similar manner is now understood as the blocking of the cytochrome-oxidase system, in one case by anoxia and in the other by the cyanide. Wittner's[971] interpretation of oxygen poisoning is that it involves inactivation of -SH groups, presumably normally functional in the folding and unfolding of the protein polymers involved in movement.[943] Wichterman's[956] observation that damage to the motile system of *Paramecium* by radiation is due to $H_2O_2$ production may be extended to include the rupture and inactivation of S-S and -SH bonds noted by Yalow,[994] cross linkage of polymers,[8] the excitation of water and other molecules to triplet state, the resonance phenomena of conjugated proteins and of other molecules with extended $\pi$ electron systems,[134, 750] and the complexity of DNA components.[510] The roles of cations and pH in the solutions around the protozoon need more interpretation in reference to oxidation-reduction potentials[622] and other membrane flux phenomena,[995] and should be interpreted in part as a function of bond angles of participating ions,[360, 437] of fixed charges in adsorption aggregates at the membrane,[594] and Gibbs-Donnan ratios of ions at membrane surfaces.[195, 436]

In brief, if we are to understand the behavior of protozoa as expressed in movement, we must learn more about the internal thermodynamic systems which power locomotion, external hydrodynamic systems which affect locomotion, and more about their interactions. These approaches have begun, as the cited recent references indicate. We need, for more complete understanding of protozoan motility, as Bishop[69] has indicated for sperm motility, "new ventures and new procedures pertinent to intracellular regulation, energy exchange, and oscillating mechanisms".

## III. THE BASIC PRIMITIVE MOTILE MECHANISM

### A. Analogy to Muscle Movements

Over a hundred years ago it was assumed that protozoan movements were due to protoplasmic contractions similar to those of muscle.[239, 240, 243, 807] This idea was widely scorned as the opinion became rooted that protozoa—particularly "the ameba"—were the "simplest" of all animals; and simple mechanisms were sought for their movements. Near the end of the 19th century and into the first two decades of the 20th, amebas were no longer believed to move actively by their own mechanisms, but were assumed to move, as do fluid droplets, by means of surface tension phenomena.[141, 143, 751] Cilia were proposed to be flaccid sacs which moved as they alternately became fluid filled and turgid, and partially emptied and limber.[795] Colloidal concepts of protoplasmic structure also arose during the first two decades of this century and in turn ruled the theories, particularly of ameboid movement, describing protoplasmic movements as due to imbibitions and synereses of colloids.[415, 697] These ideas continued into the 1930's,[950] and in adapted modern attire into the 1950's.[12, 21] Gel and sol became, almost, household words, and are still in use.[19]

However the idea that muscle and protozoan motile mechanisms are functionally akin has refused to die. New concepts of the micellar and fibrillar nature of protoplasm (review, Frey-Wyssling,[275]) the discoveries of elaborate biochemical machinery for energy processing (review, Chance[157]) and especially the discovery of macromolecular protein systems (actomyosin) which could be extracted from living muscle and made to contract, using the normally-present source of muscle energy (adenosine triphosphate) have suggested that a system of movement basic to all protoplasm may exist. Szent-Györgyi,[871] Perry[710] and Weber[943] reviewed the idea of and the search for such a basic contractile machinery in all protoplasm, similar to that in muscle. The protozoa have not been neglected, nor unproductive in this research.

Before a generally existent contractile system analogous (or homologous) to muscle could be proven present in protozoa several facts had to be established: 1) that fibrillar proteinaceous complexes are present; 2) that they contract, using ATP as an energy source; 3) that they are biochemically very similar to, if not identical with actomyosin.

## B. Fibrils in Protozoan Locomotor Organelles

The presence of fibrillar structure in the locomotor organelles of protozoa and animal sperm has long been known, although only with the refinement of electron microscopy have the details of arrangement been revealed. Engelmann[252] early suggested that fibrillar contractile materials composed of molecular filaments which he called "inotagmen" are present in cytoplasm, cilia, and flagella and are responsible for their movements. Pütter,[739] Ballowitz,[47] Dellinger,[213] and recently Wohlfarth-Bottermann[978, 979] and Roth[766, 767] also have supported a fibrillar concept of contractile protoplasm. Dellinger[213] was among the first to note the presence of fibrils in flagella, cilia and heliozoan axopods. A decade before the 20th century began, Ballowitz[46] found 7 to 10 fibrils composing the spermatozoon flagellum, and in one of his drawings clearly depicts 11 fibrils — the latter being the exact number of complex fibrils now known from precise electron microscopy to be standard in both the cilia and the flagella of cellular organisms. (see review, Pitelka[715]) Dellinger[213] described 4 fibrils in the flagellum of *Euglena*.

The burgeoning literature of electron microscopy reveals fibrils in abundance in the protozoa. Pitelka[715] states that regardless of the fixation procedure used "the cytoplasmic matrix (of protozoa) appears to consist of very fine filaments and/or granules dispersed in a low density continuum" and "if there is anything unique in the ultrastructure of protozoa, it may be the extent to which they have utilized fibrous materials in the construction of cytoplasmic organelles and organelle systems." She then lists a "bewildering profusion" of fibrillar structures in protozoa. Among these fibrils located in organelles or in regions of the cytoplasm believed to be more or less contractile, are the following: 1) banded fibrils with a period of 30 to 60 mμ, and of various widths, including accessory fibrils in flagella of *Bodo*[129] and *Entosiphon*,[35, 654] the costa of *Trichomonas*,[34] the kinetodesma of numerous ciliates, e.g., *Paramecium*,[468, 972] and of the flagellate *Oxhyrris marina*;[220] 2) cylindrical, perhaps tubular, fibrils with high density periphery and low density centers, 12 to 30 mμ in diameter, including axopodial fibrils of *Actinophrys*,[538] fibrils of all "kinetosomes", cilia and flagella, [see also reviews: Sleigh,[852] Fawcett,[259] Grimstone,[340]] fibrils in the extremities of the pellicular ribs of some gregarines,[55] and in the sucking tentacles of *Tokophrya*[771] and *Ephelota*,[770] the longitudinal pellicular fibrils of the sporozoites of *Lankesterella* and *Plasmodium*,[279, 280] and pellicular fibrils of *Euglena*[293] and *Trypanosoma*,[36, 39, 172, 492] including stalk and endoplasmic myonemes of *Vorticella*,[858] ectoplasmic network of *Gregarina rigida*,[563] fibers in the prehensile tentacles of *Ephelota*,[770] and endoplasmic myonemes of *Stentor*[258] and others. Fibrous complexes have also been found in the contractile gel of the mycetozoan *Physarum polycephalum*.[976, 977, 891] and of amebas.[189, 491, 583, 664, 665, 874, 974, 978, 979]

Roth[766, 767] suggests that filaments which form the fibrillar organelles and complexes have a basic standard diameter of 15 mμ, and that these unit filaments have much to do with the nature of filament functions, division synchrony, and replication of organelles, and Porter *et al*[727] similarly stress multiple roles for the fibrils.

In summary, fibrils have been shown to be abundantly present in the organelles of locomotion, or in sites in the protozoan cell where protoplasmic movement occurs and is contributory to locomotion.

Another role, the conduction of impulses, has often been suggested for some of the fibrils, particularly the subpellicular "kinetodesmata" of ciliates. This role will be further considered below (cf. pp. 127–132).

## C. The Role of ATP in Protozoan Movements

The presence of protein fibrils in structures that move is not necessarily proof that those fibrils are involved; but if they are shown to be composed, in part at least, of actomyosin or a similar protein complex, and show movement, contractile or otherwise, with ATP, then it is reasonable to assume that they are muscle-like fibrils.

### 1. EVIDENCE FOR ATP-ACTOMYOSIN SYSTEMS IN PROTOZOA

Accumulating evidence indicates that at least many protozoan fibrils are actomyosin-like in nature and reaction, and that they utilize ATP as an energy source. An ATP-ase-active protein complex was obtained from *Paramecium aurelia*[917] and proteins extracted from the cilia of *Tetrahymena* have some of the chemical characteristics of, and behave like actomyosin,[166, 167, 504, 941] but Gibbons[291a] notes that the ATP-ase of *Tetrahymena* cilia more nearly resembles that of the mitotic apparatus than it does that of muscle myosin. The flagella of sperm[724] and of colorless[895, 896] and green phytoflagellates[490] contain actomyosin-like proteins. In ameboid organisms an actomyosin-like protein complex was extracted first from *Physarum polycephalum* by Loewy[602] and was later shown to be functionally identical to vertebrate actomyosin-B, being able to utilize ATP extracted from rabbit muscle, and also commercially prepared vertebrate ATP.[669, 670] Simard-Duquesne and Couillard[847, 848] have extracted an ATP-reactive actomyosin-like protein from mass homogenates of *Amoeba proteus*, and a generally distributed myosin-like ATP-ase is present in its cytoplasm.[344]

Glycerine-extracted protozoan cilia and flagella free of basal bodies have been shown to use ATP from solution[166] and to move[389] or swim in ATP solutions.[123] Also, contractile movements of similarly prepared spasmonemes of vorticellids have been ATP-triggered.[390] Glycerin-extracted whole-cell models of various protozoa also contract in ATP solutions; these include hartmannellid and proteus amebas,[389, 845] trypanosomes,[387] and vorticellid peritrichs.[586, 587] Myosin-like ATP-ases have been biochemically identified in *Amoeba proteus*,[848] in *Physarum polycephalum*,[670] in flagella,[724] and cilia,[934] and have been located by cytochemical staining reactions in flagella[674, 675, 676] and cilia.[400, 410, 411, 812, 832]

Reactive sulfhydryl groups, which are inhibited by bound ATP and react as ATP is split, have been shown by cytochemical stains to be abundant in cilia[513, 589] and in myonemes and spasmonemes.[589] Metabolic blocking agents which inhibit actomyosin-like ATP-ases, e.g., 2:8 amino-Na-methyl-acrodinium-Cl (acriflavin), or para-chloromercuri-benzoic acid (PCMB), or salicyl-hydroxymercuric-methoxypropyl-amido-orthoacetate (Salygran), also inhibit ATP triggered motion of whole-cells, flagellar and ciliary models prepared from protozoa, free flagella and cilia, and the locomotion of living amebas.[2, 391, 511, 558] Iodoacetate also inhibits flagellar movements of *Euglena gracilis*,[190] and mercaptoethanol reduces pseudopodial strength of *Amoeba proteus*.[1001]

Also, the movements of cilia of intact *Paramecium* are accelerated by ATP in the medium, as are the sucking movements of suctorians[407] and the locomotor movements of amebas by ATP added to the medium[511] or injected into them.[314, 558, 1000] ATP has also been cited as an energy source for the motility of *Trypanosoma equiperdum*[432] and *Tetrahymena pyriformis*;[141] evidence consisted of the increasing and waning of motility in the latter as the available ATP increases and decreases, and the cessation of motility when ATP is entirely consumed.

## 2. GENERALITY OF ATP-ACTOMYOSIN SYSTEMS IN ORGANISMS

There is no longer any doubt of the generality of ATP-actomyosin-like motile systems in protozoa, or for that matter in organisms as a group, plant or animal, uni- or multicellular. ATP accelerates cyclotic movements in algal cells,[875] and shearing and sliding two-way motile filaments using ATP as an energy source are present in *Nitella*. (review Kamiya[502]) Jarosch[470, 472, 474] and Jahn and his co-workers[442, 443, 444, 450, 453] have commented on the similarities of plant cyclotic movements and the two-way movements of protoplasm in the filopods and axopods of foraminifera and protozoa and a possible role for such movements in the gliding of gregarines and euglenids. Nelson[675] and Afzelius[9] have also suggested that the outer peripheral fibrils of flagella (and presumably, of cilia) may "creep" against the central ones, and perhaps against one another in their contractile movements.

Therefore, it is now generally accepted that the ATP-actomyosin-like motile systems satisfy the predictions of Schaeffer,[790, 792, 793, 794] that the general features of protoplasmic streaming and of muscle contraction, wherever they occur, are similar and dependent on the same basic mechanism, and of Hill[384] that there was evidence even in 1926 to suggest that the movements of all living organisms are based on the same fundamental process. Reviews by Weber,[943] Kamiya,[502] Hoffmann-Berling,[392] Bovee,[94] and Jahn and Bovee[443, 444] further emphasize this widespread occurrence and role of ATP-using actomyosin-like motile systems, and Danielli[196] discusses the general role of phosphatases in the functions of fibrous protein systems.

## 3. FUNCTIONS OF ATP-SYSTEMS IN PROTOZOA

Just what ATP does in protozoan motile systems, other than providing an energy source, is not fully known. Hoffmann-Berling[392] considers ATP to be the only known physiological relaxing substance. Katz[514] points out that ATP effectively prevents the polymerization of actin, especially in the presence of $Ca^{++}$, blocking the reactivity of -SH groups which promote polymerization and contraction of actomyosin. Szent-Györgyi[871] has emphasized that actomyosin without ATP is stiff, and in rigor. Hayashi shows[370, 371] that both actin and myosin must be present to form a contractile complex.

$Ca^{++}$ or $K^+$ are usually suggested as cations which act as triggers for contraction, with ATP serving as the energy source. This conclusion is supported by the roles of ions, particularly critical balances and local concentrations of $Ca^{++}$, $Mg^{++}$, $K^+$ and $Na^+$, in the formation, severing, and transfer of bonds in the actomyosin complex.[82, 391, 587, 871]

At least five roles have been proposed for ATP in the motile systems of protozoa:[392] 1) relaxation; 2) elongation after binding; 3) inhibition of elongation; 4) contraction powered by ATP-splitting; 5) movement reversal. A primary role of ATP appears to be that of loading the protein complex with energy,[846] which is released by cationic triggers, particularly $Ca^{++}$, resulting in motion of or along the protein fibrils. Jarosch[473, 474] suggests that the protein fibrils may be anchored, at one end or both, and that a wave of motion progressing along the fibrils results in movement of the fibrils against one another causing shortening or elongation of the protein complex, or movements of fibrils against a surface.

Levine[587] and Hoffmann-Berling[392] assign a triggering role for $Ca^{++}$ in spasmoneme contraction of vorticellids; and Salisbury[781] a similar triggering role for $Ca^{++}$ in flagellar motion. Postma[728] contends that pseudopods, cilia and flagella are mechanical receptors which bind ATP and relax, split ATP and contract, and that contraction leads to relaxation as the vacated ATP sites refill. He also explains lengthening as due to augmentation of ATP sites which intensifies ATP-actomyosin interactions. Pautard[702] suggests that the duality of ATP in relaxation and contraction is related to: 1) low electrolyte and high (alkaline) pH and high nucleotide concentration followed by a relaxed state of actomyosin; and 2) high electrolyte, low (acid) pH and low nucleotide concentration followed by contraction or other movement of the actomyosin proteins.

Recently, Davies[207] has suggested that ATP binds myosin to actin-ADP via $Ca^{++}$ ions, thus neutralizing negative charges and triggering the contraction, dragging myosin and actin in opposite directions with a calculated force of $3 \times 10^{-7}$ dynes per ATP bridge. He assumes that sequentially formed and broken bonds thus slide the actin and myosin together.

Because of the lack of clarity concerning the roles of ATP, actomyosin, and the various cations, it is not agreed that protozoan movements are always contractile. The application of the motile mechanism and the sites of motive force are therefore still subjects of intensive experimental and observational search.

## IV. TYPES OF MOVEMENTS IN PROTOZOA

Movements of protozoa appear to be of five general categories: 1) those involving movements of the cytoplasm in a cyclic manner within the cell; or 2) along its temporary filamentous pseudopods; 3) movements of organelles, flagella, cilia and their complexes (cirri, membranelles, undulating membranes), and of fibrillar bands (spasmonemes, myonemes); 4) movements involving the cell surface against a substrate (gliding of gregarines, euglenids); and 5) undulatory movements of the body (sporozoan sporozoites).

### A. Bidirectional Filamentous Movements

#### 1. ACTIVE SHEARING MECHANISMS

Although the bidirectional streaming of protoplasmic filaments in cytoplasm and in pseudopods of protozoa, and in plant cells, has been known for over 100 years, no general significance was attached to the phenomenon until recently. Only within the past decade has an active shearing system along molecular interfaces of protoplasmic fibrils been proposed for 1) the movements of spindle fibers and chromosomes along them in mitosis;[392] 2) contraction of vertebrate muscle;[412, 413, 414] 3) cyclosis in plant cells, e.g., plant cells generally,[275, 600] the pollen tube of *Lilium*;[425] 4) movement in foraminifera;[450, 757] and suggested for 5) heliozoa and radiolaria;[443, 444] 6) cyclosis in ciliates[471] — especially *Paramecium*[443, 444] and 7) perhaps in gliding movements of gregarines.[473] At any rate, it appears that at a visual level of information protoplasmic movements in cellular organisms are not always contractile. Whether contractions occur in these bidirectional movements at the molecular level is not yet known. Perhaps the sliding movement involves reactions similar to those postulated for sliding movements of muscle fibrils involving a shift of the actin molecule along myosin, via a series of -SH, phenolic and alcoholic -OH groups in a sort of ratchet action.[943]

The bidirectional movement of protoplasm is so much a general phenomenon in protozoa, as well as in other types of cells, that it suggests a primitive universal application of the ATP-actomyosin cation triggered machinery, (reviews, Weber,[943] Kamyia[502]). Regardless of the final verdict, intensive research into these phenomena should yield much valuable data on the fundamentals of protoplasmic movements.

## 2. BIDIRECTIONAL PROTOPLASMIC MOVEMENTS

### a. Dinoflagellates

The cytoplasm of the dinoflagellate *Noctiluca* has an internal network of protoplasmic fibrils.[731] By cinematography we have confirmed (Jahn *et al.*, unpublished) the bidirectional movements of protoplasm and granules along fibrils of the network, earlier reported by Pratje.[731] These movements closely resemble similar movements of the transvacuolar filaments of *Elodea* and *Tradescantia* cells.

### b. Radiolaria

The radiolaria in which protoplasmic movements have been observed and recorded have a two-way flow of protoplasm along filose strands of the network in the vacuolated peripheral cytoplasm,[800] along the filamentous radiating filopods,[784] and in the acantharians in two-way streams from base to tip of axopod and back again, and along the axopodial filament.[383, 483, 484, 800] There are also two-way sliding movements of axopods by which they are extended and retracted; and the radiolarian may descend to the bottom, retracts its axopods, and employ filopods in locomotion and feeding much as the foraminiferans do.[800] Nothing seems to be known of the contractile mechanisms of radiolarian "myophrisks."

### c. Heliozoa

Some so-called heliozoa have filopods like those of "true" radiolarians (i.e., the non-acantharians, without axopods) in which opposing movements of protoplasm may be seen. "Typical" heliozoa with axopods, like those of acantharian radiolarians, clearly demonstrate bidirectional flow of protoplasm along the axopods[963] and may extend or retract the axopodial filaments [e.g., *Actinophrys*, Kitching,[538]]. As the helio-flagellate *Dimorpha floridanis* assumes the flagellate stage it may partly retract and fold the axopods into groups, then collapse them into a cluster covered by cytoplasm, all in response to dilution of sea water by distilled water.[91] As salt ions are suddenly added by the addition of sea water the organism may with explosive speed again extend the axopods.[91, 101] Other movements of heliozoa which may involve shearing-actions are their rolling movements on the substrate as axopods bend and straighten[705] and the slight but rapid vibrations of axopods by which they swim.[584, 705] We have made high speed cine-photomicrographs of these movements but at present can offer no theoretical explanation.

### d. Filose Testaceans

Careful but infrequent studies of testate amebas with filose pseudopods have revealed a bidirectional movement of protoplasm in their filopods [e.g., *Euglypha*, Leidy,[584] Verworn,[921] Bovee and Jahn (unpublished), *Pamphagus*, Bělař,[57] *Cyphoderia*, Berrend[62, 63] others, de Saedeleer,[779, 780] Bovee and Jahn.[97, 98]] These filopodial movements resemble those of foraminifera (cf. p. 82), and are subject to similar interpretations. One interpretation[62, 63] suggests that each filopod is extended as a gelated axial core along which slightly less gelate protoplasm advances. The core is deemed not only extensible, but also contractile and retractile, since it bends or coils.[62]

### e. "Proteomyxans"

For such a taxonomic catch-all as the "proteomyxans" no general statement of motile mechanisms is possible. In *Biomyxa vagans*, however, which Leidy[584] discovered and named, we have cinematographically confirmed his accurate observations of the bidirectional streaming in its filopodial network, and its resemblance to that of the foraminifera [Leidy,[584] Jahn and Bovee, (unpublished)]. Two-way bidirectional streaming has also been described by Nauss[673] in *Reticulomyxa filosa*, which appears to be a related organism.

### f. Foraminifera

The bidirectional movements of protoplasm and its granules along the filopods in the protoplasmic networks of foraminifera have long been known, and several times described in considerable detail.[483, 450, 584, 783] These movements, as Sandon[783] points out, are not simple, and are not describable as the gel-sol conversions of a tubular structure as in *Amoeba proteus* or *Physarum polycephalum*. Noland[684] suggests that "molecules that can orient themselves on any solid surface while others crawl forward on the backs of the first layer" are needed to explain these bidirectional movements in foraminifera.

## 3. THEORIES OF BIDIRECTIONAL MOVEMENTS

### a. Shearing Flow

Kamiya[502] on the basis of his investigations of *Nitella* has assumed that the shearing flow always occurs at gel-sol interfaces, with viscosity lower at the interface than in either the sol or gel[505] through the utilization of phosphate nucleotides, presumably in coacervates at the interface.[77] Kamiya also assumes that one or more energetically active areas of semifibrous sol could move along the interface of the gel, dragging the rest of the sol layer along.

Older concepts of the organization and movement of foraminiferan filopods suggest a central contractile gel fiber or rod covered with sol, the latter in motion along and against the gel.[808] This is almost identical with Berrend's[63] description of filopodal organization and movement in *Cyphoderia*. Neither Sandon[783] nor Jepps,[483] however, could find a solid axial core in the filopods.

Jahn and Rinaldi[450] suggest that the shearing action need not require a gel-sol interface, and that a gel-gel interface appears to function in the filopods of the foraminiferan, *Allogromia laticollaris*. They evaluate each smallest filopodial strand as being a slender gel filament bent back upon itself so that it creeps against itself, perhaps powered by a series of -SH, -OH and phenolic bonds established and severed, similar to the mechanism suggested by Weber[943] for the sliding action of muscle. The gel filament, they assume, may lack a cellular type of unit-membrane, the gel filament being apposed directly to itself as shearing surface. This concept has the advantage of eliminating the problems inherent in a multiple-shearing series of surfaces which also involves membranes surrounding filaments and bundles of filaments. They describe the rhizopodial networks as constructed of bundles and interweavings of separately moving fibrils.

Regardless of whether the surface is or is not a unit membrane, we need some mechanism which will show how, in a filopod about a micron in diameter, the *surface on one side may move distally as the opposite surface moves proximally*; such movements always occur together except possibly when the filopod is being extended or withdrawn at the same rate as one of its surfaces is moving. These facts demonstrated by Jahn and Rinaldi[450] clearly show the existence of 1) some type of active sliding mechanism, and 2) a high degree of shearing at the interface.

Sandon[784, 785] thinks the Jahn-Rinaldi hypothesis is too simple, and suggests that movement in foraminifera, as well as other sarcodines, is the combined result of a number of processes, at ionic, molecular and macro-molecular levels. This, of course, is implied in the suggestion of Jahn and Rinaldi[450] that the energy mechanism of their proposed shearing movement may be similar to and perhaps the same as in muscle. Although there is no evidence yet for an ionically-triggered, ATP-using actomyosin-like protein complex in the foraminifera, it seems likely that the bidirectional movements are mediated by some such system, since it is apparently present wherever motile protoplasm has been carefully tested.

There are other theories, however, for bidirectional movements in fora-minifera. Allen[18] and Sandon[785] reject the Jahn–Rinaldi hypothesis of naked gel filaments and self-shearing surfaces. Allen[18] considers each fila-ment a bundle of fibrils imbedded in groundplasm and surrounded by a typical cellular "unit" membrane, deriving his interpretation from the fine structure revealed by electron-microscopy for *Allogromia*.[975] They both reject the Jahn–Rinaldi hypothesis on the assumption that the "unit" membrane around each filament invalidates the Jahn–Rinaldi postulates, but this conclusion does not necessarily follow.

Allen[18] suggests that the filament anchors to the substrate at several points. He assumes tensions and contractions developed at these points which act in conjunction with propagated contractions originating at the tips of filaments as they turn back on themselves. He has not yet indicated how and where shear forces act, so he has not really proposed an alternative mechanism.

In order to evaluate properly both the Allen and the Jahn–Rinaldi theories of structure we need much more detailed electron micrographs than the preliminary ones by Wohlfarth-Botterman[975] now available.

### b. Electroconduction and Electrostriction

Another approach to bidirectional shearing movements in protoplasm is that of Osterhout[695] and Seifriz;[823] both assumed that coacervates of particles are propagated in the sol by waves of electrical potential, or depola-rization, so that both fluids and particles in the sol move along the gel interface, or along a thread of protoplasm.

### c. Helical Tension

The helical form of protein molecules has suggested to Cole[178] that protoplasmic movement may be due to the secondary coiling (and creeping) of helical protein filaments of a hydrated molecular helix (e.g., tropomyosin) as it dehydrates unilaterally against another fibrous molecule (e.g., actin).

This seems to explain partly Hayashi's[370, 371] observation that myosin alone does not contract, but when polymerized with actin it does.

Jarosch[471, 474] assumes that protein fibrils of protoplasm anchored at either end or both form a dynamic oscillating system of a polyrhythmic nature, with submicroscopic waves moving helically along the fibrils. If unanchored, the fibrils would be driven in a direction opposite that of the moving waves. This might occur in the freed flagella of sperm and *Polytoma*[123] and in the progress of free-swimming flagellates (cf. p. 139). If anchored at one, or at both ends, the fibrils would displace protoplasm within cells, or in water outside of them. By clever use of wire models Jarosch[475] has demonstrated that helical fibrils of varying pitches wound together in complex fibrillar bundles of larger diameter, might generate waves of movement along the bundle as tension is developed in the fibrils. Tensions developed locally in or along the entire length of fibrils and arising in single fibrils differentially within groups of them may cause a wave of contractile action to progress toward or away from the principal anchorage of the fibrils. He[474] proposes that the fibrils do not have to move from their relatively static locales; and that granules, protoplasm or globules adherent to or associated with the active fibrils or membranes around them might be propelled. Jarosch assumes that almost any kind of protoplasmic movement occurs in a similar manner, but there is no evidence for this theory.

## 4. Gliding Movements

Gliding has been observed in a number of protozoa, but has attracted attention mainly in the gregarine sporozoa and certain euglenid flagellates, especially *Euglena* and *Peranema*. The gregarines and euglenids also show "metabolic" or "peristaltic" movements of the body (cf. pp. 106–107).

### a. Gliding of Gregarines

The gliding of gregarines over a mucus track secreted by the protozoon has long been known. An early theory suggested that gliding was caused by an abundant secretion of slime which piled up behind the protozoon and pushed it forward as the slime accumulated,[732, 799] or that fluid was imbibed anteriorly and ejected at the rear so that it pushed the gregarine.[53] An even earlier theory[808] suggested that an external flow of protoplasm may be involved. Others have held that rippling movements[726] perhaps of myonemes against or beneath the pellicle, caused the gliding,[187, 940] and perhaps with assistance of other cytoplasmic movements.[732] Some gregarines have myonemes;[563] others apparently do not.[55] Therefore, since all gregarines glide, myonemes probably do not provide the principal mechanism.

The pellicle and adjacent protoplasm are somehow involved in gregarine gliding. Jahn and Kozloff[447] demonstrate in motion pictures that the pellicle may continue to glide after loss, by mechanical rupture, of the cytoplasm into the surrounding medium. Jarosch[472] has recently revised Schultze's[808] theory that external protoplasmic movements are involved. He suggests that an active shearing force is exerted by protoplasmic fibrils at the surface, perhaps at or between the pellicular ribs, dragging the gregarine along the surface of its self-secreted mucus in a direction opposite to that of the movement set up in the fibrils. The ripple movements attributed by earlier theories to myonemes have been reinvoked by Richter[753] who assumes that such movements occur in the pellicle, set off by movements of the protoplasmic polypeptide fibrils of molecular dimensions lying next to the pellicle.

### b. Gliding of Euglenids

*Euglena* has also been observed to glide, especially *E. intermedia* and similar species.[472] Günther[346] noted that *Euglena* always glides in one direction, and may follow old slime trails (which indicates that a reaction of some kind occurs between the cell surface and the slime as a driving mechanism). Explanations of euglenoid gliding have been similar to those proposed for gregarines. Günther[346] proposed that the euglena slides forward over a secreted mucous track by contractile waves in the pellicle, driving slime to the rear, and driving itself forward. Jarosch[472] assumes that his shearing-drive mechanism for gregarines also applies to euglenids.

Gliding movements in *Peranema*, according to Chen,[165] do not depend on the motile tip of the flagellum, and continue so long as half the length of heavy anterior flagellum is intact. What the trailing secondary flagellum, which is under the body and a part of the gliding surface,[566] does is not known. Jahn *et al*[458] have shown by high-speed cinematography that *Petalomonas* and *Peranema* glide forward smoothly although the tip of the flagellum describes power and return stroke beats, so that the flagellar beat may not be the only source of locomotor power.

### 5. CYCLOSIS

While cyclotic movements in protozoa have been known since before Ehrenberg[243] postulated his "polygastric" theory for food vacuolar movements in *Paramecium*, explanations of the cyclotic movements of protoplasm in protozoan cells are few, except for ameboid movement (cf. pp. 91–100). Tchakotine[890] found that cyclotic movements continued in *Paramecium* around areas gelated by micropuncture with ultra-violet light. He also noted that when ciliary action and contractile-vacuolar pumping ceased under nickel sulfate anesthesia, the cyclosis stopped. He therefore assumed cyclosis to be promoted by the activity of the vacuole, and by an unidentified action of the basal granules of the cilia. Yamashita[996] describes the motive force as generally distributed in the cell.

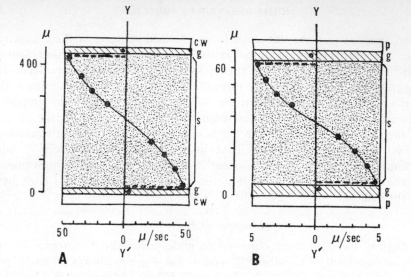

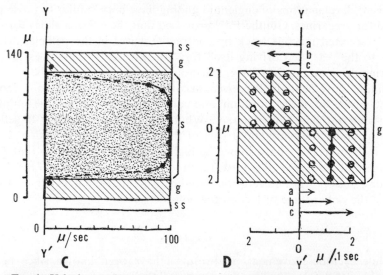

Fig. 1. Velocity profiles of protoplasmic movement. In each case zero velocity is denoted by the line y–y′, and values other than zero are denoted by the dash line in A, B, and C, and by the open, closed, and partly filled circles in D.

A, Leaf cell of *Nitella flexillis* (after Kamiya and Kuroda).

B, Cyclosis in *Paramecium multimicronucleatum.*

C, *Physarum polycephalum* (after Kamiya).

D, *Allogromia laticollaris.* If the cell body is to the left, and the pseudopod is being extended to the right, arrows labeled "c" denote velocity of the gel in each direction; if being withdrawn, arrows "a"; and if being neither extended or withdrawn, arrows "b".

cs—cell surface; g—plasmagel layer; p—plasmasol (endoplasm).

However, some preliminary studies of velocity profiles of cytoplasmic flow in cyclosis of *Paramecium*[547] are of approximately the same values as those cited by Kamiya[502] for rotational movements in large algal cells (Fig. 1). These velocity profiles indicate a shear zone between a thin layer of stationary subpellicular ectoplasm and the moving endoplasm. The source of motive energy is probably ATP.

## 6. TRICHOCYST EXTRUSION

Whatever the poorly known function of trichocysts, whether it is secretion,[464, 708] holdfast[177, 787] toxicity in food capture,[928] food entanglement,[467] defense,[629] reaction to injury,[753] or osmoregulation,[972] these all have in common an explosive extension as a mucoid or fibrous material from a capsule, i.e., they *slide* out, somehow, very rapidly, becoming thereby fibrous or mucoid strands. Those of *Paramecium* are fired by ultraviolet light, mechanical or electric shock, various chemicals, pH shifts, food etc.[953] They are, when extended, fibrous, cross-striated, possibly solid protein cylinders.[468, 972, 715] In *Paramecium* and *Frontonia* they originate and develop in the endoplasm and migrate to pellicular sites.[117, 118, 998]

An ATP-ase system is present, but ATP inhibits extrusion. $Ca^{++}$ is not bound by ATP, and easily triggers expulsion, as do also strontium or ammonium ions, and invert soaps, such as cetyltrimethylammonium-Cl. $Mg^{++}$ ions do not trigger expulsion. The $Ca^{++}$ triggered expulsion proceeds in the absence of ATP and is not blocked by Salygran. If, however, ATP is present then Salygran blocks extrusion easily, and the block remains when both ATP and Salygran are removed.[391] Some theories assume that the expulsion is somehow due to hydration of the proteins in the trichocyst capsule.[118, 468, 738] Whatever happens, extrusion appears to be an ATP-using mechanism by which fibrils slide into position and are bound there, perhaps with adsorbed water. Furthermore, there is a banded appearance and a distinct birefringence in the extruded trichocyst of *Paramecium*, indicative of an orderly bonded fibrous nature.[802]

## B. Contractile-hydraulic Movements

In protozoa with tubular or polytubular body and organelles, movement is probably due to a hydraulic pressure system powered by contractions of an outer gelated part of the tube ("ectoplasm") which drives the less gelated, and therefore more fluid (but non-Newtonian) inner content ("endoplasm") along. Locomotion is a product of this protoplasmic motility.

## 1. SHUTTLE-FLOW IN MYCETOZOA

The polytubular plasmodium of a mycetozoan (myxomycete) moves with a net rate of advance in one direction by means of rhythmic oscillations of protoplasmic flow.[821, 822] For a century the patterns have been known to be complex.[52, 929, 930] Much study has been made of this pulsating type of locomotion, and is extensively reviewed by Kamiya;[502] current opinion is expressed in a recent symposial volume on primitive motile systems[19] and by Jahn.[441] Kamiya[502] calls this shuttle-flow "polyrhythmic".

## a. Theories for Mechanics of Shuttle-flow

Most of the theories which have been mentioned in connection with bidirectional movements of protoplasm have also been used for the shuttle-flow of the mycetozoa, including: 1) gel-sol changes involving linking and unlinking of polypeptide chains in folding;[276, 404] 2) shearing at interfaces;[600] 3) counter currents of matrix propelled by a more or less contractile endoplasmic reticulum;[520] 4) shearing movement of active gel filaments with opposite displacement of filaments and adjacent protoplasm;[304, 470, 471] 5) a physical diffusion-drag gradient movement of protoplasm related to viscosity changes;[745, 862] and 6) a contractile-hydraulic mechanism in which the shuttle-flow involves the alternate contraction and relaxation of a number of centers of motive force which push a more liquid endoplasm through a polytubular ectoplasmic gel, with net unidirectional progress.[441]

Most experimental and observational studies support the last theory [reviews: Kamiya,[502] and Jahn and Bovee.[443, 444]] Except for recent papers by Stewart[861] and by Jahn and his co-workers[441, 461] most of the theories cannot or do not try to deal with the combination of the polyrhythmic movements of shuttle-flow and resultant net advance. The other theories have little support.

Only one hypothesis other than the contractile-hydraulic hypothesis has been seriously advanced in recent years. This is an adaptation of the Rashevsky[745] diffusion-drag hypothesis for cytokinesis applied to mycetozoan shuttle-flow by Stewart and Stewart.[862] Their hypothesis has serious defects, even if such diffusion-drag forces exist (their existence is as yet only hypothetical), since they must function centripetally from sites of origin; yet the mathematical formulas contain substitutions (by Rashevsky) in the integral equations for the volumetric dimensional geometry of the cell which include sign changes required by the facts of cell elongation. These substitutions in turn require that the diffusion-drag forces act centripetally along two axes, and centrifugally on a third. Since this is impossible, the equations cannot apply to cell movements of any kind.[441] Rashevsky[746] indicates still other problems in applying the diffusion-drag theory to cell movements; and Stewart[861] appears to have abandoned diffusion-drag in favor of a modified contractile-hydraulic explanation.

## b. Shuttle-flow as a Contractile-hydraulic System

### (1) The Basic Motile Materials

It is clear that the contractile substance in *Physarum* is an ATP-splitting actomyosin (myxomysin) nearly identical with vertebrate actomyosin-B.[602, 669, 670, 671, 902, 903, 904, 905] It is only necessary to assume that numerous and uniformly scattered mitochondria continuously produce ATP, that ATP is used in contraction, and that the concentration of ATP regulates viscosity, all of which occur in solutions of actomyosin or myxomyosin.[602, 871, 669] This establishes a source of energy and a mechanism for the cycle of gelation-contraction-solation, resulting in the contractile-hydraulic system responsible for shuttle-flow. This mechanism exists as a cortical meshwork of contractile gel fibrils surrounding a non-Newtonian, more or less fluid, streaming endoplasm.

It has already been shown that ATP injected locally or applied externally starts a contraction at the site.[461] When injected into, or applied externally, at any place on the plasmodium of *Physarum*, ATP at first reduces pressure, oscillation and amplitude of flow, as it is assimilated, with subsequent increases in flow, amplitude, period, and polarity of the rhythmic contraction and relaxation.[506]

## (2) "Origins" of Movement and Their Actions

Jahn[441] proposes numerous sites of contraction and relaxation, located in the gel walls of the complicated hydraulic system of tubes of various diameters, which exert hydrostatic pressure on the more fluid endoplasm. Stewart[861] says practically the same thing, but emphasizes the relaxation and elasticity rather than contraction. However, he says the tubule walls are in tension. Allen et al[24] by an elegant electronic-detection technique, found heat produced at these sites, supporting the action of a contractile, energy-using system there. There is also a changing pattern of positive birefringence in the fibrils of the tube wall which is coordinated with the contractions of the wall[20, 670a] and with the formation of more new fibrils along the wall when flow has halted. A negative birefringence, due perhaps to flow or viscous structure, or both, is present in the shuttled sol within the gel tube.[670a]

Jahn[441] calls these sites "origins", and indicates that they function in various (and variable) periods, and are therefore seldom in phase with one another. The algebraic sum of pressures from all origins, less the drop in pressure due to viscosity losses (Hagen-Poiseuille law), produces the degree of pressure at any one site. The pressure in any one tubule of the plasmodium is sequentially variable; and direction of flow in any given tubule may reverse as phase relationships change among the various contracting areas.[502]

Contraction is necessarily followed by partial solation of the gel wall[569] from inside toward the outside,[441] and the wall of the contracting origin becomes thinner and weaker. It finally becomes so thin that its tensile strength no longer overcomes the opposing hydraulic pressure. Sol flows back into the origin, and distends (relaxes) it, but the sol itself becomes gel, thickens the wall of the origin again, and thereby strengthens it so that it can again contract.

### (3) Unidirectional Progress due to Shuttle-flow

Until recently[441] no explanation had been suggested for the production of net unidirectional advance due to shuttle-flow, a lack of information stressed earlier by Noland.[684]

Stewart[861] says that net locomotion results from the forms of waves of relaxation progressing across the plasmodium, the location of sites of relaxation, and the patterns of waves from them. He believes there are sites which act "normally" as principle ones of wave origin and a stable net rhythm. He also suggests an integrative control system which he does not describe.

Jahn[441] reasons that no special integrative function is present or required. He suggests that the net additive effect of the activity of stronger origins in older regions of the plasmodium is greater in force than the net counter activity of weaker origins in newer regions. This causes greater net surge of pressure and flow from old regions toward new, overcoming the counter surge from new areas. Thus, net advance can progress only in the direction of old towards new. This depends on several principal factors: 1) gel is thicker and of greater relative volume in older tubules; 2) older tubules are of larger diameter than new ones, with greater hydrostatic pressure, rate and volume of flow;[502] 3) older gel is both more contractile[441] and more rigid[633] than new, and solates less easily under pressure than new;[571] 4) the oldest, largest, most efficient tubules are at the rear of the plasmodium, and the smaller, weaker, less efficient ones sequentially forward; 5) viscous resistance to fluid flow in a tube varies inversely as the square of the radius of the tube (Hagen-Poiseuille law), and therefore the larger tubes create and transfer hydrostatic pressures more effectively; 6) smaller tubules between the larger ones and the anterior gelating fringe exert some force against that of the larger ones, but this is easily overcome; 7) the newest, weakest gel is pumped out of the smallest weakest tubules as an anterior border forming a fringe permeated by many fine channels, but the fringe is lacking in tubular organization and has only weak contractile efficiency.

Some patterns of flow which can be described as hydrodynamic interactions of such an intricately polyrhythmic system are discussed by Jahn,[441] These include the phenomena which Stewart and Stewart[862] said were difficult to relate to contraction of gel posterior to flow, including: 1) the role of ATP-myxomyosin; 2) the parabolic velocity of flow profile in a single channel with highest velocity along the axis; 3) upstream and downstream flow reversals; 4) different rates of flow in adjacent tubules; 5) absence in tube walls of peristaltic waves; 6) effects of blocking the flow; 7) fluctuating periodicity of motive force with or without flow; 8) fluctuation of electrical potential gradients which continue after flow is blocked; 9) particle movements which are independent of general flow; and 10) an energy expenditure much greater than that used in flow only.

## c. Enigmatic Movements of Mycetozoa

The contractile-hydraulic mechanism of shuttle-flow movement does not completely explain some other phenomena of movement in mycetozoa. For example, it does not yet (but probably could) account for the cessation of shuttle-flow and locomotion during the synchronous mitotic division of the many nuclei,[348] nor is it a satisfactory description for mycetozoan movement through the narrow xylem tubules of rotting wood on a forest floor, nor does it fit the supposedly "circular" flow in a "doughnut" excised from a *Physarum* plasmodium[863] which, however, has not been confirmed (Stewart,[861] pp. 77–78). More investigation is also needed of the motile mechanisms of the early developmental stages of mycetozoa. Koevenig[548] describes at least six types of protoplasmic movements of mycetozoan swarm cells: 1) agitational streaming; 2) circulatory streaming; 3) shuttle-streaming; 4) creeping movement; 5) ameboid movement; and 6) flagellar movement. He suggests that all six types involve the same basic mechanism. In general, these movements indicate the close kinship between oscillating mycetozoan shuttle-flow and ameboid movement, suggesting that the smaller the mycetozoan body, the more nearly its movement is cyclic, as in amebas. This is also borne out by observations of McManus[648] that in the small plasmodium of *Cribraria violacea* flow is continuous for as long as 40 minutes in one direction, interrupted by a brief halt in which endoplasm slows and mixes without reversals, before continuing locomotion.

## 2. "AMEBOID" MOVEMENTS

The term "ameboid movement" has come to mean movements of a whole cell which resemble the movements of the "typical" ameba, *Amoeba proteus*; but *Amoeba proteus* is far from typical of amebas generally either in size, form, or nature of locomotion. If there is anything "typical" of amebas and "ameboid movement" it is variation. Bovee[94] and Jahn and Bovee[443] discuss some of these variations. Schaeffer,[790, 791] Penard[703, 704] and other earlier students of amebas were well aware of this diversity in amebas and their movements.

None the less, in the main, the theories of ameboid movement have developed about the movement of large amebas, such as *Amoeba proteus*.

### a. Theories of Ameboid Movement

#### (1) Older Theories

Older theories have often been reviewed previously in greater or lesser detail.[14, 15, 16, 17, 82, 143, 209, 381, 415, 751, 752, 790, 808, 899] In general, older theories stressed a hypothetical reticular, contractile organization (e.g., Heitzmann,[381]) similar to muscle with the sides and rear contracting,

4*

resulting in a forward flow.[240, 807, 936] Surface tension theories of frontal eversion supplanted these[64, 143, 751] and were countered with rebuttals by Jennings[477] who proposed a rolling-sac movement (for *Amoeba verrucosa*) and Dellinger[212] who showed that *Amoeba proteus* "walks". Hyman[415] suggested the terms *sol* and *gel*, and assumed that colloidal imbibitions and synereses were motive forces. Mast[633], who carefully documented the visible events of the movement and locomotion of *Amoeba proteus*, showed, as Hyman[415] contended, that "gel" and "sol" were two intergrading phases of protoplasm, neither one being wholly solid, nor wholly liquid, both phases of necessity being non-Newtonian. Allen[14, 15, 16] also stressed this non-Newtonian nature of ameboid protoplasm.

Rinaldi and Jahn[756] and Jahn[440] have condensed the theories and arguments, showing that all agree that some fibrillar network akin to an ATP-using actomyosin network develops in the gel, with less fibrillar material in the sol. They point out, as does also Weiss,[944] that the main area of argument and disagreement involves the mechanism of the motive force, and the location of the site or sites of contraction.

### (2) Present Electrical Theories

Bingley and Thompson[66] propose that a bioelectrical gradient, which they detect from front to rear in *Amoeba proteus*, sets off the contractile sequence by current flow, which in turn is presumed to be due to active ion flux; but they admit that ascertaining timing is difficult, and that the current flow may be the result rather than the cause of the contractile sequence, thus being associated with ionic triggering mechanisms.

Bell and Jeon[60] suggest that cytoplasmic movement is a response to an electrical signal after depolarization of and active extension of the surface membrane, drawing cytoplasm into a lengthening pseudopod; but they admit they do not have (and do not believe anyone *has*) evidence for a comprehensive theory of ameboid movement.

The supposed relationship between ion flux and electromotive force is certainly open to question.[594, 914, 245a] This does not invalidate the idea that differences in electrical potential might be associated with the locomotor mechanism, but if so, the mechanisms involved need to be identified and elucidated.

### (3) A Jet Propulsion Theory

Another recent theory is that of Kavanau[516, 517, 519, 520a] who considers the streaming to be caused by a jet propulsion pumping activity of the endoplasmic reticulum, which is assumed to push cytoplasmic matrix backward in the sol and forward in the gel; the reticulum of the gel is supposed to maintain its position in relation to the substrate, but that of the sol is assumed to be pushed forward, thereby giving rise to the observed streaming. However, since the net change in momentum produced by jet propulsion of the free swimming reticulum of the sol must be zero ([520a,] p. 482) this pumping, alone, cannot result in forward movement of the ameba. The mechanism of how some of the momentum produced by jet propulsion, presumably that of the reticulum of the gel, is transmitted to the substrate has not been explained, but it probably could be.

However, Kavanau ([520a,] p. 479) also assumes the existence of "contractile transformations and degrowth by fragmentation of certain regions of the plasmalemma (plasma membrane) and of a postulated system of double-membrane lamellae (the cortical reticulum) in the ectoplasm (plasmagel)". Existence of adequate contractile forces in the plasmalemma is questionable,[312, 313] but contraction of the gel does exist,[440] and certainly could act as Kavanau suggests. This portion of his theory of the locomotor mechanism is identical with the Mast theory that contraction of the gel exerts the locomotor force, and it has no necessary relationship to the assumed jet propulsion of the endoplasmic reticulum.

The jet propulsion theory, then, is a theory of counter current circulation of cytoplasmic matrix versus the formed cytoplasmic elements. It suggests that such a counter current exists and how it might be maintained if it does. It also states that this assumed circulation can contribute to the locomotor forces operating in amebas, but exactly which components of the momentum can contribute, and how they contribute, must be clarified.

## (4) The "Fountain-zone" Frontal Eversion Theory

Allen[14, 15, 16, 17] has proposed a frontal-eversion theory which in some aspects is a revision and extension of earlier theories[64, 381, 751, 795, 899] which involve a pulling from the anterior end. Allen proposes that gel filaments elongate and stream forward as part of a "pseudoplastic plug" in the sol; that they pack and contract at the anterior rim of the continuously formed gel tube, meantime everting more filaments from the sol. In brief, he assumes that the everting sol, as it becomes gel, *pulls* the remaining sol forward. This, he believes, negates any rearward contractile mechanism, or the need for it. The theory is derived from the cyclic streaming of sol filaments in naked ameba protoplasm under oil, and from analogous movements which occur in amebas held in glass capillaries.[23] This explanation, he believes, is made necessary by his assumption[14, 15, 16] that other theories and other observers have required that sol be and act as a true Newtonian fluid, which they definitely do not, as conclusively indicated below, [see also, Rinaldi and Jahn,[756] Jahn,[440] Jahn and Bovee[443, 444]].

## (5) The Contractile-hydraulic Theory

Although the major sites of contraction in the ameba are yet to be metabolically determined, the mass of evidence available supports a contractile-hydraulic mechanism such as proposed by Mast.[633] Almost all available data are readily explained by such a theory, including that assumed to support other theories [see Jahn,[440] Kamiya,[503] Marsland,[626] Goldacre,[313] Rinaldi and Jahn,[756] Jahn and Bovee[443, 444]].

(a) *A Brief Statement of the Theory*. The contractile-hydraulic theory, in one or another of its versions, proposes that a semi-rigid, elastic, ectoplasmic tube is continuously generated by an ameba in locomotion. This tube is composed of a three-dimensional net-like fibrous protein complex ("gel") which contracts at the rear of the ameba and drives a more fluid, less fibrous endoplasm ("sol") forward. The "sol" diverts to the rim of the gel tube anteriorly, there becoming "gel" and adding to the length of the tube. At an equal pace, the fibrous "gel" at the rear contracts and breaks up internally to become "sol". Jahn[440] outlines a concept of the movements of sol and gel, in what he has termed the contractile-hydraulic mechanism, emphasizing the nature of the motive force.[453, 443, 756, 440] Most explanations are in agreement that the more fluid endoplasm is driven forward by peripheral isometric[82] and posterior isotonic[633] contractions of the gel tube which increase in strength when the gel has become both physiologically and chronologically older as it becomes the rear end of the ameba;[22, 82, 94, 308, 311, 312, 313, 440, 592, 633, 638, 756] [see also *discussion* and *free discussion* sections, Allen and Kamiya,[19] pp. 253–255; 274–277; 323–327; 457–465; 623–633].

(b) *Data Supporting a Contractile-hydraulic System*. The contractile-hydraulic explanation is supported by much evidence which includes the following: 1) high hydrostatic pressure experiments on amebas show a close relationship between *contraction* and *solation*;[569] 2) the anterior part of the newly-formed gel tube is stretched forward as if by hydrostatic pressure;[756] 3) in newly-forming pseudopods *all* the granules throughout any whole cross-section move forward;[440, 756] 4) protein concentration is highest at the rear of a locomoting ameba;[22] 5) the pressure generated at the rear of a locomoting ameba is about that of a 1 cm column of water, and locomotion can be stopped by a counter pressure of that force;[503] 6) when a pseudopod retracts, its measured force of contraction is $10^3$ dynes/$cm^{2[311]}$, indicating an operative contractile pressure; 7) pseudopodal ridges of *Amoeba proteus* and *Chaos carolinensis* form as sol breaks through the side of the gel tube and flows forward *over* the gel tube and *under* the plasmalemma;[559, 633, 790] 8) with darkfield microscopy, fine granules can be seen moving *forward* through the gel and sometimes in the hyaline ectoplasm;[440, 451, 756] 9) neutral red dye inhibits solation when it stains the protein of the gel, causing it to become denser as it contracts and more resistant to solation, resulting in accumulation of the gel at the rear as the ameba advances;[308, 440, 894] 10) when ATP or ionic bonds break, an electrical potential and possibly current may be expected, the more bonds broken the more current,[437, 873] and measurements[66] show a gradient of increase of 1 volt/cm of length from front to rear of the ameba; 11) when an ameba slows and stops, the differential gradient of gel strength and protein concentration[22] and the bioelectrical gradient[66] fade and halt as a consequence of locomotion, interpreted by the investigators[22] as supporting a site of posterior contraction; 12) a cathodally moving ameba reacts in a direct electric current with more forcible contraction at the rear and a lack of gel formation at the front end, and the rate of its locomotion increases;[349, 645, 961] 13) a sudden increase of illumination results in a reversal of flow in the advancing pseudopods, but posterior pressure and forward flow of protoplasm continue, the ameba bulging in the center;[635] 14) if a hole is poked through the gel in a locomoting ameba with a glass needle, outflow of endoplasm occurs, even if the hole be made at the rear,[311] thus demonstrating positive peripheral and posterior pressure; and 15) granular sol bursts through the plasmagel sheet, which forms between the sol and the hyaline cap, entering the hyaline cap forcibly, demonstrating positive pressure on it.[451, 633, 635, 755, 756]

Items 12 and 13, and related observations obtained as part of a detailed study of the effects of light and electricity on protoplasm by Mast[635] and Hahnert[349] clearly support a contraction-hydraulic system, and are devastating to any frontal contraction eversion scheme. (review, Jahn[440])

(c) *Role of ATP-actomyosin in the System.* Present available evidence gives very clear support to the general description by Mast,[633] that pressure generates at the rear as the gel contracts, and drives the more fluid, non-Newtonian endoplasm anteriorly. It is also clear from the accumulated evidence on ATP-using actomyosin systems in protozoa (cf. pp. 74–77), that such a system functions in dynamic equilibrium in amebas, as proposed by Bovee,[82] elaborated with much supporting data by Landau,[569] and verified by Simard-Duquesne and Couillard;[847, 848] and by Zimmerman.[1000]

## b. Geometry and Forces Operative in Locomotion of Amoeba

If we assume that the driving force of plasmasol streaming is contraction of the posterior gel, and that flow is caused by differential hydraulic pressure at the two ends of the gel tube, it should be possible to set up equations which relate the driving force to the geometry of the system and also to include appropriate terms for whatever resistive forces exist. Since our knowledge of the forces involved is incomplete, such an equation can only be incomplete. However, attempts in this direction can be useful guides for logical consideration of the phenomena, for an evaluation of experimental results, and for the planning of future experiments. The first step was taken by Heilbrunn[375] who made a calculation of the pressure differential necessary for the observed flow, and of the tension that must be developed by the posterior gel in order to provide this pressure. In hydraulic flow the Hagen-Poiseuille law should apply. The law is

$$\frac{Q_s}{t} = \frac{\pi p r_2^4}{8 l \eta}$$

where $Q_s$ is the volume of flow of sol past a given line, $t$ is the unit of time, $p$ is the pressure differential, $r_2$ is the internal radius of the gel tube, $l$ is the length of the tube, and $\eta$ the viscosity of the sol. If $r_2$ is 20 $\mu$, $l$ is 200 $\mu$, and $\eta$ is 0.05 centipoise, the calculated value of $p$ is 8 dynes/cm².

Furthermore, Heilbrunn applied the equation for pressure developed by tension at the surface of a sphere, $p = 2T_1/r_1$, where $T_1$ is the tension developed by the gel and $r_1$ the radius of the posterior end, to calculate the value of $T_1$ necessary to produce the pressure $p$. If $r_1$ is 30 $\mu$, the calculated value of $T_1$ becomes 0.012 dynes/cm. If we apply the equation for a hemisphere ($p = T_1/r_1$) this value is doubled.

The calculated values for $p$ and for $T_1$ are extremely low. One obvious reason is that it is assumed that there is no back pressure. However, the velocity of flow is not uniform, and can be seen to increase when the plasmagel

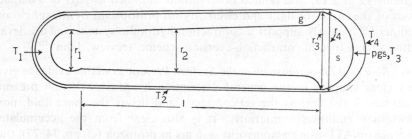

FIG. 2. Some variable forces functional in a locomoting ameba.
$l$—length of the tube; $r_1$—radius of contracting region; $r_2$—inside radius of the gel tube; $r_3$—radius of the plasmagel sheet; $r_4$—radius of the anterior plasmalemmar cap; $T_1$—tension of the posterior cortical gel; $T_2$—tension of the lateral plasmalemma; $T_3$—tension of the plasmagel sheet; $T_4$—tension of the anterior plasmalemma sheet.

sheet is ruptured. Furthermore, a certain amount of energy must be used in the filtration of the sol through the plasmagel sheet to form the hyaloplasm. For these reasons the plasmagel sheet must exert a considerable back pressure. If we use the equation for pressure in a hemisphere for defining this back pressure we can then express it as $T_3/r_3$, where $T_3$ and $r_3$ are the tension and radius of the plasmagel sheet. Similarly, if we assume a back pressure from the plasmalemma, it can be expressed as $T_4/r_4$, where $T_4$ and $r_4$ are the tension and the radius of the anterior hemispherical section of the plasmalemma. The expression for the net pressure then becomes the difference between the pressure developed by $T_1$ and the back pressure developed by $T_3$ and $T_4$.

The geometric relationships of these values are shown in Fig. 2, in which we have extended the principle applied by Heilbrunn to include $T_2$, $T_3$, $r_3$ and $r_4$.

The net pressure is the difference between that caused by the posterior cortical gel and by the two anterior membranes. If we use the symbols defined in Fig. 2, the equation for net pressure becomes

$$p = \frac{T_1}{r_1} - \frac{T_3}{r_3} - \frac{T_4}{r_4}$$

Poiseuille's law then becomes

$$\frac{Q_s}{t} = \frac{\pi r_2^4}{8\, l\eta} \left( \frac{T_1}{r_1} - \frac{T_3}{r_3} - \frac{T_4}{r_4} \right)$$

Since we now have expressions for the pressure and the flow in terms of the geometry of the ameba, the next question is whether it is possible to write an equation for the velocity of the ameba in terms of its geometry and the involved forces.

The velocity of the ameba ($V_a$) will vary directly with the volume moving per unit time, and for any given rate of volume flow will vary inversely as the total volume of the ameba ($Q_a$). Therefore

$$V_a = \frac{\pi r_2^4}{8\, l\eta\, Q_a} \left( \frac{T_1}{r_1} - \frac{T_3}{r_3} - \frac{T_4}{r_4} \right)$$

On the basis of this equation it should be possible to predict the effect on the velocity of locomotion of any treatment which will affect any one of the nine variables.

However, one of the questions most often asked in regard to locomotion of *Amoeba proteus* is "How do various environmental factors such as visible and ultra-violet light, lack of $O_2$, changes in pH, changes in temperature, and various chemicals, including ATP, affect the rate of locomotion?" Also, "How do changes in the gel/sol ratio or in the rate of rupture of the plasmagel sheet, both of which can be affected by external factors, affect locomotion, or to what extent can they be correlated with changes in the rate of locomotion?"

Some of the investigations of these questions have been very elaborate and performed with great diligence [e.g., Mast and Prosser,[642] Pitts and Mast[719, 720, 721]]. However, the experimental results obtained are complex, and such simple factors as pH and temperature yield enigmatic bimodal curves. The data have been used in compiling catalogs of the behavior of the organisms under experimental conditions, but they have not been useful in elucidating the mechanism which determines this behavior. The reason for the complex results and for the failure of investigators to pin-point the mechanism of the observed effects can be seen in the equation for the velocity of locomotion. This equation has nine variables, and presumably several of them can be affected either directly or indirectly and in an unknown manner by every one of the environmental factors which can be varied experimentally. Furthermore, the effect of each such factor may vary with time, i.e., with duration of application. On this basis it is not surprising that most of the experimental results are complex and uninterpretable in terms of mechanism.

A promising line of investigation would be the application of chemicals each known to have a specific action on only one variable. This makes the search for specific chemicals interesting and important, but so far the search has been unproductive.

### c. OTHER FACTORS IN AMEBOID MOVEMENT

#### (1) Birefringence

There is a form (textural) birefringence detectable in the cortical gel of the ameba, but none in the moving endoplasm.[656] The birefringence reported for the endoplasm may be a flow-birefringence rather than one due to structure.[13, 25] Engelmann[253] and Schmidt[803] have especially stressed the generality of birefringence in living contractile systems.

#### (2) Attachment to Substratum

It is generally recognized that in order for an ameba to move forward it must be attached to the substratum; otherwise it merely undergoes "fountain streaming" without locomotion. In large amebas the attachment is usually in the mid-region of the body, and the gel of the attached region is virtually stationary,[59, 60, 212, 440, 807] perhaps indicating an isometric tension and rigidity.[82] Near the anterior end, the gel mesh and surface membrane are stretched, and granules move forward through the gel network.[440, 576] While the mechanism of attachment is unknown and is almost an uninvestigated phase of ameboid movement, it is known that attachment varies with the nature of the substrate, and with experimental conditions.[634] It is a strong adhesion, and twice as much pressure is required to dislodge *Amoeba proteus* from its hold to the wall of a glass capillary tube as is required to stop and reverse its forward flow in the tube.[507, 508]

#### (3) The Role of the Nucleus

We do not yet know what the roles of the nucleus may be in ameboid response and motility, but Schaeffer,[790] Hirshfield,[385, 386] Landau,[569] Brachet[108, 109] and Bovee[94] consider them to be multiple and intricate. There is evidence from electromicrographs of the nucleus of amebas, that "messenger RNA" is formed by the nucleus, pinched off into vacuoles by the nuclear membrane, and presumably transported to ER sites.[109, 424] It is generally known that movement of an enucleate ameba, or in the cut-off enucleate half of an ameba, continues only briefly, then quickly slows and stops, but what the nucleus provides to maintain the locomotion is not known. Comandon and de Fonbrun[181, 182] have shown for *Thecamoeba sphaeronucleolus* that the loss of motility following enucleation is promptly and dramatically restored upon introduction of a homologous nucleus, even after 2 to 3 days of immobility, but not after 6 days. This indicates that nuclear material is important to cytoplasmic maintenance of the locomotor mechanism.

Danielli[197, 198] has shown that the nuclei of closely related amebas (*Amoeba proteus* and *Amoeba discoides*) may be interchanged; and either species of nucleus will restore full motility to an enucleate ameba of either species. It is even more significant that the pattern of locomotion is so affected that it becomes more nearly — but never entirely — like that of the species which donated the nucleus. Evidently, the organization and operation of the motile machinery is a function of the nucleus, and can be modified but not completely changed by a related nucleus. It is also significant that the nucleus of a less closely related species (e.g., *Amoeba dubia*) will only temporarily restore motility to *Amoeba proteus*; the recipient soon dies.[197, 198] The nucleus of *Amoeba dubia* is apparently incompatible with the cytoplasm of *Amoeba proteus*.

Hirshfield *et al.*[386] and Hirshfield[385] demonstrated that the nucleus is responsible for the maintenance of normal gel strength. In brief, they found that in enucleate amebas high hydrostatic pressure over a wide temperature range produces the same effect as in normal amebas, but that only half as much pressure was required. They ascribed this to a lower initial gel strength.

Sells *et al*[826] give evidence that the nucleus is involved in the rate of ATP-ase activity in the ameba; and Prescott[734] shows that *Acanthamoeba* cannot incorporate nucleic acids, and presumably cannot make RNA, unless the nucleus is present.

Brachet[109] concludes that there are mutual interactions between the nucleus and cytoplasm, related to the motile mechanism; and Goldacre[310] and Bovee[94] indicate feedback mechanisms of an oscillatory nature between nucleus and cytoplasm during the locomotor process, also stressed in earlier terminology as interactions.[790]

## (4) The Role of the Surface Membrane

The roles of the surface membrane in ameboid movement may be complex. It may possibly admit ions and enzymes which trigger contraction in the gel[82, 311] or initiate a change in EMF, or cause depolarization.[59, 60, 66] Goldacre[309, 312] believes gel cannot contract until the surface membrane is in contact with the gel, and he assumes such contact is required to trigger an ATP-ase he believes is at the membrane. It may be more likely that $Ca^{++}$ ions serve as such a trigger, and are available at the inner surface of the membrane, the ATP-ase being attached to the gel network.

While there has been some argument as to the permanence of the plasmalemma during locomotion (see Allen and Kamiya[19]), recent studies

4 a*

indicate that much of the plasmalemma on an advancing pseudopod is new surface[482] and that new surface is formed to replace that invaginated and ingested in pinocytosis.[159, 160] Several reports suggest that new surface is derived from intracellular groundplasm[623, 767] or endoplasmic reticulum.[357] Jahn[440] suggests that an ameba normally can make whatever surface membrane the circumstances may require.

### d. Other Forms of Ameboid Movement

While the contraction-hydraulic system best describes the events of movement in *Amoeba proteus* and similar amebas, it does not yet completely explain all of the details as described for other ameboid movements, such as: 1) the locomotion of thecamebas (i.e., "verrucosa" types of species) called "rolling" by Jennings[477] and recently described as a frontal-tractile system by Abé[3, 4, 5, 6] [see review, Jahn and Bovee[443, 444]]; 2) locomotion of fan shaped flabellulid amebas, e.g., *Vannella miroides*[92, 94] [see review, Jahn and Bovee[443, 444]] which considerably modifies the contraction-hydraulic system; 3) formation and movement of tapering gel pseudopods by mayorellid amebas, particularly in radiate sessile and floating stages;[80, 83, 84, 92, 94, 704, 791] 4) locomotion of certain mayorellid amebas which extend clear tapering gel pseudopods ("exolobopods", Sandon[784]) which the ameba then opens, enters, flows into and through [e.g., *Oscillosignum*, Bovee[83, 84, 94]]; and 5) rapid movements of a vibratile flagellum-like pseudopod by certain mayorellid amebas, e.g., *Flagellipodium* sp., Bovee.[94] Possibly more detailed future descriptions of locomotion in some of these organisms will permit better determination of the mechanisms involved.

### e. Aggregate Ameboid Movements

#### (1) Hartmannellid Soil Amebas

Some hartmannellid amebas which ordinarily move separately by means of an eruptive, lobopodal, contraction-hydraulic system,[89, 93, 94] with accessory filose pseudopods, may, while feeding, produce a mass aggregate movement. *Hartmannella astronyxis*[748] and *Acanthamoeba castellanii* will in several days produce clones of hundreds of amebas which concentrate on bacterial streak-colonies on agar plates. These amebas crawl over one another, so that a rolling mass of amebas, described as a "wave-front" [93, 748] moves forward slowly along the bacterial streak, devouring it. This aggregate mass moves about four times as fast as any single ameba in it, as a resultant of the combined motile activities of all of them.[748] After heavy feeding, and just prior to encystment, smaller clumps of a few hundred *Hartmanella astronyxis* will form and move about as an aggregate, movement ceasing as encystment begins.[748] *Acanthamoeba castellanii* forms plaques of layered cysts due to aggregation of amebas as food is exhausted, and mass encystment occurs.[93]

It may be that aggregation of such hartmannellid soil amebas is both ancestral to, and degenerate from, the more highly organized acrasid slime mold amebas which aggregate in a complex fashion prior to forming-cyst-like spores. Bonner[74] suggests such a relationship between hartmannellid and acrasid amebas; and Sussman[867] reports mutant acrasid strains some of which form only aggregate clumps which encyst but fail to migrate and to form fruiting stalks, or pseudo-sori, while other mutant strains will not aggregate at all.

*(2) "Social" Amebas; Acrasid "Slime Molds"*

Before aggregation these amebas individually look, move and behave like the hartmannellid amebas, presumably by the mechanism usually considered a typical ameboid movement. Although Shaffer[838] believes a "ripple movement" resembling that of tissue culture cells (review, Ambrose [33]) is a better description of their individual movements, that "ripple movement", too, is closely related to the typical movements of *Amoeba proteus*.[60]

A certain degree of "maturation" of the amebas occurs before aggregation begins. Shaffer[835] describes this process as a series of physiological states in which amebulas are at first active and feeding but non-locomotive, unresponsive to changes of light and heat and lacking the chemical (acrasin) which promotes aggregation. They pass then into a state with these capacities but do not employ them. Any one ameba may enter the next state and secrete acrasin, and others then move toward it.[834, 837]

A locomotive, extended, oriented state ensues, producing acrasin posteriorly and sensitive to it anteriorly. In this state the amebas are adhesive and migrate singly and in streams toward aggregation centers where they remain active and sensitive to acrasin. They orient mutually to form a positively directed, heat-, light-, and $CO_2$-sensitive "slug", within which the amebas are adhesive and interdigitated by their pseudopods, their individual responses driving the slug. Both individual and aggregate slug speed may depend on rates of pseudopodial formation.[782] Finally, the slug stops, becomes more $CO_2$-sensitive[76] and forms a fruiting body. The form of the fruiting body is determined by migratory activities of amebas in the slug, the posterior amebas forming the cyst-like spores by crawling over others to the top of the fruiting stalk.[74] The form of slug and fruiting body are characteristic of the species or mutant strain.[867]

As the slug is formed and locomotes, faster amebas take forward positions, slower ones rearward.[77] The slug advances through a self-secreted slime-sheath, which it leaves behind along with clumps of laggard amebas. Each "left behind" individual forms a microcyst which in some species is like that formed by each ameba in the "sorus" of the fruiting-body, but in other species is distinct.[74]

Adhesion and slime-secretion may be an antigen-antibody relationship. There are species-specific antigens in separate strains of feeding but non-aggregative amebas.[334] In the aggregated amebas a *non*-specific antigen appears so that many species and strains may mutually aggregate to form a complex slug.[334, 876] There may be other antigens, however, so that the anterior and posterior parts of a normal clonal slug may be antigenically different.[335, 876] In a complex mixed slug, the different strains and species sort out to form distinct specific sori when the slug stops and differentiation takes place.[74]

Aggregation is not triggered by the antigens, however, but is a chemotaxis triggered by "acrasin", a chemical of unknown constitution. Acrasin is a dialyzable non-protein,[834] of three component fractions in definite proportion,[868] which at room temperature is degraded by a dialyzable protein fraction.[74] Steroid hormones[989, 990] and histidine[110] stimulate aggregation, but the mechanism is just as unknown as that of stimulation by acrasin.

Physical factors also affect the aggregative process including strong light,[272] continuous light,[494, 692] light and dark cycles,[551, 552, 836] humidity,[77] food sources[951], $Ca^{++}$-chelating substances such as EDTA [74, 210, 839, 861] $CO_2$ levels,[844] and contact.[291]

## C. Taxonomic Significance of Sarcodine Movements

The absence or the presence and use of the motile units (i.e., cilia, flagella, pseudopods, etc.) has long been the basis for the principal divisions in protozoan systematics, and it has been assumed that this expressed a morphological taxonomy. Therefore, use of pseudopodal organelles in sarcodine systematics other than in positional relationships (i.e., are they radiate or not?) is shocking to classical (i.e., morphologically oriented) taxonomists. However, the obvious utility in taxonomy of ameboid organisms of the movements of pseudopods in locomotion has been pointed out by the principal students of the systematics of amebas, including Schulze,[807] Leidy,[584] Frenzel,[274] Penard,[703, 704, 705] Cash, Wailes and Hopkinson,[152] Schewiakoff,[800] Schaeffer,[791] de Saedeleer[779, 780] and Bovee,[80, 84, 94] all proposing useful schemes based on types of pseudopods and especially on their movements. Griffin[337, 338, 339] also urges the taxonomic use of other physiological and ecological factors.

### 1. ASSUMPTION OF A PHYSIOLOGICAL BASIS FOR CLASSIFICATION

Recently, Jahn and Bovee[443] have formally proposed that mechanisms of movement be used to provide the primary systematic dichotomy of the sarcodines into two classes. They use similar bases for orders.[97, 98] They assume that as locomotor mechanisms the bidirectional filamentous two-way shearing and the contractile-hydraulic mechanisms are mutually exclusive [see also Jahn and Rinaldi,[450] Jahn et al.[453]], as well as distinct morphological and physiological employments of a fundamental motile mechanism.

## 2. A Revision of Sarcodine Taxonomy

Jahn and Bovee[443] propose that the subphylum *Sarcodina* be divided into two classes: 1) Class *Autotractea* — with slender filamentous pseudopods in which two-way active shearing flow is evident; and 2) Class *Hydraulea* — with tubular or polytubular pseudopods or body in which contraction of the gel-tubes drives the more fluid contents.

This primary dichotomy cuts across previous classes of the *Sarcodina*, and requires a revision of other groups above the family level.[97, 98] Therefore, within the Class *Autotractea* they propose a division into: A) Subclass *Actinopodia* — with axopods, containing a) Order *Heliozoida* — having axopods extended from a central granule or from peripheral nuclei; and b) Order *Acantharida* — having axopods extended from the center of the body, penetrating an internal membrane; and B) Subclass *Filoreticulosia* — with filoreticulopods, but *no* axopods, containing a) Order *Hyporadiolarida* — having radiating rarely anastomosing filoreticulopods, b) Order *Radiolarida* — having peripherally-radiating basally-anastomosing distinctly-granular filoreticulopods, c) Order *Granuloreticulida* — having filoreticulopods as a mobile anastomosing network around the body, and d) Order *Filida* — having finely-granular filoreticulopods which rarely branch or anastomose.

The Class *Hydraulea* they divide into: A) Subclass *Cyclia* with ameboid, generally-unidirectional cyclic flow in steady locomotion, containing a) Order *Lobida* — having pseudopods digitate or as hemispherical waves, or as a clear border formed by protoplasmic flow, and b) Order *Acrasida* — having amebulas which aggregate to form a motile slug-like pseudoplasmode; and B) Class *Alternatia* — with a polytubular plasmodial body in which cytoplasm moves by shuttle-flow with net unidirectional advance, containing a) Order *Mycetozoida* — having amebulas which grow and/or fuse to become the plasmode of interconnected gel tubes, and b) Order *Xenophyophorida* — poorly understood marine organisms with polytubular chitinoid structure and granular internal protoplasm.

## 3. Some Major Discrepancies of Older Systems

Although already deemed a radical innovation,[715] this new system does not violate any laws of priority. It corrects a gross error in older systems based on the assumed presence of axopods in organisms with radiating pseudopods, and their absence in those which have non-radiate pseudopods [i.e., the classes *Actinopodea* and *Rhizopodea* of Calkins[146, 147]]. Trégouboff[900] has pointed out that true *Radiolarida* have *no* axopods, and he separates them from the acantharian organisms which *do* have axopods. Jahn and Bovee[443, 453] indicate also that certain organisms previously classified as heliozoa have axopods, although others do not; and they discuss other defects of older systems.

In their system the only major change from older systems is the transfer of foraminiferan and filose testacean organisms into a common relationship with axopodal "heliozoa" and "radiolaria". Other relationships will be dealt with elsewhere (Bovee and Jahn, unpublished).

To the present authors the system appears vastly superior to those used by Trégouboff[900] and by the Committee on Taxonomy of the Society of Protozoologists,[400a] both of which are similar to systems used for most of the past century, with many of the defects cited by Jahn and Bovee,[442, 443] and Jahn et al.[453] For example, those two systems retain the groups Actinopodea and Rhizopodea, and although the committee authors recognize that the Radiolaria have no axopodia, they place them in the Actinopodea. There no longer is any basis for distinguishing the old major groups except possibly the radial appearance of the Actinopodea, which is of no help in separating a radiolarian or heliozoan or an acantharian from the "radiosa" stage of an ameba[80] or foraminiferan. Retention of the old system largely for historical reasons when a rearrangement of groups is needed would prevent progress in taxonomy.[435]

## D. Non-ameboid Body Movements

Protozoa other than amebas may perform quasi-ameboid movements of part or all of the body, or may take temporary or cyclic ameboid forms. The latter are here considered truly ameboid, the others (for convenience in discussion only) are not. Certain flagellates (e.g., Cercobodo, Hexamastix) use pseudopods as well as flagella to locomote on substrates. Symbiotic polymastigid flagellates of termites ingest wood fragments pseudopodially[174, 250, 801, 869] and use both flagella and ameboid movements to advance. Gregarines show peristaltic movements of the body as well as gliding movements, and so do some euglenids (a movement called "metabolie" or metaboly). Ciliates such as Stentor, Spirostomum and Condylostoma (and probably others) contract and extend; and the contractions of the body and stalk of Vorticella are well known.

However, lack of published information and theory inhibits a detailed discussion of such movements.

### 1. MOVEMENTS OF MYONEMES

"Muscle threads" have long been assumed to be responsible for the contractions of Stentor. Tartar[877] summarizes the electron microscope studies[258, 741, 744] as indicating that the prominent myonemal bands (km or "ectomyonemes") of packed parallel longitudinal fibers, are attached all along the surface membrane and at either end of the body so that they form arcs as they contract, causing the contracted body to assume a spherical shape. Daniel and Mattern[194] contend, however, that the km fibrils are non-contractile, and suggest that a "deep tubular" system of fibrils resembling ciliary peripheral fibrils in structure are responsible. There are also less orderly fibrous cross-connected internal longitudinal bands beneath the pellicular ridges (M-bands or "endomyonemes"). What their functions may be is not known, though Tartar[877] suggests they may function in extension of the body as antagonists of *km* bundles.

There is no evidence yet of a role for ATP-actomyosin in the contractions of *Stentor*, perhaps because no such experiments seem to have been reported—an omission as astonishing as is the similar dearth of such experiments with *Paramecium*. However, older studies by Neresheimer[678, 679] indicate a quasimuscular nature of their function, e.g., curare promotes a violent contraction blocked by physostigmine, strychnine sulfate causes a normal to weak contraction, and caffeine stimulates contraction, where morphine-HCl and nicotine anesthetize. $CaCl_2$ stimulates contraction and is antagonized by 0.5% KCl, which anesthetizes the myonemes.[217] Weak solutions of $NiSO_4$ which anesthetize the cilia do not affect the myonemes.[877] Effective relaxants which permit cutting the animal without response are NaBr,[678] 0.04% $Na_2SO_4$,[217] and 1% NaI or KI.[878] A mixture of curare and strychnine sulfate anesthetizes myonemes but not cilia.[701] Nevertheless, after such treatments the myonemes still contract in mordant fixatives. According to Tartar[877] contractility of *Stentor* is one of the last functions to be lost, even after motility of cilia and swimming cease, and it persists in grossly abnormal specimens. Enucleate animals swim, contract and relax normally for about a week. If renucleated in 2–3 days they do not lose contractility, but if renucleated after 5 days contractility is completely lost and cannot be recovered, even though the renucleated ciliate lives on for several days with partial recovery of other functions and regeneration of lost organelles.[877]

In two other ciliates with long, contractile bodies, *Spirostomum* and *Condylostoma*, the principal "myonemes" are apparently identical with "kinetodesma" as indicated by electron microscopy,[264, 992, 993] those of *Condylostoma* being strikingly like the contractile *km* myonemes of *Stentor*. Finley *et al.*[264] also note other fibrillar structures in *Spirostomum* besides the *km* (lateral ectomyoneme) bands, and remark on their similarity to those of *Stentor*. Little else is known except for the observation of Kinastowski[526] that complete recovery from the effects of a stimulus which elicited a contraction requires a pause between stimuli of at least 13 minutes, and that the response is the same regardless of the kind of stimulus.[831]

Whatever the contractile elements are in *Spirostomum*, they function exceedingly rapidly.[827, 488] High speed cinematography (to 6000 ft/sec) is required to reveal the details of contraction. When stimulated with direct electric current, after a latent period of 30 msec, *Spirostomum* contracts to 50 per cent of the original length within the next 4 msec. Contraction begins at the anodal end 1 msec before contraction starts in the cathodal end. This is the fastest rate of contraction recorded for any protoplasmic material to date. Added external $Ca^{++}$ increases the rate of contraction. The rate drops in $Ca^{++}$ free and $K^+$ free solutions, but not in $K^+$ rich solutions. The data indicate that removal of $K^+$ from the anodal end of the animal raises the relative amount of bound $Ca^{++}$ to a level which triggers contraction. The Gibbs-Donnan equilibrium is probably involved.[488]

Vorticellid body myonemes contain ATP-ase, -SH groups have been shown cyto-chemically, and cysteine reduces ATP-ase activity.[588, 589] Glycerinated models of vorticellid bodies contract in the presence of ATP provided $Ca^{++}$ is present, but not after EDTA treatment.[587] The glycerinated models of spasmonemes of the vorticellid stalk react with ATP and $Ca^{++}$,[390, 587] and the spasmonemes also contain ATP-ase and -SH groups.[589] Their action is depressed by strychnine[870] and blocked by Salygran.[390] They contract with a calculated force of 75 $gm/cm^2$ per unit of sectional area, or about 0.106—0.212 mg.[910] A hydrolysis of the spasmonemal proteins is apparently involved since there is a 24 to 38 per cent loss of volume by the spasmoneme when it contracts.[865] It is assumed that ATP relaxes the spasmoneme, loading it with energy for contraction, which $Ca^{++}$ ions then trigger.[390, 391, 587] To what degree the Gibbs-Donnan equilibrium may be involved has not been investigated.

Other movements usually attributed to body myonemes, and which are not well understood, are the darting extensions and contractions of the neck of *Lacrymaria*, the movements of the probosces of *Dileptus*, *Didinium*, and *Diplodinium*, and others.

## 2. Gregarine Peristalsis

Waves of contraction in the periphery of gregarines were described by Mühl[662] and Prell[732] as "peristaltic", progressing from anterior to posterior. They considered these waves related to myonemal waves of contraction. Troisi[901] noted as many as 2 to 4 waves moving sequentially from front to rear at the same time, disappearing at the rear in *Nematocystis elmassiani*, while single waves went to the rear, and back to the front again. Each antero-posterior wave drives a surge of endoplasm in the opposite direction. Watters[942] analyzed cinematographically the peristaltic movements of *Urospora* sp. and demonstrated unidirectional contractile waves from front to rear. Carmine particles are swept the length of the body, and the wave results in a 90° torsion of the body. Although myonemes are assumed to produce the movement, Watters[942] finds a cortical birefringence not due to any resolvable myonemes.

## 3. Euglenid Metabolic Movements

Many euglenid flagellates show antero-posterior contractions resulting in central bulges, or peristaltic movements along the body (e.g., *Euglena*, *Astasia*, *Peranema*, *Heteronema*, and *Distigma*). Although often seen, they are seldom studied. The movements were called "metabolie" by Klebs,[541] who assumed them to be due to cytoplasmic movements, as did also Günther.[346] Kamiya[500] considered the metabolic movements (metaboly) of *Euglena* to be usually non-rhythmic, becoming rhythmic and oscillatory in unfavorable circumstances, presumably then pathological. Metaboly often produces torsion of the body of *Euglena mutabilis*.[380] Chen[165] observed that *Peranema* resorts to metaboly as a means of locomotion if more than 1/2 of the flagellum is absent. Acetate increases metaboly of *Khawkinea* (*Euglena*).[449] Diskus[218] suggested that the layer of protoplasm next to the pellicle is involved in the movements, and Gibbs,[293] de Haller[211] and Leedale[581, 582] have found fibrils beneath the pellicle parallel to the pellicular ridges. Roth[765] has found similar fibrils in *Peranema*. The presence of fibrils and the nature of the movements suggests myonemes, but there is no evidence yet for the function of the fibrils.

## E. Feeding Movements

Although the observations of feeding by protozoa are numerous, very little is known of what initiates the feeding process. Critical observations which might elucidate the mechanisms involved are scarce.

### 1. SUCTORIAN INGESTION OF PREY-CYTOPLASM

The seizure of prey and ingestion of its cytoplasm by the tentacles of suctorian protozoa has intrigued protozoologists for more than a century. It is probable that suctorians suck the prey-cytoplasm out of the victim.[407,532]

#### a. Adhesion to Prey

Tight adherence to the prey is a requisite of the mechanism. It is not an indiscriminate procedure, since suctoria apparently adhere to and feed mainly on certain live holotrichous and spirotrichous ciliates. They also adhere to agar models coated with fresh ciliate homogenate. Their tentacles do not ordinarily adhere to hypotrichous ciliates, or to the holotrichous *Coleps* with its hard pellicle, or to other suctoria (or their swimming ciliated small progeny), or to flagellates or amebas; nor to dead ciliates of any kind.[405] The adhesion which occurs is so firm that larger ciliates which break free always break off parts of the tentacles, carrying away the still adherent tips.[405] Recent investigations reported by Hull[406] suggest that for *Podophrya collini* an adhesive interaction occurs between some secreted substance present at the pellicle of prey and another at the tip of the suctorian tentacle which bonds the tentacle firmly to the prey. Pre-exposure of prey to acetylcholine, or to the -SH containing amino acids cysteine or methionine enhances capture; and so does addition of glutathione, methionine, or cysteine to the medium. $Ca^{++}$ is important in adhesion and addition of it restores the efficiency of capture previously reduced by depletion of free ions or by addition of monovalent cations. Concentrations of $Ca^{++}$, $Na^+$, and $Mg^{++}$ of at least $1 \times 10^{-4}$ M are necessary to completely repair the effects of the ion-depletion. Cholinesterase briefly inhibits attachment, and eserine and atropine effectively block it. Hull[406] suggests that adhesion is $Ca^{++}$ dependent and is mediated by an acetylcholine-cholinesterase system.

## b. The Ingestive Mechanism

So apparent is the sucking action of the suctoria while ingesting prey-cytoplasm that in most theories it is assumed that sucking actually occurs, as Kitching[536] says, and attempts are made to describe an effective mechanism. That tentacles alternately contract and extend during and after sucking, or on mechanical stimulation, has long been known,[170, 383, 532] and sometimes they twist and thicken while shortening.[682] Maupas[646] early suggested that the contractions might be analogous to those of muscle.

The sucking tentacles contain fibrils, often numerous, arranged somewhat like those of cilia, but central fibrils are absent.[729] The prehensile tentacles (e.g., of *Ephelota*) have 20–30 fibrils in 5 to 7 bundles.[770]

The contraction of tentacles is apparently calcium-triggered. Okajima[689] saw sustained contraction of tentacles of marine *Acineta* to 1/10 their original lengths in 1 M $CaCl_2$, and its termination by washing with sea-water. This reaction was reversible and repeatable. A similar but lesser effect was obtained with $Ba^{++}$ or $Sr^{++}$, but not $Mg^{++}$ or monovalent cations. Contractility was lost in $Ca^{++}$ free solutions. The $Ca^{++}$ dependent contractions are similar to those of vorticellid spasmonemes,[588] and both may depend upon the $K^+/\sqrt{}Ca^{++}$ ratio in the solution (i.e., a Gibbs-Donnan equilibrium). ATP does not cause contraction of tentacles, but does promote increase of their diameter in *Podophrya collini*.[407] Its role in tentacular contraction is obscure. How the tentacles may be actively extended to push away debris[708] is not known.

Contractions of tentacles have been proposed as a pumping mechanism for the ingestion of prey-cytoplasm, peristaltically[179] or by pumping with alternate contraction and extension.[722] Alternatively, retreat of predator cytoplasm from the center of the tentacle might aspirate cytoplasm from the prey.[552] These ideas have been rejected in a recent review by Canella[149] and by the studies Kitching[532, 536] and Hull.[406, 407] Also discarded is the idea that predator enzymes induce a turgor pressure in the prey which drives cytoplasm from prey into tentacles.[493]

The more recent studies confirm Penard's[707] suggestion that the body of the suctorian actively enlarges, causing a negative internal pressure in the predator which sucks the cytoplasm out of the prey.

The increased pumping rate of the contractile vacuole may lend assistance by eliminating fluid, concentrating prey cytoplasm,[407, 532] and keeping the pressure negative. However, this vacuolar pumping is not the sole cause of the suction as Eismond[246] has suggested. Furthermore, there is no evidence that the water is actually pumped out by the vacuole. For example, in *Amoeba* the vacuole is emptied by hydrostatic pressure rather than con-traction.[462]

Kitching[532] and Hull[407] both report for *Podophrya* a change of shape from pear-shaped toward spherical with instantaneous enlargement upon contact with prey. Hull calculated a 100 per cent increase in body volume only 10 per cent of which was due to the change toward spherical shape. Kitching[532] noted wrinkling of the membrane which he believed was a preliminary to size-increase. Hull[407] rejects this, but notes that as body shape changes the tentacles dilate about 2 × diameter without shortening. He saw no contractions or peristalsis of the tentacles, and attributes the suction entirely to dilation of tentacles and body expansion.

The body expansion is rapid. Hull[407] calculates that besides the 10 per cent volume increase with change of shape on contact with prey another 10 per cent was added by active body expansion.

The movements which enlarge body and tentacles may be ATP-actomyosin-like mechanisms. If 1 per cent ATP is injected into a feeding suctorian, it accelerates rate of flow of the entering prey-cytoplasm, and also the re-spiratory and contractile vacuole rates. Enlargement almost identical with that due to contact with prey occurs in a non-feeder when it is injected with 1 per cent ATP, and this enlargement also is accompanied by increased respiratory and contractile vacuole rates. The entire metabolic machinery of the suctorian appears to be involved in this feeding mechanism.[149, 407]

Previously we have had no description of a physiological mechanism for the active expansion of cortical gel or of any other layer of the suctorian which could bring about an active increase in volume. Theoretically such a mechanism might function as a reversal of an active sliding system. If contraction of muscle or of cortical gel can be brought about by active sliding of fibers, there is no reason why a cortical gel could not expand by a reverse process, provided only that the fibers are stiff. To our knowledge this ex-planation has never been suggested previously, but it is one of the newer theoretical suggestions made possible by recognition of the existence of active sliding systems.

## 2. Movements during Ingestion of Food Organisms

There are many observations of apparently elaborate motile activities on the part of carnivorous and herbivorous protozoa when seizing and ingesting whole food; but there has been little experimental or theoretical explanation of them. In many ciliates there is, plainly, a fibrillar apparatus at the base of the cystome serving as a pathway for entry of food into the cytoplasm [re-views, Taylor,[882] Pitelka[715]]. Similar, but less pronounced fibrils have also been reported in the vicinity of the cytostome of certain flagellates [e.g.,

*Peranema*, Roth,[765] *Trypanosoma*, Steinert and Novikoff[859]]. Movements of ciliate "esophageal" fibrils have been observed to occur as food vacuoles pass them, but no critical experiments indicate their mode of activity. Certain carnivorous ciliates (e.g., *Dileptus*, *Lacrymaria*, *Didinium*, *Teutophrys*, *Spathidium*) can distend the cytostome to accommodate food as large, or larger, than the diameter of their own bodies,[169, 228, 629, 632, 947, 987] and presumably the fibrils play a role in these movements.[613]

Suction also plays a part in the ingestive process, although as Wenrich[948] says: "It is difficult to understand how suction can be developed . . . but the evidence . . . favors that interpretation." At any rate, active distension of the body accompanies ingestion of prey by *Didinium*, as observed by Mast[632] and others, by *Dileptus*, as shown by cinematography by Dragesco,[228] and also by *Stentor*,[877] *Peranema*,[416, 419] *Frontonia*,[686] and several species of amebas.[90, 163, 180, 422, 617, 559, 748, 749] The suction exerted is so strong that several predators competing for the same prey may tear it apart.[228, 422, 632, 864]

Strong contractions of the cytostomal region of ciliates[43, 878] or of temporary ingestion tubes of amebas have been observed.[180, 422, 748] *Stentor*,[43] *Dileptus* or *Climastocomum*[1003] can pinch a prey ciliate in two by contraction of the cytostome, and various amebas can exert such pressure with pseudopods as to sever *Spirostomum*,[315] *Frontonia*,[56] *Vorticella*,[422] *Paramecium* or nematodes,[643, 644] rotifers,[706] or algal filaments,[584] and can exert sufficient pressure to do so while the prey struggles to escape. Traction may also be used. The flagellum of a flagellate may be seized and drawn into the cytoplasm of the predator with no distortion whatever of the body of the predator, and the body of the prey is also drawn in after the flagellum and at the same rate of progress [e.g., *Perispira ovum*, Dewey and Kidder,[216] by *Thecamoeba sphaeronucleolus*, Bovee[90]]. Traction of some sort is also applied to algal filaments, which once seized by a ciliate [*Nassula*, Fauré-Fremiet and Dragesco;[257] *Frontonia*, Oberthür,[686] *Chilodonella*, Dragesco[233] and Ivanic,[421]] or ameba [*Nebela*, MacKinlay,[617] *Pelomyxa*, Kudo,[561] Wittman,[968] *Nuclearia*, Blanch-Brude et al,[71] *Thecamoeba sphaeronucleolus*, Comandon and de Fonbrun[180]] seem to glide into the body of the predator, bending and folding, or coiling in a spiral. Food particles adhere to and are dragged toward the shell in the 2-way streaming of filoreticulopods of foraminifera[483] and by pseudopodia of some heliozoa. The struggles of large prey trapped by heliozoan axopods are followed by a sudden shortening and thickening of axopods, impaling prey on other axopods held rigid,[51] or bending around the prey and forcing it into a food cup.[232] No theories have been offered for these phenomena; an active-shearing mechanism may be involved. At least Dewey and Kidder[216] noted an increased cyclosis in the ciliate *Perispira ovum* forward to the mouth opening and back along the flagellum and the sides of the body of the prey (*Euglena*) as it was dragged into the cytoplasm. The ingestion of

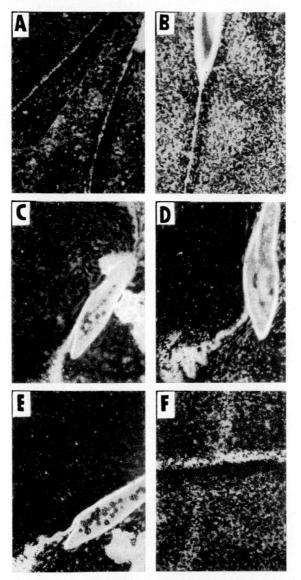

FIG. 3. A and B, tracks left by rapidly swimming *Paramecium multimicro-nucleatum*; C, D, E, tracks formed by slowly swimming almost stationary paramecia. Non-adherent granules enter the anterior end of the oral groove, and some of them leave the posterior end of the groove as an adherent stream, which may become folded, as in D and E; other non-adherent granules are driven in circular patterns by body cilia, as in C and D; F, one track, shown vertical, broken and crossed by a horizontal track; the older track is not scattered, and is probably agglutinated to the newer one.

normally motile algal filaments seems to involve little action by the predator once it has got the end of the filament into a cytostome, permanent or temporary. Possibly the presumed shearing-surface gliding movement of the alga[471] may drive it into the cytoplasm of its predator, with perhaps similar accessory action of the cytoplasm of the latter.

Other movements accompanying ingestion of prey of ciliates still lack explanation, especially the movements of the proboscis of *Dileptus* in "searching" for prey, and the bending movements thereof toward the mouth which help force the prey into the cytostome;[1003] the movements of the undulating membranes and membranelles of cannibalistic *Blepharisma* and *Stylonychia* which have also been observed to assist in forcing prey into the gullet;[294, 299] and constrictions of the "mouth" which push prey into the gullet.[169, 632]

The testate ameba, *Nebela collaris*, has been seen to assist its ingestion of other testate amebas by pushing the shell of the prey into its own shell-mouth with pseudopods, or, if the prey-shell is too large to ingest, by inserting pseudopods into the prey-shell and "scooping" the prey out.[617] *Chaos carolinensis* has been photographed in the act of pushing *Paramecium caudatum* into a food cup with a pseudopod.[319]

One of the more spectacular feeding mechanisms is that of the ciliate *Lacrymaria olor* which can dart out an extensible neck, even to a length 5–15 times that of the body and retract it instantaneously.[708] Mast[632] believed that its powerful oral membranelles dragged the neck forward in the darting maneuver, and that elastic recoil of the neck (by way of the spiral myoneme, Penard[708]) retracted the head. It seizes and swallows prey nearly its own diameter even when the neck is extended.[708]

### 3. BACTERIAL AND PARTICULATE FEEDING

The majority of holozoic protozoa are particulate feeders, partly, or entirely. Many ciliates feed on bacteria and particulate detritus; most small amebas do, likewise, and so do some flagellates.

#### a. Ciliate Mechanisms

The feeding of *Paramecium* is perhaps best known; Mast[639] restudied this mechanism, and indicated it to be entirely mechanical, with no observable mechanism for selection of particles, as proposed by others [e.g., Bragg,[111] Metalnikow[651]]. It recently has been recorded that the ciliary feeding mechanism of *Paramecium* involves a mucoid secretion.[454, 467] These investigations have demonstrated photographically that particles are agglutinated as they are driven along the oral groove of *Paramecium*, but not along ciliary tracts elsewhere. Particles that are not ingested may spill out of the oral groove in an agglutinated trail (Fig. 3). They suggest that the

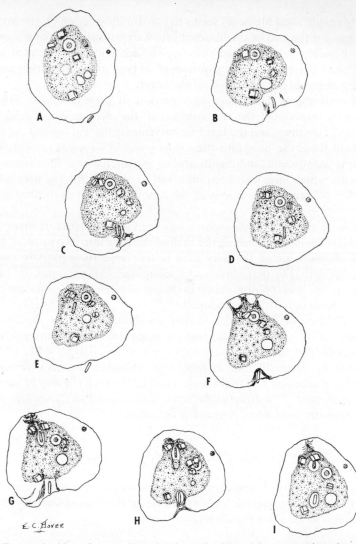

E.C. Bovee

FIG. 4. *Cochliopodium* sp. ingesting bacteria. Traced from a motion picture film, each 10th frame. A, indentation of peripheral skirt on contact with the bacterium; B, lifting of the skirt over the bacterium; C, contraction of peripheral skirt pushing bacterium beneath the body protoplasm; D, bacterium under anterior cytoplasm; E, contact made with second bacterium; F, first bacterium at rear of body, pinned down by posterior of the peripheral skirt, anterior part of the peripheral skirt indenting over second bacterium; G, tubular ingestion vacuole formed over first bacterium at the rear, second bacterium under anterior part of the peripheral skirt; H, first bacterium being sucked into posterior ingestion vacuole, second bacterium entering trap vacuole under the anterior cytoplasm; I, first bacterium in food vacuole at the rear, second bacterium still in trap vacuole under the body. Photographed at 10 frames/sec.

mucus is supplied by peristomal sacs at the bases of oral-groove cilia, and that trichocysts may also facilitate initial food entanglement. Andrews[43] reported mucus secretion on the adoral "arms" of *Folliculina*, with cilia driving a bolus of trapped food and mucus into the cytostome, which pinched off chunks of it into food vacuoles. Curds[188] says that mucus secretion by ciliates produces much of the slime which develops in sewage treatment tanks, aiding in clearing the water of flocculent particles. *Tetrahymena* also leaves mucus trails in the water,[454, 467] and the fine structure of the "mucocysts" which secrete the mucus has recently been described.[899a] Similar mucocysts have been described in *Euglena*.[581]

### b. Ameboid Movements

Amebas which engulf bacteria may do so by gliding over them, lifting them into a ventrally-formed vacuole,[85, 104] e.g., *Cochliopodium* sp. (Fig. 4), or by pinching off a mass of agglutinated bacteria by posteriorly-formed pseudopods,[747] or by adhesion of bacteria to slender pseudopods which contract, dragging the bacteria to the body surface.[86, 89, 748] The collection of food particles by the 2-way streaming protoplasm of foraminiferan reticulopods has already been mentioned (cf. p. 110).

### c. Flagellate Mechanisms

Many flagellates ingest particulate food. Symbiotic *Trichonympha* of termites feed by ameboid engulfment of wood particles at the rear end.[174, 250, 801, 869] *Peranema trichophorum* can ingest a *Euglena* or diatom as large as itself.[416, 419] In *Peranema* ingestion occurs through the "gullet"[350] and the function of the pharyngeal rods is to support the lip of the cytostome during digestion.[350, 352, 432] *Hypotrichomonas acosta* forms a feeding pouch of the body along the undulating membrane, driving particulate matter into

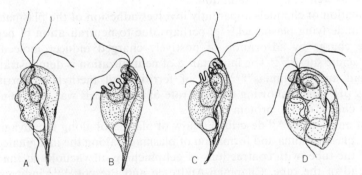

FIG. 5. A, *Hypotrichomonas acosta* before beginning vacuolar formation; B, with trailing flagellum folded toward the anterior end, pulling the body into the form of a pouch; C, with the pouch nearly closed to form a vacuole; D, after formation of four large vacuoles.

the pouch by undulations of flagellum and membrane[99] (Fig. 5). Some trypanosomes may form feeding organelles at the anterior tip,[420] or may use a mouth opening[685] to ingest particulate matter.

Collared flagellates drive particles against the collar, which contracts or marginally rolls up[568] to drag the food down to the cell surface. The collar is composed of numerous parallel finger-like processes which are connected to each other by micropseudopodia, so that the collar is a virtual net with a 2,000 Å mesh,[265, 266, 711] and the particles collect on the *outside* of the collar. The water currents produced by the flagellum enable the collar to act as a filter.[442, 443] Such water currents are atypical of a pantacronematic flagellum, but are typical of a cylindracronematic type.[442, 443]

Recently, electronmicrographs of the intracellular stages of haemosporidia show that they ingest particulate matter by pinching off part of the internal stroma of the red blood cell into food vacuoles.[772, 773, 774]

## 4. PINOCYTOTIC MOVEMENT†

Protozoa also take in dissolved nutrients from the water about them, by a process called pinocytosis[591] often at a rate more rapid than by phagotrophy. For example, *Tetrahymena pyriformis* absorbs 98 per cent of acetate and glucose it acquires through the cell surface by taking it into numerous visible vacuoles, presumably formed by coalescence of smaller ones formed in pinocytosis,[813] but the detailed mechanism is not clear.

In certain amebas, particularly *Amoeba proteus*, Mast and Doyle[640] described membrane movements which result in formation of pinocytotic channels. These movements are initiated by solutions of albumins, hypertonic salts, and calcium gluconate,[242, 640] by other basic proteins, RNAase, and toluidin blue dye,[777, 778] by gamma globulin,[624] by cytochrome-oxidase,[809] by lysozyme, methionine, mosaic virus and salts,[161] by insulin, Na-glutamate, and gelatin,[395] and by probably many other substances, as well as by UV radiation.[754]

Formation of channels apparently involves adhesion of the plasmalemma to the underlying plasmagel,[114] perhaps due to neutralization of negative surface charge by adsorption of postively charged inducer molecules at highly acidic sites.[777] The importance of neutralization is demonstrated by Marshall and Nachmias'[625] use of ferritin and methylated ferritin at various pH values, showing that the rate of pinocytosis was determined by the net charge on the protein particle.

Mast and Doyle[640] described a flow of plasmasol along the invaginated tube of plasmalemma and formation of plasmagel along the invaginated surface of the tube, with contractions of gel pinching off vacuoles at the blind inner end of the tube. Chapman-Andresen and Prescott[161] indicate that variation in form of the pinocytotic channel is related to the kind of inducer involved.

† See reviews Holter,[395, 396] Chapman-Andresen.[158]

The pinocytotic cup formed in a methionine solution is almost identical in shape with that formed in engulfing a small ciliate,[161] and also *Tetrahymena* exudes an extracellular RNA-ase[244] which may serve as an inate inducer. The effects of inducers which stimulate ingestion of *Tetrahymena* by a starved ameba are reduced if the starved ameba is first allowed to pinocytose for 20 min, before being fed *Tetrahymena*. The ameba will then ingest only about 1/10 as many *Tetrahymena* as will another starved ameba which has not pinocytosed.[159]

The membrane which lines the channel or pocket is not stretched, but is assumed to be replaced at the surface by newly-made membrane[809] perhaps derived from internal membranous vesicles,[357] as the induced layer is invaginated. Numerous pinocytotic channels may be formed all over the surface of the ameba, and locomotion stops while pinocytosis occurs.[640]

Pinocytosis apparently has two phases: 1) inducer-to-surface binding with concomitant new membrane formation, and 2) the formation of channels and cellular intake of materials. The former is insensitive to temperature, metabolic inhibitors and pH; whereas the latter is slow at lower temperatures, and is affected in rate by pH changes and by metabolic inhibitors (e.g., cyanide) in the same degree as are respiration and locomotion. Rustad[777] postulates that the streaming phase (i.e., new membrane formation and outflow of sol around the channel) is respiration independent[776] and that invagination and gel formation along the channel and pinching off of pinocytotic vacuoles are movements requiring energy sources dependent on respiration. Mast and Doyle[640] suggested that pinocytosis is brought about by the same processes which are involved in ameboid movement. Changes in surface charge, contact of plasmalemma to plasmagel, and formation of new membrane to replace that induced to move inward (or rearward) are involved in both.

Pinocytosis is well known in various types of vertebrate cells in tissue culture[395, 396, 591] and also occurs in the intestinal epithelium of vertebrates where it seems to be responsible for the absorption of vitamin $B_{12}$, but only if the vitamin is attached to the protein gastric intrinsic factor,[965] a possible but incompletely investigated example of specific protein induction. Chapman-Andresen[159] calculates that in 20 min of maximal pinocytotic activity the ameba invaginates and ingests as vesicles enough surface membrane to normally cover its entire body; and further indicates that ingestion to the limits of membrane availability is followed by cessation of pinocytosis and delay of locomotion for about 4 hrs.[160]

## F. Swimming of Sporozoan Trophozoites

Although sporozoan trophozoites have no visibly specialized organelles for locomotion, they have been known to swim since Koch[545] and Darling[204] described a spiral forward movement by *Sarcocystis muris*. Others have also observed active swimming by sporozoan trophozoites, but have suggested no mechanism for them. Allegre[11] termed the swimming movements of the sporozoites of *Gregarina rigida* "a slow lateral motion similar to that of certain nematodes." Espana *et al.*[256] described swimming movements of *Anaplasma.* Manwell and Drobeck[620] described spiral swimming, rotary and saltatory movements by *Toxoplasma,* Guimarães and Meyer[343] spiral swimming, and Jettmar,[485] six types of movements. For the sporozoites of *Eimeria necatrix* Tyzzer *et al.*[909] reported spiral swimming; and Doran, Jahn and Rinaldi[223] observed, by cinematography, intermittent spiral swimming of trophozoites of *Eimeria acervulina,* and Bovee[96] reports spiral swimming by merozoites of *Eimeria* sp. from the lizard, *Uma notata.* Doran, Jahn and Rinaldi[223] suggest that swimming is accomplished by means of a traveling helical wave in the body which is less than one wave length long. The helical wave is composed of two traveling sine waves at right angles to each other and 90° out of phase. The mechanism is essentially the same as that proposed for spirochetes.[448]

To account for this type of movement in sporozoa, Doran, Jahn and Rinaldi[223] state that presumably at least four longitudinal and one circumferential component must be present. Some reports indicate the presence of fibrils in trophozoites of *Sarcocystis,*[610] *Toxoplasma,*[281] *Lankesterella,*[279] *Plasmodium,*[280] and *Eimeria,*[222, 660] which might serve as contractile elements to produce such movements.

## G. Ciliate Movements†

### 1. ESSENTIAL SIMILARITY OF CILIA AND FLAGELLA

For convenience only, ciliary movements and flagellar movements are considered separately in this review. Older assumptions of distinctions between cilia and flagella are no longer valid either on physiological or morphological grounds. Accumulated evidence from biochemical studies, from electron photomicrographs, and from high-speed cinematography indicate an essential similarity such that, as Pitelka[715] remarks, "cilia are one of several varieties of flagella."

### *a. Structural Similarities*

All cilia and flagella so far examined by electron microscopy — except the flagella of bacteria–are structurally alike, whether protozoan or metazoan, algal or metaphytan in origin (see reviews, Afzelius,[10] Fawcett,[259] Grimstone,[340] Sleigh,[852] Pitelka[715]). Without exception the fundamental organization is that of nine peripheral doublet fibrils and two central ones extended from an attachment to a basal plate imbedded in the cytoplasm, with the peripheral fibrils continued for a short distance deeper into the

† See also reviews, Fawcett;[259] Sleigh;[852] Afzelius;[10] Rivera;[758] Jahn and Bovee; [443,444] Pitelka and Child.[716]

cytoplasm as triplet fibrils. The structure is covered, usually to the tip, by the cell membrane. The fibrils may be supplemented by additional parallel bundles of fibrils in large, strong flagella[34, 35, 36, 39] and interconnected by more slender fibrils.[259, 292, 572] Theories accounting for this universal pattern have been offered.[766, 767, 786, 833]

### b. Biochemical Similarities

Besides the structural similarities there are undeniable chemical similarities. Both cilia and flagella contain a protein complex similar to actomyosin.[167, 392, 393, 898, 941] ATP and ATP-ase are found in the peripheral fibrils[166, 675] and -SH groups are concentrated in the basal granules (i.e., inner tips of peripheral fibrils)[589] as are also phosphates and phosphatases[400, 410, 411] and apyrases.[811] Antigenic and cytochemical reactions indicate that actin forms the electron-dense periphery of the inner doublet fibrils, and myosin serves as its core.[677]

Furthermore, glycerinated models of flagella and cilia swim in ATP solutions[123, 390] and normal flagella of *Chlamydomonas moewusii* also swim [but those of a genetically paralyzed mutant strain[590] do not[122]]. All flagella and cilia operate by some series of contractions or bending tensions probably developed by the fibrils while using ATP as an energy source.

### c. Origin and Developmental Similarities

The presence of skewed microtubular triplets in both centrioles and the basal bodies, or kinetosomes, of cilia and flagella,[61] other resemblances,[278, 292, 382, 653, 767] the ability of some basal granules to function as centrioles during division [review Bĕlař[58]], and developmental studies all indicate that cilia and flagella are outgrowths of basal bodies derived from centrioles.[277, 278, 382, 653, 857] Claims that basal bodies and kinetosomes divide to allow for the growth of new cilia[58] have now been largely refuted (Pitelka, Ehret, etc.), but the conclusion that pre-existing centrioles are necessary for the formation of basal bodies, and ultimately, cilia, is incongruous with data on the ameboflagellate, *Naegleria gruberi*, which apparently has no centrioles nor flagellar basal bodies in its ameboid state, but develops both flagellar basal body and flagellum very rapidly during transformation to the flagellate state.[810]

### 2. CILIARY MOVEMENTS

The beating of cilia and the more complex organelles composed of multiple cilia (i.e., membranelles, undulating membranes, and cirri) has been carefully studied only in a few species. However, for these species an imposing mass of observation and theory is on record, the result of much excellent effort. This information needs reevaluation, but fortunately the organisms most studied, *Paramecium*, *Stentor*, *Spirostomum*, *Tetrahymena*, and *Opalina*, present enough variety and similarity to make them valuable examples for the study of the activity of cilia and ciliary organelles in general. Further-more, much of what has been considered true for ciliary movements comes from study of metazoan cilia, and this also requires reevaluation.

## a. The Nature of Ciliary Beat

### (1) The Role of Ciliary Fibrils

Since the clear demonstration of the 9/9 + 2 arrangement of ciliary fibrils by electron microscopy, and the evidence for actomyosin-like, ATP-breaking protein complexes therein, most recent theories assume that active movements are functions of the peripheral fibrils, either contractile,[852] or sliding,[471] or twisting,[474] with the central fibrils supporting the cilium,[324, 851] and perhaps conducting impulses within it.[133, 388] Both possible functions of the central fibers have been questioned. On structural grounds, based on observations with an improved polarizing microscope, Inoué[418] thinks the central fibrils may be the contractile ones. This last seems unlikely since the helical waves of flagella could not be produced except by at least four linear components such as those present in sporozoa and spirochaetes.[448] Harris[362] uses a calculation for a bending couple to assert that no biological material of the size and quantity of the central fibrils could be rigid enough physically to withstand the bending. Therefore he assumes a turgor in the cilium which confers on its membrane the neces-sary rigidity. Sleigh[852] believes that the rigidity exists in the peripheral fibrils except when they are using ATP. See also[126].

In any case there is a change of state cyclically in the cilium so that it is stiff during the power stroke, and more or less limp during the return[151] or, better perhaps, actively flexible[852] during the return stroke.

### (2) Discontinuity of Beat

It has been proposed that cilia beat incessantly so long as the supporting cell is alive.[65, 320, 894] This assumption, based mainly on observations of certain metazoan cilia, is generally true for uniformly ciliated fields among the protozoa. However, it is not true for all ciliary organelles. Many observa-tions show that protozoan cilia may stop visible action under conditions normally encountered, e.g., the "thigmotactic" response of Paramecium,[479] or the periodic cessation of movements of the "setae" of Halteria, or of the ventral and caudal cirri of Euplotes, or of the flagella of certain flagellates (e.g., Chlamydomonas, Trypanosoma, Mastigamoeba, Jahn, Fonseca and Bovee, unpublished).

### (3) The Path of Beat

It has been claimed, and widely quoted, that ciliary beat is "pendular", a supposed distinction from the "undulatory" beat of a flagellum,[320, 852] and that they beat in a plane perpendicular to the two central fibrils.[260]

Neither is necessarily true for protozoan cilia, which may move in any direction, even a funnel-shaped 3-dimensional rotary fashion,[698, 699, 912, 915] which may be an intrinsic movement, since it has been noted in cilia separated from their neighbors[921, 924] and those anesthetized enough to eliminate the power stroke but not to stop movement.[29] Pitelka[715] considers the rotary movement to be a primary one, and perhaps the simplest form of cilio-flagellar beating. Also, Jennings[477] noted that the power stroke is oblique, not straight back, as if it were a segment of an incomplete helical wave; and Parducz[699] and Okajima[687] show alteration of the direction of power stroke with force of stimulus. On the other hand, Sleigh[852] suggests that ciliary beat is a modification of the undulatory flagellar function.

Ludwig[611] calculated mathematically that a rigid ciliary shaft, swung at its base, could propel a ciliate only if the shaft bends on the return stroke. Because of a low Reynold's number (less than $10^{-4}$) the cilia, if they were straight rods hinged at the base moving with different velocities in the two directions, would not be able to exert a net locomotor force for a complete ciliary beat-cycle. Ludwig further calculated that the shape and motion of the cilia produced the greatest possible hydrodynamic efficiency for such an organelle. His computations, however, have not been experimentally verified.

### b. Reversal of Ciliary Beat

The reversal of ciliary beat performed by *Paramecium* (and many other ciliates) in the so called "avoidance reaction", by which the organism backs up several body-lengths before resuming forward motion, is an example of the "Shock reaction" discussed in Section II.

### (1) Mechanical Reversal

In the avoidance reaction of *Paramecium* caused by bumping into a solid object, all of the cilia are reversed and the organism goes almost directly backward. Earlier workers assumed that since all of the cilia reversed, there must be some type of central control, presumably a neuroid system. However, when the anterior end of a *Paramecium* strikes a solid object it is highly probable that all of the cilia are bent forcibly *forward*. The anterior end of the body is deformed on collision. Since the body is elastic there is a rebound. As the body moves backward during the rebound the cilia are moved forcibly forward in relation to the body.

Consequently, all (or almost all) cilia are subjected to the same mechanical stimulus. If this mechanical stimulus can cause reversal, then the assumption of a neuromotor system is superfluous.

It is also possible that the mechanical stimulus need not be an actual forward bending but merely a large increase in the resistance. Evidence for this second possibility is found in the fact that in highly viscous solutions *Paramecium* swims continuously backward, as in methocel solutions sometimes recommended to enable elementary students to see the "normal" movement at a low speed! Apparently in highly viscous solutions the resistance of the medium to the body and/or to the cilia slows the normal power stroke and thereby causes reversal. The exact mechanism of the reversal by viscosity is unknown. However, on the basis of the relative motion involved, reversal by viscous resistance and by anterior contact with a solid object are identical, and both types may have the same basic mechanism. Nevertheless, why *Paramecium* should continue to go backward in viscous solutions is also puzzling, because viscous resistance should be about the same in either direction.

### (2) Cationic Reversal

It has been known for several decades that certain monovalent cations cause reversal of ciliary beat in ciliates, particularly *Paramecium*. Bancroft,[49] Kamada,[497] Worley,[988] Oliphant,[690, 691] and especially Kamada and Kinosita[498] investigated these ionic effects thoroughly, with excellent results but without a satisfactory explanation. The data of Kamada and Kinosita[498] show that the greatest duration of reversal is not related to any single $K^+/Ca^{++}$ ratio or to any given ionic concentration in the solution. The $K^+/Ca^{++}$ ratio for longest duration of reversal increased with dilution from 3:1 at M/10 to 63:1 at M/640, a fact for which no adequate explanation was offered. Jahn[436] and Naitoh[668] have suggested that displacement of $Ca^{++}$ from the membrane triggers the reversal.

(a) *Membrane Adsorption. The application of the Gibbs-Donnan equilibrium.* Jahn[436] restudied the data of Kamada and Kinosita[498] and found that for organisms transferred from any given adaptation medium to various test solutions, the ratio of $K^+/\sqrt{Ca^{++}}$ (i.e., the Gibbs-Donnan ratio) of the test solution which caused maximal duration of reversal, was the same, *regardless of the dilution*. This demonstrates that the Gibbs-Donnan theory can be applied to the equilibrium between the surface and the bulk of the solution. On this basis several other conclusions can be drawn. One of these is that $Ca^{++}$ must be divalently bound. Further, it suggests[437] that any cation that binds monovalently and competes for binding sites with $Ca^{++}$, or anything that removes $Ca^{++}$ in critical amounts, such as oxalate which binds $Ca^{++}$, will cause ciliary reversal. The large size of $Ba^{++}$ and of the small bonding angle of $Mn^{++}$ (109°) limit them to monovalent binding, and therefore they induce ciliary reversal in the same way as monovalent ions. However, $Sr^{++}$ and $Mg^{++}$, with smaller sizes and with bonding angles similar to $Ca^{++}$ (180°), do bind divalently with the critically spaced carboxyl groups which normally bind $Ca^{++}$ divalently. Therefore $Sr^{++}$ and $Mg^{++}$ cause no reversal.

The principle involved is one elaborated by Danielli,[195, 196] which has generally gone unrecognized, *viz.* a critical ratio of the monovalently bindable cations to the square root of appropriate, divalently-bindable cations is needed *in solution* to produce a critical ratio of monovalently bound to divalently bound *at the membrane*. This principle, with ion-size and bond-angle, may be the key to many other cell processes.

A given ratio of monovalent/divalent cations is usually considered necessary at the membrane because divalent cations may strengthen the membrane mechanically by binding two carboxyl groups together. Other possibilities are: 1) that the divalently bound ions are required to conduct electrons between the two carboxyl groups bridged by the divalent cation;[437] and 2) that binding of the divalent cation at a "cardinal site" is followed by movement of electrons in the molecule (via electron shifts), so that "c-values" at individual cationic and anionic binding sites on the molecule are changed. According to Ling[594] c-values directly control dissociation constants of all binding groups, which kind of ion is bound (e.g., $K^+$ vs $Na^+$), and the sign of the electromotive force at the membrane where the ions are bound. Acceptable divalent ions at critical cardinal sites may produce shifts in the electron distribution pattern of protein molecules at the surface. Even without much electronic movement through the attached ions, the metabolic effects of these shifts, mostly by induction, can be extensive.

### (3) *Reversal by Direct Electrical Current*

(a) *The Ludloff Phenomenon.* Ludloff[609] observed that cilia on the surface toward the cathode reverse in direct current; but in a ciliate lying obliquely across the current cilia reverse *all around* the end of the body nearest the cathode, in relationship to a plane through the body perpendicular to the direction of current; and that up to 60 per cent of the body cilia are affected in stronger currents. This phenomenon has been confirmed by many others, but not well explained.[73, 267, 328, 329, 496, 527, 528, 667, 687, 938, 939] Another phase of the phenomenon is the rereversal by direct electrical current of cilia already chemically reversed.[496] Mast[638] assumed, without evidence, that the Ludloff phenomenon was dependent on a "neuromotor" system. Presman[735, 736] suggests that the responses of *Paramecium* to electricity are all or none responses resembling those of vertebrate nerve; and he assumes there is some sort of analogous conductile system present to yield such responses, but he gives no evidence as to its form, or location.

(b) *The Ciliate as a Core Conductor.* Jahn[434] proposed that the core-conductor theory, used to explain the stimulation of nerve and muscle, is applicable to the Ludloff phenomenon. In fact, it is even more appropriate for *Paramecium* since the conductivity of the "core" (i.e., the ciliate protoplasm) is at least ten times greater than that of the "volume conductor" (i.e., the external medium, e.g., pond water); in muscle and nerve the conductivity of "core" and "volume" are the same. Jahn's[434] reanalysis of data on the effects of electric currents on ciliates shows that a "neuromotor" system is not required in an explanation of the reversal phenomena. All

5  RP

available data may be explained by depolarization of the cell membrane, provided only that the ciliate acts as a core conductor immersed in a volume conductor. The theory is that the current will take the path of least resistance through a ciliate, regardless of angle to the electric field, that the current density for any portion of the membrane is a function of the orientation of the organism, and that as the applied current is increased the current density increases beyond the threshold for reversal (i.e., depolarization) over progressively greater area of the cathodal end of the organism. Therefore, as current is increased more cilia are depolarized and reversed. The distribution of the cilia thus theoretically reversible is exactly that observed in the Ludloff phenomenon.

## (4) Interrelationship of Electrical and Chemical Ciliary Reversals

There is undoubtedly a close relationship between the binding of ions in critical ratios at the membrane, and the effects of electrical current on ciliary reversal. Jahn[436] notes that an electrical current causes $Ca^{++}$ to leave the membrane at the cathodal end of the organism 20 per cent faster than $Na^+$, and may therefore shift the monovalent/divalent cation ratio beyond the threshold for reversal. Both the electrical effects as explained by the core-conductor theory, and their linkage to the ion effects are compatible with the Ling[594] association-induction theory.

Cutting the membrane causes local depolarization of the membrane. Cutting or otherwise locally depolarizing the membrane would alter the Gibbs-Donnan ratios and disturb ciliary functions and movements in the vicinity of the depolarized spot, whether or not any presumptive neuromotor fibrils were present and interrupted, structurally or functionally.

### c. Metachrony and Isochrony; their Causes

#### (1) Types of Metachrony

There is no question that ciliary beating over the ciliate body is coordinated. Knight-Jones[544] described these coordinations as; 1) *symplectic metachronism* with direction of ciliary beat and sequence (wave of transmission) coincident. Symplectic longitudinal waves are usually laterally isochronic in most ciliates, i.e., laterally adjacent cilia in neighboring rows beat in phase; 2) *antiplectic metachronism* with beat and wave in opposite directions; 3) *dexioplectic metachronism* with beat to the right of wave progress; and 4) *laeoplectic metachronism* with beat to the left of the wave path.

#### (2) Some Complications of the Problem

Protozoan body cilia are usually assumed to be symplectic, but Okajima[687, 688] and Párducz[699] have shown that local effects may cause considerable variation in the progress and direction of metachronal waves.

Sleigh[850] has shown the membranellar metachrony of *Stentor* to be dexioplectic, and that of *Paramecium* vestibular cilia to be antiplectic.[852]

Whole ciliates are coordinated in their ciliary movements, as are also the experimentally cut segments of *Spirostomum*[171] or *Dileptus*,[226] the anterior and posterior halves and fragments of newly cut *Paramecium*,[403] and even ciliated pellicular hulls of lysed *Paramecium*,[586] and the ciliated fragments of ectoplasm and pellicle cut from living ciliates.[988] They all have normal spiral swimming, with normal ciliary beat, and reversal of beat.

Under the influence of chloral hydrate the cilia of *Paramecium* are removed unevenly, and partially denuded organisms may have clumps of cilia remaining. In such organisms normal swimming and metachrony continue until the organism is almost bald.[564, 700] As lost cilia regrow from the basal granules they begin to beat as soon as their stubs are visible.[486, 564] However, ciliates which have been almost completely denuded of cilia cannot swim normally until cilia are nearly fully regenerated. Although ciliary beat is normal in the new cilia, even as short stubs, the metachronal rhythm is erratic until cilia are nearly fully grown; and the organism is hypersensitive to contact for some time after their complete regeneration.[564] There is experimental evidence also that local stimulation of cilia results in alterations of the metachronal waves,[688, 699] and the metachrony of *Dileptus* normally shows variation in metachronal wave and direction.[227]

### (3) *Theories for Metachrony*

Many of the recent theories which purport to explain metachrony assume tacitly, since there is little evidence (cf. p. 127), that a "neuromotor" system of fibrils mediates the metachrony.[224, 700, 763, 811, 814, 850, 852] Others assume that, with or without "neuroid" fibrils, there is some permanent physiological gradient of activity present in the subsurface cytoplasm which is responsible for relaying a stimulus,[73, 171, 564, 699, 829] or perhaps a neuromotor system at a biochemical level,[671] or a gradient analogous to the nerveless invertebrate heart.[829]

Still others have objected to such views, however, at least as a complete explanation. Gray[321] supported a mechanical interaction of cilia. Sleigh[849] indicates that the metachronal waves are at least partly due to the mechanical actions of cilia, but also suggests that a conductible stimulus is necessary to explain some observations. Potter[730] who studied the effects of viscosity of the medium on metachrony, rejected any neuroid or other subpellicular conduction to account for metachrony, pointing out that if each cilium is affected by the rate and extent of bending of its neighbors, a mechanical theory such as Gray's[321] would explain the transmission. Pigon and Szarski[712] also indicate that viscosity of the medium plays a role in the regulation of ciliary rate and metachrony.

In what ways, if any, ciliary coordination is due to functional, directive activities by the ciliate there is no evidence; yet despite the obviously possible hydro-

5*

dynamic interactions between adjacent cilia, such functionally directive relationships are often assumed,[481] without adequate evidence or explanation.

### (4) *Hydrodynamic Regulation of Metachrony*

The movements of one flagellum may affect movements of another, even though each belongs to a separate cell. For example, if sperm are swimming close together their flagella may gradually become synchronized.[616, 768] This is also true for the bodies of spirochetes.[320] Furthermore, the thousands of spirochetes attached to the surface of the flagellate, *Mixotricha paradoxa*, may exhibit perfect metachronal patterns.[176a]

Therefore, it is not always necessary to postulate a neuroid set of fibrils to carry impulses in order to cause metachrony. A hydrodynamic explanation is available by which each cilium as it moves affects its nearest neighbors, thereby controlling their activities. Such an analysis eliminates the necessity for a neuroid system and therefore any problems of how such a system works. The cilium thus serves as a sensory receptor and a transmitter by way of the compression waves it generates in the water.

Each cilium is considered to be an independently energized oscillator with its frequency and phase sensitive to compressional waves generated by other cilia. Forces caused by the movement of any one cilium affect adjacent neighbors in the direction of the power-stroke more than in other directions because the stronger pressure component moves in that direction [the pressure of the power-stroke is probably greater by 5/1 for *Paramecium* than is the pressure of return-stroke; Wichterman[953]]. Eventually a group of such oscillators which beat with an alterable but nearly identical period will synchronize their beating—as Rothschild[768] and Machin[616] have demonstrated for spirochetes and spermatozoa.

What requires an explanation is not only why metachrony occurs, but also why synchrony does not occur, i.e., why the cilia of *Paramecium* do not operate in phase, as the oars of a racing shell. The reason is that each power-stroke of a cilium starts with zero velocity and must reach a given velocity before it can create a pressure wave adequate to control the next cilium. If this delay were not present, all of the cilia would be synchronized, because the velocity of the pressure waves in water is so high that there would be almost no time differential between the beat of cilia on the same animal. This delay in creating the pressure wave therefore is what causes the ciliary beat to be metachronous rather than synchronous.

Space does not permit here a full hydrodynamic treatment of this topic, but such an analysis will be presented elsewhere by Jahn.

Temperature increases frequency of ciliary beat, decreases the wavelength of the metachronal wave and increases the velocity of the metachronal wave in *Stentor*.[849]

According to the above physical theory of metachrony an increase of viscosity should increase the metachronal wavelength, and the data of

Gosselin[317] demonstrate this very clearly. Potter[730] in a preliminary study reports the opposite for *Opalina*, but states that the data support a physical theory. This is a subject which needs further study.

Support of the role of hydrodynamics in ciliary movement is found in observations that in *Paramecium* short stubby cilia in the process of regeneration beat normally but without metachrony at first; and then later beat with only erratic "metachrony" as they grow somewhat longer.[564] This indicates that only cilia of greater than a critical length can generate enough force to stimulate other adjacent cilia and maintain metachrony; and that no internally mediated metachronal stimulus is necessary.

The most convincing evidence that a neural mechanism is *not* necessary appears in motion picture film by Cleveland[175] described by Cleveland and Grimstone,[176a] which clearly shows metachrony of the numerous motile spirochetes which are always attached by one of their ends to the body surface of the flagellate *Mixotricha paradoxa* of termites. These flagellates have no subpellicular fibrous system even analogous to "kinetodesma" of ciliates, and neither do the spirochetes. A "neuroid" explanation of this spirochete metachrony is impossible; and a hydrodynamic one must be assumed.

### d. Aggregate Swimming in Patterns

#### (1) The Nature of the Phenomenon

Another phenomenon of swimming which occurs in dense populations of protozoa, especially ciliates, but also in flagellates (see Section IV, I, 8), is "pattern swimming". Loefer and Mefferd[599] demonstrated that in critical numbers (a minimum of about 150,000/ml and in shallow media 1.5–2.0 mm. deep), *Tetrahymena* swims *en masse* in streams which form patterns. The pattern is an open polygonal network consisting of rapidly swimming organisms in macroscopic horizontal columns, four or five of which meet at each node of the net, where the organisms are packed together and fall in a vertical column toward the bottom of the container, and then swim randomly as viewed from above, but definitely upward, because of geotaxis, and rejoin the horizontal columns. This has been confirmed by Jahn et al.[445, 455, 456] When conditions are optimal, the polygonal patterns of *Tetrahymena* may be formed in less than 10 seconds. Nettleton *et al.*[680] suggest that the mass of moving organisms generates an accumulative force which interacts with their individual movements so that they are driven to swim in phase; but they do not explain the nature of the force, nor its mode of effect. Platt[723] points out that there is a resemblance of the patterns to "Benard cells" of suspended particles caused by thermal convection currents. However, he also notes that they are *not* so caused, and suggests they are due to hydrodynamic interrelations of the organisms, resulting from a "dynamic instability" related to their mass and the energy of their motions.

## (2) *Some Things which Affect Formation of Patterns*

Loefer and Mefferd[599] demonstrated that anything which affects motility affects formation of the pattern, including the distinctness of the pattern, the speed of its formation, or both. This is generally true, and some factors which alter the pattern or its rapidity of appearance include low temperatures, ultra-violet radiation, parathion, anaerobiosis, and the addition of methylcellulose to raise the viscosity of the medium. The age of the culture is also important, since younger cultures form more distinct patterns, and form them more quickly than older ones.[599] When either carbon dioxide or ammonia is added to the atmosphere above the solution the organisms (*Tetrahymena*) descend somewhat in the solution leaving a thin clear area of medium between the surface and the pattern.[455, 456] The vertical columns at the nodal junctions of the polygons of the pattern then divide into several streams with a clear space in the center of the node; and the horizontal streams also divide with a narrow clear space between the two adjacent streams.[445, 455, 456] Pattern formation may also be stimulated to develop by phenanthraquinone.[489]

## (3) *Effects of Centrifugal Force and Gravity*

If a geotaxis is involved, the patterns should not only form more rapidly as gravitational force is increased, but they should also break up if gravity is reduced to zero, reappearing again as gravity is increased. When made weightless for 12–15 sec by means of parabolic flight in an airplane, *Tetrahymena* patterns promptly break up or do not form during the weightless time, and as promptly reform upon reentry into the gravitational field. Also, they reform more rapidly if the field is $3g$ instead of $g$.[455]

## (4) *The Role of Hydrodynamic Linkage*

The hydrodynamic relationship between organisms swimming side by side tends to bring them closer together. For example, two *Tetrahymena* swimming side by side tend to move toward each other because of the nonuniform field flow caused by the complex velocity profile in the medium adjacent to the other ciliate.[445] As soon as the velocity profiles of the two organisms in the medium overlap, the organisms will be drawn together laterally. Furthermore, calculations of the mean free path of the organisms indicate that they approach one another at random at a rate of 7 per cent/sec, within a solid posterior angle of $90°$. An approach within this angle seems adequate to permit an end to end hydrodynamic linkage. Since each organism sets up a turbulent vortex ring in accordance with Newton's third law of motion, despite a low Reynolds number (about $10^{-2}$), any other organism which enters that vortex ring becomes hydrodynamically linked to the first and therefore follows it. Even dead organisms should therefore join the pattern, and do so[455, 456] although they later accumulate at the base of polygonal nodes, and to some degree beneath the horizontal streams of organisms which connect the polygonal nodes.

### e. The Ciliate Subpellicular Fibrillar System

#### (1) The "Kinotodesmal" Fibrils

(a) *Assumed "Neuroid" Structure.* Since Schuberg's[806] discovery in *Paramecium* that longitudinal fibrils apparently connect the basal bodies of cilia in each ciliary row, speculation has led to a widespread assumption that these fibrils have the principal function of stimulating and coordinating the ciliary movements of protozoa. Sharp's[840] pronouncement of these fibrils, together with the cilia, as a "neuromotor" apparatus in *Diplodinium* provided a name to accompany the concept. The reports of Rees,[749] von Gelei[288, 289, 290] and Lund[612] that a paired "neuromotorium" exists in the wall of the buccal cavity of *Paramecium* caused further acceptance of the idea.

Taylor[880, 881] seemed to show experimentally a conductile function for fibrils leading from the bases of cirri by cutting them and discoordinating the cirral movements in *Euplotes*; and Turner[908] described a "motorium" for that organism and its fibrils.

Chatton and Lwoff[164] further amplified the morphologically based assumption for a conductile activity of the fibrils by renaming them "cinetodesma" and the basal granules of the cilia "cinetosomes". These words have gained widespread usage by many ciliophorologists who deal with taxonomy [review, Corliss[186] and others who study fine structure of ciliates; (review, Pitelka[715]]. This has resulted in a tacit uncritical acceptance by many of the theory that they are primarily conductors of impulses.

(b) *Some Data from Electron Microscopy.* Certainly the fibrils are there, as repeatedly confirmed by means of electron microscopy [reviews: Fawcett,[259] Pitelka[715]]. However, it has also been shown that the basal bodies of the cilia are not directly inter-connected by these fibrils, as had been previously thought from earlier silverstaining observations. Instead, the cilia are, as was shown first by Chatton and Lwoff[164] in rows just to the *fi*ciliate's) right of the fibrils. Electron micrographs show that there is *no* (*brous connection* between the basal bodies ("kinetosomes") of cilia.[715] The longitudinal fibrils called "kinetodesma" are in most cases formed by rootlet fibrils from the ciliary basal bodies which extend to the ciliate's right and to the longitudinal fibrillar bundle, there bending forward and running parallel to or twining around the bundle for a distance, past 2 or more basal bodies forward in the row. The so-called kinetodesmal fibrils of *Stentor* are similarly composed of parallel fibrils originating at basal bodies of cilia as rootlet fibrils, but in that animal they are plainly and predominately contractile in function and their connection to the basal bodies can be assigned a structural function in contraction (see pp. 104–106).[877]

## (2) The "Kinetosome" or Ciliary Basal Body

This structure is also widely assumed to be a principal, perhaps only, route of stimulus to the ciliary unit, mainly because of the observed morphological proximity of its rootlet to the longitudinal fibrils in ciliates. Sleigh[852] for example, states unequivocally and categorically that: "the basal bodies of cilia are the site of origin of waves of contraction which pass up the cilia." In the same paragraph, however, Sleigh also indicates that the basal granule is of great value as a morphological anchor for the cilium.

However, recent observations on certain flagellates show that (1) waves of movement progress along flagella either from base to tip *or from tip to base*;[103, 443, 444, 464, 465, 466, 943] and (2) that wave propagation may occur in flagella or cilia detached from their basal bodies [Brokaw[123, 125]]. Since there is no fundamental structural difference between cilia and flagella, there is therefore much doubt as to the validity of Sleigh's categoric statement for the basal body as *the* source of stimulus for the cilium.

Sleigh[850] has suggested a version of the "neuroid" function for cilia in *Stentor*, assuming that metachronal beat in each ciliary row of a membranelle of the adoral band is begun at the first cilium in any row, which acts as "pacemaker", and that if the "pacemaker" cannot function, for whatever reason, then any other cilium which becomes functionally first in the row becomes "pacemaker". A hypothetical one-way transmission is supposed to move from the base of one cilium to the next in the row, probably by way of a fibril. The viscous drag of the medium is suggested as the initial source of the stimulus, but no explanation is offered as to why the "pacemaker" is the more sensitive of the cilia to that stimulus, nor how the stimulus is transmitted to and by way of basal granules.

## (3) Assumed "Neurochemical" Action in Protozoa

Seaman[811] contends that the presence of acetylcholine and acetylcholinesterase in certain protozoa provides critical evidence supporting a "neuroid" analogy for the "kinetodesma" of ciliates, and states that: "the same direct relationship exists between ciliary activity and AChE activity as there is between AChE activity and nerve conduction". He cites in this connection that AChE and ACh have been found in *Paramecium*,[54, 553, 830] ACh in *Trypanosoma rhodesiense*, but not in the non-motile *Plasmodium gallinaceum*[139] and AChE activity in *Tetrahymena geleii*.[812, 814] Sleigh[852] cites the same evidence, plus the report of Müller and Toth[663] that ACh bromide and eserine sulfate affect duration of the reversal response due to KC1, but Sleigh doubts a direct effect of ACh in ciliary beat. However, Aaronson,[1] while able to find AChE in *Paramecium caudatum*, could not find it in *Tetrahymena pyriformis*, nor in *Euglena*, *Ochromonas*, or *Crithidia*. Tibbs[897] found none in *Polytoma*, and only slight ("negligible") amounts in homogenates of *Tetrahymena pyriformis*. Finally, it should be noted that AChE is found in both protozoan and metazoan cells for which no neuroid function related to its presence is remotely possible, e.g., it is present in the plasmodium of *Physarum polycephalum*[671] and in mammalian red blood cells.[999]

The detection of AChE in any cell shows only that it is there where it may esterify ACh—but that is all. There is yet to be shown that it has any role in the function of protozoan cilia or flagella, particularly in connection with any supposed conduction of impulses from cilium to cilium. In that respect the assumption by Nakajima and Hatano[671] of a possible neuromotor system at a biochemical level in *Physarum*, because they found it contains AChE, is an unwarranted extrapolation, and is even less reasonable than their assumption that otherwise the AChE must be considered a "fossil enzyme".

Data concerning the action of so-called specific inhibitors of AChE are not as conclusive as is sometimes assumed. For example, Van Eys and Warnock[916] found that hexamethonium chloride reversibly inhibited ciliary movement in *Tetrahymena* and *Paramecium* for many hours and even for several days, and they assumed that this was a specific effect on the cilia. However, Jones and Jahn[487] demonstrated that in *Spirostomum ambiguum* and *S. intermedium* the drug also caused severe damage to the cell membrane, sometimes causing cytolysis while the cilia were still active, and that fed animals were more susceptible than starved animals. Hexamethonium chloride, therefore, cannot be considered a specific AChE blocking agent for cilia, as it seems to be for vertebrate neuromuscular unctions.

### (4) *Microdissection of Fibrils*

Many microdissection studies, e.g., those of Taylor,[880] Rees,[749] Chambers and Dawson,[156] Doroszewski,[224] Sleigh[850] and Okajima,[688] show that metachronal waves and local disturbances in the coordination of cilia, cirri and membranelles result on one side or the other, or on both, from a cut in a fibril associated structurally with the cilia. These disturbances have been proposed as *a priori* support for a neuroid fibrillar system. Such an assumption ignores the long known fact that cutting the cell surface (unavoidable in the experiments) results in physiological disturbances of electrostatic and electrochemical phenomena which might well alter ciliary movements (and do) if otherwise produced physically or chemically *without* cutting the membrane. Also ignored in such assumptions is the evidence that such a cut *does not* disturb the reversal response of cilia in either *Opalina*[688] or *Paramecium*.[224] The reversal response, either chemical or electrical, has often been cited as due to "neuromotor" function[477, 638] but such an assumption is not valid.[434, 436]

### (5) *Critique of a "Neuroid" Fibrillar System*

(a) *Inadequacy of the Assumptions.* Very simply, there is no critical evidence to support a conductile function for the "kinetodesmal" fibrils. Some who have carefully studied these fibrillar systems conclude that coordinated ciliary activity in metachrony, or otherwise, is not supported by their studies. Hammond[356] says that *no* fibrillar system in *Paramecium* can account for coordination of any of its cilia. Worley,[988] after much microdissection study of *Paramecium*, decided that metachronal coordination is due to surface reactions parallel to, but *not* associated with the fibrils; and Parduçz[698, 699] reached a similar conclusion. Others, most recently Seravin,[828] have rejected any morphological structures as conductive, resorting to the hypothesis of a physiological gradient in the subsurface cytoplasm. It is also difficult to explain why, if a functional "neuroid" system exists, the coordination of cilia in excised segments and fragments of ciliates is not destroyed.[171, 225, 480, 988]

Prosser and Brown[738] have indicated a weakness in the argument for such neuroid systems, namely: "It is well established that conduction in nerves is a membrane phenomenon; hence, if any ciliate fibrillae are conductile, they cannot be regarded as precursors of nerves. There is no evidence for a molecular mechanism by which intracellular fibrils might conduct signals." These statements are completely valid, even though a molecular mechanism might be postulated on the basis of the Ling[594] theory of c-values of electronic induction.

Those who have critically reviewed these fibrillar systems in ciliates are careful to indicate that no satisfactory evidence is available to support a "neuroid" function for the fibrils. Taylor [review[882]], whose own microdissection studies on *Euplotes*[880] are the most often cited in beginning texts to support a neurofibrillar system in ciliates, stated: "when, in the absence of proof, an investigator seriously contends that in these unicellular organisms any and all fibrillar differentiations perform only one elementary function, or where he assigns to these fibrils or fibrillar systems one or two functions to the exclusion of another possible function or functions, then surely that investigator thereby adopts a point of view which is inconsistent, and indefensible as well." His remarks are still valid. Pitelka[715] says that (p. 223): "Given a plethora of fibrillar designs and constructions we can scarcely conceive of enough functions to go around. A few come obviously to mind: contraction, mechanical support, information transfer," and further (p. 226): "The third possible function proposed above was information transfer, surely the most controversial of all—we are descending from an attractive probability through extreme uncertainty to total confusion."

Sandon[784] remarks that: "there is good reason to believe that the activity of a cilium is affected by the movements of those adjacent to it, and it may be that their coordination is largely, if not entirely, brought about by the purely mechanical action of one upon the other. Tempting as it is to believe that the cortical fibers serve as a kind of intraciliary nervous system, this is very far from having been proved."

However, another crucial point in the argument is that although convincing proof *for* a conductile function of such intracellular fibrils has *not* been presented, neither has there been proof that they do not or cannot conduct. The proposition is still attractive, though perhaps unnecessary.[434, 436, 784] How attractive, is indicated by Pitelka[715] who says (p. 223):

"Perhaps any structure with distinct spatial organization that is capable of transferring electrons—as protein fibers are, according to Szent-Györgyi[873]—can transmit information of a sort from one extremity to the other. Thus we do not need to think that by assigning hypothetical functions to some fibers we have excluded them as subjects for further hypotheses. Several functions of protozoan bodies seem to demand intervention of some means of information transfer more direct and precise than general cytoplasmic states or unchannelled diffusion of messenger substances. These include the careful program of morphogenetic events, the coordinated contraction and relaxation of bodies or body parts, and most conspicuously, ciliary and flagellar cooperation."

This seems like good argument, until one reflects that all those things except ciliary coordination occur in a locomoting ameba, with flagellar coordination appearing in amebo-flagellates while they have their temporary flagella. Apparently, the development of the informational programming systems may have preceded development of fibrillar systems. Therefore, if the fibrillar systems do conduct, it may be merely an evolutionary coincidence. However, as mentioned above, the association-induction theory of Ling[594] offers a mechanism by which electron shifts along a protein chain can transmit information, either with or without a visible microscopic fiber.

### (6) *Other Proposed Functions of Fibrils*

Besides the conductive hypothesis, several other functions have been proposed for the intracellular fibrils, especially the "kinetodesma", i.e., 1) contraction [reviews Pitelka;[715] Randall;[743] Tartar;[877] also Nagai;[666] Kinastowski;[525]] 2) elasticity[254, 549] 3) mechanical support;[288, 428, 521, 683, 715, 840] 4) circulation of materials;[394] and 5) ontogenetic organizers.[542, 543]

The first (i.e., contraction) appears likely for the so-called *km* myonemes of *Stentor*, for the "kinetodesma" of *Spirostomum* and *Condylostoma*, and for the spasmoneme of *Vorticella* (cf. pp. 104 and 106), but to what degree for others is uncertain. Elasticity is also probable, and so is mechanical support, the two functions obviously being interrelated. Finally there is Grimstone's[341] suggestion that a fibril (or perhaps any other intracellular structure) need not necessarily have a function; it need only exist, perhaps only later to acquire a function.

What is needed, as suggested by Taylor,[882] Wichterman,[953] Hall[351] Pitelka[715] and Sandon,[784] is the development of experimental techniques to assay the function of the fibrils to an accurate degree. These methods are presumed difficult, but not impossible [Taylor[882]].

## H. "Learning" in Ciliates

The idea that learning in a primitive form may exist in and can be studied in protozoa received early impetus from the work of Verworn[921, 927] and Jennings.[477] The latter stated that: "The writer (i.e., Jennings himself) is thoroughly convinced, after long study of the behaviour of this organism, that if *Amoeba* were a large animal, so as to come within the everyday experience of human beings, its behaviour would at once call forth the attribution to it of states of pleasure and pain, of hunger, desire and the like on precisely the same basis as we attribute these things to a dog."

The Swiss protozoologist, Penard[704] expressed similar ideas, concluding that anyone who had watched unicellular organisms in all of their activities could not but assign to them some of the abilities, however limited, which are possessed by the animal kingdom as a whole. Thomas[893] suggests that "instinct" exists at the cellular level. Such expressions have been seized upon by some experimenters, mainly psychologists, who seem to believe that they *must* find "learning" in any sequence of responses that appears to change. With its presumed "neuromotor" system, *Paramecium* has been the principal protozoan organism approached as a potential "learner". Others, e.g., *Spirostomum, Stentor, Dileptus, Amoeba, Euglena* have also been targets for such studies.

In over half a century since Jennings' comments were published, *Paramecium* has been said to "learn" to modify its "avoidance response"[112, 208, 855]; "select" food;[208, 603, 651] respond to "taste";[29, 30, 284, 285, 286] adapt to the shape of a container;[112] turn around in a tube;[208] develop "memory"[31, 32] and transmit it to offspring;[286, 287] reduce "trial and error time",[273] etc. These claims have been refuted by others, after careful reinvestigation. Mast[639] has shown that particle discrimination in feeding is apparently mechanical. Buytendijk[145] concluded that turning ability has perhaps a physiological explanation. Mirsky and Katz[655] repeated earlier work by Bramstedt,[112] Alverdes[30] and Grabowski[318] and showed that the apparently "learned" adaptation of the avoidance response with respect to light and heat was due largely to convection currents. Katz and Deterline[515] rejected Gelber's "training" of food responses by showing that the response occurred in the presence of food, regardless of whether a platinum wire dipped in food were used in "conditioning" the ciliates.

It scarcely seems worth while at present to assume a possible "learning process" in a protozoon. There are certainly no indisputably positive data in favor of that conclusion. Without proof that a "neuroid system" is present even where potentially possible in ciliates, and no morphological possibility of it in amebas, assumptions for learning based on such systems (i.e., comparable to learning in metazoa) are superfluous as well as tenuous.

## *I.* Flagella and Flagellate Movement†

### 1. FLAGELLA *vs.* CILIA?

The fundamental morphological and biochemical similarities of cilia and flagella have already been discussed (cf. pp. 116–118). It usually is assumed, however, that there is a difference in their movements. Protozoan flagellar movements have been considered helical or planar undulations from base to tip, pushing water distally[604, 605, 606, 607, 852] whereas cilia have been said to beat while stiff, moving laterally, or posteriorly (anteriorly in reversal) with a swinging movement from the base,[320, 852] thereby pushing water posteriorly or laterally.

Some recent studies, however, indicate that either cilia,[688, 699] or flagella (Jahn *et al.*, see citations below) may move in a variety of ways, removing any critically functional distinction between them. To assume a distinction now makes only convenient taxonomic sense, i.e., cilia are found on ciliates and flagella on flagellates. Hyman[417] has semantically suggested that *protozoa* have *flagella*, and *metazoa* have *cilia*—also an arbitrary dichotomy and indefensible in view of present knowledge. However, for convenience we will consider flagella, in the taxonomic sense, as separately discussable, i.e., the movements of the organelles on organisms known taxonomically as flagellates.

### 2. "CLASSICAL" FLAGELLAR MOVEMENTS

#### *a. Pusillary Function*

It has been generally held, especially by Lowndes,[604, 605, 606] that protozoan flagella generate motile waves only from the base in the body to the tip. Flagellar beating earlier described as tractellar [review: Gray[320]], e.g., of *Peranema*, were deemed by Lowndes[604] to be pusillary by way of undulations toward the tip, which was bent back towards the body. The numerous studies on the base-to-tip, pushing undulations of sperm flagella have also lent support to Lowndes' contentions.

The assumptions for an obligate basal stimulus making possible only an undulation of base-to-tip progression also perhaps arose from early observations that flagella broken from the body soon lost their motile capacities [review Grey[320]], and fit Lowndes' theories and those for sperm motility well. Nonetheless, Heidenhain[374] and Gray[320] early held that the motile machinery existed throughout the length of flagellum or cilium, an argument

---

† See also reviews, Afzelius,[10] Bishop.[68, 69]

now confirmed in part by studies on the actomyosin-ATP systems in cilia and flagella (cf. pp. 76–77).

### 3. THEORIES OF INTERNAL FLAGELLAR MECHANISMS

Most theories of flagellar movement since Gray[320] assume that movement of the flagellum (or cilium) is due to the development of an active bending force within it and along its entire length (now assumed due to ATP-acto-myosin-like systems). Also, to do its work against the viscosity of the water, the flagellum must be more or less rigidly elastic; and bending is of necessity an active energy-using and replenishing process.[124, 125, 127, 167, 326, 362]

With the revelation by electron microscopy of the standard 9/9 + 2 arrangement of fibrils from the basal body, a number of versions of a theory of commutative action were developed to explain coordinated movement from base to tip of the flagellum or cilium. Brown[133] proposed a conductile role of the two central fibrils to explain a sequence of stimuli to, and resultant wave-like activity in, the peripheral doublet fibrils. Others have employed modified but similar theories which place the basal body in the role of a stimulus generator causing base-to-tip waves of contraction along the flagellum (or cilium) with central fibrils conducting and peripheral ones contracting.[9, 292, 324, 850, 851] Various suggestions involving the relative thickness of peripheral fibrils, the sequence in which their contractions might be "fired," and relative speed of progression of stimuli and waves of activity along the fibrils, have been proposed to account for helical waves *vs.* planar waves *vs.* "ciliary" beat progressions.[45, 67, 388, 572, 981] Wolken[981] suggests that a feedback mechanism exists, also, in the various fibrils at postulated "junctions" along the flagellum, with one of the central fibrils perhaps serving as the feedback carrier. All these ideas are based entirely on the *prima facie* morphological evidence of the presence and arrangement of fibrils. They also tacitly assume that impulses must begin in, and are modulated by, the basal body.

Also, because of the proximity of the basal body of the flagellum to the nucleus of the cell in many flagellated protozoa, or because of the apparent physical connection between the basal body and the nucleus by way of a threadlike rhizoplast, it is often assumed on morphological grounds that the nucleus generates the stimulus, and relays it to the basal body, from whence it progresses, supposedly, from the base to the tip of the flagellum. The present authors can find no experimental evidence in the literature to support this; and Leedale[580] has observed that anucleate daughters and binucleate daughters of abnormal fissions in *Euglena* swim equally well.

However, as Gray[326] points out, the rhythmical activity of flagellar "models" when activated with ATP (the models being detached from the basal bodies) makes it difficult to think that anything comparable to conducted nervous impulses could be fundamentally concerned. Furthermore, recent evidence for tip-to-base movements by flagella,[103, 303, 399, 464, 465, 713, 934, 935] and a variety of other ways in which flagella may move,[556] especially as recorded in high speed cinematography by Jahn *et al.*,[464, 465, 466] indicate that basal bodies of flagella (or of cilia) may have much less to do with stimulus and modulation of beat than has been heretofore assumed.

Propagation of the wave of bending may not depend on transmission of impulses along special fibrils in the flagellum. Direct stimulation from element to element along a flagellum has been discussed by several authors, including Gray[323, 326] and Machin.[615, 616] It is assumed that bending is caused by tension in contractile elements, presumably the outer 9 fibrils, and that an increased length causes an increase in tension and therefore a shortening. However, the stretching and development of tension are not simultaneous, and the shortening is therefore delayed. This gives the fibrils the property of "delayed elasticity", and this property can account for propagation of the wave of bending. Once started, such a wave could be transmitted either distally or basally. If the reacting system is linear (reaction and applied force directly proportional), both waves may exist simultaneously as a standing wave, which, of course, cannot produce propulsion unless the waves are of different amplitudes. If there were some method of inducing a "proximal drive" (function of a basal body) in a linear system the wave could be induced to go only in one direction, i.e., distally.[615] However, if the reacting system is non-linear only the wave of greater amplitude will persist and standing waves are excluded. Assumption of non-linearity is necessary in order to avoid development of waves of an infinite amplitude, which would occur in a theoretical linear system. Also, in a non-linear system a wave externally imposed on the flagellum can, if its amplitude is sufficiently large, suppress any self-oscillation of the flagellum, and thereby produce synchrony of the flagellum with the imposed wave. If the imposed wave is produced by another flagellum, synchrony of the two flagella will occur [616, 768] This effect is also used to explain metachrony (Section IV G 2 c).

The mathematical equations used by Machin[615, 616] to predict the results of an element to element transmisson are very interesting, and tell us what can or cannot be expected on such a basis, assuming that the elements are of macromolecular dimensions, as suggested by Satir and Satir[786] and by Silvester and Holwill.[846] Brokaw and Wright[128] suggest that *activity* is *limited* to very short *transition* regions, and that the elements are much *larger*, being the crests of undulatory waves, or arcs of circles which sequentially bend and straighten to give the appearance of a traveling sine wave in motion. Equally important, however, is the fact that these principles and predictions can be used as a guide to biochemical investigations of exactly how stretching might serve as a stimulus for a delayed contraction, i.e., an elucidation of the chemical mechanism of the "delayed elasticity". *This is one of the most important unsolved problem in flagellar physiology.*

## 4. A Variety of Flagellar Movements

Some typical examples of the varied flagellar movements are tentatively classified by the geometry of the active waves as follows by Jahn *et al.*,[467] and by Jahn and Bovee.[443, 444]

### *a. Categories of Flagellar Movements*

#### (1) *Latero-posterior Beat*

This beat resembles that considered typical of cilia, with force applied at right angles to the beating position of the flagellum (Fig. 6), e.g., *Peranema, Petalomonas, Entosiphon*[443, 444, 457] and *Mastigamoeba*[94, 103, 443, 444] moving on a surface, and *Tritrichomonas* swimming.[465, 852]

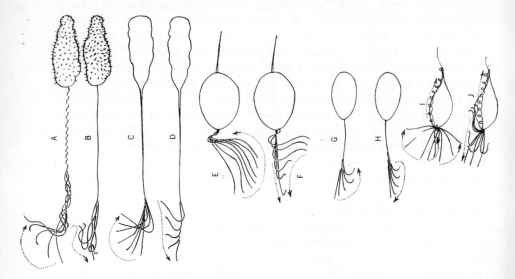

Fig. 6. Cilia-like beats of the flagella of several protozoa. A, power stroke of *Mastigamoeba setosa*, note helical wave also from tip to base, B, recovery stroke, forward by *Mastigamoeba setosa*; C, power stroke by *Peranema trichophorum*; D, recovery stroke, *Peranema trichophorum*; E, power stroke, *Entosiphon sulcatum*; F, recovery stroke, *Entosiphon sulcatum*; G, power stroke, *Petalomonas* sp.; H, recovery stroke, *Petalomonas* sp.; I, power strokes of the three anterior flagella of *Tritrichomonas foetus*, and continuous helical waves from base to tip along the trailing flagellum; J, recovery strokes of anterior flagella of *Tritrichomonas foetus*, and continuous wace along trailing flagellum. From tracings taken of motion picture films at 340 frames/second for all except *M. setosa*, which was photographed at 8 frames/second.

## (2) *Planar Undulatory Waves*

(a) *Wave Distally Directed — Pushing.* This pushes the body, i.e., exerts force toward the base of the flagellum, driving water away, e.g., *Chlamydomonas, Polytoma, Polytomella, Prymnesium,* posterior flagellum of *Ceratium*[459, 466] and most animal sperm.[69] (Fig. 7).

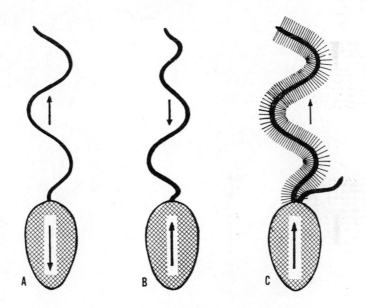

FIG. 7. A, distally directed wave pushes the cell in the direction opposite to the movement of the wave; occurs in animal spermatozoa and in the posterior flagellum of dinoflagellates, especially *Ceratium.*
B, basally directed wave pulls the cell in the direction opposite to the movement of the wave; occurs in certain trypanosomes and mastigamebas. In the latter the wave may be helical.
C, distally directed wave, flagellum with stiff mastigonemes; pulls the cell in the same direction as the movement of the wave, occurs in *Ochromonas.*
[Redrawn from Jahn and Bovee[444]]

(b) *Wave Basally Directed — Pushing.* This pulls the body, and pushes the water by means of a wave from tip to base of the flagellum, e.g., *Trypanosoma* spp.,[464, 465, 713, 934, 935] (Fig. 7) and *Strigomonas.*[399 a]

(c) *Wave Distally Directed — Pulling.* This pulls the body by forces pushing the water toward it due to action of stiff mastigonemes of a pantonematic flagellum, e.g., *Ochromonas*[460, 458, 466] (Fig. 7).

## (3) Helical Waves

(a) *Wave Distally Directed.* This pushes the body and drives water away, e.g., *Rhabdomonas* in which the flagellum and wave are positioned tangentially to the circumference of gyration of the body and do not produce a

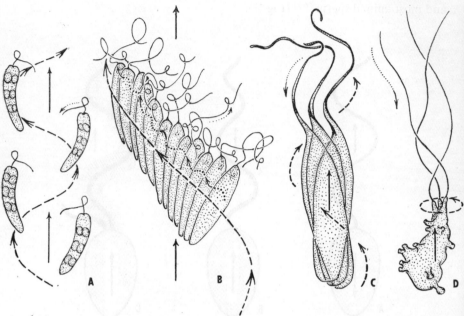

E. C. Bovee

Fig. 8. Helical wave movements of flagella. A, *Rhabdomonas* (*Menoidium*) *incurvum*, showing base-to-tip helical waves along flagellum; B, *Euglena viridis*, showing base-to-tip waves along flagellum, with latter held in trailing position; C, swimming *Peranema trichophorum*; D, swimming *Mastigamoeba steinii*. Note tip-to-base helical waves of the latter two protozoa, providing a forward drag on the body. All four species also progress by means of gyration of the body caused by beating of the flagellum, *Rhabdomonas* entirely so, *Euglena* strongly so, *Peranema* and *Mastigamoeba* only partly so. Dotted arrows, flagellar movements; dashed arrows, gyratory movements; solid arrows, forward movement. A, after Lowndes.[606] B, C and D traced from motion picture film photographed at 340 frames/second.

forwardly-directed component[604] and *Euglena* in which the anteriorly attached but posteriorly directed flagellum pushes the flagellum forward, dragging the body with it[604] (Fig. 8).

(b) *Wave Basally Directed.* This causes a tractile force directed away from the base, pulling the body forward, e.g., swimming *Mastigamoeba* (Fig. 8)[94, 103] and *Peranema*[457, 466] (Fig. 8).

(c) *Wave Directed Circumferentially in a Groove Around the Body at Right Angles to the Direction of Locomotion.* This causes a true rotary drive, e.g., the transverse flagellum of *Ceratium*[459] (Fig. 9).

Such a variety of flagellar movements suggests that many other variations are yet to be discovered, and that this classification is only temporary. As flagellar movements of other protozoa are critically analyzed, we expect to find and describe other new applications of hydrodynamic principles in microbiology.

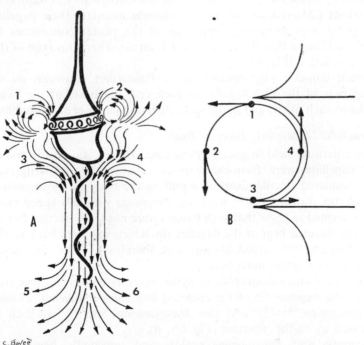

Fig. 9. A, Flagellar movements of *Ceratium*. Helical waves along the transverse flagellum in the sulcus push water posteriorly. The posterior flagellum has a distally moving planar wave series which also pushes to the rear. Both of the movements, or either one, may drive the organism forward. The arrows indicate the paths of polystyrene spheres pushed by the flagellar movements. At the girdle spheres are driven posteriorly, then outward to the sides, and are returned forward at *1* and *2*. At *3* and *4* they are driven backward by action of the transverse flagellum. Spheres at *3* and *4* move into the current driven backward by the movements of the posterior flagellum, and are driven parallel to it, then outward at *5* and *6*.
B, a cross section of the sulcus of *Ceratium* showing the directions of the force components.

### b. Latero-posterior Flagellar Movements

#### (1) "Rowing" Movements of Anterior Flagella

Jones and Lewin[490] reported for *Chlamydomonas* and *Polytoma* a "breast stroke," oar-like swinging of the two anterior flagella; and Sleigh[852] a synchronous rowing beat of the four anterior flagella of *Tritrichomonas termopsidis*, with a bending return stroke like that of cilia.

Jahn *et al.*[465, 466] confirm Sleigh's observations for trichomonads by high-speed cinematography of several other trichomonad species and Bovee and Telford[100] have seen similar movements of the anteriorflagella of *Monocercomonas* spp.

Frame by frame analysis of high speed cinematography by Jahn *et al.*[466] shows that *Chlamydomonas* and *Polytomella* undulate their flagella from base to tip with increasing amplitude of the planar (sometimes helical) waves; and shows that the rowing beat is an asynchronous type of the base to tip undulation (Fig. 11).

Certain colonial phytomonads (e.g., *Pandorina*), however, *do* show a rowing beat of the two flagella on each cell, the beats of the two being parallel to each other, and in the same direction (Jahn *et al.*, unpublished).

#### (2) Tractellar, Posteriorly Directed Beat

The anteriorly held flagella of *Peranema*, *Monas*, *Anisonema* and certain other flagellates were, from the work of Verworn[924] and Krijgsman,[556] long considered tractile, exerting a pull on the body by movements of the flagellar tip. Lowndes'[604] work on *Peranema* with low-speed cinematography seemed to show that such flagella were not truly tractile, but utilized a distally directed beat of the flagellar tip, which was bent back toward the body. Lowndes[606] urged abolishment, therefore, of the term tractellum as applied to flagellar movement.

High-speed cinematography, however, recently confirms a true tractellar beat by the flagellar tip of the euglenid flagellates *Peranema*, *Petalomonas* and *Entosiphon*[457, 466] and also *Mastigamoeba* spp.[103] in their gliding movement along the substrate (Fig. 6A, B).

*Peranema* and *Petalomonas* rapidly and repeatedly bend the distal 25 to 30 per cent of the flagellum in an arc toward the body in a vertical plane. Before the tip completes the flexing power stroke, an "unrolling" return stroke is begun which progresses outward to the tip, straightening the flagellum. In each genus certain species alternate the flagellar beat from one side to the other with a declination of about 50°. Thus the beat of the tip is a series of repeated "ciliary" strokes exerting a pulling force on the thicker extended part of the flagellum. No jerkiness in the gliding movement of the body of *Petalomonas* or *Peranema* is evident, however, which may indicate that gliding is due to an accessory mechanism (cf. p. 85).

*Entosiphon sulcatum* bends up to 90 per cent of its anterior flagellum in a similar power stroke towards the body. The recovery stroke noticeably begins to return the flagellum forward before the power stroke is completed. The power vectors produce a jerky forward movement, and a side-wise wobble on the return stroke, with the organism's body rocking from side to side on the postero-ventrally directed thick, rod-like trailing flagellum (Fig. 6 E).

*Mastigamoeba setosa* beats the anterior tip of its long slender flagellum sharply upward toward the trailing body for 20 to 50 per cent of its length,

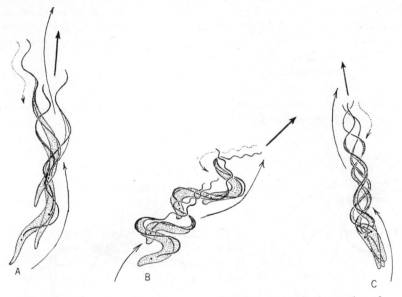

FIG. 10. Locomotion of trypanosomes. A, *Trypanosoma lewisi*, overlay of tracings from a motion picture film, each 10th frame, at 340 frames/second, dotted arrows indicate planar tip-to-base waves along the flagellum, solid arrows indicate path of forward movement; B, similar tracings for *Trypanosoma cruzi*; C, similar tracings for the leptomonad stage of *Trypanosoma cruzi*.

usually the lesser. The bent portion is then "unrolled" forward in return stroke. The power stroke is accompanied by the passage of a tight helical wave toward the base of the flagellum, adding another tractile force component. Amoeboid flow of the body also aids the forward motion (Fig. 6A, B).

All of the euglenid species discussed, and the mastigamebas, can also throw a helical wave from base to tip of the flagellum in a lashing movement which reorients the body. The heavy trailing flagellum of *Entosiphon* also shows such strong base to tip movements in reorienting the body, but it is usually motionless, as a "keel", during forward progress (Fig. 6E).

## c. Planar Undulatory Waves

### (1) Distally Directed Waves

Waves which move as undulations of a sine wave character have long been considered typical of flagella, especially for those of many animal sperm[320] (cf. p. 35). High-speed cinematography shows waves running from base to tip along the posterior flagellum of dinoflagellates, e.g., *Ceratium*,[459] pushing the body forward (Fig. 9a). Brokaw and Wright[128] contend that the undulations of the posterior flagellum of *Ceratium* are not true sine waves, but are, rather, composed of arcs of circles between which short straight segments of flagellum exist. This interpretation allows them to postulate an on-off series of bending and straightening reactions resulting in the flagellar undulations.

Similar planar undulatory waves may run from base to tip of the two flagella of *Chlamydomonas*, *Polytoma* or *Polytomella*, and of the two longer flagella of *Prymnesium parvum*, also pushing the body. The waves increase in amplitude from base to tip.[126, 466]

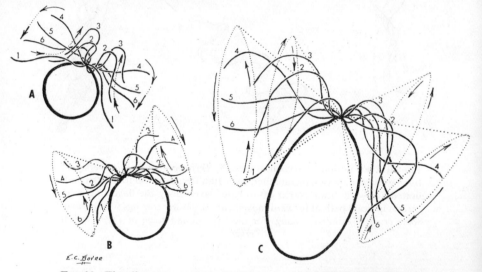

Fig. 11. Flagellar movements of *Chlamydomonas* and *Polytomella*. A, "Breast-stroke" beat of *Chlamydomonas*, waves planar and asymmetric, flagella thrown forward, then brought to the side in a rowing fashion. B, helical waves of increasing amplitude in flagella of *Chlamydomonas*, from base to tip of flagella, each flagellum describing a cone. C, helical waves along the flagella of *Polytomella*, of increasing amplitude from base to tip, somewhat asymmetrically so that flagella are bent more when moving forward than when moving to the rear; only the two flagella are shown, but conical projections indicating the approximate paths of the other two flagella are dotted in. Arrows indicate the approximate paths of the tips of flagella. Numbers indicate successive positions of flagella. Traced from motion picture films photographed at 340 frames/second.

## (2) Basally Directed Pulling Waves

Pipkin[713] and Walker and Walker[934, 935] have suggested, using slow-speed cinematography, that the waves of undulation move from tip to base along the flagellum of trypanosomes. High-speed cinematography confirms this,[399, 399a, 464, 465] and further shows that the waves are planar undulatory waves which move from tip to base of the flagellum. Some of the undulations are damped out and some reinforced (about every other one) by planar undulations of the body and undulating membrane, so that the damped undulations disappear and the augmented ones increase greatly in amplitude and the body is pulled forward. The effect of the interaction of the flagellar and body undulations is such that the free tip of the flagellum describes a complex path (Fig. 10), basically that of a figure eight, which hydrodynamically it must.[464] Motion pictures of leptomonad stages of *Trypanosoma cruzi* also indicate tip to base undulations of the flagellum, with increasing amplitude, damped out at the basal granule by the body. The body itself does not undulate, but the rear end wobbles as it progresses. At intervals the leptomonad stops, reverses the beat of the flagellum briefly (i.e., from base to tip), reorienting the body, then resumes tip-to-base flagellar waves and swims in a new direction. Gillies and Hanson[303] also report both forward and backward swimming by leptomonads, the flagellum being extended ahead of the body in forward swimming and trailing when swimming direction is reversed, but they do not describe the direction taken by undulations along the flagellum. Holwill[399a] describes both tip-to-base and base-to-tip waves in the flagellum of *Strigomonas*.

## (3) Distally Directed Pulling Waves

Normally, the distally directed planar waves push the organism as indicated above. However, certain chrysomonad flagellates, e.g., *Ochromonas danica*, *O. malhamensis* and *Chromulina* sp. generate distally directed planar sine waves from base to tip of the flagellum which *pull* the organism.[460, 458] This apparent paradox is due to the pantonematic nature of the flagellum, i.e., its surface is covered with projecting filaments (mastigonemes) so that it resembles a test tube brush [electronmicrographs, Manton;[619] Pitelka and Schooley[717]]. This converts the flagellum into a rough surfaced cylinder such that it behaves according to hydrodynamic laws proposed by Taylor[883, 884] and drives the organism forward. This is due to greater net thrust forward by roughness of the surface (i.e., net forward thrust developed by mastigonemes as each pushes backward against the water when the peak of the flagellar wave passes through the region to which the mastigonome is attached), than the opposite force developed by the undulations of the flagellar shaft.[443, 444, 459] As an analogy the flagellum may be considered as shaped like a long test tube brush with stiff bristles held rigid and at right angles at the points of attachment. A planar undulatory wave in the wire could cause a force to be exerted in the same direction as the wave, but each bristle as it passes over the peak of the wave would produce a force in the opposite direction (Fig. 12a,b,). The direction and velocity of the net locomotive progress depends therefore on the rigidity, length and diameter, numbers and positions of mastigonemes. Sleigh[853] has observed similar tractile base-to-tip waves in the flagella of *Monas*, *Actinomonas* and *Poteriodendron*, and suggests that mastigonemes are involved in those organisms.

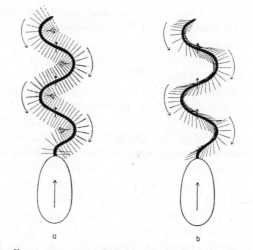

FIG. 12. Flagellar movements of *Ochromonas* spp., diagrammatic. a, the 90° fixed arrangement of mastigonemes assumed for *Ochromonas* spp., curved arrows indicate direction of movements of mastigonemes, solid arrows over flagellum indicate base-to-tip path of flagellar planar waves, solid arrow in body indicates direction of body movement; b, a theoretical system in which the mastigonemes are "hinged", and may swing between 0 and 90°, which would be still more effective, but is as yet unknown.

## d. Helical Waves

### (1) Distally Directed Waves

Such waves are seen in Lowndes'[604, 605, 606, 607] studies on *Rhabdomonas* and *Euglena*. They exert force toward the base of the flagellum where it is attached to the body. The posteriorly trailing flagellum of *Euglena* thereby pushes the anterior end of the body forward, as well as causing it to gyrate. In *Rhabdomonas* the flagellum is held at right angles to the body and exerts no push on the body to drive it forward, but instead pushes the body into gyration. The gyration, however, causes the body to assume a propeller-like action so that it thereby drives itself forward through the water (Fig. 8A,B).

### (2) Basally Directed Waves

Helical waves which move along the flagellum from tip to base are found in swimming mastigamebas[103] and *Peranema trichophorum*.[457] In these organisms the undulations pull the organism in the water, and also create a gyrational propeller-like component of the body, though not so efficient a one as that of the more flattened and rigid bodies of *Euglena* and *Rhabdomonas* (Fig. 8A, B). The vortical currents driven by the flagellum of the mastigameba may also contribute to the forward progress.

### (3) *Circumferential Waves*

In dinoflagellates the ribbon-shaped "transverse" flagellum occupies a shallow groove (girdle) which is more or less circumferential to the body. Helical waves pass from base to tip along this flagellum so that the waves are irrotational and of amplitude such that in half of each cycle the flagellum is out of the girdle. That outside portion pushes tangentially to the helix, that is, posteriorly so far as the body of the organism is concerned. In the other half of the cycle the flagellum is more or less in contact with the curved surface of the girdle, which acts as a bearing. Each half cycle therefore acts as a mechanical couple, the exposed part pushing backward against the water, the inner one against the inner surface of the anterior flange of the groove. Both serve to drive the body forward[459] (Fig. 9).

### e. Multiple Movements of the Flagellum

Krijgsman[556] clearly demonstrated that the single flagellum of *Monas* sp. could perform a variety of movements. Lowndes,[606] and others have criticized some of the movements reported by Krijgsman as possibly abnormal, due to conditions under which the observations were made; and Lowndes concluded that the "normal" movement (perhaps therefore the only effective type) was the base-to-tip undulation.

The recent studies of Jahn and his co-workers show that some organisms, e.g., *Peranema*, *Mastigamoeba*, are easily able to perform various flagellar movements, being able to reverse the direction of the wave, and perhaps alter the nature of its path, i.e., from planar to helical, or to a rowing beat. Conversely, some organisms may be unable to alter a relatively set pattern of operation, e.g., *Ceratium*, in which only distally directed movement of the waves is seen, and only planar waves in the posterior flagellum, and only helical waves in the transverse flagellum. Numerous other variations of flagellar movement are probably possible and yet to be discovered.

### 5. VALIDITY OF THE TERM TRACTELLUM

It is now certain that Lowndes[606] was wrong in his contention that flagella do not pull. It is not only evident that some do, but that flagella may show several types of traction. At least four are already known: 1) The *Peranema* type; 2) the mastigameba type; 3) the *Ochromonas* type; and 4) the trypanosome type. There are probably other types yet to be found.

## 6. The Flagellate Body as an Inclined Plane

Lowndes[606] suggested that a flagellate may be pushed forward along a helical path by only the gyrations of its body. The body of *Euglena* gyrates as the organism moves along a helical path. Lowndes demonstrated that the angle the flagellum makes with the body and also with the axis of the helix allows the flagellum to produce the body gyration and also to produce a forward component. Lowndes' contribution is the idea that the gyration of the body propels the organism forward even if the flagellum does not exert a forward component, and he demonstrated that in *Rhabdomonas* (*Menoidium*) the organism moves forward in spite of the fact that *there is no forward component of flagellar force*. In brief, *the body acts as an inclined plane and is a one bladed propeller*. The function of the flagellum is to produce gyration of the body (confirmed by Brown;[133] illustrated, Jahn and Jahn[446]). The principle applies to flagellates with cylindrical bodies, and even better to those with flattened bodies where the flat side acts as the plane. The highly ridged and twisted bodies of some species of *Phacus* [see Jahn and Jahn[446]] might be still more effective in applying this principle.

## 7. Swimming of Colonial Flagellates

Not much is known of the swimming mechanisms of colonial flagellates, neither as to the activities of individual cells, their flagella, nor as to the aggregate results.

Mast's[628, 638] early work deals mainly with the responses to certain stimuli, and reveals little about the working of the motile mechanism. Lowndes[606] assumes that the flagella on any one cell of the *Volvox* colony beat with a helical wave of increasing amplitude from base to tip, drawing his conclusions from studies of inanimate models, rather than from the study of the living organism.

The nature of the flagellar beat, the shape of the colony, the coordination of flagellar movements, and the hydrodynamics of moving the colony in the water are all involved, but few recent studies are available. Preliminary high-speed cinematographs show a parallel, synchronous beat for the two flagella on any one cell of *Pandorina* (Jahn *et al.*, unpublished) but analyses of other phases of colonial motility are not available.

## 8. Aggregate Swimming of Flagellates

The phenomenon of aggregate swimming discussed for *Tetrahymena* (see Section IV, G, 2, d) has been found under similar conditions in flagellates e.g., *Euglena*[759] and *Polytomella*.[305] The patterns formed by these flagellates differ from the open network in cultures of *Tetrahymena*. Robbins[759] described the pattern of *Euglena*, which consists of a network of triangles, but the organisms fill the triangles, so that the lines of the net are unoccupied. Gittleson and Jahn[305] found that *Polytomella* forms macroscopic horizontal patterns initially shaped like the container holding them. In circular chambers the pattern is at first circular, and becomes smaller in diameter with radiating horizontal external rays. As the diameter approaches zero, a solid point is reached from which the radiating lines emanate so that the pattern resembles an asterisk. These events occur almost entirely within 10–15 minutes after agitating a maximally active pattern forming culture and persist for at least six hours.[305] The evidence suggests that negative geotaxis and hydrodynamics produce the pattern of both ciliates and flagellates.

## 9. HYDRODYNAMICS IN FLAGELLAR MOVEMENTS

Many extrinsic factors affect flagellar movements. Application of hydrodynamics has already been made to spermatozoan swimming (review, Bishop[69]). Through use of models, both mechanical[605, 606, 883] and biological,[123, 391, 896] and by mathematical analyses of flagellar movements [320, 321, 322, 323, 324, 325, 358, 615, 616, 846, 883, 899a] it is evident that a number of hydrodynamic factors directly or indirectly affect flagellar movements and flagellate swimming, and also the movements of cilia and swimming of ciliates.

These factors include: 1) An obligate bending of the flagellum[324] required to produce patterns and amplitudes of its movements;[615, 616] 2) a negligible inertial resistance and the main resistance in the viscosity of the medium, due to a very low Reynold's number (i.e., the ratio of inertial to viscous resistance) of about $10^{-2}$ for the body and $10^{-4}$ or less for the flagellum;[883] 3) a locomotive rate which varies directly with the amplitude of the flagellar waves;[358] 4) a tangential viscous drag on the flagellum of spermatozoa and perhaps of small flagellates which makes up most of the drag of the medium, since the body is too small to present much resistance; 5) torque enough to rotate the body, generated by an asymmetric wave along the flagellum even when the flagellum itself does not rotate;[324] 6) resistance to that torque by the body;[358] 7) action by the body as an inclined plane, screwing a forward path;[604] 8) a force exerted by the roughness of a swimming cylinder, so that the net force is in the direction opposite to that due to the movement of the cylinder alone;[884] 9) interaction with dampening among the hydrodynamic and other physical factors resulting, when there is a relatively steady beating of the flagellum, in a helical path with the axis a straight line through the center of a cylinder with a diameter the same as that of the helical path. Other applications of hydrodynamics are undoubtedly involved and will be found applicable to other phenomena which may be found.

## V. SUMMARY AND POSTLUDE

Some of the major advances during the past 25 years which affect concepts of protozoan motile behavior are recognition of: 1) the obvious cellular nature of the protozoa, both morphologically and physiologically; 2) the undeniable complexity of cells, of whatever derivation; and 3) the definite similarities of all cells at fundamental physiological and morphological levels. Consequently it is no longer necessary to argue for a greater complexity of protozoan cells amounting to an acellular evolutionary drift and development. Any cell is complex enough to provide for the complexity of protozoan morphology; and the protozoa have quantitatively expanded the basic organization without any need to do it qualitatively, at least to any definitive degree.

Neither is there any need to assume that a protozoon requires a distinct, morphologically and physiologically specialized network to conduct information. Most of them do not have sufficient mass to require it, and those that might seem large enough, e.g., the mycetozoan plasmodium, do not have it. Therefore, any assumption of a neuroid system of fibrils which is primarily or solely conductive of impulses is not necessary.

However, it *is* necessary to regard the behavior of the protozoa as dependent upon and resultant from the operative biochemical and biophysical machinery of the cell. This further requires that the interpretations of these functions be based on the roles of the molecular and submolecular organizations and their interactions within the protozoon. The roles of thermodynamics and hydrodynamics and their influences are particularly important.

Conversely, the determination of behavior on the basis of the simplest applicable biophysical and biochemical principles at the molecular and submolecular levels, even if not by the most direct routes [see Szent-Györgyi[873]] eliminates any physiological concepts based on anthropomorphic interpretations, including the assumption of a neuromotor system, and all teleological explanations of behavior. This purely mechanistic concept of protozoan behavior is the only scientifically defensible concept.

Furthermore, it is no longer important to test the response of a protozoon to a "physical force" or a "chemical" (except to compile data) unless it be that the ultimate purpose of experiments is to determine how such exposures alter the flow and the pathways of energy into, through and out of the intracellular mechanisms.

Here, the cellular nature of protozoa is an asset, since most of what has been found for intracellular systems in any living cell is useful for comparative purposes. It is already known that structurally and functionally the organization of and the movements of cilia and flagella of all cells have certain basic similarities. All which have been critically examined have some adaptation of an adenosine triphosphate-using actomyosin-like protein system which is also $Ca^{++}$ dependent. At a less distinct morphological level, but no less dependent on the ATP-actomyosin $Ca^{++}$ system, are the movements of all cells which employ less permanent (but very effective) structures, i.e., "pseudopods." This biophysical and biochemical motile uniformity is further bolstered by the uniformity of other biochemical cellular functions related to energy acquisition, processing, transfer and utilization.

The search has begun for variations in the application of these mechanisms; and for pseudopods some facts are already known. There are at least two major motile mechanisms, distinguishable at the visual level of information, which promote cell movements by protozoa: 1) a contraction-hydraulic system, evident in amebas and mycetozoa, and 2) an active-shearing mechanism resulting in the sliding of filaments against one another to promote movement and locomotion, which is evident in cyclosis of at least several organisms, and exhibited in some other internal protoplasmic movements, and in foraminiferan and other sarcodinian filopods, and perhaps in the movements of the fibrils in cilia and flagella. The existence of two such visibly distinct systems presents the possibility of a long needed approach to taxonomy of protozoa, particularly the Sarcodina.

Progress has been made in the study of the motile behavior of all groups of protozoa, but the full realization of the important role of hydrodynamics in protozoan motility has only recently been apparent. The roles of water have long been overlooked, in both their external and internal effects. Any explanations of protozoan (or other cellular) movements which are in any way related to the facts must relate the movements of the protozoon to the physical principles of a body moving *itself* in a fluid, while moving a fluid (of variable viscosity, i.e., thixotropic) within itself.

Furthermore, the effects of other factors on the organism must be approached by treating the cell membrane as a living, variable, ion-exchange resin with ions and water adsorbed externally and internally; and because of connections and relationships of the membrane to the endoplasmic reticulum (which may be a vast extension of the surface membrane) the role of membrane phenomena in motile behavior may be even greater than expected.

Motion (along with growth) is one of the fundamental evidences of life, protozoan or other; and this leads to the equally intriguing accompanying question, "How does it move?"

Perhaps we are close to the answers. By applying concepts of ionic equilibria, membrane structure and ionic association, core and volume conductors, of electronic potentials, of mechanics and hydrodynamics, of modern biochemistry, and of photochemistry, it is possible to systematize much of the presently available knowledge. With purposeful experiments based on this information, using hydrodynamic and thermodynamic concepts, new principles applicable to protozoan motile behavior may soon appear.

Many other concepts are certain to enter into future research in protozoan motility. Some of these are 1) the types of electron shifts, or of electron flow in molecules and membranes of the cell, 2) the importance of membranes, particularly the method by which electromotive forces are produced across them, 3) the possibility that $K^+$ and $Na^+$ ions contribute little or nothing to the transmembrane bioelectromotive force, 4) the probability that certain chemical reactions are more likely to occur at membranes because of the existence of the triplet atomic state in molecules of the membrane, 5) selective binding of ions and organic molecules by membranes and cytoplasm, thereby making assumption of most transmembrane ion and molecular pumps unnecessary, 6) the possible existence of some ion and molecular pumps and the mechanism by which they may operate, 7) the movement of hydrogen and hydroxyl ions by proton charge transfer, thereby simplifying current ideas of secretion of acids and alkalis, and 8) molecular mechanisms of contraction and of active sliding processes.

These concepts may so affect research on motile behavior of protozoa, either directly or indirectly, that any future chapter on the subject should differ from this one more than this one does from that chapter written by Mast[638] twenty-five years ago.

TABLE 1. SENSITIVITY OF PROTOZOA TO VISIBLE LIGHT

| Organism | Wave length of maximal sensitivity m$\mu$ | Literature source |
|---|---|---|
| Chlamydomonas fluvialis | 503 | MAST, 1917 |
| Chlamydomonas globosa | 503 | MAST, 1917 |
| Chlamydomonas snowiae | 465–80 (1st peak, photo-taxis) | MAYER and POLYKOFF-MAYBER, 1959 |
| | 500 (2nd peak, phototaxis) | MAYER and POLYKOFF-MAYBER, 1959 |
| Chlamydomonas sp. | 520 (aggregation) | LOEB and MAXWELL, 1910 |
| | 535 (orientation) | LOEB and MAXWELL, 1910 |
| Chlamydomonas sp. | 492 | LUNTZ, 1931 |
| Platymonas subcordiformis | 493 (positive and negative tropotaxis) | HALLDAL, 1958 |
| Stephanoptera sp. | 493 (positive and negative tropotaxis) | HALLDAL, 1958 |
| Dunaliella sp. | 493 (positive and negative tropotaxis) | HALLDAL, 1958 |
| Eudorina elegans | 492 | LUNTZ, 1931 |
| Eudorina elegans | 524 | MAST, 1917 |
| Gonium pectorale | 524 | MAST, 1917 |
| Pandorina morum | 524 | MAST, 1917 |
| Spondylomorum quater-narium | 524 | MAST, 1917 |
| Volvox sp. | 524 | MAST, 1917 |
| Volvox minor | 492 | LUNTZ, 1931 |
| Gonyaulax sp. | 475 (positive tropotaxis) | HALLDAL, 1958 |
| Peridinium sp. | 475 (positive tropotaxis) | HALLDAL, 1958 |
| Prorocentrum sp. | 570 (positive tropotaxis) | HALLDAL, 1958 |
| Euglena viridis | 470–490 | ENGELMANN, 1882 |
| Euglena viridis | 485 (aggregation) | LOEB and MAXWELL, 1910 |
| | 460–490 (orientation) | LOEB and MAXWELL, 1910 |

TABLE 1 (cont.)

| Organism | Wave length of maximal sensitivity m$\mu$ | Literature source |
|---|---|---|
| Euglena viridis | 480–495 | OLTMANNS, 1917 |
| Euglena gracilis | 483 | MAST, 1917 |
| Euglena gracilis | 495 | BUNNING, 1956 |
| Euglena gracilis | 465 (tropotaxis) | WOLKEN, 1961 |
|  | 490 (action) | WOLKEN, 1961 |
|  | 468 (action); polarized light | WOLKEN, 1961 |
| Euglena tripteris | 483 | MAST, 1917 |
| Euglena granulata | 483 | MAST, 1917 |
| Euglena minima | 483 | MAST, 1917 |
| Phacus triqueter | 483 | MAST, 1917 |
| Trachelomonas euchlora | 483 | MAST, 1917 |
| Peranema trichophorum | 505 | MAST, 1917 |
| Chilomonas paramecium† | 366† | LUNTZ, 1931 |
| Amoeba proteus | violet | HARRINGTON and LEAMING, 1900 |
| Amoeba proteus | 430–490 | MAST, 1909 |
| Amoeba proteus | 450–490; 550 (100 ft candles) | HITCHCOCK, 1961 |
|  | 515 (20 ft candles) | HITCHCOCK, 1961 |
| Paramecium bursaria | 650–700 (an $O_2$ effect?) | ENGELMANN, 1882 |
| Stentor niger | blue, violet (aggregation) | TUFFRAU, 1957 |

† Sensitivity of chlorophyll bearing strains is the same at 336 m$\mu$ as is that of *Chilomonas*, but is higher at the 492 peak.

[For Table 2 see overleaf]

TABLE 2. MAXIMAL RATE OF MOVEMENT OF PROTOZOA AS RELATED TO TEMPERATURE

| Organism | Temperature degrees C | Rate of movement | Literature source |
|---|---|---|---|
| Euglena deses | 15 | most actively motile (crawling) | BRACHER, 1919 |
| Euglena gracilis | 30 | 80.1 $\mu$/sec (swimming) | LEE, J. W., 1954 |
| Chilomonas paramecium | 26 | 152.9 $\mu$/sec (swimming) | LEE, J. W., 1954 |
| Amoeba proteus | 22.5 | 1450 $\mu$/min (maximal locomotion recorded) | SCHWITTALA, 1924 |
| Amoeba proteus | 22–25 | 800–850 $\mu$/min (average locomotive maximum) | SCHWITTALA, 1925 |
| Amoeba proteus | 30 | 600 $\mu$/min (second average maximum) | SCHWITTALA, 1925 |
| Amoeba proteus | 22–23 | 281 $\mu$/min (average locomotive maximum) | MAST and PROSSER, 1932 |
| Amoeba proteus | 30 | 332 $\mu$/min (second average maximum) | MAST and PROSSER, 1932 |
| Flabellula mira | 27 (unadapted to new temperature) | 47 $\mu$/min (average normal maximum) | HOPKINS, 1937 |
| Flabellula mira | 38 (adapted to new temperature) | 67 $\mu$/min (second average maximum) | HOPKINS, 1937 |
| Marine ameba A | 22–25 | maximal rate | PANTIN, 1924 |
| Marine ameba B | 20 | maximal rate | PANTIN, 1924 |
| Paramecium sp. | 40 | 1200 $\mu$/sec (flight?) | GLASER, 1924 |
| | 21.5 | 750 $\mu$/sec (normal?) | GLASER, 1924 |

TABLE 3. EFFECTS OF ULTRAVIOLET RAYS ON PROTOZOAN MOVEMENT

| Organism | Wave length | Dosage | Effect on movement | Literature source |
|---|---|---|---|---|
| Chlamydomonas moewusii | 2537 Å | 10 cm; 3 min | mutants with paralysed flagella, or slow, jerky, trembling movement | LEWIN, 1952 |
| Chlamydomonas sp. | 2537 Å | 10 cm; 3 min | mutants with reduced or no swimming | LEWIN, 1960 |
| Platymonas subcordiformis | 2230 Å | $2.5 \times 10^{16}$ Q/mm² | 20% reduction of motility; 95% recovery | HALLDAL, 1961 |
| Platymonas subcordiformis | 2660 Å | $8 \times 10^{6}$ Q/mm² | 50% reduction of motility; 10% recovery | HALLDAL, 1961 |
| Platymonas subcordiformis | 2650 Å then 2230 Å | $8 \times 10^{12}$ Q/mm² | immobilization; then recovery of motility | HALLDAL, 1961 |
| Euglena sp. | 2800 Å | $3 \times 10^{16}$ Q/mm² microbeam | eyespot blinded; flagellum stopped; local contraction | TCHAKOTINE, 1935 |
| Euglena gracilis | 2537 Å | 8.54 erg/mm²/sec | prompt slowing of movement; then stops | GIESE, 1938 |
| Khawkinea halli | 2537 Å | 8.54 erg/mm²/sec | prompt slowing of movement; then stops | GIESE, 1938 |
| Peranema trichophorum | 2530 Å | 2.75 hr/4X meter can. | stopped; rounded up | SHETTLES, 1938 |
| Amoeba proteus | 2000–1250 Å | — | continued sending pseudopods away from light; part hit coagulated, sloughed | BOVIE, 1915 |
| Amoeba proteus | 2800 Å | microbeam | stops, reverses; part hit coagulated, sloughed | TCHAKOTINE, 1935 |
| Amoeba proteus | 2537 Å | 9888 erg/min | increased pinocytosis | RINALDI, 1959 |
| Amoeba proteus | 2537 Å | 9888 erg/min | increased rate of contractile vacuole | RINALDI, 1959 |
| Chaos (Pelomyxa) carolinensis | 2537 Å | 2 min | Pseudopods stop, reverse retract; rounds up | WILBER and SLANE, 1951 |
| Amoeba proteus | 2540 Å | 10,000 erg/cm³/sec for 10 (10 sec exposures) | Stops; retracts pseudopods; rounds up | BLACK, 1935 |

TABLE 3 (cont.)

| Organism | Wave length | Dosage | Effect on movement | Literature source |
|---|---|---|---|---|
| Thecamoeba verrucosa | 2800 Å | microbeam | stops; reverses; part hit coagulated, sloughed | TCHAKOTINE, 1936 |
| Arcella vulgaris | 2800 Å | microbeam | pseudopods retract when hit; part hit sloughed; internally hit part pulls away from shell | TCHAKOTINE, 1936 |
| Didymium sp. | — | — | movement abnormal | VOUK, 1913 |
| Chondrioderma sp. | — | — | movement abnormal | VOUK, 1913 |
| Physarum polycephalum | — | — | pathological effects | SEIFRIZ, 1939 |
| Fuligo sp. | — | microbeam | coagulated, red where hit; accelerated nearby | LOCQUIN, 1949 |
| Paramecium caudatum | less than 2000 Å | — | gradual loss of motility | BOVIE and HUGHES, 1918 |
| Paramecium caudatum | 2804 Å | — | little effect on motility | BOVIE and HUGHES, 1918 |
| Paramecium caudatum | less than 2000 Å | — | acceleration, then circling, erratic swimming, slowing, immobilization, then contraction | BOVIE and DALAND, 1923 |
| Paramecium caudatum | 2670 Å | $2 \times 10^{14}$ Q/mm$^2$ | random swimming, slowing, stops and pivots on rear end; immobilized; 85% recovery | BRANDT and GIESE, 1956 |
| Paramecium caudatum | 2670 Å | $30 \times 10^{14}$ Q/mm$^2$ | same as above; 10% recovery | BRANDT and GIESE, 1956 |
| Paramecium caudatum | 2804 Å | 11,200 erg/mm$^2$ | 50% of organisms immobilized | GIESE and LEIGHTON, 1935 |
| Paramecium caudatum | 2804 Å | 2800 erg/mm$^2$ | prolonged ciliary reversal | GIESE, 1945 |
| Paramecium caudatum | 2800 Å | microbeam | cilia stop where hit and cytoplasm there contracts; animal flees | TCHAKOTINE, 1935 |

TABLE 3 (cont.)

| Organism | Wave length | Dosage | Effect on movement | Literature source |
|---|---|---|---|---|
| Paramecium bursaria | — | 4 min; more | speeds up to 4 min; then slows, stops | TANG and GAW, 1937 |
| Paramecium sp. | 2800 Å | — | contracts; moves slowly, stops | RENTSCHLER, 1931 |
| Frontonia leucas | | microbeam | cilia stop where hit | TCHAKOTINE, 1935 |
| Chilodon uncinatus | — | — | produced faster swimming mutant | MacDOUGALL, 1931 |
| Fabrea salina | 2537 Å | 85.4 erg/mm²/sec | impaired movement and circling | GIESE, 1938 |
| Climastocomum sp. | 2800 Å | microbeam | adoral membranelles stop, slough when hit | TCHAKOTINE, 1936 |
| Spirostomum ambiguum | 2800 Å | microbeam | cilia stop where hit; body contracts | TCHAKOTINE, 1935 |
| Spirostomum ambiguum | 2537 Å | 5 cm, 1–10 sec | no effect | SHIRLEY and FINLEY, 1949 |
| | | 11 sec | locomotion accelerated | |
| | | 12–15 sec | increased cyclosis | |
| | | 20–24 sec | violent contractions | |
| | | 30 sec | accelerated movement | |
| | | 35–45 sec | slowing, rolling | |
| | | 70 sec | immobile; dead | |
| Blepharisma lateritium | 2800 Å | microbeam | contracts, then bulges where hit | TCHAKOTINE, 1936 |
| Bursaria truncatella | 2537 Å | 85.4 erg/mm²/sec | impaired, circling movements | GIESE, 1938 |
| Stentor coeruleus | 2800 Å | microbeam | adoral membranelles stop; slough when hit | TCHAKOTINE, 1936 |
| Stentor coeruleus | 2800 Å | microbeam | cilia stop where hit; body contracts | TCHAKOTINE, 1936 |
| Stentor coeruleus | 2800 Å | microbeam | body contracts where hit; then bulges | TCHAKOTINE, 1936 |
| Stentor roeseli | | | adoral membranelles stop; slough, when hit | TCHAKOTINE, 1936 |
| Stentor niger | 2370 Å | — | aggregates in clumps | TUFFRAU, 1937 |
| Stylonychia pustulata | 2000–1250 Å | — | continued to swim until completely cytolyzed | BOVIE, 1915 |

6*

TABLE 3 (cont.)

| Organism | Wave length | Dosage | Effect on movement | Literature source |
|---|---|---|---|---|
| Stylonychia sp. Euplotes patella | 2537 Å 2800 Å | 85.4 erg/mm²/sec microbeam | rapid backward circling cirrus not affected unless hit at base; then stops, sloughs | GIESE, 1938 TCHAKOTINE, 1936 |
| Colpidium colpoda Vorticella nebulifera | 2383 Å 2800 Å | 1000 erg/mm² microbeam | rapid immobilization spasmonene not responsive, but paralyzed where struck; spasmo-contracts if any part of body, membranelles or cilia hit | GIESE et al., 1952 TCHAKOTINE, 1936 |
| Glaucoma chattoni | 2357 Å Hg arc | one minute or more | oral membranelles stop; recover in one hour | FRANKEL, 1960 |

TABLE 4. EFFECTS OF X-RAYS, α, β OR γ RAYS ON PROTOZOAN MOVEMENT

| Organism | Source | Dosage | Effect on movement | Literature source |
|---|---|---|---|---|
| Pandorina morum | X-ray | 400,000 r | immobilized | HALBERSTAEDTER and BACK, 1942 |
| Dunaliella salina | X-ray | 18,428 r | immobilized, 2% survival | RALSTON, 1939 |
| Oxhyrris marina | X-ray | 2 hr | slowed, flagella stop; immobilized; rounded | SCHAUDINN, 1899 |
| Cryptomonas ovata | X-ray | 6 hr | stopped; rounded up | SCHAUDINN, 1899 |
| Chilomonas paramecium | X-ray | 6 hr | stopped; rounded up | SCHAUDINN, 1899 |
| Euglena acus | X-ray | 6 hr | flagella stopped; died outstretched | SCHAUDINN, 1899 |
| Euglena gracilis | X-ray | 16,500–32,000 r | slower, circular or erratic swimming, immobilization, increased metaboly, quivering | WICHTERMANN, 1955 |
| Amoeba princeps (proteus) | X-ray | 6–10 hr | slowed, retracted pseudopods, rounded up | SCHAUDINN, 1899 |
| Amoeba proteus (Chaos diffluens) | X-ray | 75,000–125,000 r | lose attachment, retract pseudopods, round up; all recover, 12–15 hr | WICHTERMAN and HONNEGER, 1957 |
|  |  | 150,000–220,000 r | same, but recovery takes 48 hr |  |
|  | X-ray | 225,000 r | same, survivors move abnormally |  |
|  |  | 240,000 r | LD 50; survivors move abnormally |  |
|  |  | 275,000 r | same; all die |  |
| Chaos carolinensis (chaos) | X-ray | — | body rounds up, fragments; some parts survive as smaller mutants | SCHAEFFER, 1946 |
| Chaos (Pelomyxa) carolinensis | X-ray | 100,000 r | loses attachment, retracts pseudopods; rounds up; most recover normally | BARRON and FLOOD, 1949 |
| Chaos carolinensis (chaos) | X-ray | 100,000–125,000 r | lose attachment, retract pseudopods; round up; 85% recover normally | WICHTERMAN and HONNEGER, 1957 |
|  |  | 150,000 r | same; 14% recover normally |  |
|  |  | 175,000–300,000 r | few recover, abnormally; all die soon |  |
| Amoeba lucida | X-ray | 4 hr | rounds up, endoplasm contracted, vacuolated | SCHAUDINN, 1899 |
| Pelomyxa palustris | X-ray | 4 hr | stops; contracts; round | SCHAUDINN, 1899 |
| Arcella vulgaris | X-ray | 10–14 hr | retracts pseudopods, rounds up in shell | SCHAUDINN, 1899 |
| Difflugia pyriformis | X-ray | 6 hr | resistant | SCHAUDINN, 1899 |

TABLE 4 (cont.)

| Organism | Source | Dosage | Effect on movement | Literature source |
|---|---|---|---|---|
| Gromia oviformis | X-ray | 6-14 hr | accelerated streaming; then retracts; rounds up inside shell | SCHAUDINN, 1899 |
| Elphidium (Polystomella) crispa | X-ray | 6-14 hr | accelerated at first; then slows, stops | SCHAUDINN, 1899 |
| Labyrinthula macrocystis | X-ray | 6-10 hr | could not normally retract to touch, after | SCHAUDINN, 1899 |
| Physarum polycephalum | X-ray | — | cessation of spreading streaming slowed | SEIFRIZ, 1936 |
| Actinosphaerium eichhorni | X-ray | 6 hr | pseudopods retract; body vacuolated | SCHAUDINN, 1899 |
| Acanthocystis turfacea | X-ray | 6 hr | extends pseudopods further | SCHAUDINN, 1899 |
| Trichosphaerium sieboldi | X-ray | 6 hr | not affected | SCHAUDINN, 1899 |
| Paramecium caudatum | X-ray | 200,000–250,000 r | movement altered, metachrony lost, swim back and forth | BACK and HALBERSTAEDTER, 1945 |
| Paramecium caudatum | X-ray | 400,000 r<br>50,000–100,000 r<br>200,000–450,000 r<br>340,000 r | immobilization and death<br>increased swimming rate; full recovery<br>retarded swimming<br>LD 50; slow recovery; gliding first; full recovery several hours | WICHTERMAN, 1955 |
| Paramecium multimicro-nucleatum | X-ray | 500,000 r<br>1,800,000 r (cummulative) | immobilized; no recovery<br>permanently reduced swimming rate; altered behavior; ellipsoid form in survivors | WICHTERMAN, 1957 |
| Spathidium spatula | X-ray | 4,000–10,000 r | recover; feed; division delayed; strain death | WILLIAMS, 1959 |
| Colpidium colpoda | X-ray | 1–1.5 coul.<br>2.5 coul. | accelerated excited movement<br>zig-zag sway; stops | CROWTHER, 1926 |
| Tillina magna | X-ray | 25,000–50,000 r<br>100,000–200,000 r | no effect on movement<br>circling; cyclosis and contractile vacuole slowed; rounds up | BRIDGMAN and KIMBALL, 1954 |
| Spirostomum ambiguum | X-ray | 6-10 hr | stopped (died) outstretched; then contracted | SCHAUDINN, 1899 |
| Karyolysus lacertorum | X-ray | 10 hr | no effect | SCHAUDINN, 1899 |
| Adalea ovata | X-ray | 10 hr | no effect | SCHAUDINN, 1899 |
| Eimeria (Coccidium) schneideri | X-ray | 10 hr | no effect | SCHAUDINN, 1899 |

| Organism | Source | Dosage | Effect on movement | Literature source |
|---|---|---|---|---|
| Clepsidira (Gregarina) polymorpha | X-ray | 6 hr | killed in host | SCHAUDINN, 1899 |
| Polytoma uvella | α-rays | $1/\mu^2/\text{sec}$ | some slowed, erratic; others immobilized | HOLWECK and LACASSAGNE, 1931 |
| Fuligo sp. | β-rays | "proper amount" | accelerated rate of protoplasmic flow | LOCQUIN, 1949 |

## VI. REFERENCES

1. AARONSON, S. (1963) Is there a protozoan analog of the metazoan nervous system? I. Acetylcholine and acetylcholinesterase. *J. Protozool.* **10** (Suppl.), 8.
2. ABÉ, S. (1963) The effect of P-chloromercurobenzoate on amoeboid movement, flagellar movement and gliding movement. *Biol. Bull.* **124**, 107–114.
3. ABÉ, T. H. (1961) Morpho-physiological study of ameboid movement. I. Dynamic organization of striata amebae. *Cytologia* **26**, 378–407.
4. ABÉ, T. H. (1962) Morpho-physiological study of ameboid movement. II. Ameboid movement and organization pattern in a striata ameba. *Cytologia* **27**, 111–139.
5. ABÉ, T. H. (1963) Morpho-physiological study of ameboid movement. 3. Invisible gel structures in the endoplasm of an ameba of the verrucosa type. *J. Protozool.* **10**, 94–101.
6. ABÉ, T. H. (1964) Mechanisms of ameboid movement based on dynamic organization. Morphophysiological study of ameboid movement, *In* ALLEN, R. D. and N. KAMIYA (eds.), *Primitive Motile Systems in Cell Biology*, pp. 221–236. Academic Press, New York.
7. ACKERMAN, E. (1952) Cellular fragilities and resonances observed by means of some sonic vibrations. *J. Cell. Comp. Physiol.* **39**, 167–190.
8. ADLER, G. (1963) Cross-linking of polymers by radiation. *Science* **141**, 321–329.
9. AFZELIUS, B. A. (1959) Electron microscopy of the sperm tail. Results obtained with a new fixative. *J. Biochem. Biophys. Cytol.* **5**, 269–278.
10. AFZELIUS, B. A. (1961) Some problems of ciliary structure and ciliary function. *In* GOODWIN, T. W. and O. LINDBERG (eds,), *Biological Structure and Function, Vol. II*, pp. 557–567. Academic Press, London.
11. ALLEGRE, C. F. (1948) Contributions to the life history of a gregarine parasitic in grasshoppers. *Trans. Am. Microscop. Soc.* **67**, 211–226.
12. ALLEN, R. D. (1955) Protoplasmic streaming in amoeba. *Biol. Bull.* **109**, 339–340.
13. ALLEN, R. D. (1958) Polarization optical studies on amebae. *Biol. Bull.* **115**, 327.
14. ALLEN, R. D. (1961a) A new theory of ameboid movement and protoplasmic streaming. *Exptl. Cell Res.* **8** (Suppl.), 17–31.
15. ALLEN, R. D. (1961b) Ameboid movement. *In* Brachet, J. and A. E. MIRSKY (eds.), *The Cell*, Vol. II, pp. 135–216. Academic Press, New York.
16. ALLEN, R. D. (1961c) Structure and function in amoeboid movement. *In* GOODWIN, T. W. and O. LINDBERG (eds.), *Biological Structure and Function*, Vol. II, pp. 549–556. Academic Press, London.
17. ALLEN, R. D. (1962) Amoeboid movement. *Sci. Amer.*, **206** (2), 112-122.
18. ALLEN, R. D. (1964) Cytoplasmic streaming and locomotion in marine foraminifera. *In* ALLEN, R. D. and N. KAMIYA (eds.), *Primitive Motile Systems in Cell Biology*, pp. 407–432. Academic Press, New York.
19. ALLEN, R. D., and KAMIYA, N. (eds.) (1964) *Primitive Motile Systems in Cell Biology*. Academic Press, New York. 642 pp.
20. ALLEN, R. D., and NAKAJIMA, H. (1965) Two-exposure, film densitorometric method of measuring phase retardations due to weak birefrigence in fibrillar or membranous cell constituents. *Exptl. Cell Res.* **37**, 230–249.
21. ALLEN, R. D., and ROSLANSKY, J. D. (1958) An anterior-posterior gradient of refractive index in the ameba and its significance in ameboid movement. *J. Biophys. Biochem. Cytol.* **4**, 517–524.
22. ALLEN, R. D., and ROSLANSKY, J. D. (1959) The consistency of ameba cytoplasm and its bearing on the mechanism of ameboid movement I. An analysis of endoplasmic velocity profiles of *Chaos chaos* (L.). *J. Biophys. Biochem. Cytol.* **6**, 437–446.
23. ALLEN, R. D., COOLEDGE, J. W., and HALL, P. J. (1960) Streaming in cytoplasm dissociated from the giant amoeba *Chaos chaos. Nature* **187**, 896–899.
24. ALLEN, R. D., PITTS, W. R., JR., SPEIR, D., and BRAULT, J. (1963) Shuttle streaming: Synchronization with heat production in slime mold. *Science* **142**, 1485–1487.

25. ALLEN, R. D., FRANCIS, D. W., and NAKAJIMA, H. (1965) Pseudopodial birefringence and the motive force of ameboid movement. *Absts. 9th Meet. Biophys. Soc., San Francisco*, 1965, 151.

26. ALLEN, P. J., and PRICE, W. H. (1950) The relation between respiration and protoplasmic flow in the slime mold *Physarum polycephalum*. *Am. J. Bot.* **37**, 393–402.

27. ALSUP, F. W. (1939) Relation between the responses of *Amoeba proteus* to alternating current and sudden illumination. *Physiol. Zool.* **12**, 85–95.

28. ALSUP, F. W. (1942) The Effects of light alone and photodynamic action on the relative viscosity of amoeba protoplasm. *Physiol. Zool.* **15**, 168–183.

29. ALVERDES, F. (1922) Studien an Infusiorien über Flimmerbewegung, Lokomotion und Reizbeantwortung. *Arb. Geb. D. exptl. Biol.* **3**, 1–123.

30. ALVERDES, F. (1937) Das Lernvermögen der einzelligen Tiere. *Zeit. Tierpsychol.* **1**, 35–38.

31. ALVERDES, F. (1939) Weiteres über die Marburger Dressurversuche an niederen Tieren. *Verh. D. zool. Ges.* **41**, 103–110.

32. ALVERDES, F., and BRAMSTEDT, F. (1939) Erwiderung auf das Koehlersche Nach- und Schlußwort. *Verh. D. zool. Ges.* **41**, 470–473.

33. AMBROSE, E. J. (1961) The movements of fibrocytes. *Exptl. Cell Res.* **8** (Suppl.), 54–73.

34. ANDERSON, E. (1955) The electron microscopy of *Trichomonas muris*. *J. Protozool.* **2**, 114–124.

35. ANDERSON, E. (1962) The cytoarchitecture of *Entosiphon sulcatum*. *Am. Zool.* **2**, 386–387.

36. ANDERSON, E., SAXE, H. L., and BEAMS, H. W. (1956) Electron microscope observations of *Trypanosoma equiperdum*. *J. Parasitol.* **42**, 11–16.

37. ANDERSON, J. D. (1951) Galvanotaxis of slime mold. *J. Gen. Physiol.* **35**, 1–16.

38. ANDERSON, J. D. (1964) Regional differences in ion concentration in migrating plasmodia. *In* ALLEN, R. D. and N. KAMIYA (eds.), *Primitive Motile Systems in Cell Biology*, pp. 125–134. Academic Press, New York.

39. ANDERSON, W. A. (1964) Ultrastructure of the flagellum and pellicle of *Trypanosoma lewisi*. *J. Cell Biology* **23**, 5A.

40. ANDREJEWA, E. W. (1930) Die elektrische Ladung und die Bewegungsgeschwindigkeit der Infusioren *Paramaecium caudatum*. *Kolloid Zeitschr.* **51**, 348–356.

41. ANDREJEWA, E. W. (1931) Zur Frage über die physikalisch-chemische Bestimmung der Korrelation einiger physiologischer Prozesse bei *Paramaecium caudatum*. *Arch. Protistenk.* **73**, 346–360.

42. ANDREWS, E. A. (1945) Stentor's anchoring organs. *J. Morphol.* **77**, 219–232.

43. ANDREWS, E. A. (1946) Ingestion organs in folliculinids and in stentors. *J. Morphol.* **79**, 419–444.

44. ANGERER, C. A. (1936) The effects of mechanical agitation on the relative viscosity of *Amoeba* protoplasm. *J. Cell. Comp. Physiol.* **8**, 329–345.

45. ASTBURY, W. T., BEIGHTON, E., and WEIBULL, C. (1955) The structure of bacterial flagella. *Symp. Soc. Exptl. Biol.* **9**, 282–305.

46. BALLOWITZ, E. (1888) Untersuchungen über die Struktur der Spermatozoen zugleich ein Beitrag zur Lehre vom feineren Bau der contraktilen Elemente. *Arch. Mikros. Anat.* **32**, 401–473.

47. BALLOWITZ, E. (1890) Fibrilläre Struktur und Contraktilität. *Pflüger's Arch. ges. Physiol.* **46**, 433–464.

48. BAMFORTH, S. S., and LORENZ, L. K. (1962) Tolerance of four ciliates to low oxygen concentrations. *Am. Zool.* **2**, 503.

49. BANCROFT, F. W. (1905) On the validity of Pflüger's law for the galvanotropic reactions of *Paramecium*. *Univ. Calif. Publ. Physiol.* **2**, 193–215.

50. BARNES, T. C., and JAHN, T. L. (1934) Properties of water of biological interest. *Quart. Rev. Biol.* **9**, 292–341.

51. BARRETT, J. M. (1953) The mechanisms of food capture in *Actinosphaerium eichhorni* Ehrenberg. *Proc. Soc. Protozool.* **3**, 19.

52. BARY, A. DE (1864) *Die Mycetozoen* (Schleimpilze). 2nd ed. W. Engelmann, Leipzig. 132 pp.

53. BASTIN, A. (1919) Contribution à l'étude des Grégarines monocystides. *Bull. Biol.* **53**, 325–375.

54. BAYER, G., and WENSE, T. (1936) Über den Nachweis von Hormonen in einzelligen Tieren. I. Mitteilung. Cholin und Acetylcholin im *Paramecium. Pflüger's Arch. ges. Physiol.* **237**, 417–422.

55. BEAMS, H. W., TAHMISIAN, T. N., DEVINE, R. L., and ANDERSON, E. (1959) Studies on the fine structure of a gregarine parasitic in the gut of the grasshopper, *Melanoplus differentialis. J. Protozool.* **6**, 136–146.

56. BEERS, C. D. (1924) Observations on *Amoeba* feeding on the ciliate *Frontonia. J. Exptl. Biol.* **1**, 335–341.

57. BĚLAŘ, K. (1921) Untersuchungen über Thecamöben der Chlamydophrys-Gruppe. *Arch. Protistenk.* **43**, 287–354.

58. BĚLAŘ, K. (1926) *Der Formwechsel der Protistenkerne.* Fischer, Jena. 420 pp.

59. BELL, L. G. E. (1963) How locomotion and division are linked in living cells. *New Scientist* **18**, 103–105.

60. BELL, L. G. E., and JEON, K. W. (1963) Locomotion of *Amoeba proteus. Nature* **198**, 675–676.

61. BERNHARD, W., and HARVEN, E. DE (1960) L'ultrastructure du centriole et d'autres élémentes de l'appareil achromatique. *Verh. IV Intern. Kongr. Elektronmikroskopie, Berlin,* 1958 **2**, 217–227.

62. BERREND, R. E. (1958) Filopodial movement in *Cyphoderia ampulla* (Ehr.). Ph. D. thesis, U. Wisc., Madison; Univ. Microfilms, Ann Arbor, Michigan. 68 pp.

63. BERREND, R. E. (1964) Filopodial movement in *Cyphoderia ampulla* (Ehr.). *In* ALLEN, R. D., and N. KAMIYA (eds.), *Primitive Motile Systems in Cell Biology,* pp. 433–443. Academic Press, New York.

64. BERTHOLD, G. (1886) *Studien über Protoplasmamechanik.* A. Felix, Leipzig. 332 pp.

65. BIDDER, G. P. (1923) The relation of the form of a sponge to its currents. *Quart J. Microscop. Sci.* **67**, 293–323.

66. BINGLEY, M. S., and THOMPSON, C. M. (1962) Bioelectric potentials in relation to movement in amocbac. *J. Theoret. Biol.* **2**, 16–32.

67. BISHOP, D. W. (1958) Motility of the sperm flagellum. *Nature* **182**, 1638–1640.

68. BISHOP, D. W. (1962a) Reactivation of extracted sperm cell models in relation to the mechanism of motility. *In* BISHOP, D. W. (ed.), *Spermatozoan Motility,* pp. 251–268; Epilogue pp. 285–295. Am. Assoc. Adv. Sci., Washington, D. C.

69. BISHOP, D. W. (1962b) Sperm motility. *Physiol. Rev.* **42**, 1–59.

70. BITTAR, E. E. (1964) *Cell pH.* Butterworth, Washington. 129 pp.

71. BLANCH-BRUDE, R., SKREB, Y., and DRAGESCO, J. (1955) Sur la biologie de *Nuclearia delicatula* (Cienkowski). *Bull. Microscop. Sci. Appl.* **5**, 113–117.

72. BLUM, H. (1941) *Photodynamic action and Diseases Caused by Light.* Reinhold, New York, 309 pp.

73. BONAVENTURE, N. (1955) L'électrocinèse dans le galvantropisme de *Paramoecium caudatum.* Étude de l'action du courant galvanique sur les battements ciliares. *Comp. Rend. Soc. Biol. Paris* **149**, 2230–2232.

74. BONNER, J. T. (1959a) Differentiation in social amoebae. *Sci. Am.* **201** (6), 152–162.

75. BONNER, J. T. (1959b) *The Cellular Slime Molds.* Princeton Univ. Press, Princeton, New Jersey, 150 pp.

76. BONNER, J. T. (1963) How slime molds communicate. *Sci. Am.* **209** (2), 84–93.

77. BONNER, J. T., and ADAMS, M. S. (1958) Cell mixtures of different species and strains of cellular slime moulds. *J. Embryol. and Exptl. Morphol.* **6**, 346–356.

78. Booij, H. L., and Bungenberg, H. G. de Jong (1956). Biocolloids and their interactions. *Protoplasmatologia* 1, 2, 1–162.
79. Borgers. J. A., and Kitching, J. A. (1956) Reactions of the flagellate, *Astasia longa* in gradients of dissolved carbon dioxide. *Proc. Roy. Soc. London* B 144, 507–519.
80. Bovee, E. C. (1951a) The non-existence and suggested abolishment of *Amoeba radiosa* as a separate and taxonomically valid species. *Proc. Am. Soc. Protozool.* 2, 5.
81. Bovee, E. C. (1951b) Some observations on *Trichamoeba osseosaccus* (Schaeffer). *Trans. Am. Microscop. Soc.* 70, 47–56.
82. Bovee, E. C. (1952) A possible explanation of the gel-sol changes in ameboid movement based on the muscle contraction theories of Szent-Györgyi. *Proc. Iowa Acad. Sci.* 59, 428–434.
83. Bovee, E. C. (1953a) *Oscillosignum* nov. gen. *proboscidium* nov. sp. type form of its genus, Family Mayorellidae, Order Amoebida. *Trans. Am. Microscop. Soc.* 72, 328–332.
84. Bovee, E. C. (1953b) Morphological identification of free-living amoebida. *Proc. Iowa Acad. Sci.* 60, 599–615.
85. Bovee, E. C. (1956a) Some observations on the morphology and activities of a new ameba from citrus wastes, *Flamella citrensis* n. sp. *J. Protozool.* 3, 151–155.
86. Bovee, E. C. (1956b) Some observations on a marine ameba of intertidal zones, *Vexillifera telmathalassa* n. sp. *J. Protozool.* 3, 155–158.
87. Bovee, E. C. (1958) Optimal temperatures for amebas based on their incidences in water samples of known temperatures. *J. Protozool.* 5 (Suppl.), 20.
88. Bovee, E. C. (1959) Studies on the amebo-flagellates. I. The general morphology and mastigonts of *Trimastigamoeba philippinensis* Whitmore 1911. *J. Protozool.* 6, 69–75.
89. Bovee, E. C. (1960a) Studies concerning the effects of nutrition on morphology of amebas. I. *Mayorella cultura* Bovee, on abundant and starvation quantities. *Am. Midl. Nat.* 63, 257–169.
90. Bovee, E. C. (1960b) Studies on the feeding behavior of amebas. I. Ingestion of thecate rhizopods and flagellates by verrucosid amebas, particularly *Thecamoeba sphaeronucleolus*. *J. Protozool.* 7, 55–61.
91. Bovee, E. C. (1960c) Studies on the helioflagellates. I. The morphology and fission of *Dimorpha floridanis* n. sp. *Arch. Protistenk.* 104, 503–514.
92. Bovee, E. C. (1963a) Locomotion and pseudopod formation by a flabellulid ameba. *J. Protozool.* 10 (Suppl.), 10.
93. Bovee, E. C. (1963b) Studies concerning the effects of nutrition on morphology of amebas. II. *Acanthamoeba castellani* Douglas on abundant and starvation quantities. *Am. Midl. Nat.* 69, 173–181.
94. Bovee, E. C. (1964) Morphological differences among pseudopodia of various small amebae and their functional significance. *In* Allen, R. D., and N. Kamiya (eds.), *Primitive Motile Systems in Cell Biology*, pp. 189–219. Academic Press, New York.
95. Bovee, E. C. (1965) An ecological study of amebas from a small stream in northern Florida. *Hydrobiologia* 25, 69–87.
96. Bovee, E. C. Movement and locomotion of Eimerian Merozoites. *Trans. Am. Microscop. Soc.* (in press).
97. Bovee, E. C., and Jahn, T. L. (1960) Locomotion and the classification of Amoebida and Testacida. *J. Protozool.* 7 (Suppl.), 8.
98. Bovee, E. C., and Jahn, T. L. (1965) Mechanisms of movement in taxonomy of Sarcodina. II. The organization of subclasses and orders in relation to the classes *Autotractea* and *Hydraulea*. *Am. Midl. Nat.* 73, 293–298.
99. Bovee, E. C., and Telford, S. R., Jr. (1961) The feeding behavior of *Hypotrichomonas acosta*, inquilinic in Florida reptiles. *J. Protozool.* 8 (Suppl.), 6.

6 a*

100. BOVEE, E. C., and TELFORD, S. R., JR. (1964) On the movements of the anterior flagella of monocercomonads from reptiles. *Trans. Am. Microscop. Soc.* **84**, 86–88.

101. BOVEE, E. C., and WILSON, D. E. (1961) An ameboid stage in the feeding behavior of the helioflagellate protozoan *Dimorpha floridanis. Am. Zool.* **1**, 345.

102. BOVEE, E. C., and WILSON, D. E. (1963) Growth of the "sewage" amoeba, *Entamoeba moshkovskii*, in relation to temperature and aeration. *Develop. Indust. Microbiol.* **4**, 350–354.

103. BOVEE, E. C., JAHN, T. L., FONSECA, J., and LANDMAN, M. (1963) Flagellar movements in some species of mastigamebas. *Absts. 7th Ann. Meet. Biophys. Soc.*, New York, 1963, MD 2.

104. BOVEE, E. C., WILSON, D. E., and JAHN, T. L. (1964) Feeding behavior of an ameba, *Cochliopodium* sp. *Am. Zool.* **4**, 306–307.

105. BOVIE, W. T. (1915) The visible effects of the Schumann rays on protoplasm. *Bot. Gaz.* **59**, 149–153.

106. BOVIE, W. T., and KLEIN, A. (1918) Sensitization to heat due to exposure to light of short wave lengths. *J. Gen. Physiol.* **1**, 331–336.

107. BOVIE, W. T., and HUGHES, D. M. (1918) The effect of quartz ultra violet light on the rate of division of *Paramecium caudatum. J. Med. Res.* **39**, 223–231.

108. BRACHET, J. T. (1959) Cytoplasmic dependence in amoebae. *Ann. N. Y. Acad. Sci.* **78**, 688–695.

109. BRACHET, J. (1961) Nucleocytoplasmic interactions in unicellular organisms. *In* BRACHET, J., and MIRSKY, A. E. (eds.), *The Cell*, Vol. II, pp. 771–841. Academic Press, New York.

110. BRADLEY, S. G., SUSSMAN, M., and ENNIS, M. L. (1956) Environmental factors affecting the aggregation of the cellular slime mold, *Dictyostelium discoideum. J. Protozool.* **3**, 33–38.

111. BRAGG, A. N. (1936) Selection of food in *Paramecium trichium. Physiol. Zool.* **9**, 433–442.

112. BRAMSTEDT, F. (1935) Dresserversuche mit *Paramecium caudatum* und *Stylonychia mytilus. Zeit. vergl. Physiol.* **22**, 490–516.

113. BRANDT, C. L., and GIESE, A. C. (1956) Photoreversal of nuclear and cytoplasmic effects of short ultraviolet radiation on *Paramecium caudatum. J. Gen. Physiol.* **39**, 735–751.

114. BRANDT, P. W. (1958) A study of the mechanism of pinocytosis. *Exptl. Cell Res.* **15**, 300–313.

115. BRINLEY, F. J. (1928) Effects of cyanide on the protoplasm of ameba. *J. Gen. Physiol.* **12**, 201–206.

116. BRINLEY, F. J. (1929) Action of $H_2S$ on the protoplasm of *Amoeba proteus. Science* **69**, 336.

117. BRODSKY, A. (1908) Observations sur la structure intime du *Frontonia leucas* Ehrbg. *Rev. Suisse Zool.* **16**, 75–130.

118. BRODSKY, A. (1924) Die Trichocysten der Infusorien. *Arch. russ. Protistol.* **3**, 23–37.

119. BROKAW, C. J. (1958a) Chemotaxis of bracken spermatozoids; implications of electrochemical orientation. *J. Exptl. Biol.* **35**, 197–212.

120. BROKAW, C. J. (1958b) Chemotaxis of bracken spermatozoids. The role of bimalate ions. *J. Exptl. Biol.* **35**, 192–196.

121. BROKAW, C. J. (1959) Random and oriented movements of bracken spermatozoids. *J. Cell. Comp. Physiol.* **54**, 95–101.

122. BROKAW, C. J. (1960) Decreased adenosine triphosphatase activity of flagella from a paralyzed mutant of *Chlamydomonas moewusii. Exptl. Cell. Res.* **19**, 430–432.

123. BROKAW, C. J. (1961) Movement and nucleoside polyphosphate activity of isolated flagella from *Polytoma uvella. Exptl. Cell. Res.* **22**, 151–162.

124. BROKAW, C. J. (1962a) Flagella. *In* LEWIN, R. A. (ed.), *Physiology and Biochemistry of Algae*, pp. 595–602. Academic Press, New York.

125. BROKAW, C. J. (1962b) Studies on isolated flagella. *In* BISHOP, D. W. (ed.), *Spermatozoan Motility*, pp. 269–278. Am. Assoc. Adv. Sci. Washington, D. C.
126. BROKAW, C. J. (1963) Movement of the flagella of *Polytoma uvella*. *J. Exptl. Biol.* **40**, 149–156.
127. BROKAW, C. J. (1965) The stiffness of flagella and cilia. *Absts. 9th Ann. Meet. Biophys. Soc., San Francisco* 1965, 148.
128. BROKAW, C. J., and WRIGHT, L. (1963) Bending waves of the posterior flagellum of *Ceratium*. *Science*, **142**, 1169–1170.
129. BROOKER, B. E. (1964) Mastigonemes in a zooflagellate. *J. Protozool.* **11** (Suppl.), 41.
130. BROWN, D. E. S., and MARSLAND, D. A. (1936) The viscosity of amoeba at high hydrostatic pressure. Amoeboid movement at high hydrostatic pressure. *J. Cell. Comp. Physiol.* **8**, 159–178.
131. BROWN, E. B., JR., and GOOTT, B. (1963) Intracellular hydrogen ion changes and potassium movement. *Am. J. Physiol.* **204**, 765–770.
132. BROWN, F. A., JR. (1962) Response of the planarian *Dugesia* and the protozoan, *Paramecium*, to very weak horizontal magnetic fields. *Biol. Bull.* **123**, 264–281.
133. BROWN, H. P. (1945) On the structure and mechanics of the protozoan flagellum. *Ohio J. Sci.* **45**, 247–301.
134. BROWN, J. S., and FRENCH, C. S. (1959) Absorption spectra and relative photostability of the different forms of chlorophyll in *Chlorella*. *Plant Physiology* **34**, 305–309.
135. BRUCE, V. G. (1959) Some investigations of the phototactic rhythm in *Euglena*. *J. Protozool.* **6** (Suppl.), 11.
136. BRUCE, V. G., and PITTENDRIGH, C. S. (1957) Temperature independence of a unicellular clock. *Proc. Natl. Acad. Sci.* **42**, 676–682.
137. BRUCE, V. G., and PITTENDRIGH, C. S. (1958) Resetting the *Euglena* clock with a single light stimulus. *Am. Nat.* **92**, 295–306.
138. BRUCE, V. G., and PITTENDRIGH, C. S. (1960) An effect of heavy water on the phase and period of the circadian rhythm of *Euglena*. *J. Cell. Comp. Physiol.* **56**, 25–31.
139. BULBRING, E., LOURIE, E. M., and PARDOE, A. U. (1949) The presence of acetylcholine in *Trypanosoma rhodiesiense* and its absence from *Plasmodium gallinaceum*. *Brit. J. Pharmacol. Chemother.*, **4**, 290–294.
140. BULLINGTON, W. E. (1930) A further study of spiraling in the ciliate *Paramecium*, with a note on morphology and taxonomy. *J. Exptl. Zool.* **56**, 423–449.
141. BURNASHEVA, S. A., and EFREMENKO, M. V. (1962) Rol adenozintrifosfornoi kisloty v avigatel noi funktsii infuzorii vida *Tetrahymena pyriformis*. (in Russian; English abstract). *Biokhimiya* **27**, 167–172.
142. BÜTSCHLI, O. (1882) Protozoa. *In* BRONN, H. E. (ed.), *Klassung und Ordnung des Thierreichs*, pp. 1–1097. Winter, Leipzig.
143. BÜTSCHLI, O. (1891) Über die Struktur des Protoplasma. *Verh. Deutsch. zool. Ges.* **1**, 14–19.
144. BUTZEL, H. M., JR., BROWN, L. H., and MARTIN, W. B., JR. (1960) Effects of detergents upon electro-migration of *Paramecium aurelia*. *Physiol. Zool.* **33**, 39–41.
145. BUYTENDIJK, F. J. J. (1919) Acquisition d'habitudes par des êtres unicellulaires. *Arch. Neerl. Physiol.* **3**, 455–468.
146. CALKINS, G. N. (1909) *Protozoology*. Lea and Febiger, New York, 349 pp.
147. CALKINS, G. N. (1926) *The Biology of the Protozoa*. Lea and Febiger, New York, 623 pp.
148. CALKINS, G. N. (1933) *The Biology of the Protozoa*, 2nd Ed. Lea and Febiger, New York, 607 pp.
149. CANELLA, M. F. (1957) Studie Ricerche sui Tentaculiferi nel quadro della Biologia generale. *Ann. Univ. Ferrara Sect. 3, Biol. Anim.* **1**, 1–716.
150. CARLSON, F. D. (1962) A theory of the survival value of motility. *In* BISHOP, D. W. (ed.), *Spermatozoan Motility*, pp. 137–146. Am. Assoc. Adv. Sci., Washington, D. C.
151. CARTER, G. S. (1924) On the structure and movements of the latero-frontal cilia of the gills of *Mytilus*. *Proc. Roy. Soc. London* **B 96**, 115–122.

152. CASH, J., WAILES, G. W., and HOPKINSON, J. (1905; 1908) *British Freshwater Rhizopoda and Heliozoa*. Vol. I, II. Ray Society, London, 148 pp.; 166 pp.
153. CHALKLEY, H. W. (1929) Changes in water content in *Amoeba* in relation to changes in its protoplasmic structure. *Physiol. Zool.* **2**, 535–574.
154. CHALKLEY, H. W. (1935) The mechanism of cytoplasmic fission in *Amoeba proteus*. *Protoplasma* **24**, 607–621.
155. CHAMBERS, R. (1928) Intracellular hydrion studies. I. The relation of the environment to the pH of protoplasm and of its inclusion bodies. *Biol. Bull.* **55**, 369–376.
156. CHAMBERS, R., and DAWSON, J. A. (1925) The structure of the undulating membrane in the ciliate *Blepharisma. Biol. Bull.* **48**, 240–242.
157. CHANCE, B. (1959) Control of oxygen utilization. *In* WOLSTENHOLME, G.E.W. and O'CONNOR C. M. (eds.), *CIBA Foundation Symposium on the Regulation of Cell Metabolism*, pp. 91–129. J. and A. CHURCHILL, London.
158. CHAPMAN-ANDRESEN, C. (1962) Studies on pinocytosis in amoebae. *Compt. Rend. Trav. Lab. Carlsberg* **33**, 73–264.
159. CHAPMAN-ANDRESEN, C. (1963) Pinocytosis in *Amoeba proteus*. Some observations on the utilisation of membrane during pinocytosis. *Progress Protozool.* **1**, 267–270.
160. CHAPMAN-ANDRESEN, C. (1964) Surface Renewal in *Amoeba proteus*. *J. Protozool.* **11** (Suppl.), 11.
161. CHAPMAN-ANDRESEN, C., and PRESCOTT, D. M. (1956) Studies on pinocytosis in the amoebae *Chaos chaos* and *Amoeba proteus. Compt. Rend. Trav. Lab. Carlsberg, Ser. Chim.* **30**, 57–78.
162. CHASE, A. M., and GLASER, O. (1930) Forward movement of *Paramecium* as a function of the hydrogen ion concentration. *J. Gen. Physiol.* **13**, 627–636.
163. CHATTON, E., and BRODSKY, A. (1909) Les parasitisme d'une Chytridinée du genre *Sphaerita* Dangeard chez *Amoeba limix* Dujard. Étude comparative. *Arch. Protistenk.* **17**, 1–18.
164. CHATTON, E., and LWOFF, A. (1935) Le constitution primitive de la strie ciliare des infusoires. La desmodexie. *Compt. Rend. Soc. Biol. Paris* **118**, 1068–1072.
165. CHEN, Y. T. (1950) Investigations of the biology of *Peranema trichophorum* (Eugleninae). *Quart. J. Microscop. Sci.* **91**, 279–308.
166. CHILD, F. M. (1959) The characterization of the cilia of *Tetrahymena pyriformis*. *Exptl. Cell. Res.* **18**, 258–267.
167. CHILD, F. M. (1961) Some aspects of the chemistry of cilia and flagella. *Exptl. Cell. Res.* **8** (Suppl.), 47–53.
168. CHRISTENSEN, E., cited in GIESE, A. C. (1953) Protozoa in photobiological research. *Physiol. Zool.* **26**, 1–22.
169. CLAFF, C. L., DEWEY, V. C., and KIDDER, G. W. (1941) Feeding mechanisms and nutrition in three species of *Bresslaua. Biol. Bull.* **81**, 221–244.
170. CLAPARÉDE, E., and LACHMANN, J. (1858–61) *Études sur les Infusoires et les Rhizopodes*. Vaney, Genève, 773 pp.
171. CLARK, A. M. (1946) The reactions of isolated parts of *Spirostomum. J. Exptl. Biol.* **22**, 88–94.
172. CLARK, T. B., and WALLACE, F. G. (1960) A comparative study of kinetoplast ultrastructure in the Trypanosomatidae. *J. Protozool.* **7**, 115–124.
173. CLAYTON, R. K. (1964) Phototaxis in microorganisms. *In* GIESE, A. C. (ed.), *Photophysiology*, Vol. II, pp. 51–77. Academic Press, New York.
174. CLEVELAND, L. R. (1925) The method by which *Trichonympha campanula*, a protozoon in the intestine of termites, ingests solid particles of wood for food. *Biol. Bull.* **48**, 282–288.
175. CLEVELAND, L. R. (1963) Microcinematography of flagellates from Australian termites (16 mm. film). *J. Protozool.* **10** (Suppl.), 6.

176. CLEVELAND, L. R., and BURKE, A. W., JR. (1956) Effects of temperature and tension on oxygen toxicity for the protozoa of *Cryptocercus. J. Protozool.* **3**, 74–77.

176a. CLEVELAND, L. R., and GRIMSTONE, A. V. (1964) The fine structure of the flagellate, *Mixotricha paradoxa. Proc. Roy. Microscop. Soc.* **B 159**, 668–685.

177. CLOYD, W. J., and JONES, A. W. (1951) The adhesive function of the trichocysts of *Paramecium. J. Tenn. Acad. Sci.* **26**, 148–149.

178. COLE, A. (1963) Molecular model for biological contractility. Implications in muscle and chromosome structure and function. *Absts. 7th Meet. Biophys. Soc.* New York, *1963*, MF 6.

179. COLLIN, B. (1912) Étude monographique sur les Acinetiens. II. Morphologie, physiologie, systématique. *Arch. Zool. exp. gen.* **51**, 1–457.

180. COMANDON, J., and FONBRUNE, P. DE (1936) Mécanisme de l'ingestion d'Oscillaires par des Amibes, enregistrement cinématographique. *Compt. Rend. Soc. Biol. Paris* **123**, 1170–1172.

181. COMANDON, J., and FONBRUNE, P. DE (1938) Mécanisme de la préhension des microbes et absorption de bulles d'air par une Amibe, *Amoeba terricola*. Enregistrement cinématographique. *Compt. Rend. Soc. Biol. Paris* **124**, 634–636.

182. COMANDON, J., and FONBRUNE, P. DE (1942) Influence de stades evolutifs du cytoplasm et du noyau greffé d'*Amoeba sphaeronucleus* sur leurs volumes réspectifs et sur le déclenchement de la caryokinèse. *Compt. Rend. Soc. Biol. Paris* **136**, 763–764.

183. COOK, J. R., and JAMES, T. W. (1960) Light-induced synchrony in *Euglena gracilis* var. *bacillaris. Exptl. Cell. Res.* **21**, 583–589.

184. COPE, F. W. (1963) A theory of enzyme kinetics based on electron conduction through the enzymatic particles, with applications to cytochrome oxidases and to free radical decay in melanin. *Arch. Biochem. Biophys.* **103**, 352–365.

185. CORLISS, J. O. (1960) *Tetrahymena chironomi* sp. nov., a ciliate from midge larvae, and the current status of facultative parasitism in the genus *Tetrahymena. Parasitology* **50**, 111–153.

186. CORLISS, J. O. (1961) *The Ciliated Protozoa.* Pergamon Press, New York. 310 pp.

187. CRAWLEY, H. (1902) The progressive movement of gregarines. *Proc. Acad. Nat. Sci. Philadelphia*, **54**, 4–20.

188. CURDS, C. R. (1963) The flocculation of suspended matter by ciliated protozoa. *J. Protozool.* **10**, (Suppl.), 30–31.

189. DANEEL, S. (1964) Identifizierung der kontraktilen Elemente im Cytoplasma von *Amoeba proteus. Naturwissenschaften* **15**, 368–369.

190. DANFORTH, W., and ERVE, P. (1964) Personal communication.

191. DANIEL, G. E., and MAY, G. H. (1950) Observations on the reaction of *Pelomyxa carolinensis* subjected to a direct current electric field. *Physiol. Zool.* **23**, 231–236.

192. DANIEL, J. F. (1908) The adjustment of *Paramecium* to distilled water and its bearing on the problem of the necessary inorganic salt control. *Am. J. Physiol.* **23**, 48–63.

193. DANIEL, J. W., and RUSCH, H. P. (1962) Method of inducing sporulation of pure cultures of the myxomycete *Physarum polycephalum. J. Bacteriol.* **83**, 234–240.

194. DANIEL, W. A., and MATTERN, C. F. T. (1965) Some observations on the fine structure of the perisomial membranelle of *Spirostomum ambiguum. J. Protozool.* **12**, 14–27.

195. DANIELLI, J. F. (1937) The relations between surface pH, ion concentrations and interfacial tension. *Proc. Roy. Soc. London* **B 122**, 155–174.

196. DANIELLI, J. F. (1954) Phosphatases and other enzymes considered in relation to active transport and the functions of fibrous protein structures. *Proc. Roy. Soc. London*, **B 142**, 146–154.

197. DANIELLI, J. F. (1955) The transfer of nuclei from cell to cell as a method of studying differentiation. *Exptl. Cell. Res.* **3** (Suppl.), 98–101.

198. DANIELLI, J. F. (1959) The cell-to-cell transfer of nuclei in amoebae and a comprehensive cell theory. *Ann. N.Y. Acad. Sci.* **78**, 675–687.

199. DANIELS, E. W. (1951) Studies on the effects of X-irradiation upon *Pelomyxa carolinensis* with special reference to nuclear division and plasmotomy. *J. Exptl. Zool.* **117**, 189–209.
200. DANIELS, E. W. (1955) X-irradiation of the giant amoeba *Pelomyxa illinoisensis* I. Survival and cell division following exposure. Therapeutic effects of whole protoplasm. *J. Exptl. Zool.* **130**, 183–197.
201. DANIELS, E. W. (1959) Micrurgical studies on irradiated *Pelomyxa. Ann. N.Y. Acad. Sci.* **78**, 662–674.
202. DANIELS, E. W. (1962) Limits of transplantation tolerance in large amoebae. I. Microfusion studies using *Amoeba proteus, Pelomyxa illinoisensis,* and three strains of *Pelomyxa carolinensis. J. Protozool.* **9**, 183–187.
203. DANIELS, E. W., and VOGEL, H. H., JR. (1959) Effects of nonirradiated protoplasm on recovery of amoebae exposed to supralethal doses of fission neutrons. *Radiation Research* **10**, 584–596.
204. DARLING, S. T. (1909) Sarcosporidiosis, with report of a case in man. *Arch. Internal Med.* **3**, 183–192.
205. DAUGHERTY, K. (1937) The action of anesthetics on amoeba protoplasm. *Physiol. Zool.* **10**, 473–483.
206. DAVENPORT, C. B. (1897) *Experimental Morphology,* Vol. I. New York, 180 pp.
207. DAVIES, R. E. (1963) A molecular theory of muscle contraction: Calcium dependent contractions with hydrogen bond formation plus ATP-dependent extensions of part of the myosin-actin cross bridges. *Nature* **199**, 1068–1074.
208. DAY, L. M., and BENTLEY, M. (1911) A note on learning in *Paramecium. J. Anim. Behav.* **1**, 67–73.
209. DEBRUYN, P. P. H. (1947) Theories of ameboid movement. *Quart. Rev. Biol.* **22**, 1–24.
210. DEHAAN, R. L. (1959) The effects of the chelating agent ethelynediamine tetra-acetic acid on cell adhesion in the slime mould *Dictyostelium discoideum. J. Embryol. and Exptl. Morphol.* **7**, 335–343.
211. DEHALLER, G. (1960) Contribution á la cytologie d'*Euglena viridis. Verh. 4th Intern. Kongr. Elektronmikros.* Berlin, 1958, **2**, 517–520.
212. DELLINGER, O. P. (1906) Locomotion of amoebae and allied forms. *J. Exptl. Zool.* **3**, 337–358.
213. DELLINGER, O. P. (1909) The cilium as a key to the structure of contractile protoplasm. *J. Morphol.* **20**, 171–210.
214. DEMBOWSKI, J. (1923) Über die Bewegung von *Paramaecium caudatum. Arch. Protistenk.* **47**, 25–54.
215. DEMBOWSKI, J. (1931) Die Vertikalbewegungen von *Paramaecium caudatum.* III. Polemische und experimentelles. *Arch. Protistenk.* **74**, 153–187.
216. DEWEY, V. C., and KIDDER, G. W. (1941) Growth studies on ciliates. VI. Diagnosis, sterilization and growth characteristics of *Perispira ovum. Biol. Bull.* **79**, 255–271.
217. DIERKS, K. (1926) Lähmungsversuche an *Stentor coeruleus* durch Kaliumionen. *Zool. Anz.* **67**, 207–218.
218. DISKUS, A. (1955) Färbestudien an den Schleimkörperchen und Schleimausscheidungen einiger Euglenen. *Protoplasma* **45**, 460–477.
219. DOBELL, C. C. (1911) The principles of protistology. *Arch. Protistenk.* **23**, 269–308.
220. DONHAM, R. T. (1960) Electrophoresis studies on the protozoan, *Tetrahymena pyriformis.* M. S. thesis, New York Univ., typewritten, 44 pp.
221. DONIACH, I. (1939) A comparison of the photodynamic activity of some carcinogenic and noncarcinogenic compounds. *J. Exptl. Pathol.* **20**, 227–235.
222. DORAN, D. J. (1963) Personal communication.
223. DORAN, D. J., JAHN, T. L., and RINALDI, R. A. (1962) Excystation and locomotion of *Eimeria acervulina* sporozoites. *J. Parasitol.* **48** (Suppl.), 32–33.

224. DOROSZEWSKI, M. (1958) Experimental studies on the conductive role of ectoplasm and the silverline system in ciliates. *Acta Biol. Exptl.* **18**, 69–88.

225. DOROSZEWSKI, M. (1961) Reception areas and polarization of ciliary movement in the ciliate *Dileptus*. *Acta Biol. Exptl.* **21**, 15–34.

226. DOROSZEWSKI, M. (1963a) The response of the ciliate *Dileptus* and its fragments to the water shake. *Acta Biol. Exptl.* **23**, 3–10.

227. DOROSZEWSKI, M. (1963b) Some features of the ciliary activity in *Dileptus*. *Acta Protozool.* **1**, 187–192.

228. DRAGESCO, J. (1948) Étude microcinématographique de la capture et de l'ingestion de proies chez les ciliés holotriches gymnostomes. *Compt. Rend. Intern. Congr. Zool.* Paris, 1948 **13**, 227.

229. DRAGESCO, J. (1952) The mucoid trichocysts of flagellates and ciliates. *Proc. Soc. Protozool.* **3**, 15.

230. DRAGESCO, J. (1960) Ciliés Mesopsammiques Littoraux. (Systématique, morphologie, écologie). *Trav. Sta. Biol. Roscoff* **12**, 1–356.

231. DRAGESCO, J. (1962) On the biology of sand dwelling ciliates. *Science Progress* **50**, 353–363.

232. DRAGESCO, J. (1964) Capture et ingestion de proies chez *Actinosphaerium eichhorni*. *Arch. zool. exp. gen.* **104**, 163–175.

233. DRAGESCO, J., FAURÉ-FREMIET, E., and CORLISS, J. O. (1953) Feeding in vegetative and carnivorous gymnostome ciliates. *Proc. Soc. Protozool.* **4**, 4.

234. DRYL, S. (1959) The velocity of forward movement of *Paramecium caudatum* in relation to pH of medium. *Bull. Acad. Sci. Pol. Ser. Sci. biol.* **9**, 71–74.

235. DRYL, S. (1961) The ciliary reversal in *Paramecium caudatum* induced by the simultaneous action of barium and calcium ions. *J. Protozool.* **8** (Suppl.), 16.

236. DRYL, S. (1963) Oblique orientation of *Paramecium caudatum* in electric field. *Acta Protozool.* **1**, 193–199.

237. DRYL, S. (1964) The inhibitory action of chemical, electrical and mechanical stimuli on the periodic ciliary reversal in *Paramecium caudatum* induced by $Ba^{++}/Ca^{++}$ and $Sr^{++}/Ca^{++}$ factors. *J. Protozool.* **11** (Suppl.), 30.

238. DUGGAR, B. M. (1936) *Biological Effects of Radiation*, 2 Vols. McGraw-Hill, New York, 1343 pp.

239. DUJARDIN, F. (1835) Recherches sur les organismes inférieurs. *Ann. Sci. nat., Zool.* Ser. 2, **4**, 343–377.

240. ECKER, A. (1849) Zur Lehre von Bau und Leben der contraktilen Substanz der niedersten Tiere. *Zeit. wiss. Zool.* A **1**, 218–245.

241. ECKERT, R. Spontaneous potentials and tentacle movements in the dinoflagellate, *Noctiluca*. *Abst. 23rd. Intern. Physiol. Sci. Congr.* (in press).

242. EDWARDS, J. G. (1925) Formation of food cups in *Amoeba* induced by chemicals. *Biol. Bull.* **48**, 236–239.

243. EHRENBERG, C. G. (1838) *Die Infusiorentierchen als vollkommene Organismen*. Felix, Leipzig, 547 pp.

244. EICHEL, H. J., CONGER, N., and FIGUEROA, E. (1963) Extracellular ribonuclease of *Tetrahymena pyriformis* and comparison of its properties with intracellular ribonuclease. *J. Protozool.* **10** (Suppl.), 6.

245. EIGEN, M., and MAYER, L. DE (1958) Self dissociation and protonic charge transport in water and ice. *Proc. Roy. Soc. London* A **247**, 505–533.

245a. EISENMAN, G. (1963) The influence of Na, K, Li, Rb, and Cs on cellular potentials and related phenomena. *Bol. Inst. Estud. Med. Biol.* **21**, 155–183.

246. EISMOND, J. (1890) Zur Frage über den Saugmechanismus bei Suctorien. *Zool. Anz.* **13**, 721–723.

247. ELLIOTT, A. M. (1933) Isolation of *Colpidium striatum* Stokes in bacteria free cultures and the relation of growth to pH of the medium. *Biol. Bull.* **65**, 45–56.

248. ELLIOTT, A. M. (1935) Effects of certain organic acids and protein derivates on the growth of *Colpidium*. *Arch. Protistenk.* **84**, 472–494.
249. ELLIOTT, A. M., TRAVIS, D. M., and BAK, I. J. (1962) Carbon dioxide inhibition of growth and respiration in *Tetrahymena*. *Biol. Bull.* **123**, 487–488.
250. EMIK, L. O. (1941) Ingestion of food by *Trichonympha*. *Trans. Am. Microscop. Soc.* **60**, 1–6.
251. ENGLEMANN, T. W. (1869) Beiträge zur Physiologie des Protoplasm. *Pflüger's Arch. Ges. Physiologie.* **2**, 307–322.
252. ENGLEMANN, T. W. (1879) Physiologie der Protoplasma- und Flimmerbewegung. *In Hermann's Handbuch der Physiologie* 1, pp. 343–408. Vozel, Leipzig.
253. ENGLEMANN, T. W. (1906) Zur Theorie der Contraktilität. *Sitzb. Kgl. Preuss. Akad. Wiss.* **1906**, 698–724.
254. ENTZ, G. (1893) Die elastischen und kontraktilen Elemente der Vorticellen. *Math. Naturw. Ber. Ung.* **10**, 1–48.
255. EPSTEIN, S. S., and SMALL, M. (1963) Some practical applications of the photodynamic response of *Paramecium caudatum* to polycyclic aromatic hydrocarbons. *J. Protozool.* **10** (Suppl.), 8.
256. ESPANA, C., ESPANA, E. M., and GONZALES, D. (1959) *Anaplasma marginale.* 1. Studies with phase contrast and electron microscopy. *Am. J. Vet. Res.* **20**, 795–805.
257. FAURÉ-FREMIET, E., and DRAGESCO, J. (1949) Mécanismes physiques de l'ingestion des proies chez certains ciliés. *Compt. Rend. 13e Congr. Intern. Zool.*, Paris, 1948, **13**, 222.
258. FAURÉ-FREMIET, E., ROUILLER, C., and GAUCHERY, M. (1956) Les structures myoides chez les ciliés. Étude au microscope électronique. *Arch. anat. microscop.* **45**, 139–161.
259. FAWCETT, D. W. (1961) Cilia and flagella. *In* BRACHET, J. and MIRSKY, A. E. (eds.), *The Cell*, Vol. II, pp. 218–297. Academic Press, New York.
260. FAWCETT, D. W., and PORTER, K. R. (1954) A study of the fine structure of ciliated epithelia. *J. Morphol.* **94**, 221–282.
261. FINLEY, H. E. (1930) Toleration of freshwater protozoa to increased salinity. *Ecology* **11**, 337–347.
262. FINLEY, H. E. (1952) Sexual differentiation in peritrichous ciliates. *Proc. Soc. Protozool.* **3**, 7.
263. FINLEY, H. E., and WILLIAMS, H. B. (1955) Chromatographic analysis of the asexual and sexual stages of a ciliate (*Vorticella microstoma*). *J. Protozool.* **2**, 13–18.
264. FINLEY, H. E., BROWN, C. A., and DANIEL, W. A. (1964) Electron microscopy of the ectoplasm and infraciliature of *Spirostomum ambiguum*. *J. Protozool.* **11**, 264–280.
265. FJERDINGSTAD, E. J. (1961a) The ultrastructure of choanocyte collar cells in *Spongilla lacustris* (L). *Zeitschr. Zellforschung.* **53**, 645–657.
266. FJERDINGSTAD, E. J. (1961b) Ultrastructure of the collar of the choanoflagellate *Codonosiga botrytis* (Ehrenb.). *Zeitschr. Zellforschung.* **54**, 499–510.
267. FLICK, E. W. (1951) An electrical response in *Homalozoon vermicularis*. *Proc. Am. Soc. Protozool.* **2**, 14.
268. FOLGER, H. T. (1925) A quantitative study of reactions to light in *Amoeba*. *J. Exptl. Zool.* **41**, 261–291.
269. FOLGER, H. T. (1926) The effects of mechanical shock on locomotion in *Amoeba proteus*. *J. Morphol. and Physiol.* **42**, 359–370.
270. FOLGER, H. T. (1947) The period of quiescence in the response to light by *Amoeba*. *Biol. Bull.* **93**, 45–51.
271. FRAENKEL, G. S., and GUNN, D. L. (1940) *The Orientation of Animals, Kineses, Taxes and Compass Reactions*. Oxford Univ. Press, New York, 352 pp.
272. FRANCIS, D. W. (1964) Some studies on phototaxis of *Dictyostelium*. *J. Cell. Comp. Physiol.* **64**, 131–138.
273. FRENCH, J. W. (1940) Trial and error learning in *Paramecium*. *J. Exptl. Psychol.* **26**, 609–613.

274. FRENZEL, J. (1892) Untersuchungen über die mikroskopische Fauna Argentiniens. Die Protozoen. I. Abt. Die Rhizopodien und Helioamöben. *Bibl. Zool.* **12**, 1–82.
275. FREY-WYSSLING, A. (1949) Das Plasmagel. *Exptl. Cell. Res.* **1** (Suppl.), 33–42.
276. FREY-WYSSLING, A. (1953) *Submicroscopic Morphology of Protoplasm*, 2nd Ed. Elsevier, Amsterdam. 411 pp.
277. FUCHS, H. (1904) Über Beobachtungen an Sekret- und Flimmerzellen. *Anat. Hefte* **25**, 501–678.
278. GALL, J. G. (1961) Centriole replication. A study of spermatogenesis in the snail *Vivaparus. J. Biophys. Biochem. Cytol.* **10**, 163–193.
279. GARNHAM, P. C. C., BAKER, J. R., and BIRD, R. G. (1962) The fine structure of *Lankasterella garnhami. J. Protozool.* **9**, 107–114.
280. GARNHAM, P. C. C., BIRD, R. G., BAKER, J. R., and BRAY, R. S. (1961) Electron microscope studies of motile stages of malaria parasites. II. The fine structures of the sporozoite of *Laverania* (= *Plasmodium*) *falciparum. Trans. Roy. Soc. Trop. Med. Hyg.* **55**, 98–102.
281. GAVIN, M. A., WANKO, T., and JACOBS, L. (1962) Electron microscope studies of reproducing and interkinetic *Toxoplasma. J. Protozool.* **9**, 222–234.
282. GAW, H. Z. (1936) Physiology of the contractile vacuole in ciliates. 4. The effect of heavy water. *Arch. Protistenk.* **87**, 213–224.
283. GEISSMAN, T. A. (1949) A theory of the mechanism of enzyme action. *2. Rev. Biol.* **24**, 309–327.
284. GELBER, B. (1952) Investigations of the behavior of *Paramecium aurelia*: I. Modification of behavior after training with reinforcement. *J. Comp. Physiol. Psychol.* **45**, 58–65.
285. GELBER, B. (1956) Investigations of the behavior of *Paramecium aurelia*. III. The effect of the presence and absence of light on the occurrence of a response. *J. Genetic Psychol.* **88**, 31–36.
286. GELBER, B. (1961) Autogamy *vs.* responsiveness in *Paramecium aurelia. J. Protozool.* **8** (Suppl.), 17.
287. GELBER, B. (1963) Different responses to the same training in syngen 1 and syngen 4 of *Paramecium aurelia. Proc. 16th Intern. Congr. Zool., Washington, 1963*, **16** (2), 3.
288. GELEI, G. v. (1929) Über das Nervensystem der Protozoen. *Allatt. Kozlem (Zool. Mitt.)* **26**, 186–190.
289. GELEI, G. v. (1937) Ein neues Fibrillensystem im Ectoplasma von *Paramecium*; zugleich ein Vergleich zwischen dem neuem und dem alten Gittersystem. *Arch. Protistenk.* **89**, 133–162.
290. GELEI, G. v. (1939) Das äußere Stützgerüstsystem des *Paramecium* Körpers. *Arch. Protistenk.* **92**, 245–272.
291. GERISCH, G. (1964) Die Bildung des Zellverbandes bei *Dictyostelium minutum.* I. Übersicht über die Aggregation und den Funktionswechsel der Zellen. *Arch. Entwicklungsmech.* **155**, 342–357.
291a. GIBBONS, I. R. (1963) Studies on the protein components of cilia from *Tetrahymena pyriformis. Proc. Nat. Acad. Sci.* **50**, 1002–1010.
292. GIBBONS, I. R., and GRIMSTONE, A. V. (1960) On flagellar structure in certain flagellates. *J. Biophys. Biochem. Cytol.* **7**, 697–716.
293. GIBB, S. P. (1960) The fine structure of *Euglena gracilis* with special reference to the chloroplasts and pyrenoids. *J. Ultrastr. Res.* **4**, 127–148.
294. GIESE, A. C. (1938) Cannibalism and gigantism in *Blepharisma. Trans. Am. Microscop. Soc.* **57**, 245–255.
295. GIESE, A. C. (1945) The ultraviolet action spectrum for retardation of division of *Paramecium. J. Cell. Comp. Physiol.* **26**, 47–55.
296. GIESE, A. C. (1946) An intracellular photodynamic sensitizer in *Blepharisma. J. Cell. Comp. Physiol.* **28**, 119–127.

297. GIESE, A. C. (1953) Protozoa in photobiological research. *Physiol. Zool.* **26**, 1–22.
298. GIESE, A. C. (1964) Studies on ultraviolet radiation action upon animal cells. *In* GIESE, A. C. (ed.), *Photophysiology*, Vol. II, pp. 203–246. Academic Press, New York.
299. GIESE, A. C., and ALDEN, R. H. (1938) Cannibalism and giant formation in *Stylonychia. J. Exptl. Zool.* **78**, 117–134.
300. GIESE, A. C., and CROSSMAN, E. B. (1946) Sensitization of cells to heat by visible light in the presence of photodynamic dyes. *J. Gen. Physiol.* **29**, 193–202.
301. GIESE, A. C., and LEIGHTON, P. A. (1935) Quantitative studies on the photolethal effects of quartz ultra-violet radiation upon *Paramecium. J. Gen. Physiol.* **18**, 557–571.
302. GIESE, A. C., SHEPARD, D. C., BENNETT, J., FARMANFARMAIAN, A., and BRANDT, C. L. (1956) Evidence for thermal reactions following exposure of *Didinium* to intermittent ultraviolet radiations. *J. Gen. Physiol.* **40**, 311–325.
303. GILLIES, C., and HANSON, E. D. (1963) A new species of *Leptomonas* parasitizing the marconucleus of *Paramecium trichium. J. Protozool.* **10**, 467–473.
304. GIMESI, N. I., and POZSAR, B. I. (1956) About the physiology of protoplasmic movements. *Acta Biol. Acad. Sci. Hung.* **8**, 113–132.
305. GITTLESON, S. M., and JAHN, T. L. (1964) Pattern formation by *Polytomella agilis. J. Protozool.* **11** (Suppl.), 13.
306. GITTLESON, S. M., and SEARS, D. F. (1964) Effects of $CO_2$ on *Paramecium multimicronucleatum. J. Protozool.* **11**, 191–199.
307. GODWARD, M. B. E. (1962) Invisible radiations. *In* LEWIN, R. A. (ed.), *Physiology and Biochemistry of Algae*, pp. 551–556. Academic Press, New York.
308. GOLDACRE, R. J. (1952) The action of general anesthetics on amoebae and the mechanism of the response to touch. *Symp. Soc. Exptl. Biol.* **6**, 128–144.
309. GOLDACRE, R. J. (1954) The cell membrane, head-tail polarity and the maintenance of cell organization in *Amoeba proteus. Excerpta Medica Sec I*, **8**, 408–409.
310. GOLDACRE, R. J. (1958) The regulation of movement and polar organisation in amoeba by intracellular feedback. *Proc. 1st Intern. Congr. Cybernetics*, Namur, 1956 **1**, 715–725.
311. GOLDACRE, R. J. (1961a) Active transport and membrane expansion-contraction cycles. *In* GOODWIN, T. W. and LINDBERG, O. (eds.), *Biological Structure and Function*, pp. 633–643. Academic Press, London.
312. GOLDACRE, R. J. (1961b) The role of the cell membrane in the locomotion of amoebae, and the source of the motive force and its control by feedback. *Exptl. Cell. Res.* **8** (Suppl.), 1–16.
313. GOLDACRE, R. J. (1964) On the mechanism and control of amoeboid movement. *In* ALLEN, R. D. and KAMIYA, N. (eds.), *Primitive Motile Systems in Cell Biology*, pp. 237–255. Academic Press, New York.
314. GOLDACRE, R. J., and LORCH, I. J. (1950) Folding and unfolding of protein molecules in relation to cytoplasm streaming, amoeboid movement and osmotic work. *Nature* **166**, 497–500.
315. GOLDSTEIN, L. C. (1943) An unusual food reaction of *Chaos chaos* Schaeffer. *Am. Midl. Nat.* **29**, 252–254.
316. GÖSSEL, I. (1957) Über das Aktionsspektrum der Phototaxis chlorophyllfreier Euglenen und über die Absorption des Augenflecks. *Arch. Mikrobiol.* **27**, 288–305.
317. GOSSELIN, R. E. (1958) Influence of viscosity on metachronal rhythm of cilia. *Fed. Proc.* **17**, 372.
318. GRABOWSKI, U. (1939) Experimentelle Untersuchungen über das angebliche Lernvermögen von *Paramecium. Zeit. Tierpsychol.* **2**, 265–282.
319. GRAVE, E. V. (1964) Reisenamöbe fängt ein Pantoffeltier. *Mikrokosmos* **53**, 321–25.
320. GRAY, J. (1928) Ciliary Movement. Cambridge. Univ. Press, London, 162 pp.
321. GRAY, J. (1931) *A Textbook of Experimental Cytology*. Cambridge Univ. Press, London, 516 pp.

322. GRAY, J. (1937) Pseudo-rheotropism in fishes. *J. Exptl. Biol.* **14**, 95–103.

323. GRAY, J. (1953) Undulatory propulsion. *Quart. Journ. Microscop. Sci.* **94**, 551–578.

324. GRAY, J. (1955) The movement of sea-urchin spermatozoa. *J. Exptl. Biol.* **32**, 775–801.

325. GRAY, J. (1958) The movement of the spermatozoa of the bull. *J. Exptl. Biol.* **35**, 96–108.

326. GRAY, J. (1962) Introduction: Flagellar propulsion. *In* BISHOP, D. W. (ed.), *Spermatozoan Motility*, pp. 1–12. Am. Assoc. Adv. Sci., Washington, D.C.

327. GRAY, W. D. (1938) The effect of light on the fruiting of myxomycetes. *Am. J. Bot.* **25**, 511–522.

328. GRĘBECKI, A. (1963) Galvanotaxie transversale et oblique chez les ciliés. *Acta Protozool.* **1**, 91–98.

329. GRĘBECKI, A. (1963) Rebroussement ciliare et galvanotaxie chez *Paramecium caudatum. Acta Protozool.* **1**, 99–112.

330. GRĘBECKI, A. (1964) Rôle des ions K+ et Ca²+ dans l'excitabilité de la cellule protozoaire. 1. Equilibrement des ions antagonistes. *Acta Protozool.* **2**, 69–79.

331. GRĘBECKI, A., and KUŹNICKI, L. (1963) The influence of external pH on the toxicity of inorganic ions for *Paramecium caudatum. Acta Protozool.* **1**, 157–164.

332. GREELEY, A. W. (1901) On the analogy between the effects of loss of water and lowering of temperature. *Am. J. Physiol.* **6**, 122–128.

333. GREELEY, A. W. (1904) Experiments on the physical structure of the protoplasm of *Paramecium*, and its relation to the reactions of the organism to thermal, chemical and electrical stimuli. *Biol. Bull.* **7**, 3–32.

334. GREGG, J. H. (1956) Serological investigations of cell adhesion in the slime molds, *Dictyostelium discoideum, Dictyostelium purpureum* and *Polysphondylium violaceum. J. Gen. Physiol.* **39**, 813–820.

335. GREGG, J. H. (1961) An immunoelectrophoretic study of the slime mold *Dictyostelium discoideum. Developm. Biol.* **3**, 757–766.

336. GREGG, J. H. (1964) Developmental processes in cellular slime molds. *Physiol. Rev.* **44**, 631–656.

337. GRIFFIN, J. L. (1962) The large amebae: Physiological specialization and criteria for classification. *Absts. 2nd Ann. Meet. Am. Soc. Cell. Biol.* San Francisco, 1962, 61.

338. GRIFFIN, J. L. (1963) Light and electron microscopy of ameba membranes. *J. Cell. Biol.* **19**, 29–30A.

339. GRIFFIN, J. L. (1964) The comparative physiology of movement in the giant multinucleate amebae. *In* ALLEN, R. D. and N. KAMIYA (eds.), *Primitive Motile Systems in Cell Biology*, pp. 303–322. Academic Press, New York.

340. GRIMSTONE, A. V. (1961) Fine structure and morphogenesis in protozoa. *Biol. Rev.* **36**, 97–150.

341. GRIMSTONE, A. V. (1963) The fine structure of some polymastigote flagellates. *Proc. Linn. Soc. London* **174**, 49–52.

342. GRODZYNSKI, Z. (1961) Reactions of amoebas irradiated by a microbeam of UV rays. *Acta Biol. Cracova Ser. Zool.* **4**, 47–57.

343. GUIMARÃES, F. N., and MEYER, H. (1942) Cultivo de *Toxoplasma* Nicolle et Manceaux 1909, em culturas de Tecidos. *Rev. Brasil Biol.* **2**, 123–129.

344. GUINDON, A., and COUILLARD, P. (1964) Localisation par histochimie de l'ATPase de type myosine chez *Amoeba proteus. Rev. Canad. Biol.* **23**, 123–28.

345. GUNN, D. L., and WALSHE, B. M. (1941) Klino-kinesis of *Paramecium. Nature* **148**, 564–565.

346. GUNTHER, F. (1927) Über den Bau und die Lebensweise der Euglenen, besonders der Arten *E. terricola, geniculata, proxima, sanguinea* und *lucens* nov. spec. *Arch. Protistenk.* **60**, 511–590.

347. GUTTES, E., GUTTES, S., and RUSCH, H. P. (1961) Morphological observations on growth and differentiation of *Physarum polycephalum* grown in pure culture. *Developm. Biol.* **3**, 588–614.

348. GUTTES, E., and GUTTES, S. (1963) Arrest of plasmodial motility during mitosis in *Physarum polycephalum*. *Exptl. Cell, Res.* **30**, 242–244.
349. HAHNERT, W. F. (1932) A quantitative study of reactions to electricity in *Amoeba proteus*. *Physiol. Zool.* **5**, 491–525.
350. HALL, R. P. (1933) The method of ingestion in *Peranema trichophorum* and its bearing on the pharyngeal rod ("Staborgan") problem in the Euglenida. *Arch. Protistenk.* **81**, 308–317.
351. HALL, R. P. (1953) *Protozoology.* Prentice-Hall, New York. 680 pp.
352. HALL, R. P., and POWELL, W. N. (1928) Morphology and binary fission of *Peranema trichophorum* (Ehrbg.) Stein. *Biol. Bull.* **54**, 36–64.
353. HALLDAL, P. (1961) Photoinactivations and their reversals in growth and motility of the green alga *Platymonas* (Volvocales). *Physiol. Plantarum* **14**, 558–575.
354. HALLDAL, P. (1962) Taxes. *In* LEWIN, R. A. (ed.), *Physiology and Biochemistry of Algae*, pp. 583–594. Academic Press, New York.
355. HALLDAL, P. (1964) Phototaxis in Protozoa. *In* HUTNER, S. H. (ed.), *Biochemistry and Physiology of Protozoa*, Vol. III, pp. 277–296. Academic Press, New York.
356. HAMMOND, J. C. (1935) Physiological dominance as a factor in ciliary coordination in the protozoa. *Ohio J. Sci.* **35**, 304–306.
357. HAN, S. S. (1964) The possible origin of membranes concerned with pinocytosis and phagocytosis from compound vacuoles. *J. Cell. Biol.* **23**, 119A.
358. HANCOCK, G. J. (1953) The self-propulsion of microscopic organisms through liquids. *Proc. Roy. Soc. London* **A 217**, 96–121.
359. HANSON, E. D. (1963) Personal communication.
360. HARRIS, E. J. (1960) *Transport and Accumulation in Biological Systems*, Academic Press, New York.
361. HARRIS, H. (1961) Chemotaxis. *Exptl. Cell. Res.* **8** (Suppl.), 199–208.
362. HARRIS, J. E. (1961) The mechanics of ciliary movement. *In* RAMSAY, J. A. and V. E. WIGGLESWORTH (eds.), *The Cell and the Organism*, pp. 22–36. Cambridge Univ. Press, London.
363. HARRIS, R. J. C. (ed.) (1961) *Cell Movement and Cell Contact.* Academic Press, New York, 281 pp.
364. HARVEY, E. N. (1934) Biological effects of heavy water. *Biol. Bull.* **66**, 91–96.
365. HARVEY, E. N., and LOOMIS, A. L. (1928) High frequency sound waves of small intensity and their biological effects. *Nature*, **122**, 622–624.
366. HARVEY, E. N., HARVEY, E. B., and LOOMIS, A. L. (1928) Further observations on the effect of high frequency sound waves on living matter. *Biol. Bull.* **55**, 459–469.
367. HASSETT, C. C. (1941) The effect of dyes on the response to light in *Peranema trichophorum*. *Biol. Bull.* **81**, 285.
368. HASSETT, C. C. (1944) Photodynamic action in the flagellate *Peranema trichophorum* with special reference to motor response to light. *Physiol. Zool.* **17**, 270–278.
369. HASTINGS, J. W., and BODE, V. C. (1962) Biochemistry of rhythmic systems. *Ann. N.Y. Acad. Sci.* **98**, 876–889.
370. HAYASHI, T. (1962) Muscle research and flagellar movement. *In* BISHOP, D. W. (ed.), *Spermatozoan Motility*, pp. 279–283. Am. Assoc. Adv. Sci., Washington, D.C.
371. HAYASHI, T., ROSENBLUTH, R., SATIR, P., and VOZICK, M. (1958) Actin participation in actomyosin contraction. *Biochim. Biophys. Acta* **28**, 1–8.
372. HECHT, S. (1918) The photic sensitivity of *Ciona intestinalis*. *J. Gen. Physiol.* **1**, 147–166.
373. HECHT, S. (1919) Sensory equilibrium and dark adaptation in *Mya arenaria*. *J. Gen. Physiol.* **1**, 545–558.
374. HEIDENHAIN, M. (1911) *Plasma und Zelle.* Eine allgemeine Anatomie der lebenden Masse, Vol. I. Fischer, Jena, 507 pp.

375. HEILBRUNN, L. V. (1937) *An Outline of General Physiology*. Saunders, W. B. Philadelphia, 603 pp.

376. HEILBRUNN, L. V. (1952) *An Outline of General Physiology*, 3rd. Ed. Saunders, W. B. Philadelphia, 818 pp.

377. HEILBRUNN, L. V. (1958) The viscosity of protoplasm. *Protoplasmatologia* 2, 1–109.

378. HEILBRUNN, L. V., and DAUGHERTY, K. (1932) The action of sodium, potassium, calcium, and magnesium ions on the plasmagel of *Amoeba proteus*. *Physiol. Zool.* 5, 254–274.

379. HEILBRUNN, L. V., and DAUGHERTY, K. (1933) The action of ultraviolet light on amoeba protoplasm. *Protoplasma* 18, 596–619.

380. HEIN, G. (1953) Über *Euglena mutabilis* und ihr Verhalten zu sauren Medien. *Arch. Hydrobiol.* 47, 516–525.

381. HEITZMANN, C. (1873) Untersuchungen über das Protoplasma. I. Bau des Protoplasmas. *Sitzber. K. Akad. wiss. Math.-Naturwiss. Cl. III. Abt.* 67, 100–115.

382. HENNEGUY, L. F. (1897) Sur les rapports des cils vibratiles avec les centrosomes. *Arch. Anat. Microscop.* 1, 481–496.

383. HERTWIG, R. (1876) Über *Podophrya gemmipara* nebst Bemerkungen zum Bau und zur systematischen Stellung der Acineten. *Morphol. Jahr* 1, 20–82.

384. HILL, A. V. (1926) The laws of muscular motion. *Proc. Roy. Soc. London* B 100, 87–108.

385. HIRSHFIELD, H. I. (1959) Introduction. Nuclear control of cytoplasmic activities. *Ann. N.Y. Acad. Sci.* 78, 405–406; 647–654.

386. HIRSHFIELD, H. I., ZIMMERMANN, A. M., and MARSLAND, D. (1958) The nucleus in relation to plasmagel structure in *Amoeba proteus*; a pressure-temperature analysis. *J. Cell. Comp. Physiol.* 52, 269–274.

387. HÖBER, K. (1945) *Physical Chemistry of Cells and Tissues*. Blakiston, Philadelphia, 676 pp.

388. HODGE, A. J. (1949) Electron microscopic studies of spermatozoa II. The morphology of the human spermatozoon. *Austral. J. Sci. Res.* B 2, 368–378.

389. HOFFMANN-BERLING, H. (1953) Die Wasser-Glyzerin-extrahierte Zelle als Modell der Zellmotilität. *Biochim. Biophys. Acta* 10, 628–633.

390. HOFFMANN-BERLING, H. (1955) Geisselmodelle und Adenosintriphosphat (ATP). *Biochim. Biophys. Acta* 16, 146–154.

391. HOFFMANN-BERLING, H. (1958) Der Mechanismus eines neuen, von der Muskelkontraktion verschiedenen Kontraktionszyklus. *Biochim. Biophys. Acta* 27, 247–255.

392. HOFFMANN-BERLING, H. (1960) Other mechanisms producing movements. *In* FLORKIN, M. and MASON, H. S. (eds.), *Comparative Biochemistry*, Vol. II (2), pp. 341–370. Academic Press, New York.

393. HOFFMANN-BERLING, H. (1964) Relaxation of fibroblast cells. *In* ALLEN, R. D. and KAMIYA, N. (eds.), *Primitive Motile Systems in Cell Biology*, pp. 365–375. Academic Press, New York.

394. HÖFKER, J. (1928) Das neuromotorische Apparat der Protozoen. *Tijdschr. Nederlendsch.* 1, 34–38.

395. HOLTER, H. (1959a) Problems of pinocytosis with special reference to amoebae. *Ann. N.Y. Acad. Sci.* 78, 524–537.

396. HOLTER, H. (1959b) Pinocytosis. *Int. Rev. Cytol.* 8, 481–504.

397. HOLWECK, F., and LACASSAGNE, A. (1931a) Action de rayons α sur *Polytoma uvella*. Determination des "cibles" correspondent aux principles lésions observées. *Compt. Rend. Soc. Biol. Paris* 107, 812–814.

398. HOLWECK, F., and LACASSAGNE, (1931b) Essaie d'interprétation quantique des diverse lésions produites dans les cellules par les radiations. *Compt. Rend. Soc. Biol. Paris* 107, 814–817.

399. HOLWILL, M. E. J. (1964) High-speed cinephotography of certain of the *Trypanosomatidae*. *J. Protozool.* 11 (Suppl.), 40–41.

399a. HOLWILL, M. E. J. (1965) The motion of *Strigomonas oncopelti*. *J. Exptl. Biol.* **42**, 125–137.

400. HONIGBERG, B. M. (1955) Distribution of phosphatase in *Paramecium caudatum*. *J. Protozool.* **2** (Suppl.), 4.

400a. HONIGBERG, B. M., BALAMUTH, W., BOVEE, E. C., CORLISS, J. O., GOJDICS, M., HALL, R. P., KUDO, R. R., LEVINE, N. D., LOEBLICH, A. R., JR., WEISER, J., and WENRICH, D. H. (1964) A revised classification of the phylum Protozoa. *J. Protozool.* **11**, 7–20.

401. HOPKINS, D. L. (1926) The effect of hydrogen-ion concentration on locomotion and other life-processes in *Amoeba proteus*. *Proc. Natl. Acad. Sci.* **12**, 311–315.

402. HOPKINS, D. L. (1928) The effects of certain physical and chemical factors on locomotion and other life-processes in *Amoeba proteus*. *J. Morphol. Physiol.* **45**, 97–119.

403. HORTON, F. M. (1935) On the reaction of isolated parts of *Paramecium caudatum*. *J. Exptl. Biol.* **12**, 13–16.

404. HOSOI, T. (1937) Protoplasmic streaming in isolated pieces of *Paramecium*. *J. Fac. Sci. Imp. Univ. Tokyo, Zool.* **4**, 299–305.

405. HULL, R. W. (1954) Feeding processes in *Solenophrya micraster* Penard 1914. *J. Protozool.* **1**, 178–182.

406. HULL, R. W. (1961a) Studies on suctorian protozoa. The mechanism of prey adherence. *J. Protozool.* **8**, 343–350.

407. HULL, R. W. (1961b) Studies on suctorian protozoa: The mechanism of ingestion of prey cytoplasm. *J. Protozool.* **8**, 351–359.

408. HULL, R. W. (1962) Using the "Paramecium assay" to screen carcinogenic hydrocarbons. *J. Protozool.* **9** (Suppl.), 18.

409. HULPIEU, H. R. (1930) The effect of oxygen on *Amoeba proteus*. *J. Exptl. Zool.* **56**, 321–361.

410. HUNTER, N. W. (1951) Cytochemical demonstration of some enzymes of *Opalina carolinensis* Metcalf. *Proc. Am. Soc. Protozool.* **2**, 15.

411. HUNTER, N. W. (1959) Enzyme systems of *Stylonychia pustulata*. II. Miscellaneous systems (Hydrases, hydrolases and dehydrogenases). *J. Protozool.* **6**, 100–104.

412. HUXLEY, A. F., and NIEDERGERKE, R. (1954) Structural changes in muscle during contraction. *Nature* **173**, 971–973.

413. HUXLEY, H. E. and HANSON, J. (1954) Changes in the cross striations of muscle during contraction and stretch and their structural interpretation. *Nature*, **173**, 973–976.

414. HUXLEY, H. E. and HANSON, T. (1959) The structural basis of the contraction mechanism in striated muscle. *Ann. N.Y. Acad. Sci.* **81**, 403–408.

415. HYMAN, L. H. (1917) Metabolic gradients in *Amoeba* and their relation to the mechanism of amoeboid movement. *J. Exptl. Zool.* **24**, 55–99.

416. HYMAN, L. H. (1936) Observations on protozoa. I. The impermanence of the contractile vacuole in *Amoeba vespertilio*. II. Structure and mode of food ingestion by *Peranema. Quart. J. Microscop. Sci.* **79**, 43–56.

417. HYMAN, L. H. (1940) *The Invertebrates*: Protozoa through Ctenophora. McGraw-Hill, New York, 716 pp.

418. INOUÉ, S. (1959) Motility of cilia and the mechanism of mitosis. *In* ZIRKLE, R. E. (ed.), *Biophysical Science, A Study Program* II. *Rev. Mod. Physics* **31**, 402–408.

419. IVANIĆ, M. (1935) Zur Kenntnis der rhizopodialen Nahrungsaufnahme bei *Peranema trichophorum* Stein. *Zool. Anz.* **109**, 19–23.

420. IVANIĆ, M. (1936a) Sur l'ingestion des alimentes et la division nucléaire chez le *Trypanosoma equiperdum* Doflein. *La Cellule* **45**, 149–168.

421. IVANIĆ, M. (1936b) Die Nahrungsaufnahme mittels Reusenapparats bei Chilodon-Arten (*Chilodon cucullulus* Ehrbg. und *Chilodon uncinatus* Ehrbg.). *Zool. Anz.* **114**, 26–28.

422. Ivanić, M. (1936c) Recherches nouvelles sur l'ingestion des alimentes au moyen de cytostomes chez quelques amibes d'eau douce (*Amoeba vespertilio* Pénard et *Hartmannella maasi* Ivanić). *La Cellule* 45, 179–206.

423. Ivanov, I. I., and Umanskaya, M. V. (1945) Chemical transformations as the source of energy for the motility of *Trypanosoma equiperdum* (in Russian). *Compt. Rend. (Doklady) Acad. Sci. U.R.S.S. (N.S.)* 48, 337–338.

424. Iverson, R. M. (1962) Passage of material containing uracil-$^{14}$C between the nucleus and cytoplasm of *Amoeba proteus*. *Exptl. Cell. Res.* 27, 125–131.

425. Iwanami, Y. (1956) Protoplasmic movement in pollen grains and tubes. *Phytomorphology* 6, 288–295.

426. Jacobs, M. H. (1922) The effects of carbon dioxide on the consistency of protoplasm. *Biol. Bull.* 42, 14–30.

427. Jacobs, M. H. (1940) Some aspects of cell permeability to weak electrolytes. *Cold Spring Harbor Symp. Quant. Biol.* 8, 30–39.

428. Jacobsen, I. (1931) Fibrilläre Differenzierungen bei Ciliaten. *Arch. Protistenk.* 75, 31–100.

429. Jahn, T. L. (1934) Problems of population growth in the protozoa. *Cold Spring Harbor Symp. Quant. Biol.* 2, 167–180.

430. Jahn, T. L. (1936) Effect of aeration and lack of $CO_2$ on growth of bacteria-free cultures of protozoa. *Proc. Soc. Exptl. Biol. Med.* 33, 494–498.

431. Jahn, T. L. (1941) Respiratory metabolism. *In* Calkins, G. N. and Summers, F. M. (eds.), *Protozoa in Biological Research*, pp. 352–403. Columbia Univ. Press, New York.

432. Jahn, T. L. (1946) The euglenoid flagellates. *Quart. Rev. Biol.* 21, 246–274.

433. Jahn, T. L. (1947) Basic concepts in the interpretation of visual phenomena. *Proc. Iowa Acad. Sci.* 54, 325–343.

434. Jahn, T. L. (1961a) The mechanism of ciliary movement. I. Ciliary reversal and activation by electric current; the Ludloff phenomenon in terms of core and volume conductors. *J. Protozool.* 8, 369–380.

435. Jahn, T. L. (1961b) Man versus machine: A future problem in protozoan taxonomy. *Systematic Zoology*, 10, 179–192.

436. Jahn, T. L. (1962a) The mechanism of ciliary movement. II. Ion antagonism and ciliary reversal. *J. Cell. Comp. Physiol.* 60, 217–228.

437. Jahn, T. L. (1962b) A theory of electronic conduction through membranes and of active transport of ions, based on redox transmembrane potentials. *J. Theoret. Biol.* 2, 129–138.

438. Jahn, T. L. (1963a) The use of computers in systematics. *J. Parasitol.* 48, 656–663.

439. Jahn, T. L. (1963b) A possible mechanism for the amplifier effect in the retina. *Vision Res.* 3, 25–28.

440. Jahn, T. L. (1964a) Relative motion in *Amoeba proteus*. *In* Allen, R. D., and Kamiya, N. (eds.), *Primitive Motile Systems in Cell Biology*, pp. 279–302. Academic Press, New York.

441. Jahn, T. L. (1964b) Protoplasmic flow in the mycetozoan *Physarum* II. The mechanism of flow; a re-evaluation of the contraction-hydraulic theory and of the diffusion-drag hypothesis. *Biorheology* 2, 133–152.

442. Jahn, T. L., and Bovee, E. C. (1965) Mechanisms of movement in taxonomy of Sarcodina. I. As a basis for a new major dichotomy into two classes, *Autotractea* and *Hydraulea*. *Am. Midl. Nat.* 73, 30–40.

443. Jahn, T. L., and Bovee, E. C. (1964) Protoplasmic movements and locomotion of Protozoa. *In* Hutner, S. H. (ed.), *Physiology and Biochemistry of Protozoa*, III, pp. 61–129. Academic Press, New York.

444. Jahn, T. L., and Bovee, E. C. (1965) Locomotion of Microorganisms. *Ann. Rev. Microbiol.* 19, 21–58.

445. Jahn, T. L., and Brown, M. (1961) The mechanism of pattern formation in ciliate cultures. *Am. Zool.* 1, 454.

446. JAHN, T. L., and JAHN, F. F. (1949) *How to Know the Protozoa.* Brown, Dubuque, Iowa, 234 pp.
447. JAHN, T. L., and KOZLOFF, E. (unpublished).
448. JAHN, T. L., and LANDMAN, M. D. (1965) Locomotion of spirochaetes. *Trans. Am. Microscop. Soc.* **84**, 395–406.
449. JAHN, T. L., and McKIBBEN, W. R. (1937) A colorless euglenoid flagellate, *Khawkinea halli* n. gen. n. sp. *Trans. Am. Microscop. Soc.* **56**, 48–54.
450. JAHN, T. L., and RINALDI, R. A. (1959) Protoplasmic movement in the foraminiferan *Allogromia laticollaris*; and theory of its mechanism. *Biol. Bull.* **117**, 100–118.
451. JAHN, T. L., and RINALDI, R. A. (1963) Tracks of granules during ameboid movement (*Amoeba proteus.*) *Absts. 7th Ann. Meet. Biophys. Soc.* New York 1963, MD1.
452. JAHN, T. L., and WULFF, V. J. (1950) Photoreception. *In* PROSSER, C. L. (ed.), *Comparative Animal Physiology*, pp. 381–446. Saunders, Philadelphia.
453. JAHN, T. L., BOVEE, E. C., and SMALL, E. B. (1960) Mechanisms of movement: The basis for a new major dichotomy of the Sarcodina. *J. Protozool.* **7** (Suppl.), 8.
454. JAHN, T. L., BROWN, M., and WINET, H. (1961a) Secretory activity of oral groove of *Paramecium. J. Protozool.* **8** (Suppl.), 18.
455. JAHN, T. L., BROWN, M., and WINET, H. (1961b) Pattern formation in cultures of *Tetrahymena. Am. Zool.* **1**, 454.
456. JAHN, T. L., BROWN, M., and WINET, H. (1962) The mechanism of pattern formation in ciliate cultures. *Excerpta Medica* Ser. **48**, 638.
457. JAHN, T. L., FONSECA, J. R., and LANDMAN, M. (1963) Mechanisms of locomotion of flagellates. III. *Peranema, Petalomonas* and *Entosiphon. J. Protozool.* **10** (Suppl.), 11.
458. JAHN, T. L., FONSECA, J. R., and LANDMAN, M. D. (1964) The mechanism of locomotion in flagellates. II. Function of the mastigonemes of *Ochromonas. J. Protozool.* **11**, 291–296.
459. JAHN, T. L., HARMON, W. M., and LANDMAN, M. D. (1963) Locomotion of flagellates. I. *Ceratium. J. Protozool.* **10**, 358–363.
460. JAHN, T. L., LANDMAN, M., and FONSECA, J. (1963) Hydrodynamic function of mastigonemes of a marine chrysomonad. *Proc. XVI Intern. Congr. Zool.* Washington, D.C., **2**, 292.
461. JAHN, T. L., RINALDI, R. A., and BROWN, M. (1964) Protoplasmic flow in the mycetozoan, *Physarum* — I. Geometry of the plasmodium and the observable facts of flow. *Biorheology* **2**, 123–131.
462. JAHN, T. L., WIGG, D., and RINALDI, R. A. (1964) The water expulsion of *Amoeba proteus. J. Protozool.* **11** (Suppl.), 32.
463. JAHN, T. L., WILSON, D. E., and FONSECA, J. R. (1964) Locomotion and flagellar ultrastructure of a choanoflagellate. *J. Protozool.* **11** (Suppl.), 32.
464. JAHN, T. L., BOVEE, E. C., FONSECA, J. R., and LANDMAN, M. (1964a) Mechanisms of locomotion of flagellates. V. *Trypanosoma lewisi* and *Trypanosoma cruzi. J. Protozool.* **11** (Suppl.), 31.
465. JAHN, T. L., BOVEE, E. C., FONSECA, J. R., and LANDMAN, M. (1964b) Flagellar Movements: (1) Trypanosomes. (2) Trichomonads. *J. Parasitol.* **50** (Suppl.), 42.
466. JAHN, T. L., BOVEE, E. C., FONSECA, J. R., and LANDMAN, M. (1964c) Mechanisms of flagellate locomotion. *Symp. Fine Structure and Cytochemistry. Xth Intern. Botan. Congr., Edinburgh*, 1964, 218–219.
467. JAHN, T. L., BOVEE, E. C., DAUBER, M., WINET, H., and BROWN, M. Secretory activity of the oral apparatus of ciliates: Trails of adherent particles left by *Paramecium caudatum* and *Tetrahymena pyriformis. In* JAKOWSKA, S. (ed.), *Mucus Secretion in Invertebrates.* Pergamon Press, New York (in press).
468. JAKUS, M. S., and HALL, C. E. (1946) Electron microscope observations of the trichocysts and cilia of *Paramecium. Biol. Bull.* **91**, 141–144.

469. JAMES, T. W. (1959) Synchronization of cell division in amoebae. *Ann. N.Y. Acad. Sci.* **78**, 501–514.
470. JAROSCH, R. (1957) Zur Mechanik der Protoplasmafibrillenbewegung. *Biochim. Biophys. Acta* **25**, 204–205.
471. JAROSCH, R. (1958) Zur Gleitbewegung der niederen Organismen. *Protoplasma* **50**, 277–289.
472. JAROSCH, R. (1962) Gliding. In LEWIN, R. A. (ed.), *Physiology and Biochemistry of Algae*, pp. 573–582. Academic Press, New York.
473. JAROSCH, R. (1963) Grundlagen einer Schrauben-Mechanik des Protoplasmas. *Protoplasma* **57**, 448–500.
474. JAROSCH, R. (1964a) Screw-mechanical basis of protoplasmic movement. In ALLEN, R. D., and N. KAMIYA (eds.), *Primitive Motile Systems in Cell Biology*, pp. 599–622. Academic Press, New York.
475. JAROSCH, R. (1964b) Zur Mechanik schnell rotierender elastischer Schrauben. *Biorheology* **2**, 37–53.
476. JENNINGS, H. S. (1899) Studies on reactions to stimuli in unicellular organisms. IV. Laws of chemotaxis in *Paramecium*. *Am. J. Physiol.* **2**, 355–379.
477. JENNINGS, H. S. (1904) *Contributions to the Study of the Behavior of Lower Organisms*. Carnegie Inst., Washington, D.C., 252 pp.
478. JENNINGS, H. S. (1905) The basis for taxis and certain other terms in the behavior of Infusoria. *J. Comp. Neurol.* **15**, 138–143.
479. JENNINGS, H. S. (1931) *Behavior of the Lower Organisms*. Columbia Univ. Press, New York, 366 pp.
480. JENNINGS, H. S., and JAMIESON, C. (1902) Studies on reactions to stimuli in unicellular organisms. X. The movements and reactions of pieces of ciliate infusoria. *Biol. Bull.* **3**, 225–234.
481. JENSEN, D. D. (1959) A theory of the behavior of *Paramecium aurelia* and behavioral effects of feeding, fission, and ultraviolet microbeam irradiation. *Behaviour* **15**, 82–122.
482. JEON, K. W., and BELL, L. G. E. (1964) Behaviour of cell membrane in relation to locomotion in *Amoeba proteus*. *Exptl. Cell. Res.* **33**, 531–539.
483. JEPPS, M. W. (1942) Studies on *Polystomella* Lamarck (Foraminifera). *J. Mar. Biol. Assoc.* **25**, 607–666.
484. JEPPS, M. W. (1956) *The Protozoa. Sarcodina*. Oliver and Boyd, Edinburgh, 183 pp.
485. JETTMAR, H. M. (1953) Zum Bewegungsmodus der Toxoplasmen. *Arch. Hyg. Bakt.* **137**, 477–486.
486. JOHNSON, W. H., and EVANS, F. E. (1941) Dedifferentiation and redifferentiation of cilia in cysts of *Woodruffia metabolica*. *Trans. Am. Microscop. Soc.* **60**, 7–16.
487. JONES, A. R., and JAHN, T. L. (1964) The effect of hexamethonium chloride in ciliary and myonemal systems of *Spirostomum*. *J. Protozool.* **11** (Suppl.), 32.
488. JONES, A. R., JAHN, T. L., and FONSECA, J. R. C. (1965) Cinematographic analysis of the anodally stimulated contraction of *Spirostomum ambiguum*. *Excerpta Med.*, **91**, 245–246.
489. JONES, P. F., and BAKER, H. G. (1946), Formation of aggregations of *Glaucoma pyriformis* Kahl by means of phenathraquinone and other substances. *Nature* **157**, 554.
490. JONES, R. F., and LEWIN, R. A. (1959) The chemical nature of the flagella of *Chlamydomonas moewusii*. *Exptl. Cell Res.* **19**, 408–410.
491. JOYON, L., and CHARRET, R. (1962) Sur l'ultrastructure du Thecamebien *Hyalosphenia papilio* (Leidy). *Compt. Rend. Acad. Sci.* **255**, 2661–2663.
492. JUDGE, D. M., and ANDERSON, M. S. (1964) Ultrastructure of *Trypanosoma lewisi*. *J. Parasitol.* **50**, 757–762.
493. KAHL, A. (1933) Anmerkungen zu der Arbeit von Bruno Pestel: Beiträge zur Morphologie und Biologie des *Dendrocometes paradoxus* Stein. *Arch. Protistenk.* **80**, 64–71.

494. KAHN, A. J. (1964) The influence of light on cell aggregation in *Polysphondylium pallidum. Biol. Bull.* **127**, 85–97.
495. KAMADA, T. (1928) The time-intensity factors in the electro-destruction of the membrane of *Paramecium. J. Fac. Sci. Imp. Univ. Tokyo, sec. 4*, **2**, 41–49.
496. KAMADA, T. (1931) Polar effect of electric current on the ciliary movements of *Paramecium*. Reversal of the electric polar effect in *Paramecium* according to the change of current strength. *J. Fac. Sci. Imp. Univ. Tokyo* **2**, 285–307.
497. KAMADA, T. (1940) Ciliary reversal of *Paramecium. Proc. Imp. Acad. Tokyo* **16**, 241–247.
498. KAMADA, T., and KINOSITA, H. (1940) Calcium-potassium factor in ciliary reversal of *Paramecium. Proc. Imp. Acad. Tokyo* **16**, 125–130.
499. KAMADA, T., and KINOSITA, H. (1945) Protoplasmic contraction of *Paramecium. Proc. Jap. Acad. Sci.* **31**, 349–58.
500. KAMIYA, N. (1939) Die Rhythmik des metabolischen Formwechsels der Euglenen. *Ber. Dtsch. Bot. Gesel.* **57**, 231–240.
501. KAMIYA, N. (1953) The motive force responsible for protoplasmic streaming in the myxomycete plasmodium. *Ann. Repts. Sci. Works Osaka Univ.* **1**, 53–83.
502. KAMIYA, N. (1959) Protoplasmic streaming. *Protoplasmatologia* **8** (3a), 1–199.
503. KAMIYA, N. (1964) The motive force of ameboid motion. *In* ALLEN, R. D. and KAMIYA, N. (eds.), *Primitive Motile Systems in Cell Biology*, pp. 257–276. Academic Press, New York.
504. KAMIYA, T. (1960) Acid soluble phosphate compounds of the ciliate protozoon *Tetrahymena geleii* W. *J. Biochem. Tokyo* **47**, 69–76.
505. KAMIYA, N., and KURODA, K. (1958) Studies on the velocity distribution of the protoplasmic streaming in the myxomycete plasmodium. *Protoplasma* **49**, 1–4.
506. KAMIYA, N., NAKAJIMA, H., and ABÉ, S. (1957) Simultaneous measurement of respiration and the motive force of protoplasmic streaming in the myxomycete plasmodium. II. The effect of cyanide. *Proc. Japan. Acad. Sci.* **33**, 407–419.
507. KANNO, F. (1964a) An analysis of ameboid movement. I. The velocity of endoplasmic streaming of *Amoeba* in a glass capillary under the effect of various pressure gradients. *Annot. Zool. Jap.* **37**, 1–11.
508. KANNO, F. (1964b) An analysis of ameboid movement. II. Mechanical properties of surface structures of *Amoeba. Annot. Zool. Jap.* **37**, 12–19.
509. KANNO, F. (1964c) An analysis of ameboid movement. III. Ionic effect on the mechanical properties of surface structure of *Amoeba. Annot. Zool. Jap.* **37**, 63–73.
509a. KANNO, F. (1965) *Ibid.* IV. Cinematographic analysis of movement of granules with special reference to the theory of amoeboid movement. *Annot. Zool. Jap.* **38**, 45–63.
510. KAPLAN, H. S., and MOSES, L. E. (1964) Biological complexity and radiosensitivity. *Science* **145**, 21–25.
511. KÄPPNER, W. (1961) Bewegungsphysiologische Untersuchungen an der Amoebe *Chaos chaos* L. I. Die Einflüsse des pH der Medien auf das bewegungsphysiologische Verhalten von *Chaos chaos* L. II. Die Wirkung von Salygren, cystein an ATP. *Protoplasma* **53**, 81–105; 504–529.
512. KASSEL, K., and KOPAC, M. J. (1953) Experimental approaches to the evaluation of fractionation media I. The action of ions on the protoplasm of *Amoeba proteus* and *Pelomyxa carolinensis. J. Exptl. Zool.* **124**, 279–301.
513. KATOH, A. K. (1960) Localization of sulfhydryl compounds in *Tetrahymena. J. Protozool.* **7** (Suppl.), 21.
514. KATZ, A. N. (1962) The influence of cations on the SH reactivity of actin. *Proc. 2nd Meet. Soc. Cell. Biol.* San Francisco, 1962, 89.
515. KATZ, M. S., and DETERLINE, W. A. (1958) Apparent learning in the *Paramecium. J. Comp. Physiol. Psychol.* **51**, 243–247.

516. KAVANAU, J. L. (1962a) Countercurrent streaming in liquid surfaces and its relevance to protoplasmic movement. *Science* **136**, 652–653.

517. KAVANAU, J. L. (1962b) On the genesis of cytoplasmic streaming. *Life Sci.*, 1962, 177–183.

518. KAVANAU, J. L. (1962c) Twilight transitions and biological rhythmicity. *Nature* **194**, 1293–1295.

519. KAVANAU, J. L. (1963a) A new theory of amoeboid locomotion. *J. Theoret. Biol.* **4**, 124–141.

520. KAVANAU, J. L. (1963b) Protoplasmic streaming as a process of jet propulsion. *Developm. Biol.* **7**, 22–37.

520a. KAVANAU, J. L. (1964; 1965) *Structure and Function of Biological Membranes*, *Vols. I and II.* Holden-Day, San Francisco. 321 pp., and 760 pp.

521. KENNEDY, J. R., JR. (1963) The fine structure of the fibrillar system of *Blepharisma undulans*. *J. Protozool.* **10** (Suppl.), 23.

522. KIMBALL, R. F. (1957) Nongenetic effects of radiation on microorganisms. *Ann. Rev. Microbiol.* **11**, 199–220.

523. KIMBALL, R. F. (1958) Experiments with *Stentor coeruleus* on the nature of the radiation-induced delay in fission in the ciliates. *J. Protozool.* **5**, 151–155.

524. KIMBALL, R. F., and GAITHER, N. (1951) The influence of light upon the action of ultraviolet on *Paramecium aurelia*. *J. Cell. Comp. Physiol.* **37**, 211–231.

525. KINATOWSKI, W. (1963a) Die Einflüsse der mechanischen Reize auf die Kontraktilität von *Spirostomum ambiguum* Ehrbg. *Acta Protozool.* **1**, 201–222.

526. KINASTOWSKI, W. (1963b) Das Problem "des Lernens" bei *Spirostomum ambiguum* Ehrbg. *Acta Protozool.* **1**, 223–236.

527. KINOSITA, H. (1936) Electric excitation and electric polarization in *Paramecium*. *J. Fac. Sci. Imp. Univ. Tokyo* **4**, 155–161.

528. KINOSITA, H. (1954) Electrical potentials and ciliary response in *Opalina*. *J. Fac. Sci. Imp. Univ. Tokyo* **7**, 1–14.

529. KING, R. L., and BEAMS, H. W. (1941) Some effects of mechanical agitation on *Paramecium caudatum*. *J. Morphol.*, **68**, 149–159.

530. KITCHING, J. A. (1939a) The physiology of contractile vacuoles. IV. A note on the sources of water evacuated and on the function of contractile vacuoles. *J. Exptl. Biol.* **16**, 34–37.

531. KITCHING, J. A. (1939b) On the activity of protozoa at low oxygen tensions. *J. Cell. Comp. Physiol.* **14**, 219–236.

532. KITCHING, J. A. (1952) The physiology of contractile vacuoles. VIII. Observations on the mechanism of feeding in the suctorian *Podophrya*. The water relations of the suctorian during feeding. *J. Exptl. Biol.* **29**, 255–266; 363–371.

533. KITCHING, J. A. (1954) Effects of high hydrostatic pressure on *Actinophrys sol* (Heliozoa). *J. Exptl. Biol.* **34**, 511–517.

534. KITCHING, J. A. (1956a) Effects of high hydrostatic pressure on a feeding suctorian. *Protoplasma* **46**, 475–480.

535. KITCHING, J. A. (1956b) Contractile vacuoles of protozoa. Food vacuoles of protozoa. *Protoplasmatologia* **III D(3a)**, 1–45; **III D(3b)**, 1–54.

536. KITCHING, J. A. (1957a) On suction in suctoria. *Colston Papers* **VII**, 197–203.

537. KITCHING, J. A. (1957c) Effects of high hydrostatic pressure on the activity of flagellates and ciliates. *J. Exptl. Biol.* **34**, 494–510.

538. KITCHING, J. A. (1964) The axopods of the sun animalcule, *Actinophrys sol* (Heliozoa). *In* ALLEN, R. D. and KAMIYA, N. (eds.), *Primitive Motile Systems in Cell Biology*, pp. 445–456. Academic Press, New York.

539. KITCHING, J. A., and PEARSE, D. C. (1939) The liquefaction of the tentacles of suctorian protozoa at high hydrostatic pressures. *J. Cell. Comp. Physiol.* **14**, 410–412.

540. KITCHING, J. A., and PIRENNE, M. H. (1940) The influence of low tensions of oxygen on the protoplasmic streaming of myxomycetes. *J. Cell. Comp. Physiol.* **16**, 131–133.

541. KLEBS, G. (1881–83) Über die Organisation einiger Flagellatengruppen und ihre Beziehungen zu Algen und Infusioren. *Unters. Bot. Inst. Tübingen* **1**, 1–13.

542. KLEIN, B. M. (1942) Reaktionen des neuroformativ Systems bei bedeutenden Infusioren im Leibesinneren eines Raub-Infusors. *Ann. naturh. Mus. Wien* **52**, 54–65.

543. KLEIN, B. M. (1958) Das neurofomativ System als nervliche Urstufe in der Haut Einzelliger. *Acta Neurovegetat.* **18**, 344–351.

544. KNIGHT-JONES, E. W. (1954) Relations between metachronism and the direction of ciliary beat in metazoa. *Quart. J. Microscop. Sci.* **95**, 503–521.

545. KOCH, M. (1902) Über Sarcosporidien. *Verh. Intern. Zool. Kongr. V, Berlin*, 1902, **5**, 674–684.

546. KOEHLER, O. (1930) Über die Geotaxis von *Paramecium*. II. *Arch. Protistenk.* **70**, 279–307.

547. KOENUMA, A. (1964) The velocity distribution of the cyclosis in *Paramecium caudatum*. *Annot. Zool. Jap.* **36**, 66–71.

548. KOEVENIG, J. L. Three educational films on myxomycetes with a study of the life cycle of *Physarum gyrosum* Rost. Ph.D. thesis, Univ. Iowa (unpublished), 225 pp.

548a. KOGAN, A. B., and TIKHONOVA, N. A. (1965) The effect of constant magnetic fields on paramecium movement. *Biofizika* **10**, 292–296.

549. KOLTZOFF, N. K. (1911) Studien über die Gestalt der Zelle. III. Untersuchungen über die Kontraktilität des Vorticellinenstiels. *Arch. Zellforsch.* **7**, 344–423.

550. KONIJN, T. M., and RAPER, K. B. (1961) Cell aggregation in *Dictyostelium discoideum*. *Developm. Biol.* **3**, 725–756.

551. KONIJN, T. M., and RAPER, K. B. (1962) Influence of light on cell aggregation in the *Dictyosteliaceae*. *Am. J. Bot.* **49**, 667.

552. KORMOS, J. (1938) Bau und Funktion der Saugröhrchen der Suctorien. *Allat. Kozlem.* **35**, 150–153.

553. KOSHTOYANTS, K. S., and KOKINA, N. N. (1957) On the role of acetylcholine and cholinesterase systems in galvanotaxis and summation of stimuli in *Paramecium* (in Russian). *Biofizika* **2**, 46–50.

554. KOSTIR, W. C. (1952) Factors which induce motility or passivity in *Euglena*. *Proc. Soc. Protozool.* **3**, 5.

555. KOTYK, A. (1962) Uptake of 2-4-dinitrophenol by the yeast cell. *Folia Microbiol.* **7**, 109–114.

556. KRIJGSMAN, B. J. (1925) Beiträge zum Problem der Gießelbewegung. *Arch. Protistenk.* **52**, 478–488.

557. KRISZAT, G. (1949) Die Wirkung von Adenosintriphosphat auf Amöben (*Chaos chaos*). *Ark. Zool. Ser.* 2, **1**, 81–86.

558. KRISZAT, G. (1954) Die Wirkung von Para-Chlor Mercurobenzoesäure und ATP auf Amöben (*C. chaos*). *Ark. Zool. Ser.* 2, **6**, 195–201.

559. KUDO, R. R. (1946) *Pelomyxa carolinensis* Wilson. I. General observation on the Illinois stock. *J. Morphol.* **78**, 317–351.

560. KUDO, R. R. (1954) *Protozoology*, 4th Ed. Thomas, Springfield, Illinois. 966 pp.

561. KUDO, R. R. (1957) *Pelomyxa palustris* Greeff. I. Cultivation and general observations. *J .Protozool.* **4**, 154–164.

561a. KÜHNE, W. (1864) Untersuchungen über das Protoplasma und die Contractilität, Leipzig, 158 pp.

562. KÜHNE, W. (1898) Über die Bedeutung von Sauerstoff für die vitale Bewegung. Zweite Mitteilung. *Zeit. Biol.* **36**, 425–522.

563. KÜMMEL, G. (1958) Die Gleitbewegung der Gregarinen. Elektronenmikroskopische und experimentelle Untersuchungen. *Arch. Protistenk.* **102**, 501–522.

564. KUZNICKI, L. (1963) Recovery in *Paramecium caudatum* immobilized by chloral hydrate treatment. *Acta Protozool.* **1**, 177–185.

565. LACKEY, J. B. (1925) The fauna of Imhoff tanks. *Bull. New Jersey Agr. Exp. Stat.* **417**, 1–39.

566. LACKEY, J. B. (1929) Studies in the life histories of Euglenida, II. The life cycles of *Entosiphon sulcatum* and *Peranema trichophorum. Arch. Protistenk.* **67**, 128–156.

567. LACKEY, J. B. (1938) A study of some ecologic factors affecting the distribution of protozoa. *Ecol. Mongr.* **8**, 501–527.

568. LACKEY, J. B. (1959) Morphology and biology of a species of *Protospongia. Trans. Am. Microscop. Soc.* **78**, 202–206.

569. LANDAU, J. V. (1959) Sol-gel transformations in amoebae. *Ann. N.Y. Acad. Sci.* **78**, 487–500.

570. LANDAU, J. V. (1965) High hydrostatic pressure effects on *Amoeba proteus. J. Cell. Biol.* **24**, 332–336.

571. LANDAU, J. V., ZIMMERMAN, A. M., and MARSLAND, D. A. (1954) Temperature pressure experiments on *Amoeba proteus*; plasmagel structure in relation to form and movement. *J. Cell. Comp. Physiol.* **44**, 211–232.

572. LANG, N. J. (1963) Additional ultrastructural components of flagella. *J. Protozool.* **10** (Suppl.), 23–24.

573. LATIMER, P. (1958) Apparent shifts of absorption bands of cell suspensions and selective light scattering. *Science* **127**, 29–30.

574. LATIMER, P. (1959) Erroneous absorption spectra of live cells caused by anomalous light scattering. *Proc. 1st. Natl. Biophys. Conf.* Columbus, 51–58.

575. LEE, J. J. (personal communication).

576. LEE, J. W. (1954a) The effect of pH on forward swimming in *Euglena* and *Chilomonas. Physiol. Zool.* **27**, 272–275.

577. LEE, J. W. (1954b) The effect of temperature on forward swimming in *Euglena* and *Chilomonas. Physiol. Zool.* **27**, 275–280.

578. LEE, J. W. (1956) The effect of pH on the velocity of ciliary movement in *Paramecium J. Protozool.* **3** (Suppl.), 9.

579. LEEDALE, G. F. (1959a) Periodicity of mitosis and cell division in the *Euglenineae. Biol. Bull.* **116**, 162–174.

580. LEEDALE, G. F. (1959b) Formation of anucleate cells of *Euglena gracilis* by miscleavage. *J. Protozool.* **6** (Suppl.), 26.

581. LEEDALE, G. F. (1964) Pellicle structure in *Euglena. British Phycol. Bull.* **2**, 291–306.

582. LEEDALE, G. F., MEEUSE, B. J. D., and PRINGSHEIM, E. G. (1965) Structure and physiology of *Euglena spirogyra.* I and II. *Arch. Mikrobiol.* **50**, 68–102.

583. LEHMANN, F. E. (1950) Globular Partikele als submikroskopische Elemente des tierischen Zytoplasmas. *Experentia* **6**, 382–384.

584. LEIDY, J. (1879) Freshwater rhizopods of North America. *U.S. Geol. Surv. Territories* **12**, 1–324.

585. LEPOW, S. S. (1938) Some reactions of slime mold protoplasm to certain alkaloids and snake venoms. *Protoplasma* **31**, 161–179.

586. LEPȘI, J. (1926) Zellphysiologische Experimente mit Ciliaten. *Mikrokosmos* **20**, 54–56.

587. LEVINE, L. (1956) Contractility of glycerinated Vorticellae. *Biol. Bull.* **111**, 319.

588. LEVINE, L. (1959) ATPase of vorticellan contractile apparatus. *J. Protozool.* **6**, (Suppl.), 16.

589. LEVINE, L. (1960) Visualization of sulfhydryl groups in *Vorticella convallaria. Anat. Rec.* **138**, 364–365.

590. LEWIN, R. A. (1952) Studies on the flagella of algae. I. General observations on *Chlamydomonas moewusii* Gerloff. *Biol. Bull.* **103**, 74–79.

591. LEWIS, W. H. (1931) Pinocytosis. *Bull. Johns Hopkins Hospital* **49**, 17–27.

592. Lewis, W. H. (1942) The relation of viscosity changes of protoplasm to ameboid locomotion and cell division. *In* Seifriz, W. (ed.), *The Structure of Protoplasm*, pp. 163–197. Iowa State College Press, Ames, Iowa.

593. Lindeman, R. L. (1942) Experimental simulation of winter anaerobiosis in a senescent lake. *Ecology* **23**, 1–13.

594. Ling, G. N. (1962) *A Physical Theory of the Living State: The Association Induction Hypothesis.* Blaisdell, New York, 680 pp.

595. Locquin, M. (1949) L'utilization de rayonnement $\beta$ du radium pour l'étude des courants protoplasmiques dans les plasmodes de myxomycètes. *Trav. Bot. (Algiers).* **2**, 209–214.

596. Loeb, J. (1924) *Die Eiweißkörper und die Theorie der kolloidalen Erscheinungen.* Springer, Berlin, 306 pp.

597. Loefer, J. B. (1935) Relation of hydrogen ion concentration to growth of *Chilomonas* and *Chlorogonium. Arch. Protistenk.* **85**, 209–223.

598. Loefer, J. B. (1935) Effect of certain carbohydrates and organic acids on growth of *Chlorogonium* and *Chilomonas. Arch. Protistenk.* **84**, 456–471.

599. Loefer, J. B., and Mefferd, R. B., Jr. (1952) Concerning pattern formation by free-swimming organisms. *Am. Nat.* **86**, 325–329.

600. Loewy, A. C. (1949) A theory of protoplasmic streaming. *Proc. Am. Phil. Soc.* **93**, 326–329.

601. Loewy, A. C. (1950) Protoplasmic streaming under anaerobic conditions in a myxomycete. *J. Cell. Comp. Physiol.* **35**, 151–153.

602. Loewy, A. C. (1952) An actomyosin-like substance from the plasmodium of a myxomycete. *J. Cell. Comp. Physiol.* **40**, 127–156.

603. Losina-Losinskiy, L. K. (1931) Zur Ernährungsphysiologie der Infusioren: Untersuchungen über die Nahrungsauswahl und Vermehrung bei *Paramecium caudatum. Arch. Protistenk.* **74**, 18–120.

604. Lowndes, A. G. (1941) On flagellar movement in unicellular organisms. *Proc. Roy. Soc. London* **A 111**, 111–134.

605. Lowndes, A. G. (1943) The swimming of unicellular flagellate organisms. *Proc. Zool. Soc. London* **A 113**, 99–107.

606. Lowndes, A. G. (1944) The swimming of *Monas stigmatica* Pringsheim and *Peranema trichophorum* (Ehrbg.) Stein and *Volvox* sp. Additional experiments on the working of a flagellum. *Proc. Roy. Zool. Soc. London* **A 114**, 325–338.

607. Lowndes, A. G. (1947) Recent work on flagellar movement. *Science Progress* **35**, 61–68.

608. Luce, R. H. (1926) Orientation to the electric current and to light in *Amoeba. Anat. Rec.* **32**, 55.

609. Ludloff, K. (1895) Untersuchungen über den Galvanotropismus. *Pflüger's Arch. Ges. Physiol.* **59**, 525–554.

610. Ludvik, J. (1960) The electron microscopy of *Sarcocystis miescheriana* Kuhn 1865. *J. Protozool.* **7**, 128–135.

611. Ludwig, W. (1930) Zur Theorie der Flimmerbewegung (Dynamik, Nutzeffekt, Energiebilanz). *Zeit. vergl. Physiol.* **13**, 397–504.

612. Lund, E. E. (1933) A correlation of the silverline and neuromotor systems of *Paramecium. Univ. Calif. Publ. Zool.* **39**, 35–75.

613. Lund, E. E. (1941) The feeding mechanisms of various ciliated protozoa. *J. Morphol.* **69**, 563–573.

614. Lund, E. J., and Logan, G. A. (1925) The relation of the stability of protoplasmic films in *Noctiluca* to the duration and intensity of an applied electric potential. *J. Gen. Physiol.* **7**, 461–471.

615. Machin, K. E. (1958) Wave propagation along flagella. *J. Exptl. Biol.* **35**, 796–806.

616. Machin, K. E. (1963) The control and synchronization of flagellar movement. *Proc. Roy. Soc. London* **B 158**, 88–104.

617. MacKinlay, R. B. (1936) Observations on *Nebela collaris* Leidy (*pro parte*) a testate amoeba of moorland waters. Part I. *J. Roy. Microscop. Soc.* **56**, 307–325.
618. Mandeville, S. E., Crespi, H. L., and Katz, J. J. (1964) Fully deuterated *Euglena gracilis*. *Science* **146**, 769–770.
619. Manton, I. (1952) The fine structure of plant cilia. *Symp. Soc. Exptl. Biol.* **6**, 306–319.
620. Manwell, R. D., and Drobeck, H. P. (1953) The behavior of *Toxoplasma* with notes on its taxonomic status. *J. Parasitol.* **39**, 577–584.
621. Mark, M. F., Imparato, A. M., Hutner, S. H., and Baker, H. (1963) Estimate of toxicity of radio-opaque agents by means of a ciliate. *Angiology* **14**, 383–389.
622. Marsh, G., and Jahn, T. L. (1964) The non-existence of the short-circuited state of bioelectric systems and the incompetence of the short-circuiting theory. *Absts. 8th Ann. Meet. Biophys. Soc.* Chicago 1964, FG 12.
623. Marshall, J. M., Jr. (1964) Intracellular transport in the amoeba *Chaos chaos*. *Excerpta Med.* **77**, 30.
624. Marshall, J. M. Jr., Schumaker, V. N., and Brandt, P. W. (1959) Pinocytosis in amoebae. *Ann. N.Y. Acad. Sci.* **78**, 515–523.
625. Marshall, J. M., Jr., and Nachmias, V. T. (1960) Protein uptake by pinocytosis in amoebae. *Science* **132**, 1496.
626. Marsland, D. A. (1964) Pressure-temperature studies on ameboid movement and related phenomena. An analysis of the effects of heavy water ($D_2O$) on the form, movement and gel structure of *Amoeba proteus*. In Allen, R. D., and Kamiya, N. (eds.), *Primitive Motile Systems in Cell Biology*, pp. 173–188. Academic Press, New York.
627. Marsland, D. A., and Brown, D. E. S. (1936) Amoeboid movement at high hydrostatic pressure. *J. Cell. Comp. Physiol.* **8**, 167–178.
628. Mast, S. O. (1907) Light reactions in lower organisms. II. *Volvox globator*. *J. Comp. Neurol.* **17**, 99–180.
629. Mast, S. O. (1909) The reactions of *Didinium nasutum* Stein with special reference to the feeding habits and the function of trichocysts. *Biol. Bull.* **16**, 91–118.
630. Mast, S. O. (1910) Reactions in *Amoeba* to light. *J. Exptl. Zool.* **9**, 265–277.
631. Mast, S. O. (1911a) *Light and the Behavior of Lower Organisms*. Wiley, New York, 410 pp.
632. Mast, S. O. (1911b) Habits and reactions of the ciliate *Lacrymaria*. *J. Anim. Behavior* **1**, 229–243.
633. Mast, S. O. (1926) Structure, movement, locomotion and stimulation in *Amoeba*. *J. Morphol.* **41**, 347–425.
634. Mast, S. O. (1928) Factors involved in changes in form of *Amoeba*. *J. Exptl. Zool.* **51**, 97–120.
635. Mast, S. O. (1931a) The nature of the action of electricity in producing response and injury in *Amoeba proteus* (Leidy) and the effect of electricity on the viscosity of protoplasm. *Zeit. vergl. Physiol.* **15**, 309–238.
636. Mast, S. O. (1931b) The nature of response to light in *Amoeba proteus* (Leidy). *Zeit. vergl. Physiol.* **15**, 139–147.
637. Mast, S. O. (1932) Localized stimulation, transmission of impulses and the nature of response in *Amoeba*. *Physiol. Zool.* **5**, 1–15.
638. Mast, S. O. (1941) Motor responses in unicellular animals. In Calkins, G. N., and Summers, F. M. (eds.), *Protozoa in Biological Research*, pp. 271–351. Columbia Univ. Press, New York.
639. Mast, S. O. (1947) The food-vacuole in *Paramecium*. *Biol. Bull.* **92**, 31–72.
640. Mast, S. O., and Doyle, W. L. (1934) Ingestion of fluid by *Amoeba*. *Protoplasma* **20**, 555–560.
641. Mast, S. O., and Nadler, J. E. (1926) Reversal of ciliary action in *Paramecium caudatum*. *J. Morphol.* **43**, 105–117.

642. MAST, S. O., and PROSSER, C. L. (1932) Effect of temperature, salts and hydrogen-ion on rupture of the plasmagel sheet, rate of locomotion and gel-sol ratio in *Amoeba proteus*. *J. Cell. Comp. Physiol.* **1**, 333–354.

643. MAST, S. O., and ROOT, F. M. (1916a) Observations on *Ameba* feeding on infusoria, and their bearing on the surface tension theory. *Proc. Natl. Acad. Sci.* **2**, 188–189.

644. MAST, S. O., and ROOT, F. M. (1916b) Observations on *Amoeba* feeding on rotifers, nematodes and ciliates, and their bearing on the surface-tension theory. *J. Exptl. Zool.* **21**, 33–49.

645. MAST, S. O., and STAHLER, N. (1937) The relation between luminous intensity, adaptation to light, and rate of locomotion in *Amoeba proteus* (Leidy). *Biol. Bull.* **73**, 126–133.

646. MAUPAS, E. (1881) Contribution à l'étude des Acinétiens. *Arch. zool. exp. gen.* **9**, 299–368.

647. MCMANUS, M. A. (1961) Culture of *Stemonitis fusca* on glass. *Am. J. Bot.* **48**, 582–588.

648. MCMANUS, M. A. (1963) The plasmodium of the myxomycete, *Cribraria violacea*. *Proc. Iowa Acad. Sci.* **70**, 97–100.

649. MEFFERD, R. B., JR., and LOEFER, J. B. (1952) Lethality of ultraviolet radiation for *Tetrahymena*. *Proc. Soc. Protozool.* **3**, 17.

650. MERTON, H. (1923) Studien über Flimmerbewegung. *Pflüger's Arch. Ges. Physiol.* **198**, 1–28.

651. METALNIKOW, S. (1912) Contributions à l'étude de la digestion intracellulaire chez les protozoaires. *Arch. Zool. exp. gen.* **49**, 373–499.

652. METZ, C. B., PITELKA, D. R., and WESTFALL, J. A. (1953) The fibrillar systems of ciliates as revealed by the electron microscope. I. *Paramecium*. *Biol. Bull.* **104**, 408–425.

653. MEVES, F. (1903) Über oligopyrene und apyrene Spermien und über ihre Entstehung, nach Beobachtungen an *Paludina* und *Pygaera*. *Arch. mikroskop. Anat.* **61**, 1–84.

654. MIGNOT, J.-P. (1964) Observations complémentaires sur la structure des flagelles d'*Entosiphon sulcatum* (Duj.) Stein, Flagelle Euglenien. *Compt. rend. Acad. Sci.* **258**, 3360–3363.

655. MIRSKY, A. F., and KATZ, M. S. (1958) Avoidance "conditioning" in *Paramecia*. *Science* **127**, 1498–1499.

656. MITCHISON, J. M. (1950) Birefringence of amoebae. *Nature* **166**, 313–314.

657. MITCHISON, J. M. (1961) Some questions for the cell. *In* RAMSAY, J. A., and V. B. WIGGLESWORTH (eds.), *The Cell and the Organism*, pp. 37–59. Cambridge Univ. Press, London.

658. MOEWUS, F. (1939) Über die Chemotaxis von Algengameten. *Arch. Protistenk.* **92**, 485–526.

659. MONTGOMERY, P. O'B., BONNER, W. A., HUNDLEY, L. L., and ASHWORTH, C. T. (1961) Biological effects of UV irradiation in *Chaos chaos*. *J. Roy. Microscop. Soc.* **80**, 19–24.

660. MOSSEVITCH, T. N., and CHEISSIN, E. M. (1961) Certain data on electron microscope study of the merozoites of *Eimeria intestinalis* from rabbit intestine (in Russian). *Tsitologia* **3**, 34–39.

661. MUGARD, H., and RENAUD, P. (1960) Étude sur l'effet des ultrasons sur un infusoire cilié *Paramecium caudatum*. *Arch. biol.* **71**, 73–91.

662. MÜHL, D. (1921) Beitrag zur Kenntnis der Morphologie und Physiologie der Mehlwurm-Gregarinen. *Arch. Protistenk.* **43**, 361–414.

663. MÜLLER, M., and TOTH, E. (1959) Effect of acetylcholine and eserine on the ciliary reversal in *Paramecium multimicronucleatum*. *J. Protozool.* **6** (Suppl.), 28.

664. NACHMIAS, V. T. (1964a) Fibrillar structures in the cytoplasm of *Chaos chaos*. *J. Cell. Biol.* **23**, 183–187.

665. NACHMIAS, V. T. (1964b) Cytoplasmic fibrils in *Chaos chaos* by electron microscopy. *J. Cell. Biol.* **23**, 122A.

666. NAGAI, T. (1956) Elasticity and contraction of *Paramecium* ectoplasm. *Cytologia* **21**, 65–75.

667. NAITOH, Y. (1958) Direct current stimulation of *Opalina* with intracellular micro-electrode. *Annot. Zool. Japon.* **31**, 59–73.

668. NAITOH, Y. (1964) Ciliary responses of Paramecium to the external application of various chemicals under different ionic conditions. (in Japanese; English Abst.) *Dobutsugaku Zasschi* **73**, 207–212.

669. NAKAJIMA, H. (1956) Some properties of a contractile protein in a slime mold. (in Japanese) *Seitaino Kagaku* **7**, 49–52; 256–259.

670. NAKAJIMA, H. (1960) Some properties of a contractile protein in a myxomycete plasmodium. *Protoplasma.* **52**, 413–436.

670a. NAKAJIMA, H., and ALLEN, R. D. (1965) The changing pattern of birefringence in plasmodia of the slime mild, *Physarum polycephalum. J. Cell. Biol.* **25**, 361–374.

671. NAKAJIMA, H., and HATANO, S. (1962) Acetylcholinesterase in the plasmodium of the myxomycete *Physarum polycephalum. J. Cell. Comp. Physiol.* **59**, 259–263.

672. NATHAN, H. A., and FRIEDMAN, W. (1962) Chlorpromazine affects permeability of resting cells of *Tetrahymena pyriformis. Science*, **135**, 793–794.

673. NAUSS, R. N. (1949) *Reticulomyxa filosa* gen. et sp. nov., a new primitive plasmodium. *Bull. Torrey Bot. Club* **76**, 161–173.

674. NELSON, L. (1954) Enzyme distribution in fragmented bull spermatozoa I. Adenyl-pyrophosphatase. *Biochim. Biophys. Acta* **14**, 312–320.

675. NELSON, L. (1958) ATP—an energy source for sperm motility. *Biol. Bull.* **115**, 326–327.

676. NELSON, L. (1962) Cytochemical aspects of spermatozoan motility. *In* BISHOP, D. W. (ed.), *Spermatozoan Motility*, pp. 171–187. Am. Assoc. Adv. Sci., Washington, D.C.

677. NELSON, L., and PLOWMAN, K. (1963) Actin in the ultrastructure of the sperm flagellum. *Absts. 7th Ann. Meet. Biophys. Soc.*, New York, 1963, MD4.

678. NERESHEIMER, E. R. (1903) Über die Höhe histologischer Differenzierung bei heterotrichenen Ciliaten. *Arch. Protistenk.* **2**, 305–324.

679. NERESHEIMER, E. R. (1907) Nachmals über *Stentor coeruleus. Arch. Protistenk.* **9**, 137–138.

680. NETTLETON, R. M., JR., MEFFERD, R. B., JR., and LOEFER, J. B. (1953) Pattern formation in concentrated particulate suspensions. *Am. Nat.* **67**, 117–118.

681. NICHOLS, S. P. (1925) The effect of wounds upon the rotation of the protoplasm in the internodes of *Nitella. Bull. Torrey Bot. Club* **52**, 351–363.

682. NOBLE, A. E. (1932) On *Tokophrya lemnarum* Stein (Suctoria) with an account of its budding and conjugation. *Univ. Calif. Publ. Zool.* **37**, 477–520.

683. NOIROT-TIMOTHÉE, C. (1960) Étude d'une famille des ciliés: les "Ophryoscolescidae". Structures et ultrastructures. *Ann. Sci. Nat. Zool. Biol. Animal, Ser.* **12**, 2, 527–718.

684. NOLAND, L. E. (1957) Protoplasmic streaming: A perennial puzzle. *J. Protozool.* **4**, 1–6.

685. NOVIKOFF, A. B. (1961) Mitochondria (chondriosomes). Lysosomes and related particles. *In* BRACHET, J., and A. E. MIRSKY (eds.), *The Cell.*, pp. 299–488. Vol. II. Academic Press, New York.

686. OBERTHÜR, K. (1937) Untersuchungen an *Frontonia marina* Fabre-Dom. aus einer Binnenland-Salzquelle unter besonderer Berücksichtigung der pulsierenden Vakuole. *Arch. Protistenk.* **88**, 387–420.

687. OKAJIMA, A. (1953) Studies on the metachronal wave in *Opalina* I. Electrical stimulation with the micro-electrode. *Japan. J. Zool.* **11**, 87–100.

688. OKAJIMA, A. (1954) Studies on the metachronal wave of *Opalina*. II. The regulating mechanism of ciliary metachronism and of ciliary reversal. *Annot. Zool. Japon.* **27**, 40–45.

689. OKAJIMA, A. (1957) Protoplasmic contraction observed on the tentacles of the Suctorian I. Effects of electrolytes in the medium. *Annot. Zool. Japon.* **30**, 51–62.

690. OLIPHANT, J. F. (1938) The effect of chemicals and temperature on reversal in ciliary action in *Paramecium. Physiol. Zool.* **11**, 19–30.

691. OLIPHANT, J. F. (1942) Reversal of ciliary action in *Paramecium* induced by chemicals. *Physiol. Zool.* **15**, 443–452.

692. OLIVE, L. S., and STOIANOVICH, C. (1960) Two new members of the Acrasiales. *Bull. Torrey Bot. Club* **87**, 1–20.

693. ORD, M. J., and DANIELLI, J. F. (1956) The site of damage in amoebae exposed to X-rays. *Quart. J. Microscop. Sci.* **97**, 29–37.

694. Not applicable.

695. OSTERHOUT, W. J. V. (1952) Some aspects of protoplasmic motion. *J. Gen. Physiol.* **35**, 519–527.

696. OSTERHOUT, W. J. V., and HILL, S. E. (1933) Anesthesia produced by distilled water. *J. Gen. Physiol.* **17**, 87–98.

697. PANTIN, C. F. A. (1923) On the physiology of ameboid movement. *J. Mar. Biol. Assoc.* **13**, 24–69.

698. PÁRDUCZ, B. (1956) Reizphysiologische Untersuchungen an Ziliaten IV. Über das Empfindungs- bzw. Reaktions-Vermögen von *Paramecium. Acta. Biol. Acad. Sci. Hungar.* **6**, 289–316.

699. PÁRDUCZ, B. (1957) *Ibid.* VII. Das Problem der vorbestimmten Leitungsbahnen. *Acta Biol. Acad. Sci. Hungar.* **8**, 219–251.

700. PÁRDUCZ, B. (1962) On the nature of metachronal ciliary control in *Paramecium. J. Protozool.* **9** (Suppl.), 27.

701. PARISIS, N. G. (1956) cited in TARTAR, V. (1961) *The Biology of Stentor.* Pergamon Press, London, pp. 242.

702. PAUTARD, F. G. E. (1962) Biomolecular aspects of spermatozoan motility. *In* BISHOP, D. W. (ed.), *Spermatozoan Motility,* pp. 189–232. Am. Assoc. Adv. Sci., Washington, D.C.

703. PENARD, E. (1890) Étude sur les rhizopodes d'eau douce. *Mem. Soc. Phys. Hist. Nat. Genève* **31**, 1–230.

704. PENARD, E. (1902) *Faune rhizopodique du Bassin du Leman.* Kündig, Genève, 714 pp.

705. PENARD, E. (1904) *Les Heliozoaires d'eau douce.* Kündig, Genève, 341 pp.

706. PENARD, E. (1905) Observations sur les Amibes à pellicule. *Arch. Protistenk.* **6**, 175–206.

707. PENARD, E. (1920) Études sur les Infusoires tentaculifères. *Mem. Soc. Phys. Hist. Nat. Genève* **39**, 131–229.

708. PENARD, E. (1922) *Études sur les Infusoires d'eau douce.* George, Genève, 331 pp.

709. PENARD, E. (1947) Habituation. *J. Roy. Microscop. Soc.* **67**, 43–45.

710. PERRY, S. V. (1956) Relation between chemical and contractile function and structure of the skeletal muscle cell. *Physiol. Rev.* **36**, 1–76.

711. PETERSEN, J. B., and HANSEN, J. B. (1954) Electron microscope observations on *Codonosiga botrytis* (Ehr.) James Clark. *Botan. Tidssk.* **51**, 281–291.

712. PIGON, A., and SZARSKI, H. (1955) The velocity of the cilia and the force of the ciliary beat in *Paramecium caudatum. Bull. Acad. Polonaise Sci. Cl.* 2, **3**, 99–102.

713. PIPKIN, A. C. (1962) Microcinematographic studies on the life cycle of *Trypanosoma cruzi. J. Parasitol.,* **48** (Suppl.), 50.

714. PISHA, B. V., and RUDZINSKA, M. A. (1952) The influence of ultra violet rays on *Amoeba dubia. Proc. Soc. Protozool.* **3**, 9.

715. PITELKA, D. R. (1963) *Electron-microscopic Structure of Protozoa.* Pergamon Press-MacMillan, New York, 269 pp.

716. PITELKA, D. R., and CHILD, F. M. (1964) The Locomotor Apparatus of Ciliates and Flagellates: Relations Between Structure and Function. *In* HUTNER, S. H. (ed.),

*Biochemistry and Physiology of Protozoa*, Vol. III. pp. 131–198. Academic Press, New York.

717. PITELKA, D. R., and SCHOOLEY, C. N. (1955) Comparative morphology of some protistan flagella. *Univ. Calif. Publ. Zool.* **61**, 79–127.

718. PITTENDRIGH, C. S. (1960) Circadian rhythms and the circadian organization of living systems. *Cold Spring Harbor Symp. Quant. Biol.* **25**, 159–184.

719. PITTS, R. F., and MAST, S. O. (1934a) The relation between inorganic salt concentration, hydrogen ion concentration and physiological processes in *Amoeba proteus*. I. Rate of locomotion, gel sol ratio and hydrogen ion concentration in balanced salt solutions. *J. Cell. Comp. Physiol.* **3**, 449–462.

720. PITTS, R. F., and MAST, S. O. (1934b) *Ibid.* II. Rate of locomotion, gel/sol ratio and hydrogen ion concentration in solutions of single salts. *J. Cell. Physiol.* **4**, 237–256.

721. PITTS, R. F., and MAST, S. O. (1934c) *Ibid.* III. The interaction between salts (antagonism) in relation to hydrogen ion concentration and salt concentration. *J. Cell. Comp. Physiol.* **4**, 435–455.

722. PLATE, L. (1886) Untersuchungen einiger an den Kiemenblättern des *Gammarus pulex* lebenden Ektoparasiten. *Zeit. wiss. Zool.* **43**, 175–241.

723. PLATT, J. R. (1961) "Bioconvection patterns" in cultures of free-swimming organisms. *Science* **133**, 1766–1767.

724. PLOWMAN, K. M., and NELSON, L. (1962) An actin-like protein isolated from starfish sperm. *Biol. Bull.* **123**, 478.

725. POLJANSKY, G. I., and POSNANSKAJA, T. M. (1964) A long lasting culture of *Paramecium caudatum* at 0° C, (in Russian; English summary) *Acta Protozool.* **2**, 272–278.

726. PORTER, J. F. (1897) Two new Gregarinida. *J. Morphol.* **14**, 1–20.

727. PORTER, K. R., LEDBETTER, M. C., and BADENHAUSEN, S. (1964) The microtubule in cell fine structure as an accompaniment of cytoplasmic movements. *Excerpta Med.* **77**, 36–37.

728. POSTMA, N. (1959) The aggregate of motile and postural functions in the animal kingdom and its differentiation. *Proc. 15th Intern. Congr. Zool.*, London, 1958 **15**, 523–525.

729. POTTAGE, R. H. (1959) Electron microscopy of the adults and migrants of *Discophrya piriformis*. *Proc. 15th Intern. Congr. Zool.* London, 1958 **15**, 472–473.

730. POTTER, N. B. (1960) The effect of an increase in viscosity of the medium on transmission of metachronal rhythm of *Opalina*. *J. Protozool.* **7** (Suppl.), 24.

731. PRATJE, A. (1921) *Noctiluca miliaris* Suriray. Beiträge zur Morphologie, Physiologie und Cytologie. I. Morphologie und Physiologie (Beobachtungen an der lebenden Zelle). *Arch. Protistenk.* **42**, 1–98.

732. PRELL, H. (1921) Zur Theorie der sekretorischen Ortsbewegung. *Arch. Protistenk.* **42**, 99–175.

733. PRESCOTT, D. M. (1955) Relations between cell growth and cell division I. Reduced weight, cell volume, protein content and nuclear volume of *Amoeba proteus* from division to division. *Exptl. Cell. Res.* **9**, 328–337.

734. PRESCOTT, D. M. (1960) The nuclear dependence of RNA synthesis in *Acanthamoeba* sp. *Exptl. Cell. Res.* **19**, 29–34.

735. PRESMAN, A. S. (1963a) Vozbudimost' u parametsii pri razdrazhenii impul'sami postoyanoggo i peremennogie toka (in Russian). *Biofizika* **8**, 138–140.

736. PRESMAN, A. S. (1963b) Deistoie mikrovoln na parametsii (in Russian). *Biofizika* **8**, 258–260.

737. PRINGSHEIM, E. G., and ONDRAČEK, K. (1939) Untersuchungen über die Geschlechtsvorgänge bei *Polytoma*. *Beih. bot. Zentralbl.* **59** A, 117–172.

738. PROSSER, C. L., and BROWN, F. A., JR. (1961) *Comparative Animal Physiology*, 2nd Ed. Saunders, Philadelphia, 688 pp.

739. Putter, A. (1893) Die Flimmerbewegung. *Ergeb. Physiol. Jahrg.* **2** (2), 1–102.
740. Puytorac, P. de, Andrivon, C., and Serre, F. (1963) Sur l'action cytonarcotique de sels de nickel chez *Paramecium caudatum* Ehrb. *J. Protozool.* **10**, 10–19.
741. Randall, J. T. (1957) Observations on contractile systems. *J. Cell. Comp. Physiol.* **49** (Suppl. 1), 199–220.
742. Randall, J. T. (1959a) Contractility in the stalks of *Vorticellidae*. *J. Protozool.* **6** (Suppl.), 30.
743. Randall, J. T. (1959b) Comparative studies of fine structure and function in ciliates. *Proc. 15th Intern. Congr. Zool.*, London, 1958, **15**, 468–470.
744. Randall, J. T., and Jackson, S. F. (1958) Fine structure and function in *Stentor polymorphus*. *J. Biophys. Biochem. Cytol.* **4**, 807–830.
745. Rashevsky, N. (1948) *Mathematical Biophysics. Physicomathematical Foundations of Biology*, Revised Ed. Univ. Chicago Press, Chicago, 669 pp.
746. Rashevsky, N. (1952) Some suggestions for a new theory of cell division. *Bull. Math. Biophys.* **14**, 293–305.
747. Ray, D. L. (1951) Agglutination of bacteria: A feeding method in the soil amoeba *Hartmanella* sp. *J. Expt. Zool.* **118**, 443–465.
748. Ray, D. L., and Hayes, R. E. (1954) *Hartmannella astronyxis*: a new species of free-living amoeba. *J. Morphol.* **95**, 159–188.
749. Rees, C. W. (1922) The neuromotor apparatus of *Paramaecium*. *Univ. Calif. Publ. Zool.* **20**, 333–365.
750. Reid, C. (1960) Quantum phenomena in biology. *Science* **131**, 1078–1084.
751. Rhumbler, L. (1898) Physikalische Analyse von Lebenserscheinungen von Zellen. I. Bewegung, Nahrungsaufnahme, Defäkation, Vacuolen-Pulsation und Gehäusebau bei lobosen Rhizopoden. *Arch. Entwicklungsmech.* **7**, 103–350.
752. Rhumbler, L. (1925) Rhizopoda oder Sarkodina, Wurzelfüßen. *In* Krumbach, T. (ed.), *Handbuch der Zoologie*, Abt. I., pp. 1–114, de Gruyter, Berlin.
753. Richter, I. E. (1959) Bewegungsphysiologische Untersuchungen an polycystiden Gregarinen unter Anwendung Mikrozeitrafferfilms. *Protoplasma* **51**, 197–241.
754. Rinaldi, R. A. (1959) The induction of pinocytosis in *Amoeba proteus* by ultraviolet radiation. *Exptl. Cell. Res.* **18**, 70–75.
755. Rinaldi, R. A. (1964) Pictographs and flow analysis of the hyaline cap in *Chaos chaos*. *Protoplasma* **58**, 603–620.
756. Rinaldi, R. A., and Jahn, T. L. (1963) On the mechanism of ameboid movement. *J. Protozool.* **10**, 344–357.
757. Rinaldi, R. A., and Jahn, T. L. (1964) Shadowgraphs of protoplasmic movement in *Allogromia laticollaris* and a correlation of this movement to striated muscle contraction. *Protoplasma* **58**, 369–90.
758. Rivera, J. A. (1962) *Cilia, Ciliated Epithelium and Ciliary Activity*. Pergamon Press, New York, 167 pp.
759. Robbins, W. J. (1952) Patterns formed by motile *Euglena gracilis* var. *bacillaris*. *Bull. Torrey Botan. Club.* **79**, 107–109.
760. Rosenbaum, J. L. and Child, F. M. (1964) Incorporation of tritiated precursors into regenerating flagella of two flagellates. *J. Protozool.* **11** (Suppl.), 22.
761. Rosenberg, B. (1962a) Electrical conductivity of proteins. *Nature* **193**, 364–365.
762. Rosenberg, B. (1962b) Electrical conductivity of proteins. II. Semiconduction in crystalline bovine hemoglobin. *J. Chem. Phys.* **36**, 816–823.
763. Rosenberg, L. E. (1937) The neuromotor system of *Nyctotherus hylae*. *Univ. Calif. Publ. Zool.* **41**, 249–276.
764. Roth, L. E. (1956) Aspects of ciliary fine structure in *Euplotes patella*. *J. Biophys. Biochem. Cytol.* **2** (Suppl.), 235–240.
765. Roth, L. E. (1959) An electron microscope study of the cytology of the protozoan *Peranema trichophorum*. *J. Protozool.* **6**, 107–116.

766. ROTH, L. E. (1962) A unifying concept for filaments in the mitotic apparatus, cilia and protozoan infraciliature. *Absts. 2nd Ann. Meet. Soc. Cell. Biol.*, San Francisco, 1962, 158.
767. ROTH, L. E. (1964) Motile Systems with continuous filaments. *In* ALLEN, R. D., and KAMIYA, N. (eds.), *Primitive Motile Systems in Cell Biology*, pp. 527–548. Academic Press, New York.
768. ROTHSCHILD, L. (1955) The spermatozoa of the honeybee. *Trans. Roy. Ent. Soc. London* **107**, 289–294.
769. ROTHSCHILD, L. (1962) Sperm movement—Problems and observations. *In* BISHOP, D. W. (ed.), *Spermatozoan Motility*, pp. 13–29. Am. Assoc. Adv. Sci., Washington, D.C.
770. ROUILLER, C., FAURÉ-FREMIET, E., and GAUCHERY, M. (1956) Les tentacles d'*Ephelota*: Étude au microscope electronique. *J. Protozool.* **3**, 194–200.
771. RUDZINSKA, M. A., and PORTER, K. R. (1954) Electron microscope study of intact tentacles and disc in *Tokophrya infusionum*. *Experientia* **10**, 460–462.
772. RUDZINSKA, M. A., and TRAGER, W. (1957) Intracellular phagotrophy by malarial parasites: An electron microscope study of *Plasmodium lophurae*. *J. Protozool.* **4**, 190–199.
773. RUDZINSKA, M. A., and TRAGER, W. (1962) Intracellular phagotrophy in *Babesia rodhaini* as revealed by electron microscopy. *J. Protozool.* **9**, 279–288.
774. RUDZINSKA, M. A., BRAY, R. S., and TRAGER, W. (1960) Intracellular phagotrophy in *Plasmodium falciparum* and *Plasmodium gonderi*. *J. Protozool.* **7** (Suppl.), 24–25.
775. RUPERT, C. S. (1964) Photoreactivation of ultraviolet damage. *In* GIESE, A. C. (ed.), *Photophysiology*, Vol. II, pp. 283–327. Academic Press, New York.
776. RUSTAD, R. C. (1958) The effects of temperature and respiration inhibitors on pinocytosis. *J. Protozool.* **5** (Suppl.), 14.
777. RUSTAD, R. C. (1959) Molecular orientation at the surface of amoebae during pinocytosis. *Nature* **183**, 1058–1059.
778. RUSTAD, R. C., and RUSTAD, L. C. (1960) Studies on the binding site of pinocytosis inducers. *Biol. Bull.* **121**, 377.
779. SAEDELEER, H. DE (1932) Recherches sur les pseudopodes des rhizopodes testacés. Les concepts pseudopodes lobosa, filosa et granulo-reticulosa. *Arch. zool. exp. gen.* **74**, 597–626.
780. SAEDELEER, H. DE (1934) Beitrag zur Kenntnis der Rhizopoden: morphologische und systematische Untersuchungen und ein Klassifikationsversuch. *Mem. Mus. R. Hist. Nat. Belg.* **60**, 1–112.
781. SALISBURY, G. W. (1962) Ionic and osmotic conditions in relation to metabolic control. *In* BISHOP, D. W. (ed.), *Spermatozoan Motility*, pp. 59–87. Am. Assoc. Adv. Sci., Washington, D. C.
782. SAMUEL, E. W. (1961) Orientation and rate of locomotion of individual amebas in the life cycle of the the cellular slime mold *Dictyostelium mucoroides*. *Developm. Biol.* **3**, 317–335.
783. SANDON, H. (1934) Pseudopodial movements of foraminifera. *Nature* **133**, 761–762.
784. SANDON, H. (1963) *Essays on Protozoology*. Hutchinson, London, 143 pp.
785. SANDON, H. (1964) Some observations on reticulose pseudopodia. *Progress Protozool.* **1**, 166–169.
786. SATIR, P., and SATIR, B. (1964) A model for ninefold symmetry in $\alpha$ keratin and cilia. *J. Theor. Biol.* **7**, 123–128.
787. SAUNDERS, J. T. (1925) The trichocysts of *Paramecium*. *Proc. Cambr. Phil. Soc., Biol. Sci.* **1**, 249–269.
788. SCHAEFFER, A. A. (1917a) Choice of food in *Amoeba*. *J. Anim. Behav.* **7**, 220–258.
789. SCHAEFFER, A. A. (1917b) Reactions of ameba to light and the effect of light on feeding. *Biol. Bull.* **32**, 45–74.

790. SCHAEFFER, A. A. (1920) *Ameboid Movement.* Princeton Univ. Press, Princeton, New Jersey, 156 pp.

791. SCHAEFFER, A. A. (1926a) The taxonomy of the amebas, with descriptions of thirty-nine new marine and freshwater species. *Carnegie Inst. Wash. Publ.* **345**, 1–116.

792. SCHAEFFER, A. A. (1926b) Recent discoveries in the biology of ameba. *Q. Rev. Biol.* **1**, 95–118.

793. SCHAEFFER, A. A. (1931) On molecular organization in ameban protoplasm. *Science* **74**, 47–51.

794. SCHAEFFER, A. A. (1948) Is the 14-day left-right spiraling rhythm of general occurrence in ameboid cells? *Anat. Rec.* **101**, 664.

795. SCHÄFER, E. A. (1891) On the structure of ameboid protoplasm with a comparison between the nature of the contractile process in ameboid cells and in muscular tissue and a suggestion regarding the mechanism of ciliary action. *Proc. Roy. Soc. London* **49**, 193–198.

796. SCHAUDINN, F. (1899) Über den Einfluß der Röntgenstrahlen auf Protozoen. *Pflüger's Arch. ges. Physiol.* **77**, 29–43.

797. SCHERBAUM, O. H., and LOEFER, J. B. (1964) Environmentally induced growth oscillations in protozoa. *In* HUTNER, S. H. (ed.), *Physiology and Biochemistry of Protozoa*, Vol. III, pp. 9–59. Academic Press, New York.

798. SCHERBAUM, O. H., LOUDERBACK, A. L., and BROWN, A. (1960) Soluble sulfhydryls in growing and synchronously dividing *Tetrahymena. J. Protozool.* **7** (Suppl.), 25.

799. SCHEWIAKOFF, W. (1894) Über die Ursache der fortschreitenden Bewegung der Gregarinen. *Zeit. wiss. Zool.* **58**, 340–354.

800. SCHEWIAKOFF, W. (1926) Acantharia. *Fauna Flora Naples* **37**, 1–755.

801. SCHMIDT, H. (1951) Aufnahme und Speicherung von Holzteilchen im Zellplasma der Termitenflagellaten. *Verhandl. D. Zool. Ges.*, 1950, 165–170.

802. SCHMIDT, W. J. (1939) Über die Doppelbrechung der Trichocysten von *Paramecium. Arch. Protistenk.* **92**, 527–536.

803. SCHMIDT, W. J. (1941) Die Doppelbrechung des Protoplasmas und ihre Bedeutung für die Erforschung seines submikroskopischen Baues. *Ergebn. Physiol.* **44**, 27–95.

804. SCHMITT, F. O. (1929) Ultrasonic manipulation. *Protoplasma* **7**, 332–340.

805. SCHOENBORN, H. W. (1953) Lethal effect of ultraviolet and X-radiation on the protozoan flagellate *Astasia longa. Physiol. Zool.* **26**, 312–319.

806. SCHUBERG, M. (1905) Über Cilien und Trichocysten einiger Infusorien. *Arch. Protistenk.* **6**, 61–110.

807. SCHULZE, F. E. (1875) Rhizopodien Studien. IV. *Arch. mikroskop. Anat.* **11**, 329–353.

808. SCHULTZE, M. (1865) Die Bewegung der Diatomeen. *Arch. mikroskop. Anat.* **1**, 376–402.

809. SCHUMAKER, V. N. (1958) Uptake of protein from solution by *Amoeba proteus. Exptl. Cell. Res.* **15**, 314–331.

810. SCHUSTER, F. (1963) An electron microscope study of the amoebo-flagellate *Naegleria gruberi* (Schardinger). I. The amoeboid and flagellate stages. *J. Protozool.* **10**, 297–313.

811. SEAMAN, G. R. (1955) Metabolism of free-living ciliates. *In* HUTNER, S. H., and LWOFF, A. (eds.), *Biochemistry and Physiology of Protozoa*, Vol. II, pp. 91–158. Academic Press, New York.

812. SEAMAN, G. R. (1960) Large-scale isolation of kinetosomes from the ciliated protozoan *Tetrahymena pyriformis. Exptl. Cell. Res.* **21**, 292–302.

813. SEAMAN, G. R. (1961) Some aspects of phagotrophy in *Tetrahymena. J. Protozool.* **8**, 204–212.

814. SEAMAN, G. R., and HOULIHAN, R. K. (1951) Enzyme systems in *Tetrahymena geleii* S II. Acetylcholinesterase activity. Its relation to motility of the organism and to coordinated ciliary action in general. *J. Cell. Comp. Physiol.* **37**, 309–321.

815. SEARS, D. F., and ELVEBACK, L. (1961) A quantitative study of the movement of *Paramecium caudatum* and *P. multimicronucleatum*. *Tulane Studies Zool.* **8**, 127–139.
816. SEARS, D. F., and GITTLESON, S. M. (1960) Effects of carbon dioxide on Paramecia. *Physiologist.* **3**, 140.
817. SEARS, D. F., and GITTLESON, S. M. (1961) Narcosis of Paramecia with xenon. *Fed. Proc.* **2**, 142.
818. SEARS, D. F., and GITTLESON, S. M. (1964) Cellular narcosis of *Paramecium multimicronucleatum* by xenon and other chemically inert gases. *J. Protozool.* **11**, 538–546.
819. SEIFRIZ, W. (1936) Reaction of protoplasm to radium radiation. *Protoplasma* **25**, 196–200.
820. SEIFRIZ, W. (1939) Pathological changes in protoplasm. *Protoplasma* **32**, 538–550.
821. SEIFRIZ, W. (ed.) (1942) *The Structure of Protoplasm.* Iowa State Press, Ames, 283 pp.
822. SEIFRIZ, W. (1952) The rheological properties of protoplasm. *In* FREY-WYSSLING, A. (ed.), *Deformation and Flow in Biological Systems*, pp. 3–156. Elsevier, Amsterdam.
823. SEIFRIZ, W. (1953) Mechanism of protoplasmic movement. *Nature* **171**, 1136–1138.
824. SEIFRIZ, W., and EPSTEIN, N. (1941) Shock anesthesia in myxomycetes. *Biodynamica* **3**, 191–197.
825. SEIFRIZ, W., and URAGUCHI, M. (1941) The toxic effects of heavy metals on protoplasm. *Am. J. Bot.* **28**, 191–197.
826. SELLS, B. H., SIX, N., and BRACHET, J. (1961) The influence of the nucleus on adenosine triphosphatase activity in *Amoeba proteus*. *Exptl. Cell. Res.* **22**, 246–256.
827. SERAVIN, L. N. (1959) Rhythmic activity of the ciliate *Spirostomum ambiguum* (in Russian). *In Coord. Conf. Problem Fund. Questions Cytol.* Leningrad. pp. 143–144.
828. SERAVIN, L. N. (1962a) Mekhanism reversii bieniya resnits u infusoria *Spirostomum ambiguum* (in Russian). *Tsitologia* **4**, 652–660.
829. SERAVIN, L. N. (1962b) Fiziologischeskie gradienty infusorii *Spirostomum ambiguum* (in Russian). *Tsitologia*, **4**, 545–554.
830. SERAVIN, L. N. (1963) O roli sistemy atsetilkholin-kholinesteraza v koordinatsii bieniya resnichek u infuzorii (in Russian). *S.B. Rabot Inst. Tsitol. Akad. Nauk S.S.S.R.* **3**, 111–122.
831. SERAVIN, L. N. (1964) Ritmicheskaya aktivnost' sokratilelnoi sistemy odnokletochnych organizmov i usloviya ee vesniknovinaya. *Tsitologia*, **6**, 516–520.
832. SERGEJEVA, G. I. (1964) Activity of acid phosphatase at different stages of the life cycle of *Nyctotherus cordiformis* (Ehrbg.). Stein (Ciliata). (in Russian; English summary) *Acta Protozool.* **2**, 163–174.
833. SERRA, J. A. (1960) Flagella cilia have 1 + 9 pair of fibres. *Exptl. Cell Res.* **20**, 395–400.
834. SHAFFER, B. M. (1956) Acrasin, the chemotactic agent in cellular slime molds. *J. Exptl. Biol.* **33**, 645–657.
835. SHAFFER, B. M. (1957) Aspects of aggregation in cellular slime moulds. I. Orientation and chemotaxis. *Am. Nat.* **91**, 19–35.
836. SHAFFER, B. M. (1958) Integration in aggregating cellular slime moulds. *Quart. J. Microscop. Sci.* **99**, 103–121.
837. SHAFFER, B. M. (1961) The cells founding aggregation centers in the slime mold *Polysphondylium violaceum*. *J. Exptl. Biol.* **38**, 833–849.
838. SHAFFER, B. M. (1962) The acrasina. *Adv. Morphogen.* **2**, 109–182.
839. SHAFFER, B. M. (1964) Intracellular movement and locomotion of cellular slime-mold amoebae. *In* ALLEN, R. D., and KAMIYA, N. (eds.), *Primitive Motile Systems in Cell. Biology*, pp. 387–405. Academic Press, New York.
840. SHARP, R. G. (1914) *Diplodinium ecaudatum* with an account of its neuromotor apparatus. *Univ. Calif. Publ. Zool.* **13**, 42–123.
841. SHETTLES, L. B. (1937) Response to light in *Peranema trichophorum* with special reference to dark-adaptation and light-adaptation. *J. Exptl. Zool.* **77**, 215–249.

842. SHIBATA, K. (1959) Spectrophotometry of intact biological materials. Absolute and relative measurements of their transmission, reflection and absorption spectra. *J. Biochem.* **45**, 599–623.

843. SHILO, M., and SHILO, M. (1961) Osmotic lysis of *Prymnesium parvum* by weak electrolytes. *Verhandl. Intern. Verein. Limnol.* **14**, 905–911.

844. SHOOPMAN, J. (1963) *Dictyostelium diminitivum* sp. nov., a new cellular slime mold from Mexican soils. M.S. Thesis, Univ. Wisc., Madison.

845. SHORTESS, G. S. (1942) The relation between temperature, light, and rate of locomotion in *Peranema trichophorum* and response to changes in temperature. *Physiol. Zool.* **15**, 184–195.

846. SILVESTER, N. R., and HOLWILL, M. E. J. (1965) Molecular hypothesis of flagellar activity. *Nature* **205**, 665–668.

847. SIMARD-DUQUESNE, N., and COUILLARD, P. (1962a) Ameboid movement I. Reactivation of glycerinated models of *Amoeba proteus* with adenosinetriphosphate. *Exptl. Cell. Res.* **28**, 85–91.

848. SIMARD-DUQUESNE, N., and COUILLARD, P. (1962b) Ameboid movement II. Research of contractile proteins in *Amoeba proteus*. *Exptl. Cell. Res.* **28**, 92–98.

849. SLEIGH, M. A. (1956) Metachronism and frequency of beat in the peristomal cilia of *Stentor*. *J. Exptl. Biol.* **33**, 15–28.

850. SLEIGH, M. A. (1957) Further observations on co-ordination and the determination of frequency in the peristomal cilia of *Stentor*. *J. Exptl. Biol.* **34**, 106–115.

851. SLEIGH, M. A. (1960) The form of beat in cilia of *Stentor* and *Opalina*. *J. Exptl. Biol.* **37**, 1–10.

852. SLEIGH, M. A. (1962) *The Biology of Cilia and Flagella*. Pergamon Press, London, 242 pp.

853. SLEIGH, M. A. (1964) Flagellar movement of the sessile flagellates *Actinomonas*, *Codonosiga*, *Monas* and *Poteriodendron*. *Quart. J. Microscop. Sci.* **105**, 405–414.

854. SMAGINA, A. P. (1948) Mercatnelnogie Dvizenie. Moskva, Medgiz.

855. SMITH, S. (1908) The limits of educability in *Paramecium*. *J. Comp. Neurol. Psychol.* **18**, 499–510.

856. SOLLBERGER, A. (1962) General properties of biological rhythms. *Ann. N.Y. Acad. Sci.* **98**, 757–774.

857. SOTELLO, J. R., and TRUJILLO-CENÓZ, O. (1958) Electron microscope study of the development of ciliary components of the neural epithelium of the chick embryo. *Zeit. Zellforsch.* **49**, 1–12.

858. SOTELLO, J. R., and TRUJILLO-CENÓZ, O. (1959) The fine structure of an elementary contractile system. *J. Biophys. Biochem. Cytol.* **6**, 126–128.

859. STEINERT, M., and NOVIKOFF, A. B. (1960) The existence of a cytostome and the occurrence of pinocytosis in the trypanosome *Trypanosoma mega*. *J. Biophys. Biochem. Cytol.* **8**, 563–569.

860. STERN, D. H. (1959) Observations on the biology of *Pelomyxa palustris* Greeff collected under polysaprobic conditions. *Virginia Acad. Sci.* **10**, 264.

861. STEWART, P. A. (1964) The organization of movement in slime mold plasmodia. *In* ALLEN, R. D., and KAMIYA, N. (eds.), *Primitive Motile Systems in Cell Biology*, pp. 69–78. Academic Press, New York.

862. STEWART, P. A., and STEWART, B. T. (1959) Protoplasmic movement in slime mold plasmodia: The diffusion drag force hypothesis. *Exptl. Cell. Res.* **17**, 44–58.

863. STEWART, P. A., and STEWART, B. T. (1961) Circular streaming paterns in a slime mold plasmodium. *Nature* **192**, 1206–1207.

864. STUMP, A. B. (1936) Observations on the feeding of *Difflugia*, *Pontigulasia* and *Lesquereusia*. *Biol. Bull.* **69**, 136–142.

865. SUGI, H. (1961) Volume change during contraction in the stalk muscle of *Carchesium*. (in Japanese; English summary) *J. Fac. Sci. Univ. Tokyo Sec. 4, Zool.* **9**, 155–170.

866. Sussman, M. (1961) Cellular differentiation in the slime mold. *In* Zarrow, M. X. (ed.), *Growth in Living Systems*, pp. 221–239. Basic Books, New York. 759 pp.

867. Sussman, M. (1955) Developmental physiology of the ameboid slime molds. *In* Hutner, S. H., and Lwoff, A. (eds.), *Biochemistry and Physiology of Protozoa*, Vol. II, pp. 201–223. Academic Press, New York.

868. Sussman, M., Lee, F., and Kerr, N. S. (1956) Fractionation of acrasin, a specific chemotactic agent for slime mold aggregation. *Science* 123, 1171–1172.

869. Swezy, O. (1923) The pseudopodial method of feeding by the trichonymphid flagellates parasitic in wood-eating termites. *Univ. Calif. Publ. Zool.* 20, 391–400.

870. Swindle, P. F., and Kriz, R. A. (1924) Depressing effects of strychnine on the *Vorticella* and other unicellular forms. *Am. Nat.* 58, 457–467.

871. Szent-Györgyi, A. (1953) *Chemical Physiology of Contraction in Body and Heart Muscle*. Academic Press, New York, 135 pp.

872. Szent-Gyorgyi, A. (1960a) Remarks on muscle. *In* Bourne, G. H. (ed.), *Structure and Function of Muscle*, III, pp. 445–451. Academic Press, New York.

873. Szent-Gyorgyi, A. (1960b) *Introduction to Submolecular Biology*. Academic Press, New York, 135 pp.

874. Szubinska, B. (1964) Electron microscopy of the interaction of ruthenium violet with the cell membrane complex of *Amoeba proteus*. *J. Cell. Biol.* 23, 92A.

875. Takata, M. (1958) Protoplasmic streaming in *Acetabularia calyculus*. (in Japanese). *Kagaku* 28, 142.

876. Takeuichi, I. (1961) Immunochemical and histochemical studies on the development of the cellular slime mold *Dictyostelium mucoroides*. *Am. J. Bot.* 48, 530–531.

877. Tartar, V. (1961) *The Biology of Stentor*. Pergamon Press, London. 413 pp.

878. Tartar, V. (1962) Effects of extreme alteration of the nucleo-cytoplasmic ratio in *Stentor coeruleus*. *J. Protozool.* 9 (Suppl.), 16.

879. Tasaki, I., and Kamiya, N. (1964) A study on electro-physiological properties of carnivorous amoebae. *J. Cell. Comp. Physiol.* 63, 365–380.

880. Taylor, C. V. (1920) Demonstration of the function of the neuromotor apparatus in *Euplotes* by the method of microdissection. *Univ. Calif. Publ. Zool.* 19, 403–471.

881. Taylor, C. V. (1929) Experimental evidence of the function of the fibrillar system in certain protozoa. *Am. Nat.* 63, 328–345.

882. Taylor, C. V. (1941) Fibrillar systems in ciliates. *In* Calkins, G. N., and Summers, F. M. (eds.), *Protozoa in Biological Research*, pp. 191–270. Columbia Univ. Press, New York.

883. Taylor, G. I. (1951) Analysis of the swimming of microscopic organisms *Proc. Roy. Soc. London* A 209, 447–461.

884. Taylor, G. I. (1952) The action of waving cylindrical tails in propelling microscopic organisms. *Proc. Roy. Soc. London* A 211, 225–239.

885. Tchakotine, S. (1935a) L'effet d'arrêt de la fonction de la vacuole pulsatile de la paramécie par micropuncture ultraviolette. *Compt. rend. soc. biol.* 120, 782–784.

886. Tchakotine, S. (1935b) Recherche physiologiques sur les protozoaires faites au moyen de la micropuncture ultraviolette. *Compt. Rend. Acad. Sci. Paris* 200, 2217–2219.

887. Tchakotine, S. (1936a) La résistance de la paramécie et d'autres infusoires aux manipulations multiples dans la microexperimentation. *Bull. Soc. franc. microscop.* 5, 61–64.

888. Tchakotine, S. (1936b) Irradiation localisée du myonème du pedoncle des Vorticelles par micropuncture ultraviolette. *Compt. rend. Acad. Sci. Paris.* 202, 1114–1116.

889. Tchakotine, S. (1936c) La fonction du stigma chez la flagellé, *Euglena*, étudiée au moyen de la micropuncture ultraviolette. *Compt. rend. soc. biol.* 121, 1162–1165.

890. Tchakotine, S. (1939) Analyse du mécanisme de la cyclose chez la Paramécie au moyen de la micropuncture ultra-violette. *Compt. rend. soc. biol. Paris* 130, 738–740.

891. TERADA, T. (1962) Electron microscope studies on the slime mold, *Physarum poly-cephalum. Ann. Repts. Sci. Works Fac. Sci. Osaka Univ.* **10**, 47–58.

892. TERRA, N. DE, and RUSTAD, R. C. (1959) The dependence of pinocytosis on tempera-ture and aerobic respiration. *Exptl. Cell. Res.* **17**, 191–195.

893. THOMAS, R. (1957) Activité psychique chez les unicellulaires. *Trav. Lab. Inst. Botan. Fac. Med. Pharm. Bordeaux* **1957**, 1–3.

894. THOMPSON, D'A. W. (1942) *On Growth and Form.* Cambridge, Univ. Press, London, 1116 pp.

895. TIBBS, J. (1957) The nature of algal and related flagella. *Biochim. Biophys. Acta* **23**, 275–288.

896. TIBBS, J. (1958) The properties of algal and sperm flagella obtained by sedimentation. *Biochim. Biophys. Acta,* **28**, 636–637.

897. TIBBS, J. (1960) Acetylcholinesterase in flagellated systems. *Biochim. Biophys. Acta* **41**, 115–122.

898. TIBBS, J. (1962) Adenosine triphosphatase and acetylcholinesterase in relation to sperm motility. *In* BISHOP, D. W. (ed.), *Spermatozoan Motility,* pp. 233–250. Am. Assoc. Adv. Sci., Washington, D. C.

899. TIEGS, O. W. (1926) On the surface tension changes which underlie muscular and amoeboid movement. *Austral. J. Exptl. Biol. Med. Sci.* **3**, 1–10.

899a. TOKUYASU, K., and SCHERBAUM, O. H. Ultrastructure of mucocysts and pellicle of *Tetrahymena pyriformis. J. Cell. Biol.* **24**, (in press).

900. TRÉGOUBOFF, G. (1953) Classes d'Acanthaires; Radiolaires; Hélizoaires. *In* GRASSÉ, P.-P. (ed.), *Traité de Zoologie,* I (II), pp. 270–491. Maisson, Paris.

901. TROISI, A. (1940) Further studies on *Nematocystis elmassiani* (Protozoa; Sporozoa) from oligochaete annelids. *J. Morphol.* **66**, 561–579.

902. Ts'O, P. O. P., JR., BONNER, J., EGGMAN, L., and VINOGRAD, J. (1956) Observations on an ATP-sensitive protein system from the plasmodia of a myxomycete. *J. Gen. Physiol.* **39**, 325–347.

903. Ts'O, P. O. P., EGGMAN, L., and VINOGRAD, J. (1956) The isolation of myxomyosin, an ATP-sensitive protein from the plasmodium of a myxomycete. *J. Gen. Physiol.* **39**, 801–812.

904. Ts'O, P. O. P., EGGMAN, L., and VINOGRAD, J. (1957a) The interaction of myxomyosin with ATP. *Arch. Biochim. Biophys.* **66**, 64–70.

905. Ts'O, P. O. P., EGGMAN, L., and VINOGRAD, J. (1957b) Physical and chemical studies of myxomyosin, an ATP-sensitive protein in cytoplasm. *Biochim. Biophys. Acta* **25**, 532–542.

906. TSUBO, Y. (1961) Chemotaxis and sexual behavior in *Chlamydomonas. J. Protozool.* **8**, 114–121.

907. TUFFRAU, M. (1957) Les facteurs essentiels du phototropisme chez le cilié heterotriche. *Stentor niger. Bull. Soc. Zool. France* **82**, 354–356.

908. TURNER, J. P. (1933) The external fibrillar system of *Euplotes* with notes on the neuromotor apparatus. *Biol. Bull.* **64**, 53–66.

909. TYZZER, E. E., THEILER, H., and JONES, E. E. (1932) Coccidiosis in gallinaceous birds. II. A comparative study of species of *Eimeria* of the chicken. *Am. J. Hyg.* **15**, 319–393.

910. UEDA, K. (1952) Studies on the stalk muscle of *Carchesium* I. (in Japanese; English summary) *Dobutsugaku Zasshi (Tokyo)* **61**, 367–371.

911. UEDA, K. (1956) Intracellular calcium and ciliary reversal in *Opalina. Jap. J. Zool.* **12**, 1–10.

912. ULEHLA, V. (1911) Ultramikroskopische Studien über Geisselbewegung. *Biol. Zen-tralbl.* **31**, 645–654; 657–676; 689–705; 721–731.

913. UMRATH, K. (1959) Galvanotaxis. *In* RUHLAND, W. (ed.), *Handbuch der Pflanzenphy-siologie,* 17 (1), pp. 164–167. Springer, Berlin.

914. USSING, H. H., and ZERAHN, K. (1951) Active transport of sodium as the source of electric current in the short-circuited isolated frog skin. *Acta Physiol. Scand.* **23**, 110–127.

915. VALENTIN, G. (1842) Flimmerbewegung. In WAGNER, R. (ed.), *Handwörterbuch der Physiologie*, Vol. I, pp. 484–516. Braunschweig, Vieweg.

916. VAN EYS, J., and WARNOCK, L. G. The inhibition of motility of ciliates through methonium drugs. *J. Protozool.* **10**, 465–467.

917. VAN WAGTENDONK, W. J., and VLOEDMAN, D. A. JR., (1951) Evidence for the presence of a protein with ATP-ase and antigenic specificity in *Paramecium aurelia* variety 4, stock 51. *Biochim. Biophys. Acta* **7**, 335–336.

918. VAVRA, J., and AARONSON, S. (1962) Instability of the stigma in apochloric *Euglena gracilis* var. *bacillaris*. *J. Protozool.* **9** (Suppl.), 28.

919. VERAIN, A., and VERAIN, A. (1956) Influence des ultrasons sur *Plasmodium berghei*. *Compt. Rend. Soc. Biol.* **150**, 1189–1190.

920. VERAIN, A., VERAIN, A., and FILLIATRE, M. LE (1956) Influence des ultrasons sur *Trypanosoma equiperdum*. *Compt. Rend. Soc. Biol. Paris* **150**, 1529–1530.

921. VERWORN, M. (1889a) *Psycho-physiologische Protistenstudien. Experimentelle Untersuchungen*. Fischer, Jena, 218 pp.

922. VERWORN, M. (1889b) Die polare Erregung der Protisten durch den galvanischen Strom. *Pflüger's Arch. ges. Physiol.* **45**, 1–36.

923. VERWORN, M. (1889c) Die polare Erregung der Protisten durch den galvanischen Strom. *Pflüger's Arch. ges. Physiol.* **46**, 269–303.

924. VERWORN, M. (1890) Studien zur Physiologie der Flimmerbewegung. *Pflüger's Arch. ges. Physiol.* **48**, 149–180.

925. VERWORN, M. (1894) *Allgemeine Physiologie*. Fischer, Jena, 574 pp.

926. VERWORN, M. (1896) Untersuchungen über die polare Erregung der lebendigen Substanz durch den konstanten Strom. IV. Mitteilung. *Pflüger's Arch. ges. Physiol.* **65**, 47–62.

927. VERWORN, M. (1913) *Irritability*. Yale Univ. Press, New Haven, 264 pp.

928. VISSCHER, J. P. (1923) Feeding reactions in the ciliate *Dileptus gigas* with special reference to the functions of trichocysts. *Biol. Bull.* **45**, 113–143.

929. VOUK, V. (1910) Untersuchungen über die Bewegung der Plasmodien. I. Die Rhythmik der Protoplasmaströmung. *S.B. kais. Akad. Wiss. Wien, math.-naturwiss.-Kl.* **119**, 853–876.

930. VOUK, V. (1913) Untersuchungen über die Bewegung der Plasmodien. II. Studien über die Protoplasmaströmung. *Denkschr.kais. Akad. Wiss. Wien, math.-naturwiss.-Kl.* **88**, 652–692.

931. WADDELL, W. J., and BUTLER, T. C. (1959) Calculation of intracellular pH from the distribution of 5,5-dimethyl-2,4-oxazolidinedione (DMO). Application to skeletal muscle of the dog. *J. Clin. Investig.* **38**, 720–729.

932. WAGER, H. (1900) On the eye-spot and flagellum in *Euglena viridis*. *J. Linn. Soc. London (Zoology)* **27**, 463–481.

933. WALD, G. (1961) The molecular organization of vision systems. In MCELROY, W. D., and GLASS, B. (eds.), *Light and Life*, pp. 724–749. Johns Hopkins Press, Baltimore, Md.

934. WALKER, P. J. (1961) Organization of function in Trypanosome flagella. *Nature* **189**, 1017–1018.

935. WALKER, P. J., and WALKER, J. C. (1963) Movement of trypanosomes flagella. *J. Protozool.* **10** (Suppl.), 32.

936. WALLICH, G. C. (1863) On an undescribed indigenous form of *Amoeba*. *Ann. Mag. Nat. Hist.*, Ser. 3 **11**, 287–291.

937. WARNOCK, L. G., and EYS, J. VAN (1963) Observations on *Tetrahymena pyriformis* relating to the Pasteur effect. *J. Cell. Comp. Physiol.* **61**, 309–316.

938. WATANABE, I. (1955) On the ciliary reversal in *Spirostomum ambiguum*. (in Japanese; English summary) *Dobutsugaku Zasshi* **64**, 334–337.

939. WATANABE, I. (1959) Studies on the reversal action of cirri in *Stylonychia* (Ciliata). (in Japanese; English summary) *Dobutsugaku Zasshi* **68**, 281–285.

940. WATSON, M. E. (1916) Studies on Gregarines. *Univ. Ill. Mongr. Biol.* **2** (3), 3–258.

941. WATSON, M. R., and HOPKINS, J. M. (1962) Isolated cilia from *Tetrahymena pyriformis*. *Exptl. Cell. Res.* **28**, 280–295.

942. WATTERS, C. D. (1962) Analysis of motility in a new species of gregarine. *Biol. Bull.* **123**, 514.

943. WEBER, H. H. (1958) *Motility of Muscle and Cells*. Harvard Univ. Press, Cambridge, Massachusetts, 69 pp.

944. WEISS, P. (1961) Guiding principles in cell locomotion and aggregation. *Exptl. Cell. Res.* **8** (Suppl.), 260–281.

945. WEISZ, P. B. (1955) Chemical inhibition of regeneration in *Stentor coeruleus*. *J. Cell. Comp. Physiol.* **46**, 517–527.

946. WELLS, M. M. (1962) Nuclear differentiation in *Tetrahymena pyriformis* as affected by near infra-red and X-radiation. *Diss. Absts.* **22** (11), 3824–3825.

947. WENRICH, D. H. (1929) Observations on some freshwater ciliates (Protozoa) I. *Teuthophrys trisulcata* Chatton and de Beauchamp and *Stokesia vernalis* n.g., n.sp. *Trans. Am. Microscop. Soc.* **48**, 221–237.

948. WENRICH, D. H. (1939) Food habits of *Entamoeba muris*. *Biol. Bull.* **77**, 313–314.

949. WENRICH, D. H. (1941) Observations on the food habits of *Entamoeba muris*, and *Entamoeba ranarum*. *Biol. Bull.* **81**, 324–340.

950. WHITEHOUSE, S. W. (1931) Amoeboid motion as the product of protein swelling. *Science* **73**, 325–326.

951. WHITTINGHAM, W. F., and RAPER, K. B. (1957) Environmental factors influencing the growth and fructification of *Dictyostelium polycephalum*. *Am. J. Bot.* **44**, 619–627.

952. WICHTERMAN, R. (1952) A method for obtaining abundant dividing stages of *Paramecium*. *Trans. Am. Microscop. Soc.* **71**, 303–305.

953. WICHTERMAN, R. (1953) *The Biology of Paramecium*. Blakiston, New York, 527 pp.

954. WICHTERMAN, R. (1955) Survival and other effects following X-irradiation of the flagellate, *Euglena gracilis*. *Biol. Bull.* **109**, 371.

955. WICHTERMAN, R. (1956) Attempts to breed an X-ray resistant clone of *Paramecium*. *Biol. Bull.* **111**, 315.

956. WICHTERMAN, R. (1957) Biological effects of radiation on protozoa. *BIOS* **28**, 3–20.

957. WICHTERMAN, R. (1961) Survival and reproduction of *Paramecium* after X-irradiation. *J. Protozool.* **8**, 158–162.

958. WICHTERMAN, R., and HONNEGER, C. M. (1958) Action of X-rays on the two common amoebas, *Chaos diffluens* and *Chaos chaos*. *Proc. Pa. Acad. Sci.* **32**, 240–253.

959. WICHTERMAN, R., SOLOMON, H., and FIGGE, F. H. J. (1958) The influence of protoporphyrin-nitroresorcinol and other phenols on X-radiation sensitivity of *Paramecium caudatum*. *Biol. Bull.* **115**, 369–370.

960. WIERCINSKI, F. J. (1955) The pH of animal cells. *Protoplasmatologia* **II B 2c**, 1–56.

961. WILBER, C. G., and SLANE, G. M. (1951) The effect of ultra violet light on the protoplasm in *Pelomyxa carolinensis*. *Trans. Am. Microscop. Soc.* **70**, 265–271.

962. WILLIAMS, M. (1925) Some observations on the action of radium on certain plant cells. *Ann. Bot.* **39**, 547–562.

963. WILSKA, A. (1954) Observations with the anoptral microscope. *Mikroskopie* **9**, 1–80.

964. WILSON, B. W., BUETOW, D. E., JAHN, T. L., and LEVEDAHL, B. H. (1959) A differential effect of pH on cell growth and respiration. *Exptl. Cell. Res.* **18**, 454–465.

965. WILSON, T. H. (1963) Intestinal absorption of vitamin $B_{12}$. *Physiologist* **6**, 11–26.
966. WINER, B. J., and MOORE, A. R. (1941) Reactions of the plasmodium *Physarum polycephalum* to physico-chemical changes in the environment. *Biodynamica* **3**, 323–345.
967. WISE, B. N. (1962) Effects of localized damage, by ultraviolet microbeam, on morphogenesis in *Euplotes*. *J. Protozool.* **9** (Suppl.), 13.
968. WITTMAN, H. (1950) Untersuchungen zur Dynamik eines Lebensvorganges von *Amoeba sphaeronucleolosus* (Greeff) bei natürlichen "Zeitmoment" und unter Zeitraffung. *Protoplasma* **39**, 450–482.
969. WITTNER, M. (1955) Inhibition and reversal of oxygen poisoning in *Paramecium*. *J. Protozool.* **2** (Suppl.), 4–5.
970. WITTNER, M. (1957a) Effects of temperature and pressure on oxygen poisoning of *Paramecium*. *J. Protozool.* **4**, 20–23.
971. WITTNER, M. (1957b) Inhibition and reversal of oxygen poisoning in *Paramecium*. *J. Protozool.* **4**, 24–29.
972. WOHLFARTH-BOTTERMANN, K. E. (1953) Experimentelle und elektronenoptische Untersuchungen zur Funktion der Trichocysten von *Paramecium caudatum*. *Arch. Protistenk.* **98**, 169–226.
973. WOHLFARTH-BOTTERMANN, K. E. (1959) Protistenstudien VIII. Weitere Untersuchungen zur Feinstruktur der Axopodia von Helizoen. *Zool. Anz.* **163**, 1–10.
974. WOHLFARTH-BOTTERMANN, K. E. (1960) Protistenstudien X. Licht- und elektronenmikroskopische Untersuchungen an der Amöbe *Hyalodiscus simplex* n. sp. *Protoplasma* **52**, 58–107.
975. WOHLFARTH-BOTTERMANN, K. E. (1961) Cytologische Studien VIII. Zum Mechanismus der Cytoplasmaströmung in dünnen Faden. *Protoplasma* **54**, 1–26.
976. WOHLFARTH-BOTTERMANN, K. E. (1962) Weitreichende fibrilläre Protoplasmadifferenzierungen und ihre Bedeutung für die Protoplasmaströmung I. Elektronenmikroskopischer Nachweis und Feinstruktur. *Protoplasma* **54**, 514–539.
977. WOHLFARTH-BOTTERMANN, K. E. (1963) Weitreichende fibrilläre Protoplasmadifferenzierungen und ihre Bedeutung für die Protoplasmaströmung II. Lichtmikroskopische Darstellung. *Protoplasma* **57**, 747–761.
978. WOHLFARTH-BOTTERMANN, K. E. (1964a) Differentiations of the ground cytoplasm and their significance for the generation of the motive force of ameboid movement. *In* ALLEN, R. D., and KAMIYA, N. (eds.), *Primitive Motile Systems in Cell Biology*, pp. 79–109. Academic Press, New York.
979. WOHLFARTH-BOTTERMANN, K. E. (1964b) Cell structures and their significance for ameboid movement. *Intern. Rev. Cytol.* **16**, 61–131.
980. WOLFSON, C. (1935) Observations on *Paramecium* during exposure to sub-zero temperature. *Ecology* **16**, 630–639.
981. WOLKEN, J. J. (1961) *Euglena*. Rutgers Univ. Press, Rutgers, New Jersey, 173 pp.
982. WOLKEN, J. J., and SHIN, E. (1958) Photomotion in *Euglena gracilis* I. Photokinesis II. Phototaxis. *J. Protozool.* **5**, 39–46.
983. WOLKENSTEIN, M. V. (1962) The theory of cooperative processes as the foundation of molecular biophysics. *Biophys. J.* **2**, 189–201.
984. WOODS, R. W. (1955) Acoustic resonance of microorganisms to supersonic vibrations. *Proc. Soc. exp. Biol. Med.* **89**, 406–409.
985. WOODS, R. W., and LOOMIS, A. L. (1927) The physical and biological effects of high frequency sound waves of great intensity. *Phil. Mag. 7th Ser.* **4**, 417–436.
986. WOODRUFF, L. L., and BUNZEL, H. H. (1909) The relative toxicity of various salts and acids toward *Paramecium*. *Am. J. Physiol.* **25**, 190–194.
987. WOODRUFF, L. L., and SPENCER, H. (1922) Studies on *Spathidium spathula* I. The structure and behavior of *Spathidium*, with special reference to the capture and ingestion of prey. *J. Exptl. Zool.* **35**, 189–205.

988. WORLEY, L. G. (1934) Ciliary metachronism and reversal in *Paramecium, Spirostomum* and *Stentor. J. Cell. Comp. Physiol.* **5**, 53–72.
989. WRIGHT, B. E. (1958) Effects of steroids on aggregation in the slime mold *Dictyostelium discoideum. Bacteriol. Proc.* **58**, 115.
990. WRIGHT, B. E. (1964) Biochemistry of Acrasiales. *In* HUTNER, S. H. (ed.), *Biochemistry and Physiology of Protozoa, Vol. III*, pp. 341–381. Academic Press, New York.
991. YAGI, K. (1961) The mechanical and colloidal properties of Amoeba protoplasm and their relations to the mechanism of amoeboid movement. *Comp. Biochem. Physiol.* **3**, 73–91.
992. YAGUI, R., and SHIGENAKA, Y. (1959) Electron microscopical observation of *Condylostoma spatiosum* Ozaka and Yagui in ultra thin section. IV. The fibrils between the basal granule and the longitudinal fibrillar bundle (in Japanese; English summary) *Dobutsugaku Zasshi* **68**, 414–418.
993 YAGUI, R., and SHIGENAKA, Y. (1963) Electron microscopy of the longitudinal fibrillar bundle and the contractile fibrillar system in *Spirostomum ambiguum. J. Protozool.* **10**, 364–369.
994. YALOW, R. S. (1957) Production of sulfhydryl groups as a result of the indirect or direct effect of ionizing radiation. *Absts. Natl. Conf. Biophysics*, Columbus, 1957, 169–173.
995. YAMAGUCHI, T. (1964) Time changes in Na, K, and Ca contents in *Paramecium caudatum* after $\gamma$ irradiation (in Japanese; English summary) *Annot. Zool. Jap.* **36**, 55–65.
996. YAMASHITA, Y. (1964) Effects of mechanical deformation and electric current on protoplasmic streaming in *Paramecium* (in Japanese; English summary). *Dobutsugaku Zasshi* **73**, 39–44.
997. YAPP, W. B. (1941) Klino-kinesis of *Paramecium. Nature* **148**, 754.
998. YUSA, A. (1963) An electron microscope study on regeneration of trichocysts in *Paramecium caudatum. J. Protozool.* **10**, 253–262.
999. ZAJICEK, J., and DATTA, N. (1953) Investigation on the acetylcholinesterase activity of erythrocytes, platelets, and plasma in different animal species. *Acta Haematol.* **9**, 115–121.
1000. ZIMMERMAN, A. M. (1962) Action of ATP on *Amoeba. J. Cell. Comp. Physiol.* **60**, 271–280.
1001. ZIMMERMAN, A. M. (1964) The effects of mercaptoethanol upon form and movement of *Amoeba proteus. Biol. Bull.* **127**, 538–546.
1001 a. ZIMMERMAN, A. M., and RUSTAD, R. C. (1965) Effects of high pressure on pinocytosis in *Amoeba proteus. J. Cell. Biol.* **25**, 397–400.
1002. ZIMMERMAN, A. M., LANDAU, J. V., and MARSLAND, D. A. (1958) The effects of adenosinetriphosphate and dinitro-o-cresol upon the form and movement of *Amoeba proteus*. A pressure-temperature study. *Exptl. Cell. Res.* **15**, 484–495.
1003. ZINGER, J. (1937) Zur Biologie der Infusioren. *Biol. Zhurnal.*, (in Russian; German summary) **6**, 425–436.
1004. ZIRKLE, R. E. (1957) Partial-cell radiation. *Adv. Biol. Med. Phys.* **5**, 104–146.
1005. ZUELZER, M. (1905) Über die Einwirkung der Radiumstrahlen auf Protozoen. *Arch. Protistenk.* **5**, 358–369.

# RESPIRATORY METABOLISM

WILLIAM F. DANFORTH

*Department of Biology, Illinois Institute of Technology, Chicago, Illinois*

# CONTENTS

# GENERAL INTRODUCTION †

In introducing the subject of the respiratory metabolism of protozoa, we may recall the reasons for studying respiration in protozoa.[168] Measurement and analysis of the respiratory metabolism of an organism provide information about "the rate at which it uses energy, the substrate from which this energy is derived, and the mechanism by which it is obtained from the substrate".[168] The emphasis on energy is well placed; knowledge of the mechanisms and characteristics of the respiratory process take on their greatest significance when considered as aspects of the larger problem of the means by which organisms maintain, direct, and control the flow of energy on which all of their life processes depend.

These considerations, of course, apply equally well to all organisms. What are the reasons for giving special consideration to the respiratory metabolism of the protozoa? The first, and probably the most important reason is the belief, justified by the entire history of biology, that the thorough study of any single species, together with the comparisons between diverse species, is a rich source of discoveries and insights which advance our understanding of the processes common to all living things. It is hazardous to attempt to predict the nature of such discoveries; more frequently than not, they arise unexpectedly in the course of work directed toward some more modest goal.

Recognizing the likelihood of the unexpected, it is nevertheless possible to suggest areas of general biological interest in which studies of protozoan respiratory metabolism might be expected to yield especially valuable understanding.

One such area is the evolutionary modification of energy metabolism. The protozoa are an extraordinarily diverse group, including organisms adapted to habitats ranging from snowfields to the interior of mammalian cells; phototrophic species, predatory species, and species which are both; organisms closely allied to higher animals or plants, and organisms which have diverged widely, and in unique ways, from the "main lines" of evolution. Included in this diversity are, almost certainly, organisms which have retained many of the characteristics of the common ancestors of multicellular plants and animals. It would be astonishing if systematic understanding of the respiratory metabolism of the protozoa did not give insights into the evolutionary history of biological energy transfer and its relations to other life processes.

† Supperted in part by PHS Research Grant GM 07918 from the Division of General Medical Sciences, Public Health Service.

A second area in which studies of the protozoa are likely to be of especial value is that of the regulation and direction of energy metabolism, the mechanisms by which the rates and pathways of the various processes of energy transfer are adjusted to conform with each other, and with the varying demands on the organism as a whole. In the protozoa (as in the bacteria, and many algae and fungi), this problem appears in a special light, because the unit being considered is at once a single cell and a complete, independent organism; the burden of adjustments rests solely on intracellular mechanisms. The analysis of such processes as enzyme induction and repression and feedback inhibition of metabolic reactions in bacteria strongly emphasizes the value of microorganisms in such studies. While the bacteria will probably continue to play a central role in such studies, the more complex organization and behavior of the protozoa, while increasing the difficulty of study, may be expected to reveal additional levels of metabolic control.

Finally, in addition to these general concerns, there are innumerable specific reasons for wishing to understand the respiratory metabolism of particular species or groups of protozoa. For example, such knowledge may lead to control of diseases caused by protozoan parasites, to better understanding of the part played by protozoa in the ecology of natural communities, and to more effective use of protozoa as "tools" for such practical purposes as vitamin assay or the support of human beings in space.

It would be impractical to attempt to review all studies of respiratory metabolism of protozoa within the available time and space. Instead, I have attempted to concentrate on those relatively few species (or groups of related species) about which there is sufficient information to permit at least partial recognition of the overall patterns of respiratory metabolism. Also, emphasis has been limited to work bearing more or less directly on the nature and rates of the normal pathways of energy metabolism. To keep the subject matter within a manageable scope, isolated measurements of metabolic rates or enzymatic activities in less-thoroughly studied organisms have been omitted, as have studies of the effects of chemotherapeutic agents on respiration of parasitic species (except where such studies throw light on the normal respiratory mechanisms), and studies where respiratory measurements have been incidental to studies of non-respiratory processes. In general, this review is intended to cover the period from 1941 (the date of Jahn's[168] review) to the time of the writing, mid-1963. Papers published before 1941 have been cited when they contained information not available in the more recent literature, while some papers published after 1941 have been omitted because they reported results which have been extended or superseded by more recent studies cited here.

Von Brand's excellent review of the carbohydrate metabolism of protozoa[317a] covers much of the information included in this chapter.

Because there is so much diversity within the Phylum Protozoa, and because our information concerns only a small sample of this diversity, it

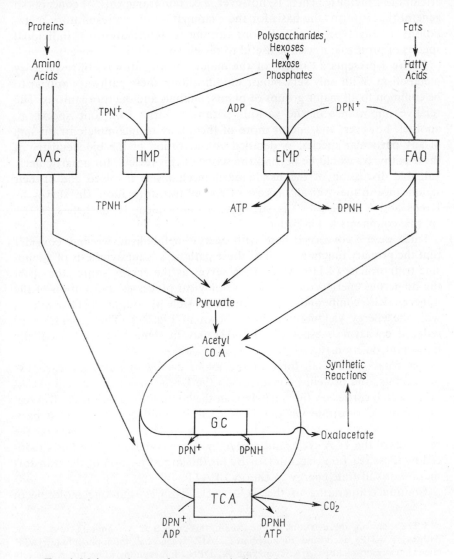

FIG. 1. Major pathways of energy metabolism. No attempt has been made to represent the quantitative aspects of the pathways. Pathways depicted are: amino acid catabolism (AAC); Emden-Meyerhof-Parnas glycolysis (EMP); fatty acid oxidation (FAO); glyoxylate cycle (GC); hexose monophosphate shunt (HMP); and tricarboxylic acid cycle (TCA). Other abbreviations: ADP, adenosine diphosphate; ATP, adenosine triphosphate; Co A, coenzyme A; $DPN^+$ and DPNH, oxidized and reduced diphosphopyridine nucleotide; $TPN^+$ and TPNH, oxidized and reduced triphosphopyridine nucleotide.

seemed preferable to consider individual species separately, rather than to attempt to generalize. There is, however, a certain framework of concepts so general that it forms the basis for the examination of the respiratory metabolism of any type of cell. Before turning to information on individual species of protozoa, it well be useful to review some of these concepts.

Figure 1 presents a "map" of the major known pathways of respiratory metabolism. With only very minor modifications, these pathways appear to be common to all major groups of plants, animals and microorganisms. The relative importance of the various pathways varies from one species to another, however, and one or more of them may be incomplete or missing in any particular species. A detailed consideration of the biochemistry of these pathways would be beyond the scope of this review; for a particularly valuable discussion of the biochemical mechanisms involved and of their significance in the over-all process of energy transformation, the survey by Krebs and Kornberg[176] is strongly recommended. Nevertheless, a few specific comments are in order.

Since we are concerned here with energy metabolism, we may consider that the primary function of all of these pathways is the synthesis of adenosine triphosphate (ATP), which then serves as the energy source for all of the numerous energy-consuming physiological processes. Formation of the "energy rich" compound, ATP, is made possible by coupling ATP synthesis with the energy yielding reactions shown in Fig. 1.† (The generation of reduced coenzymes, especially TPNH, may in some cases be an equally important function.)

The catabolism of all three of the major classes of nutrients, carbohydrates, fats, and proteins, converges on the Krebs tricarboxylic acid (TCA) cycle, which carries on the final steps in the complete oxidation of all three. Oxidation of substrate via the TCA cycle is coupled, for the most part, with the reduction of DPN. Where such complete oxidation occurs, the reactions of the TCA cycle, and especially the reoxidation of the DPN reduced by these reactions, account for by far the largest portion of the transformation of substrate energy to energy of ATP.

Continued operating of the TCA cycle requires that one molecule of

---

† The following abbreviations will be used in this chapter: AAC, amino acid catabolic pathways; ADP, adenosine diphosphate; AMP, adenosine monophosphate; ATP, adenosine triphosphate; Co A, coenzyme A; DPN, diphosphopyridine nucleotide (coenzyme I, nicotinamide adenine dinucleotide, NAD); DPN$^+$, oxidized DPN; DPNH, reduced DPN; EMP, Emden-Meyerhof-Parnas glycolysis pathway; GC, glyoxylate cycle; HMP, hexosemonophosphate shunt (pentose shunt); P$_i$, inorganic phosphate; Q$_{O_2}$, $\mu$l. O$_2$ consumed per mg. dry weight per hour; Q$_{10}$, factor by which a rate increases with a 10 °C temperature increase; RC, pathway(s) of catabolism of intracellular reserves; RQ, respiratory quotient (CO$_2$ produced/O$_2$ consumed); SA, pathway(s) of substrate assimilation; SC, pathway(s) of substrate catabolism; TCA cycle, Krebs tricarboxylic acid cycle; TPN, triphosphopyridine nucleotide (coenzyme II, nicotinamide adenine dinucleotide phosphate, NADP); TPN$^+$, oxidized TPN; TPNH, reduced TPN.

oxalacetate be regenerated for each two-carbon fragment oxidized by way of the cycle. When substrates such as acetate, ethanol, or fatty acids serve as both carbon and energy sources, some of the TCA intermediates are diverted into synthetic reactions, and an additional source of oxalacetate is required if the TCA cycle is to remain in operation. In many micro-organisms, this need is satisfied by the glyoxylate cycle,[173, 174, 175] whose net effect is the conversion of two molecules of acetyl CoA to one molecule of oxalacetate. The glyoxylate cycle involves several of the same enzymes as the TCA cycle, plus two additional enzymes, isocitrate lyase (isocitratase) and malate synthase (malate synthetase).

Two alternative pathways of carbohydrate catabolism, both leading into the TCA cycle, are of widespread importance. The first of these, Emden-Meyerhof-Parnas (EMP) glycolysis, results in the conversion of carbohydrate to pyruvic acid, with the coupled reduction of DPN, and the synthesis of a small number of ATP molecules. The second, the hexosemonophosphate (HMP) shunt or pentose pathway, results in the conversion of a hexose unit to three molecules of $CO_2$ and one molecule of glyceraldehyde-3-phosphate, coupled with the reduction of TPN. Of these, the EMP route appears usually to be the major pathway, of energy metabolism, while the HMP pathway apparently serves as a source of pentose and reduced TPN. There are, however, some organisms in which the HMP reactions seem to be the main pathway of carbohydrate breakdown.[304a] Synthesis of carbohydrate has been found to involve a general reversal of the EMP reaction, with special mechanisms for bypassing a few difficultly reversible steps.

In the oxidation of fats, the glycerol portion of the fat molecule is phosphorylated and channelled into the EMP glycolytic pathway, while the fatty acids are oxidized by a cyclic series of reactions (fatty acid oxidation cycle, FAO cycle) which involve successive removal of molecules of acetyl coenzyme A, and reduction of DPN and flavin coenzymes. The acetyl coenzyme A, in turn, enters the TCA cycle.

Preliminary oxidation of proteins cannot be readily summarized, since the pathways for the several amino acids differ considerably. In general, however, the processes involve deamination or transamination, conversion of the carbon skeleton to one of the acids of the TCA cycle, and reduction of DPN or flavin.

All of these pathways involve oxidation of the substrate, coupled with reduction of one or more of the electron acceptors, DPN, TPN, or flavin. In most aerobic organisms, reoxidation of reduced DPN (DPNH) and flavin occurs via the "electron transfer system" ("cytochrome system") (Fig. 2), with oxygen as the ultimate electron acceptor. It is this series of reactions which accounts for most of the oxygen consumed in respiratory metabolism.

During this sequence of oxidation-reduction reactions, further ATP is produced, two ATP molecules per flavin or three per DPN. The over-all process of coenzyme oxidation and ATP formation is known as "oxidative phosphorylation". Reoxidation of reduced TPN (TPNH) is less well understood. Direct reoxidation via the electron transfer system does not seem to occur. Mechanisms for transfer of electrons from TPN to DPN, and thence to the electron transfer system are known, but in general it appears that reduced TPN is used mainly as a source of electrons for reductive synthetic reactions, rather than participating in oxidative phosphorylation.

In the absence of oxygen, reoxidation of coenzymes via the cytochrome system is impossible. Oxidative phosphorylation is eliminated, and the energy yield of catabolic reactions greatly reduced. Moreover, the oxidative reactions can occur anaerobically only to the extent that some mechanism other than the cytochrome system is available to maintain a supply of oxidized coenzymes. In general no such alternative mechanisms are known for the TCA cycle or for fatty acid oxidation, so that these systems function only in the presence of oxygen (although individual part-reactions of both pathways may occur anaerobically).

A variety of anaerobic mechanisms are known by which carbohydrates can be partially broken down (fermented) without the participation of oxygen (Fig. 2). The best known of these are lactic acid fermentation, in which reduction of pyruvate to lactate serves to reoxidize reduced DPN, and alcohol fermentation, in which pyruvate is decarboxylated to acetalde-

Electron Transfer System

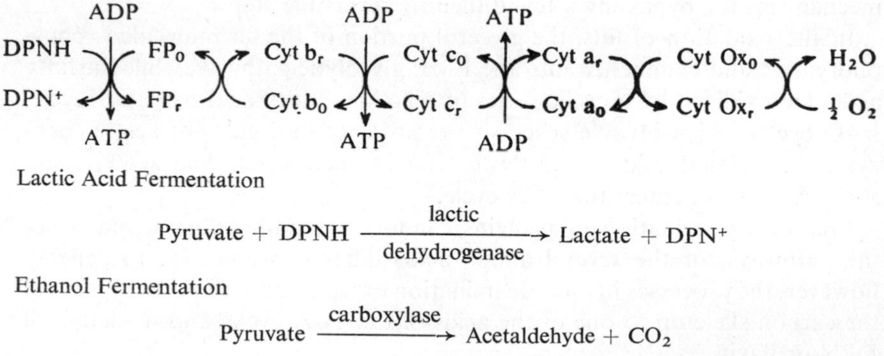

$$\text{DPNH} \xrightarrow{\text{ADP}} \text{FP}_0 \quad \text{Cyt b}_r \xrightarrow{\text{ADP}} \text{Cyt c}_0 \xrightarrow{\text{ATP}} \text{Cyt a}_r \quad \text{Cyt Ox}_0 \quad \text{H}_2\text{O}$$
$$\text{DPN}^+ \xleftarrow{} \text{FP}_r \quad \text{Cyt b}_0 \xleftarrow{} \text{Cyt c}_r \quad \text{Cyt a}_0 \quad \text{Cyt Ox}_r \quad \tfrac{1}{2}\text{O}_2$$
$$\text{ATP} \quad\quad\quad\quad \text{ATP} \quad\quad\quad \text{ADP}$$

Lactic Acid Fermentation

$$\text{Pyruvate} + \text{DPNH} \xrightarrow[\text{dehydrogenase}]{\text{lactic}} \text{Lactate} + \text{DPN}^+$$

Ethanol Fermentation

$$\text{Pyruvate} \xrightarrow{\text{carboxylase}} \text{Acetaldehyde} + \text{CO}_2$$

$$\text{Acetaldehyde} + \text{DPNH} \xrightarrow[\text{dehydrogenase}]{\text{alcohol}} \text{Ethanol} + \text{DPN}^+$$

FIG. 2. Mechanisms for the reoxidation of reduced diphosphopyridine nucleotide. Vertical arrows indicate the sites of oxidative phosphorylation in the electron transfer system. For simplicity, several known or suspected additional components of the electron transfer system have been omitted. Abbreviations: Cyt. a, b and c; cytochromes a, b and c; Cyt. Ox., cytochrome oxidase (cytochrome $a_3$); FP, flavoprotein; subscripts "o" and "r", respectively, indicate the oxidized and the reduced form of the components; other abbreviations as in Fig. 1.

hyde, and reduction of the acetaldehyde to alcohol is coupled with DPN oxidation. In certain cases (some to be discussed below), other DPN-linked reductions may serve the same purpose. Since neither the TCA cycle nor oxidative phosphorylation occurs, the yields of ATP per substrate molecule are much lower than in the case of complete aerobic oxidation.

Fermentation of individual amino acids, and mixed fermentations of amino acids and carbohydrates are known to occur in bacteria,[116a] but

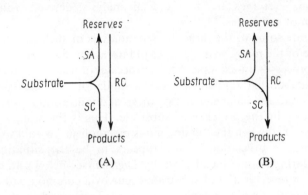

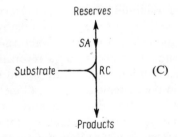

FIG. 3. Possible interactions between substrate metabolism and metabolism of intracellular reserves. Abbreviations: RC, catabolism of reserves; SA, assimilation of substrate; SC, catabolism of substrate. See discussion in text.

it is questionable whether anaerobic breakdown of protein is of any general importance as an energy source.

In the absence of an external supply of nutrients, most of the organisms to be discussed carry on a measurable "endogenous" respiratory metabolism at the expense of intracellular reserves. Addition of exogenous substrates often (though not necessarily) increases the respiratory rate. At the same time, a portion of the external substrate may be assimilated to form cellular material, while the remainder is broken down via the respiratory pathways to provide energy. Such "oxidative assimilation" or "fermentative assimilation" is essential, of course, where a single substrate serves as sole source of both carbon and energy, but is by no means limited to such cases.

The fact that all three processes, catabolism of endogenous reserves, catabolism of substrate, and assimilation of substrate into reserves, may go on simultaneously greatly complicates quantitative studies of substrate utilization. The complexity has been further compounded by the use of the ambiguously defined terms "endogenous metabolism" and "exogenous (substrate) metabolism" to discuss such situations, and by the fact that the "endogenous" reserves are, in the final analysis, derived from previous assimilation of substrates.[335a]

To illustrate some of the difficulties in analysis of such situations, Fig. 3 shows three of the many possible types of interaction between these different metabolic processes. In example A, the processes of reserve catabolism (RC), substrate catabolism (SC) and substrate assimilation (SA) are assumed to be entirely separate and independent; synthesis and utilization of reserves go on simultaneously in the presence of substrate. This is the situation which is usually envisioned when the "endogenous metabolism" is said to "continue during substrate utilization", and appears to be the situation actually occurring during acetate metabolism by *Euglena* (see below). In example B, catabolism of reserves and of substrate occur by a common pathway, while substrate assimilation is independent. In this case, addition of substrate might be expected to inhibit catabolism of reserves to a degree depending on the extent of competition for the common pathway. In example C, not only do substrate catabolism and reserve catabolism share a common pathway, but substrate assimilation occurs by a reversal of certain steps of reserve catabolism. Here, addition of substrate would markedly reduce catabolism of reserves and, in the extreme case, overall metabolism (measured as respiratory rate or rate of production of end products) might not increase at all during utilization of substrates. A situation of this sort is described in connection with *Plasmodium berghei*. It may not always be necessary to distinguish between these, and other, possible alternatives so long as one is interested only in the energy balance of the cell as a whole, and if complete balance sheets can be constructed for the overall metabolic conversions. Where balance sheets are incomplete, however, or where such intracellular processes as metabolic regulation are under study, failure fully to analyse these relationships may lead to entirely erroneous conclusions.

Such analysis is not easy; extensive and systematic studies using both chemical and isotopic tracer techniques are essential, and considerable ingenuity is necessary for the design of meaningful experiments. At present, real progress in the solution of such problems has been made in the case of a very few organisms (protozoan or otherwise), and in no case has anything like a complete analysis been achieved. Such knowledge, however, is absolutely essential to a full understanding of the energetics and economics of normal intact cells.

## PHYTOFLAGELLATES

The energy metabolism of the phytoflagellates is of particular interest because these organisms bridge the gap between photosynthethic and heterotrophic modes of obtaining energy, and because organisms in this group are generally believed to have been ancestral to the other protozoa and to higher plants and animals.

Photosynthesis and heterotrophy are combined in a variety of ways in the phytoflagellates. Frequently, as in many species of *Euglena* and *Chlamydomonas*, the two energy sources appear to be freely interchangeable; the organisms survive and grow equally well photoautotrophically, or in the dark with a single organic carbon and energy source. In many strains, chlorophyll and photosynthetic ability have been lost, making heterotrophy obligatory, without any other increase in nutritional requirements. In contrast to such versatility, we find organisms like *Ochromonas malhamensis*, which require both light and complex organic nutrients for optimal growth, and such obligate phototrophs as *Chlamydomonas moewusii*.

The metabolism of the phytoflagellates is discussed in reviews by Hutner and Provasoli[164, 165] and Lwoff.[188]

## Ochromonas

The chrysomonads *Ochromonas* and *Poteriochromonas* differ markedly in their nutritional behavior from the other phytoflagellates discussed in the following sections. In addition to photosynthesis and heterotrophic utilization of dissolved carbon and energy sources, these flagellates ingest and digest particulate food. In *O. malhamensis* and *P. stipitata*, photosynthesis appeared to be, at best, only a supplementary source of carbon and energy: only very slow growth was possible in light unless heterotrophic carbon and energy sources were also present.[166, 215] Even at saturating light intensities, the rate of photosynthesis was so low that in the presence of a good carbon source such as glucose, photosynthesis did not compensate for respiration; there was a net consumption of $O_2$ even in light.†

Sugars or glycerol were required for dark growth and for more than minimal growth in the light.[166, 215, 239] Krebs cycle acids and amino acids did not replace sugars in this role, but markedly stimulated growth in the presence of sugar.

† Vishniac and Reazin,[314] however, have presented evidence that this apparent weakness of photosynthesis is actually a limited ability to evolve $O_2$ photosynthetically, and that the role of organic substrates in light is to serve as hydrogen donors for photoreduction ($CO_2$ reduction without $O_2$ evolution). Whatever may be the case in light, it seems clear that in darkness these substrates (glucose and glycerol) serve as both carbon and energy sources. *O. danica* is much more active photosynthetically than is *O. malhamensis*.[1, 239]

Respiration was stimulated by sugars, intermediates of the glycolysis and citric acid cycles, triacetin, acetate, and higher fatty acids.[244] There was evidence of adaptive increase in the ability to oxidize palmitate. Acetate was seemingly oxidized completely, with no assimilation. This lack of assimilation of acetate (and perhaps other Krebs cycle intermediates) may explain the failure to utilize such compounds as sole carbon and energy sources.

*Ochromonas malhamensis* grew anaerobically in light, but not in darkness.[215] In the absence of $O_2$, sugar was fermented to alcohol and $CO_2$. Tracer studies indicated that sugar catabolism was by way of the EMP glycolysis pathway.[245]

The carbohydrate reserves of *O. malhamensis* were found to consist of a $\beta$-1,3-linked polysaccharide of glucose, resembling the paramylon of the euglenoids.[13]

## Euglena and Astasia

The respiratory metabolism of the euglenoids *Euglena* and *Astasia* has been more thoroughly studied than that of any other group of phytoflagellates. Of the numerous species of *Euglena*, *Euglena gracilis* var. *bacillaris* has been the subject of most respiratory studies, although enough information is available concerning other strains of *E. gracilis* to demonstrate clear-cut strain differences. The related colorless euglenoids, *Astasia klebsii* and *A. longa*, have likewise been the subject of investigation. Present information indicates that with respect to respiratory metabolism, the differences between *Astasia* and *Euglena* are no greater than those between the several strains of *E. gracilis*.

Like the other phytoflagellates, *Euglena* is of interest because its energy metabolism bridges the gap between photosynthetic and oxidative heterotrophic metabolism. *E. gracilis* var. *bacillaris* grew at the same rate photoautotrophically or by oxidation of organic carbon sources in the dark.[76] For the Mainx and Vischer strains of *E. gracilis* photosynthesis appeared to be more effective than heterotrophic sources of carbon and energy, while other species of *Euglena* have been reported to be obligatory phototrophs.[164, 165, 188] *Astasia* and the various "bleached" (chlorophyll-lacking) strains of *Euglena gracilis* are, of course, obligate heterotrophs.

In addition, *Euglena* effectively bridges the gap between the "acetate flagellates" and organisms for which sugars are usual carbon sources. Some strains of *Euglena* seem not to utilize sugars, others utilize glucose under certain restrictive conditions, while still others use glucose and other sugars readily under all circumstances.[238] The nature of these differences will be discussed below.

While there is practically no published information on the metabolic behavior of *Euglena* or *Astasia* under anaerobic conditions, oxygen was

required for growth, but not survival, of *Astasia*.[335] Certainly the metabolism of these organisms has been found to be oxidative whenever oxygen
is available.

## ENZYMATIC PATHWAYS

While the evidence is far from complete, it seems likely that oxygen consumption by *Euglena* and its relatives occurs chiefly via a cytochrome system
similar to those found in the majority of aerobic organisms. In *Astasia
klebsii*, Von Dach[324] found spectroscopic absorption bands at wavelengths
corresponding approximately to those of cytochromes a, b, and c of other
organisms. The bands disappeared on aeration, and the disappearance was
blocked by cyanide, as would be expected for a functional cytochrome
system. Cyanide markedly inhibited oxygen consumption, although respiration continued at a low rate (equal to about one-half the endogenous rate)
in the presence of 0.01 M cyanide. The presence of slow cyanide-insensitive
respiration is typical of many organisms in which the cytochrome system is
the main pathway of respiratory electron transfer.

Three different cytochrome pigments, all of the cytochrome c type, have
been isolated from *Euglena gracilis*, one from the *bacillaris* variety[225] and
two from the z strain.[125] Two of these were present only in light-grown
cells, disappearing with the loss of chlorophyll which occurs in the absence
of light, and hence were considered likely to function in photosynthesis rather
than respiration. The third type was found only in dark-grown cells, and
hence may be concerned in respiration. Its spectrum, however, was more like
the photosynthetic cytochromes than like the respiratory cytochrome c.
Clearly, much further work will be required to sort out the various *Euglena*
cytochromes and identify their functions. The development of methods for
the differential isolation of mitochondria and chloroplasts from *Euglena*
would provide a major step toward differentiating the respiratory from the
photosynthetic cytochromes.

Of the enzymes of EMP glycolysis, hexokinase, aldolase, isomerase,
DPN-linked phosphoglyceraldehyde dehydrogenase, and alcohol dehydrogenase have been reported in *E. gracilis* var. *bacillaris* while lactic dehydrogenase was not detected.[33, 159] The presence of two D-lactic dehydrogenases, one DPN-linked and the other not, has been reported in *E. gracilis*
strain z, however.[237a] A TPN-linked phosphoglyceraldehyde dehydrogenase was also present in green strains of *E. gracilis*, but absent in dark-
grown or permanently bleached strains.[47, 11] The amount of this enzyme
closely paralleled the amount of chlorophyll, suggesting that its activity was
involved in photosynthetic rather than respiratory metabolism. Fructose-1,
6-diphosphatase, also found in *Euglena*, is likewise believed to be concerned
in photosynthesis.[293] In *Astasia longa*, hexokinase, phosphoglucomutase,
and lactic dehydrogenase were detected; tracer studies indicated that the EMP
pathway, rather than the HMP shunt, was the main route of glucose cata-

bolism.[28] The major phosphorylated intermediates of glycolysis were found in *Euglena*.[9]

Of the enzymes of the HMP shunt, glucose-6-phosphate dehydrogenase and 6-phosphogluconate dehydrogenase (both TPN-linked) were found in *Euglena*.[159]

The presence of uridine diphosphoglucose pyrophosphorylase in *Euglena*[159] suggests that, as in other organisms,[182, 253] polysaccharide synthesis is by way of uridine diphosphoglucose.

Of the TCA cycle enzymes, acetic thiokinase, the citrate "condensing enzyme", aconitase, TPN-linked isocitric dehydrogenase, succinic dehydrogenase, fumarase, and malic dehydrogenase have been demonstrated in *A. longa*, and malonate was found to inhibit acetate oxidation.[150] In *E. gracilis* var. *bacillaris*, most of the TCA cycle acids stimulated respiration of either intact cells or homogenates; synthesis of citrate from oxalacetate and pyruvate was demonstrated; and malonate and fluoroacetate were found to inhibit acetate metabolism.[79, 80] Citrate accumulated in fluoroacetate poisoned cells of *E. gracilis* and *A. longa*.[141]

The characteristic enzymes of the glyoxylate cycle have been demonstrated in *E. gracilis*.[131, 246]

Taken together, these data leave little doubt that the usual pathways of carbohydrate oxidation are present and functional in *Euglena* and *Astasia*.

Mechanisms of lipid synthesis in *E. gracilis* z have been partially characterized by Cheniae.[63]

## ENDOGENOUS RESPIRATION

Von Dach[324] found that *Astasia klebsii* cells harvested during the logarithmic phase of growth showed an initial endogenous respiratory rate of about $10 \mu l \ O_2$/million cells/hr. The rate declined sharply during the first two hours in inorganic medium and stabilized at about $4 \mu l \ O_2$/million cells/hr. This latter rate remained essentially constant through at least the seventh hour after harvesting. Similar results were obtained for cells harvested in the later, stationary phase of the growth curve, except that the absolute rates of respiration were considerably lower: $4 \mu l \ O_2$/million cells/hr initially, decreasing to a steady rate of $2 \mu l$/million cells/hr. Danforth and Wilson[84] and Buetow and Levedahl[52] reported similar results with bleached *E. gracilis* var. *bacillaris*. In both *Euglena* and *Astasia* these rates were essentially independent of the pH of the incubation medium, and at least in the case of *Euglena*, of the composition of the growth medium.

In *Euglena*, the final, steady rate of endogenous metabolism persisted for long periods of incubation (up to 26 hr in one experiment) in the absence of substrates,[84] indicating the presence of extensive reserves. Danforth and Wilson[84] found an average respiratory quotient of 1.05; Von Dach[324] found an average RQ of 0.96 with *Astasia*. These values suggest that carbohydrate (theoretical RQ, 1.00) was the major substrate of endogenous metabolism. This conclusion is in keeping with the fact that the euglenoids possess extensive polysaccharide reserves in the form of paramylon granules.[69, 120, 177] Starvation was followed by the disappearance of these granules[122, 236, 335] and marked decreases (81 %) in the paramylon content.[50] Fluoracetate was found to inhibit the endogenous respiration of Euglena by 68 per cent; a 66.7 per cent inhibition would be expected for oxidation of carbohydrate via aerobic glycolysis and the tricarboxylic acid cycle.[84] It seems, therefore, that the endogenous respiration resulted from the oxidation of paramylon stores via the conventional pathways of carbohydrate metabolism.

This being the case, it is more than a little surprising that studies by a variety of methods[81, 84, 335a, 337] indicate that the same process of reserve oxidation continues at an unchanged rate during the oxidation of exogenous acetate and ethanol,† since these substrates might be expected to compete for many of the same enzymes involved in endogenous metabolism. Whether the lack of competition is due to compartmentation within the cell, to chemical differences in the endogenous and exogenous metabolic pathways, or to other causes, remains unknown.

## UTILIZATION OF EXOGENOUS SUBSTRATES

Acetate supported heterotrophic growth and stimulated respiration of all strains of *Euglena gracilis* and *Astasia* which have been tested.[76, 80, 150, 324] A variety of other low molecular weight fatty acids, alcohols, and tricarboxylic acid intermediates likewise stimulated respiration, but the particular compounds which were effective in this regard varied from one strain to another. Thus, respiration of *E. gracilis* var. *bacillaris* was stimulated by all the tricarboxylic acid cycle acids tested except α-ketoglutaric acid, *cis*-aconitic, and citrate, and was also stimulated by acetate, propionate, butyrate, pyruvate, lactate, and ethanol.[80] In *Astasia longa*, most of the same acids, plus α-ketoglutarate and citrate, caused stimulation.[150] In *A. klebsii*, on the other hand, neither fumarate nor succinate stimulated respiration.[324] Although respiratory data are lacking, growth studies[76] suggest that the Vischer strain of *E. gracilis* is even more limited in its range of substrates.

The limitations in the ability to utilize exogenous substrates are certainly due in part to the limited permeability of the cell membrane. Thus, Dan-

† It has been customary to describe such a situation by saying that the "endogenous metabolism continues in the presence of exogenous substrate". The complications discussed in connection with Fig. 3 make the use of the term "endogenous metabolism" undesirable in situations where external substrates are present. See also the discussion of acetate metabolism by *Euglena*.

forth[80] found that metabolites such as $\alpha$-ketoglutarate and *cis*-aconitate, which were not utilized by intact *Euglena* cells, stimulated the respiration of homogenates, and Hunter and Lee[150] obtained similar results with *Astasia*. Studies of the effect of pH on respiration also support the belief that cellular permeability is a major factor limiting the availability of exogenous substrates. It is well known that, in general, undissociated molecules penetrate cell membranes far more readily than do ions. Thus, one would expect the availability of the weakly acidic tricarboxylic acid cycle intermediates to be increased in acid media, where the proportion of undissociated molecules is greater than in neutral or basic media. This expectation has ample experimental confirmation, for *E. gracilis* var. *bacillaris*,[80, 336]† for *A. klebsii*[324, 325] and for *A. longa*.[150] As would be expected, tricarboxylic acids were found to be less readily utilized than dicarboxylic, while monocarboxylic acids were most readily available to the cells.

Weak monocarboxylic acids, such as acetic and butyric, were toxic to *E. gracilis* var. *bacillaris* and *A. longa* in acidic media.[80, 150] The more acid the medium, the lower the concentration at which toxic effects are apparent. This phenomenon, which has been observed with other phytoflagellates (see below), probably results from a tendency for the concentration of undissociated acid molecules to equilibrate across the cell membrane. When the pH of the medium is appreciably lower than that of the cytoplasm, such equilibration would result in the accumulation of high concentrations of acid anions within the cells[167, 336] and eventually to overpowering the intracellular buffering systems and acidification of the cytoplasm.‡

Not all of the differences in availability of substrates can be attributed to differences in simple, passive permeability. Cells of *E. gracilis*§ var. *bacillaris* utilized acetate readily at pH 7-8, although more than 99 per cent of the acetate is in ionic form at this pH. From the effects of pH and of acetate concentration on respiratory rate, it was concluded[83] that acetate entered the cells by two distinct mechanisms, simple diffusion of *undissociated molecules* and penetration of acetate *ions* by a process whose kinetics resembled enzymatic reactions rather than diffusion. The ionic mechanism appeared to be partially adaptive, since it was more effective in cells grown on acetate than in cells grown on other substrates, and since its activity sometimes increased suddenly during incubation on acetate. Similar ion-ransfer systems may explain the utilization of lactate, pyruvate, and oxalace-

---

† Rates of endogenous respiration, and of respiration on ethanol, are independent of pH within the same range.

‡ It is worth noting here that the effects of pH on the rates of substrate oxidation bear no consistent relationship to the effects of growth on the same substrates. In *E. gracilis* var. *bacillaris*, for example, respiration on succinate is almost twice as great at pH 5 as at pH 7, while the growth rate is highest at pH 7, where respiration barely exceeds the endogenous rate.[336]

§ As do all other strains of *Euglena* and *Astasia* whose respiration has been studied.

tate[80] at pH 7 by *E. gracilis* var. *bacillaris*. Lactate and pyruvate (oxalace-tate was not tested) did not stimulate respiration of *A. klebsii* in neutral media,[325] suggesting that these transfer systems are substrate specific and that the several strains of euglenoids possess different combinations of such systems.

The failure to stimulate respiration cannot, unfortunately, be taken as proof that the metabolite in question does not penetrate the cell membrane. As has been mentioned previously, compounds such as succinate and fuma-rate supported growth under conditions where they produced little or no stimulation of respiration.[336]†

Early studies on substrate utilization suggested that the euglenoids were typical "acetate flagellates", incapable of utilizing glucose or other sugars as substrates for growth and respiration. Cramer and Myers,[76] however, showed that *E. gracilis* var. *bacillaris* (but not the Vischer strain of *E. gracils*) was capable of growth on glucose.

In order for glucose utilization to occur, several rather restrictive condi-tions had to be fulfilled: (a) glucose had to be present during a long "adap-tation" period before growth began. (b) an acid medium was required, and (c) aeration with 5 % $CO_2$ greatly stimulated growth. Pringsheim[238] found that the cultured strains of *E. gracilis* fell into three groups with respect to their ability to utilize sugars for growth. One group, including the Vischer strain and the Mainx strain, appeared unable to use glucose under any conditions. A second group, typified by the *bacillaris* and z strains, grew on sugar under conditions similar to those described by Cramer and Myers. The third group, designated *E. gracilis* var. *saccharophila*, utilized sugar readily under ordinary growth conditions.

In the case of those strains which did not use sugar under any conditions, cellular impermeability to the sugar molecules appeared to account for this failure. Barry[28] obtained a glucose-utilizing mutant from a parental strain of *Astasia longa* which was unable to grow on sugars. Intact cells of the mutant strain produced $^{14}CO_2$ when incubated with radioactive glucose; cells of the parent strain did not. However, homogenates or extracts of both parental and mutant strains produced radioactive $CO_2$ from radioactive glucose, and hexokinase, phosphoglucomutase, and lactic dehydrogenase were detected in extracts of the parental as well as the mutant strain. Thus, the parental strain possessed the enzymatic equipment for oxidation of sugar, and failure of intact cells to carry out this reaction must probably be attributed to a permeability barrier.

Some progress has been made in untangling the peculiar requirements for sugar utilization by *E. gracilis* strains of the *bacillaris* and z type. In general, the finding of Cramer and Myers that low pH, adaptation, and high $CO_2$ tension favored growth on glucose has been confirmed. Meat extract, yeast

† In each case, respiration on these substrates averaged about 10 per cent above the endogenous rate, but this increase was within the range of probable error of the experi-ments.

8*

extract, tricarboxylic acid cycle acids such as pyruvate, succinate, and amino acids such as glutamic acid, aspartic acid, asparagine, and glycine also stimulated utilization, apparently substituting for $CO_2$ in this respect.[21, 159, 163, 238] In all cases the stimulatory effect was catalytic and the stimulatory compounds were effective in amounts too small to serve as sole carbon sources. Moreover, growth on sugar was "sparked" by compounds such as citrate, ethylenediamine tetraacetic acid, and glycine, which could not by themselves support growth of the strains in question. In the case of citrate and ethylenediamine tetraacetic acid, the "sparking" effect seems to be related to the ability to bind metal ions in chelate complexes.[159] There is apparently some interaction between the sparking effects of low molecular weight carbon compounds and the effects of pH, since heavy growth may be obtained on glucose in neutral media containing citrate or glycine[159] but not in the absence of such substances.

Although glucose supported excellent growth of *E. gracilis* var. *bacillaris* (provided the conditions described above are met), it has proved difficult or impossible to demonstrate any stimulation of respiration in the presence of glucose under similar conditions.[159] The reasons for the failure of glucose to stimulate respiration are unknown; one possibility is that glucose metabolism (unlike acetate metabolism) replaces, rather than sums with, the reserve catabolism (Fig. 3). In contrast, Barry[28] found that glucose caused appreciable stimulation of the respiration of the glucose-utilizing mutant of *A. longa*.

## ACETATE OXIDATION AND ASSIMILATION

Using cells harvested by the usual centrifugal methods, most workers have found the respiratory rate of acetate grown *E. gracilis* var. *bacillaris* on acetate to be about 20–30 μl/million cells/hr.[49, 52, 83] Buetow,[48] however, found that centrifugation markedly decreased the respiratory rate. Cells harvested with only 1 min centrifugation respired at a rate of 54 μl $O_2$/ million cells/hr and it was estimated that the rate might be more than 60 μl/million cells/hr with no centrifugation. As with the endogenous respiration, the rate of acetate respiration of *E. gracilis* and *A. longa* was also depressed by "crowding" to cell concentrations greater than 50 thousand cells per ml.[335] The rate of acetate oxidation by cells grown on ethanol or other substrates was somewhat lower than that of acetate-grown cells.[83]

Von Dach[324] reported respiratory rates of 40–60μl $O_2$/million cells/hr for logarithmic phase *Astasia klebsii* on acetate; rates of stationary phase cells were about half this great.

During heterotrophic nutrition, a single major organic substrate often serves as both an energy and carbon source. A portion of the substrate carbon is oxidized to $CO_2$, providing energy for assimilation of the remainder of the carbon into cellular material. In the case of acetate, nonphotosynthetic

*E. gracilis* var. *bacillaris* and *Astasia longa* converted 42 per cent of the acetate carbon to $CO_2$, while the remaining 58 per cent was assimilated.[81, 337, 335a] This oxidation-assimilation ratio was found to be constant under all experimental conditions tested, including conditions which greatly altered the *rate* of acetate utilization.

Studies of the carbon-oxygen balance and tracer studies of this oxidative assimilation process indicate that the major product of acetate assimilation has the empirical composition of carbohydrate, and that the polysaccharide, paramylon, is the main assimilatory product under these conditions.[200, 337] This preferential synthesis of carbohydrate, instead of the mixture of cellular components required for balanced growth, may have resulted from experimental conditions which minimized cell multiplication (i.e. media deficient in nitrogen, minerals, and $CO_2$,† dense cell populations, and constant shaking). Partial carbon-balance experiments on growing *Astasia*, however, indicated an identical oxidation-assimilation ratio, and hence probably similar assimilatory products.[335a] Possibly acetate is initially assimilated as carbohydrate, and the carbohydrate later converted to proteins, fats, and other cellular constituents. If so, the procedure of the carbon balance studies would have included these later conversions in the "endogenous metabolism", rather than in the acetate carbon balance.

Danforth[81] used radioactive carbon to study separately the fates of the carboxyl and methyl carbons during the oxidative assimilation of acetate. The carbon distribution agreed with that previously found for starch synthesis from acetate by *Polytomella*, (see below) and was in close agreement with the theoretical distribution expected if assimilation involved synthesis of oxalacetate via the glyoxylic acid cycle, decarboxylation of the oxalacetate to pyruvate, and conversion of pyruvate to carbohydrate by a process resembling reversal of glycolysis.

Although oxidation of reserves continues during oxidation of exogenous acetate, Danforth and Wilson[84] presented evidence that assimilation of acetate "dilutes" the reserves with carbon derived from the acetate. Thus, when [14]C-labeled *Euglena* were incubated with unlabeled acetate, the extent of labeling of the $CO_2$ decreased with time, until 70–90 per cent of the "endogenous" $CO_2$ was derived from the unlabeled acetate carbon. This dilution of the reserves is far greater than would be expected if the acetate carbon mixed freely with the total carbohydrate reserves. To explain these results, Danforth and Wilson, [84] postulated that a pool of "labile reserve" materials, constituting a small fraction of the total reserves, was both the immediate product of acetate assimilation and the immediate substrate of endogenous metabolism.‡

† $CO_2$ is essential for the growth of several species of flagellates,[167a, 240] but not for normal respiratory rates.[237]

‡ It is quite possible that this "labile reserve" is simply the surface layers of the paramylon granules.

Marzullo,[199, 200] found that the products of acetate assimilation could be separated into two fractions on the basis of solubility in 60 per cent ethanol. The ethanol-soluble fraction increased rapidly at first, but soon reached a plateau at a relatively low level. The rate of formation of the ethanol-insoluble fraction was slow at first, but increased rapidly to a linear rate which persisted as long as acetate assimilation continued. Kinetic analysis indicated that the ethanol-soluble fraction was composed of two subfractions, of which the first to appear was probably the precursor of the insoluble fraction. The insoluble fraction was shown to be composed almost entirely of paramylon; the composition of the soluble subfractions is still unknown.

In synchronized cultures of *A. longa*, the respiratory rate per cell on acetate remained constant throughout the entire life cycle.[337a] This finding implies that there was no increase in respiratory activity during interphase, although cell weight increased appreciably during this phase, and that the respiratory rate doubled rather suddenly at approximately the time of cell division.

## ETHANOL METABOLISM

Like acetate, ethanol is oxidatively assimilated by *E. gracilis* var. *bacillaris*. The rates of respiration on ethanol average about the same as those on acetate, but in individual batches of cells, respiration may be either faster, slower, or equal to that on acetate.[83, 107a] The rate of respiration on ethanol shows considerable dependence on the ethanol concentration, decreasing with decreasing ethanol concentrations below about 10 mM.

For each molecule of ethanol consumed (in the absence of a useful nitrogen source) 0.97 molecules of $O_2$ were consumed, and 0.29 molecules of $CO_2$ produced,[107a, 337] indicating that about 85 per cent of the ethanol carbon was assimilated and only about 15 per cent oxidized to $CO_2$. Unlike the findings with acetate, the RQ was incompatible with the assumption that carbohydrate was the major assimilatory product, and suggested that appreciable amounts of more reduced products, perhaps lipids, were produced during ethanol assimilation.

The presence of ethanol plus acetate usually resulted in a respiratory rate higher than that on acetate alone,[49, 81] while the rate of acetate consumption was unchanged.[81] Thus, acetate and ethanol are oxidized simultaneously when both substrates are present. Under these conditions, however, a larger proportion of acetate carbon (67–80%) was assimilated than when acetate was the sole substrate (58%), and carbon balance studies suggested assimilation of acetate carbon into products more reduced than carbohydrate. As would be expected, the effects of ethanol metabolism were more striking in ethanol-grown than in acetate-grown cells.

## Chilomonas paramecium

*Chilomonas paramecium*, a non-photosynthetic cryptomonad, is one of the most thoroughly studied of the typical "acetate flagellates." It did not grow on glucose, glucose-1-phosphate, hexose diphosphate, dihydroxy-acetone, or any of some twenty naturally-occurring $\alpha$-amino acids. The only compounds which have been found to serve as carbon and energy sources are acids related to the Krebs tricarboxylic acid cycle[141] and even number straight chain fatty acids and alcohols.[74] Odd numbered fatty acids and alcohols were toxic,† and the branch-chained compounds inert.

Cytochrome c and cytochrome oxidase have been detected in *Chilomonas*.[160]

Of the compounds tested by Holz,[141] all of those which supported growth also stimulated respiration, and *vice versa*. It seems probable that the higher fatty acids and alcohols which support growth would also stimulate respiration, but this remains to be tested.

A variety of other indications point to the tricarboxylic acid cycle as the major pathway of respiratory metabolism in this species. Oxidation of pyruvate, acetate, $\alpha$-ketoglutarate and succinate was inhibited by malonate and by fluoroacetate. The malonate inhibition was somewhat reversed by succinate, and citrate accumulated during fluoroacetate inhibition.[141]

Limitations of permeability apparently are important in determining which substrates may be utilized. Thus, citric, *cis*-aconitic, and isocitric acids did not support either growth or respiration, although the accumulation of citrate during fluoroacetate poisoning clearly implicated these tricarboxylic acids as metabolic intermediates. These bulky, strongly-ionized hydrophilic compounds are, however, precisely those which the cell membrane might be expected to exclude. In the case of those acidic substrates which were utilized, utilization was dependent on the pH of the medium and in general, the stronger the acid, the lower the optimal pH, suggesting that the cells are relatively impermeable to the anionic forms of the acids. Pyruvate and lactate were exceptions to this rule, being utilized over a wide range of pH. The failure to utilize amino acids, even those immediately related to Krebs cycle intermediates, may well be due to impermeability; Cirillo[63a] found amino acids to be ineffective as nitrogen sources for *Chilomonas*.

Possible reasons for the failure of acetate flagellates to utilize glucose and related compounds will be discussed below.

Hutchens and co-workers[36, 160-62] have made extensive and valuable studies on the carbon and energy balance of acetate utilization by *Chilomonas*. For cells in logarithmic growth (generation time about 5.5 hr), the balance sheet shown in Table I (see p. 290) was derived.[162] Cellular protein, carbohydrate,‡

---

† Probably because they interfere with the metabolism of $\beta$-alanine and pantothenate.[311]

‡ The polysaccharide reserves of *C. paramecium* are composed of starch containing approximately equal proportions of amylose and amylopectin.[12, 162]

and fat, plus $CO_2$, accounted for some 88 per cent of the acetate carbon consumed; no organic carbon was released into the medium. Two independent methods of estimation (respiration measurements and cellular carbon determinations) indicated that 50–55 per cent of the acetate carbon was assimilated, and the remainder oxidized to $CO_2$.

Measurements were also made of heat production during the utilization of acetate and ethanol.[36] From the heat produced during acetate consumption, and the heats of formation of fat, carbohydrate, and $CO_2$ from acetate, it was estimated that 57 per cent of the acetate was oxidized and 43 per cent assimilated. Since no accurate values for the heat of formation of protein were available (the calculations, in effect, assumed that the heat cost of protein synthesis equaled that of starch synthesis) these estimates of carbon balance are reasonably close to those derived previously by chemical methods. In the absence of ammonia, to eliminate protein synthesis, similar calculations indicated oxidation of 40 per cent of the acetate carbon, a value in very close agreement with that already cited for *Euglena* under similar conditions.

From these data, tentative calculations of the free-energy efficiency of acetate utilization could be made. In the absence of ammonia, some 31 per cent of the available free energy appeared to be used for synthetic purposes, while only about 18 per cent was used in the presence of ammonia. The latter figure is less certain, because of the unknown energetics of protein synthesis; lower efficiency would probably be expected, however, for the growth process in the presence of ammonia than for the simple conversion of acetate to fat and carbohydrate reserves.

Similar, though less extensive, studies were made on ethanol metabolism, and carbon and free energy efficiencies calculated on the assumption that ethanol is oxidized to acetate, some of which is oxidized and the remainder assimilated. These estimates, however, are subject to considerable uncertainty because the products of ethanol assimilation were assumed, without evidence, to be identical with those of acetate assimilation.

Estimations of free-energy efficiency of growth and substrate assimilation involve many theoretical and practical difficulties. The estimates just cited for *Chilomonas* are among the best recorded for any organism, and those publications plus the review by Hutchens[161] should be consulted for an appreciation of the problems involved and the methods available.

## Polytomella caeca

*Polytomella caeca*, a nonphotosynthetic phytomonad, is another acetate flagellate, differing somewhat from *Chilomonas* in its abilities to utilize exogenous carbon sources. Glucose, maltose, sucrose, and trehalose failed to support growth,[189, 190] while glyceraldehyde permitted a doubtful growth which may have been due to contaminants.[342] This failure to utilize exogenous carbohydrate is particularly striking in view of the well-documented occurrence of intracellular starch synthesis and utilization (see below), and of the demonstration of glucose-1-phosphate, glucose 6-phosphate, fructose-6-phosphate, triose phosphate, phosphoglycerate, and phosphoenolpyruvic acid in homogenates.[343]

Like *Chilomonas paramecium*, *Polytomella caeca* grew on a variety of tricarboxylic acid cycle acids, straight-chain fatty acids, and alcohols. There are, however, significant differences in the pattern of substrates utilized by the two species. *Polytomella* was unable to grow on fumarate, malate, or lactate, ($\alpha$-ketoglutarate gave questionable growth). On the other hand, odd-numbered fatty acids, which were toxic for *Chilomonas*, supported growth of *Polytomella*.[342, 343] Once again cellular permeability seems to be a major factor limiting the availability of substrates, since Wise[344] found evidence for lactic, malic, succinic, and $\alpha$-ketoglutaric dehydrogenases, and for fumarase in homogenates of *P. caeca*.

Less extensive studies indicated that *P. agilis* has a similar (though not necessarily identical) pattern of substrate specificity.[186]

As in other flagellates, utilization of acidic substrates (in contrast to the corresponding alcohols) was markedly dependent on the pH of the growth medium. In general, the lower the $pK_a$ of the substrate, the lower the optimum pH for utilization. Wise[342, 343, 344] found that with most acids, the optimal pH range narrowed and shifted in the alkaline direction with increasing acid concentration. These are the relationships which would be expected if on the one hand, only the undissociated acid molecules penetrated the cell membrane, while on the other hand, suboptimal pH caused accumulation of toxic amounts of acid within the cell.

In the case of acetate, however, chloroacetic acid was found to inhibit oxidation by intact cells, but not by homogenates.[344] This probably indicates that chloroacetate interferes with transport of acetate across the cell membrane, which in turn suggests that penetration of acetate, at least, occurs by some substrate-specific transport system rather than by simple diffusion.

*P. caeca* grown on acetate or ethanol stored large amounts of carbohydrate in the form of starch.[40, 189, 190] The presence of isocitrate lyase, as well as other evidence,[131] suggests that the glyoxylate cycle is operative in starch synthesis in *P. caeca* and *P. agilis*. The properties and metabolism of this starch have been extensively studied by Bourne and his co-workers and are reviewed by Barker and Bourne.[27] The starch was similar to that of higher plants, consisting of a mixture of amylose (straight chain) and amylopectin (branched) components; the amylose content was somewhat lower than that typical of most higher plants.[40] Phosphorylase activity and glucose-1-phosphate were demonstrated in cell-free extracts, while amylosucrase and amylomaltase could not be detected.[30, 189, 190] In view of the similarity of starch metabolism of *P. caeca* to that of plants in general, it seems probable that the phosphorylase acts primarily in starch degradation, and that synthesis will be found to occur via the uridinediphosphoglucose pathway.[182, 253] Conversion of amylose to amylopectin was catalyzed by a "Q-enzyme"; indeed, *Polytomella* has served as an important source of enzyme for studies of the characteristics and mechanism of this conversion.[26, 30, 31]

When starch was synthesized from $^{14}C$-labeled acetate, a much larger porportion of the acetate methyl carbon than of the carboxyl carbon was incorporated into starch; more of the carboxyl than of the methyl carbon was converted to $CO_2$. The distribution of methyl and carboxyl carbons is consistent with the conversion of acetate to oxalacetate via the glyoxylate cycle, decarboxylation of the oxalacetate to pyruvate, and conversion of pyruvate to starch by a reversal of EMP glycolysis.[27, 34, 35] Similar results and conclusions concerning paramylon synthesis from acetate by *Euglena* have already been cited.

## Polytoma

*Polytoma uvella* is another nonphotosynthetic acetate flagellate (Phytomonadida), resembling *Chilomonas* and *Polytomella* in many respects. Cirillo[64, 65, 66] has studied the respiration of *P. uvella* on acetate and higher fatty acids. The endogenous respiration of this organism was very low, about 0.5 $\mu l$ $O_2$/million cells/hr,[64] as compared with rates of 25–50 $\mu l$ million cells/hr on acetate.[65] The presence of a nitrogen source ($NH_4Cl$) stimulated the rate of respiration on acetate about 15 per cent, and increased the fraction of acetate oxidized from 43 to 49 per cent, with a corresponding decrease in the fraction assimilated. The rates and efficiencies of acetate utilization thus appear to resemble those of *Euglena* and the other acetate flagellates described above.

Cells grown on acetate oxidized butyrate and caproate very slowly at first but the rate of respiration increased as much as 6-fold during continued incubation on these substrates. This adaptation to fatty acid oxidation occurred within a few hours, and apparently involved the induced synthesis of one or more of the enzymes of fatty acid oxidation. A nitrogen source was required for the induction process, and the induction was inhibited by ultraviolet irradiation.[64, 65] The induction was reversed by 24 hr in acetate medium.

In addition to this short-term adaptation to fatty acid *oxidation*, there was a second, long-term adaptive process which permitted *growth* on the same substrates.[66] The generation time of acetate-grown cells on butyrate continued to decrease for some ten generations in butyrate media. This increase in growth rate was, nevertheless, too rapid to be accounted for by any probable rate of mutation and selection. Adaptation to butyrate and caproate was sequential, prior growth on butyrate decreased but did not eliminate the lag on caproate. Adaptation to growth on these substrates persisted for more than fifty generations in acetate medium, although the oxidative rates dropped to the non-induced level within three to four generations.

Attempts to adapt *P. uvella* to utilization of odd-numbered fatty acids have been unsuccessful.[66]

The glyoxylate cycle has been reported to occur in *P. uvella*.[173]

"Respiratory deficient mutants" of *P. uvella*, produced by carcinogens, have been reported.[117]

## Chlamydomonas and Related Flagellates

When grown in the dark, certain species of the photosynthetic genera *Chlamydomonas*, *Chlorogonium*, etc., like their non-photosynthetic counterparts, showed the characteristics of typical acetate flagellates, while others have been reported to utilize sugars. Studies of the respiration of these organisms have been rather few; most of the information relating to their "dark metabolism" has been derived from growth studies.[164, 165, 168, 296] As is pointed out elsewhere in this chapter, attempts to infer respiratory characteristics from growth, or *vice versa*, can be extremely misleading.

In certain species of *Chlamydomonas*, the ability to utilize exogenous organic compounds for growth was found to be highly limited. Lewin[184] found that *C. dysosmos* grew well on acetate, and slightly on pyruvate and lactate, but not on succinate, malate, citrate, glutamate, glycerol or glucose. Sager and Granick[265] found that only acetate out of some 33 sugars, Krebs cycle acids, lower fatty acids, alcohols, etc., permitted dark growth of *C. reinhardi*. Other species appear to have carried this restriction of heterotrophic abilities to its logical extreme, being obligate phototrophs, unable to grow in darkness on any substrate so far tested.

J. C. Lewin[183] made an extensive study of obligate phototrophy in *Chlamydomonas moewusii*. None of some 64 compounds, including essentially all of those which are known to support growth of other phytoflagellates and algae, permitted dark growth. Cell extracts, hydrolysates, or filtrates of light-grown cells were likewise ineffective, nor was there any evidence that toxic materials accumulated in the absence of light. Wetherell[331] made similar studies of *C. eugametos*. Cell division and protein synthesis were found to stop within 9 hours after removal from light, although motility and utilization of starch reserves continued well beyond this time. Supplementation of the medium with a wide variety of potential substrates and growth factors did not permit dark growth, nor did such supplements increase growth at limiting light intensities.

We have seen that restricted cellular permeability was found to be a major factor limiting the ability of other flagellates to utilize exogenous substrates, and it might be thought that obligate phototrophy is simply an extreme example of this limitation, in which the cell is impermeable to all potentially useful substrates. While it seems probable that such limitations

8a*

of permeability contribute to the phenomenon of obligate photoautotrophy, it is certain that they are not the complete explanation. This is shown by the fact that acetate, pyruvate, and succinate stimulated respiration of *C moewusii*.[183] A mixture of Krebs cycle acids stimulated respiration of *C eugametos*, although glucose did not,[331] and acetate stimulated respiration of an obligately phototrophic mutant of the normally heterotrophic species, *C. dysosmos*.[184] Clearly, substrates which support respiration must be entering the cells, and their failure to support growth cannot be attributed to permeability limitations.

R. A. Lewin[184] compared acetate metabolism of an obligately phototrophic mutant of *C. dysosmos* with that of the wild-type, which will grow on acetate in the dark. In both strains, addition of acetate stimulated respiration to about twice the endogenous rate, and increased the respiratory quotient from ~ 0.9 to ~ 1.0. Oxidation of cellular reserves continued during oxidation of acetate. With the mutant strain, 2 moles of $O_2$ were consumed for every mole of acetate utilized, indicating that all the acetate carbon was oxidized to $CO_2$, and none assimilated into cellular material. In the wild type, similar results were obtained immediately after addition of acetate, but on continued exposure to acetate, the $O_2$ : acetate ratio declined from ~ 2 to ~ 1, indicating that the ability to assimilate acetate carbon developed adaptively on exposure to acetate. No such adaptation occurred in the mutant. If the mutation to obligate phototrophy caused a block in the glyoxylate cycle but not in the TCA cycle, these findings would be accounted for. There is evidence that just such a block does occur.[131] The inability of the mutant strain to utilize acetate carbon for the synthesis of cellular materials provided a sufficient and satisfying explanation for the failure of this strain to grow on acetate. Azide and 2,4-dinitrophenol, which are known to "uncouple" oxidative phosphorylation, prevented dark growth of the wild-type on acetate, mimicking the effect of the mutation in this respect.[184]

The same explanation cannot, unfortunately, account for obligate phototrophy in other species of *Chlamydomonas*. In *C. moewusii* and in an obligately phototrophic mutant of *C. debaryana*, only 1.0–1.5 moles of $O_2$ were consumed per mole of acetate utilized, indicating that 25–50% of the acetate carbon was assimilated. The inability of these species to grow on acetate remains unexplained. In *C. mundana*, acetate metabolism and assimilation were stimulated many-fold by light.[107, 119] In this case, it has been suggested that photosynthetic phosphorylation provided ATP required for acetate assimilation.†

The respiratory quotient of 1.0 for oxidative assimilation of acetate by wild-type *C. dysosmos*, suggests, as in other phytoflagellates, that carbohydrate is the major assimilatory product of acetate.

† Studies of obligate phototrophy in algae are reviewed by Danforth.[82] Information from other algae sheds little additional light on the causes of the phenomenon in the phytoflagellates.

## General Discussion, Phytoflagellates

Insofar as enzymatic pathways are concerned, the respiratory metabolism of the phytoflagellates seems to be fairly conventional, with a strong emphasis on EMP glycolysis and the TCA cycle. Most of the peculiarities of the group appear to result from severely limited cellular permeability. Low permeability certainly plays a major role in determining which exogenous substrates are utilized and which are not. In the case of the acetate flagellates, failure to utilize glucose probably results from this cause rather than, as was once thought, from a deficiency of hexokinase or some other enzyme. The demonstration of hexokinase in wild-type *Astasia longa*, a strict acetate flagellate, and the finding that disrupted cells of this strain oxidized glucose, leaves little doubt that in this case only impermeability prevents utilization of exogenous sugars. By analogy, it seems likely that the same is true of other strict acetate flagellates. If so, the peculiar dependence of glucose metabolism on environmental factors in some strains of *Euglena gracilis* may reflect the sensitivity of a sugar "permease" system to these variables.

Similar permeability restrictions, and probably also enzymatic deficiencies, almost certainly contribute to the phenomenon of obligate photoautotrophy. In only a few cases has this phenomenon been fully accounted for; multiple causes are clearly involved, and in the majority of cases no completely adequate explanation is available.

The glyoxylate cycle appears to account for the ability of many phytoflagellates to use acetate and other two-carbon compounds as sole carbon and energy sources.

## TRYPANOSOMIDAE

The respiratory metabolism of the Trypanosomidae has been described in several excellent reviews,[191, 315, 316, 317] so the emphasis in the present discussion will be on the literature appearing after 1955.

## General Characteristics

The respiratory metabolism of all of the Trypanosomidae so far studied showed two very striking characteristics: (1) carbohydrates were by far the most readily utilized sources of carbon and energy, and (2), carbohydrate metabolism, although accompanied by rapid $O_2$ consumption, was incomplete, resulting in end-products less oxidized than $CO_2$. The major pathway of energy metabolism was thus a process of aerobic fermentation.

Rates of oxygen consumption on glucose were among the highest found in any protozoan group, when calculated on the basis of dry weight or of nitrogen content (rates per cell appear relatively low because of the small size of the cells). In view of the incomplete oxidation of the substrate, such rates indicate an extremely rapid carbohydrate consumption. Von Brand[315] has calculated that bloodstream forms of the African pathogenic trypanosomes consumed in one hour glucose equivalent to 50–100 per cent of their own dry weight.

The trypanosomids parasitic on vertebrates, with a few exceptions, pass through a complex life cycle, alternating between vertebrate and insect hosts. Vertebrate and insect stages of the same species differ markedly in morphology, and probably also in their metabolic characteristics. At least, in many species of trypanosomes, it has been shown that the metabolism of the culture form, the morphology of which resembles that of the insect stage, differs markedly from that of the bloodstream form in the vertebrate host.[264, 315, 316, 317] The biological and evolutionary significance of these differences will be discussed below.

Among the various species of *Trypanosoma*, differences in respiratory pattern show considerable correlation with the taxonomic groupings proposed by Hoare[138] (Table II, see p. 290) on the basis of morphological characteristics. The procedure in the following discussion, therefore, will be to describe in some detail the metabolism of one member in each taxonomic category, with briefer comments on other similar species.

## Trypanosoma cruzi (Group I)

Trypanosomes of the lewisi group (Group I) differ from those of all other groups in a number of respects.[316] The rate of glucose utilization of the bloodstream forms in this group was much lower than that found in other groups. The respiration of organisms in this group was markedly inhibited by cyanide, but relatively insensitive to iodoacetic acid and similar inhibitors of sulfhydryl enzymes; the reverse was true of members of the other groups. Of the members of the lewisi group, *T. cruzi* (also called *Schizotrypanum cruzi*) has been most thoroughly studied.

### ELECTRON TRANSFER

The sensitivity of the $O_2$ consumption of *T. cruzi* to cyanide and to azide,[14, 115, 263, 349] suggests the operation of a cytochrome system in this species. There is reason to doubt, however, that a conventional cytochrome system, if present at all, can be the major pathway of electron transfer to oxygen. Cytochrome c could not be detected by spectroscopic means, although absorption peaks resembling those of cytochromes a and b were present.[14, 115, 263] Baernstein[14] found that oxygen consumption, unlike that mediated by cytochrome c oxidase, was almost entirely insensitive to carbon monoxide, though Fulton and Spooner[115] found approximately 30 per cent inhibition with CO. Little[281] or no[14] cytochrome c oxidase activity could be detected in homogenates. Succinic dehydrogenase ([124, 275, 281,] but compare[7]) and a number of DPN-linked dehydrogenases[14, 15] from

*T. cruzi* reduced cytochrome c *in vitro*, indicating the presence of cytochrome c reductases.

Thus, the nature of the electron transfer system in *T. cruzi* remains a mystery. While the failure to demonstrate cytochrome c spectroscopically and the low or negative cytochrome c oxidase activities do not eliminate the possibility that these components are present in small amounts, the insensitivity of the respiration to carbon monoxide, if confirmed, almost certainly indicates that a typical cytochrome oxidase is not involved in the major pathway of oxygen utilization. On the other hand, the sensitivity of the respiration to cyanide and azide, the presence of substances resembling cytochromes a and b, and the presence of cytochrome c reductase activity all suggest that cytochrome-like pigments are somehow involved in electron transport. The glycerophosphate oxidase system which appears to function in electron transfer in other trypanosomes (see below) does not seem to be a major pathway of oxygen utilization in *T. cruzi*.[124]

## ENZYMATIC PATHWAYS

A number of enzymes of the EMP glycolysis pathway have been demonstrated in the culture form of *T. cruci*. These included aldolase, triose phosphate isomerase and DPN-linked 3-phosphoglyceraldehyde dehydrogenase.[14, 18, 241] Negative results were obtained for $\alpha$-glycerophosphate dehydrogenase and lactic dehydrogenase,[14] but against this negative evidence must be balanced the finding that the organism produced lactic acid[56, 263] and oxidized glycerol,[347] and that glycerophosphate stimulated respiration of cell extracts.[124] The question of the presence of $\alpha$-glycerophosphate dehydrogenase deserves reinvestigation, particularly in the bloodstream form, in view of the importance of this enzyme in electron transfer in the bloodstream forms of trypanosomes of other groups. While the evidence is not conclusive, it seems probable that the EMP pathway plays an important role in the glucose metabolism of *T. cruzi*.

Of the HMP cycle enzymes, glucose-6-phosphate dehydrogenase and 6-phosphogluconic acid dehydrogenase were found,[241] but inability to convert ribose-5-phosphate to lactate suggests that other HMP enzymes may be lacking. On the basis of indirect evidence, Raw[241] has suggested that the Entner-Doudoroff pathway (discussed below in connection with *Entamoeba histolytica*) may occur in *T. cruzi*.

Of the enzymes of or related to the tricarboxylic acid cycle, aconitase,[241] TPN-linked isocitric dehydrogenase,[8, 241] succinic dehydrogenase,[7, 14, 15, 281] fumarase,[241] fumaric hydrogenase,† DPN-linked malic dehydro-

---

† Fumaric hydrogenase catalyses the reduction of fumarate to succinate:

Fumarate + reduced flavoprotein → Succinate + oxidized flavoprotein

by a reaction which is not identical with the reversal of succinic dehydrogenase.[15]

genase,[14, 15] and "malic enzyme"[241] have been demonstrated in the culture form of *T. cruzi*.

A number of transaminases, which would permit oxidation of a variety of amino acids via the Krebs cycle, have been demonstrated in *T. cruci*.[14,15,29]

## ENDOGENOUS RESPIRATION

In the absence of exogenous substrates, cultured *T. cruzi* consumed $O_2$ at a rate† of 70–170 $\mu$l/mg N/hr[263, 318, 326, 346] at 30°C. The endogenous respiration of the bloodstream form at 37°C was almost identical to that of the culture form at 30°.[263] The nature of the endogenous substrate is unknown. It is unlikely that this substrate was carbohydrate, since analysis indicated that the total carbohydrate content of the cells was only about 0.25 per cent of their dry weight, none of which was glucose polysaccharide,[319, 334] since the RQ of endogenous metabolism was about 0.77 as compared with an RQ of 1.0 for glucose metabolism by this species, and since endogenous acid production was much less than that associated with carbohydrate metabolism.[263] The release of about 0.4 moles $NH_3$ per mole of $O_2$ utilized suggests that proteins or amino acids were being oxidized.[263] Lipid metabolism may also occur, since the cells have been found to contain a considerable amount of lipid.[319] Attempts to guess the substrate from the RQ are perilous in an organism known to carry out incomplete oxidations.

*T. cruzi* and other trypanosomes of the lewisi group appear to resemble the insect and plant trypanosomids in their ability to survive and, in the case of *T. cruzi*, to maintain active motility and respiration in the absence of exogenous substrates[263, 346] in contrast to the other mammalian trypanosomes which rapidly lose motility and die under endogenous conditions.

## SUBSTRATE UTILIZATION

The presence of glucose-stimulated respiration; oxygen consumption on glucose ranged from 1.5 to 4.5 times that in the absence of substrate.[263, 326, 346, 348] Stimulation occured in both the culture and bloodstream forms. Oxidation of glucose was markedly incomplete, with the consumption of only about 3.6 moles $O_2$/mole of glucose by the bloodstream form and about 2.5 for the culture form, as compared with a theoretical value of 6.0 for complete oxidation of glucose. Correspondingly, values for $CO_2$ production were 3.3 and 2.6 for bloodstream and culture forms respectively, again as compared with 6.0 for complete oxidation. Aside from $CO_2$, the major

---

† To facilitate comparisons, the respiratory rates of the Trypanosomidae have, when necessary, been recalculated to $\mu$l/mg N/hr by assuming that 1 mg/N is equivalent to 10 mg dry weight and $10^9$ cells. These proportions are correct within ± 50 per cent for all species of Trypanosomidae for which they have been determined;[259, 315, 326] no greater accuracy is claimed for the values presented here. Warren[326] gives reasons for preferring N content over cell number or dry weight as a basis for expressing respiratory rates.

end products of glucose metabolism were succinic and acetic acids; smaller amounts of lactic acid and traces of pyruvic acid were also produced by the bloodstream form. Acetic acid production was higher, and succinic acid production lower in the culture form than in the bloodstream form. In both cases, recovery of carbon was incomplete, suggesting that other, unknown, products may also be formed.[263]

Under anaerobic conditions, there was of course, no $O_2$ consumption and $CO_2$, instead of being produced, was actually consumed. Glucose consumption was increased by anaerobiosis and considerably more succinate was produced per mole of glucose.[263]

Fructose, galactose, mannose, maltose, and glucosamine were more or less readily oxidized by T. cruci, while a variety of other sugars caused little or no stimulation. Glycerol was utilized, but at a much lower rate than glucose and other sugars. Some stimulation of respiration occurred with 2-desoxyglucose, which is more commonly found to be an inhibitor of glucose metabolism.[347]

Since trehalose had been reported to induce infectivity in noninfective culture forms of trypanosomes, Bowman et al.[45] tested the ability of T. cruzi to utilize this sugar. No utilization was found except in the presence of a trehalase (splitting trehalose to glucose) originating in the blood used in culture media.

Of the Krebs cycle acids, pyruvate, isocitrate, $\alpha$-ketoglutarate, succinate, and malate stimulated oxygen consumption, though to a considerably lesser extent than glucose. Citrate, cis-aconitate, and fumarate produced little or no stimulation. Stimulation was greatest in acid media, indicating that permeability limited the ability of T. cruzi to utilize these substances. Malonate inhibited respiration, and the inhibition was reversed by succinate.[318, 348] Asparagine, glutamine, glutamic, and aspartic acids also stimulated respiration, presumably because they can be converted to the corresponding Krebs cycle acids.[347]

Although the evidence is not complete, the available data suggest that T. cruzi possesses the apparatus for carrying out all the reactions of the Krebs tricarboxylic acid cycle and hence for the complete oxidation of glucose. It is surprising, therefore, that in actual fact the oxidation of glucose has been found to be so markedly incomplete. In particular, as Von Brand[317] has pointed out, it is peculiar to find that succinic acid accumulated as a major metabolic end product when both succinic dehydrogenase and the succinate cleaving enzyme were present. It is possible, of course, that the activities of several of the Krebs cycle enzymes are simply too low to oxidize the products of glycolysis as fast as these products are formed, with a resulting accumulation of intermediates. The reported activities in extracts of these enzymes do not appear particularly low, however. It is also possible that peculiarities of the incompletely understood electron transport system limit the rates of one or more of the oxidative steps in the Krebs cycle, or that the action of these enzymes *in vivo* is inhibited by some other, unknown mechanism.

The mechanism of formation of particular end products is also doubtful in some cases. Pyruvic acid presumably is a direct end-product of the glycolytic reactions. Acetate might be formed through the decarboxylation of pyruvate, or from succinate by way of the succinate cleaving enzyme. Net accumulation of succinate cannot be accounted for solely on the basis of the reactions of the Krebs cycle, since formation of a mole of succinate by this route requires the consumption of a mole of oxalacetate, which in turn must be derived from succinate. The very active $CO_2$ fixation observed in *T. cruzi*,[263] and the observation that succinate formation in *Strigomonas oncopelti* was dependent on $CO_2$ tension (see also below), suggest, however, that succinate is derived by way of carboxylation of pyruvate to oxalacetate or malate. The enzymes of the glyoxylate cycle, if present in *T. cruzi*, might provide an alternative pathway for succinate formation.

Seaman[281] has suggested that the succinate cleavage reaction:

$$\text{Succinate} + \text{DPNH} + 2\,\text{CoA} \rightarrow 2\,\text{Acetyl-CoA} + \text{DPN}$$

may serve to reoxidize reduced DPN in a fashion analogous to the formation of lactate or ethanol in muscle or yeast fermentation. Aerobically this process is presumably unnecessary, since oxygen can serve as an electron acceptor for DPN oxidation,[124] while the finding that anaerobiosis decreases the production of acetic acid relative to succinic[263] does not support this hypothesis.

### Trypanosoma lewisi (Group I)

*Trypanosoma lewisi*, a second member of the lewisi group, shares a number of characteristics with *T. cruzi*. Thus, its respiration was found to be sensitive to cyanide and relatively insensitive to sulfhydryl inhibitors.[115, 259, 315, 316, 317] It also oxidized glucose with an RQ of about 1.0 and the formation of a variety of acidic end-products.[259, 263]

Unlike *T. cruzi*, *T. lewisi* has been shown to contain an essentially complete cytochrome system. Spectroscopic studies showed a band corresponding to cytochrome c, as well as bands for the other cytochromes. Inhibition of respiration by carbon monoxide, and reversal of this inhibition by light have been demonstrated unequivocally.[115, 259] Oxidation of DPNH, succinate and $\alpha$-glycerophosphate were sensitive to cyanide and to antimycin A, as in the conventional system.[124] The only evidence tending to cast doubt on the presence of a functional cytochrome system in *T. lewisi* is the failure to obtain more than very low cytochrome oxidase activity in extracts of this organism.[115] Further studies on this point are clearly desirable. The $\alpha$-glycerophosphate oxidase system seems to play a minor role, if any, in electron transport.[124]

The endogenous respiration of *T. lewisi* (bloodstream form) has been reported as 40–200 $\mu$l $O_2$/mg N/hr, decreasing sharply with time. The organisms survived several hours in the absence of substrate, but lost their motility. The endogenous RQ was about 0.8, and ammonia was produced.[259, 302]

Addition of glucose, fructose, or mannose stimulated $O_2$ consumption greatly, to about 600 $\mu$l/mg N/hr,[212, 213] while a variety of other carbohydrates and carbohydrate derivatives were ineffective. Glutamine was oxidized even more rapidly than glucose; glycerol, asparagine, and glutamic acid more slowly. Lactate, succinate, and several other Krebs cycle acids and amino acids caused little or no stimulation of respiration at pH 7.3, although lactate and succinate were oxidized by cell extracts.[124, 212, 259, 302] Malonate was found to cause some inhibition.[213]

The products of glucose metabolism resembled those of *T. cruzi*, with $CO_2$, acetate, lactate, and succinate accounting for most of the carbon. Anaerobically, there was net $CO_2$ fixation and a considerable increase in the amounts of succinate and lactate formed per glucose molecule.[259, 263]

The rate of respiration increased, and the rate of glucose consumption decreased, with the "age" of infection, so that the oxygen/glucose ratio increased from 1 to 3. $CO_2$ production and malonate inhibition increased during this time, suggesting that the extra $O_2$ consumption in "old" organisms was due to Krebs cycle oxidation.[213]

### Schizotrypanum vespertilionis (Group I)

*Schizotrypanum vespertilionis*, another member of the lewisi group, appears to be almost identical to *T. cruzi* in all aspects of respiratory metabolism so far studied.[346, 347, 348, 349]

### Trypanosoma vivax (Group II)

The trypanosomes so far considered have belonged to Section A of the genus *Trypanosoma*, which is believed to include the most primitive members of the genus. Groups II (vivax), III (congolense) and IV (brucei) belong to Section B, whose members are considered evolutionarily more advanced. Of these, the vivax group is regarded, on morphological grounds, as most, and the brucei group as least closely related, to the members of Section A.

*Trypanosoma vivax* is the only member of the vivax group for which respiratory data are available. Desowitz[86] has reported that, in keeping with its supposed intermediary position, the bloodstream form of *T. vivax* was moderately cyanide sensitive. Ryley[263] and Fulton and Spooner,[115] however, found no cyanide or carbon monoxide inhibition of respiration, and no spectroscopic evidence that any of the cytochrome pigments were present. Fulton and Spooner have suggested that the cyanide inhibition reported by Desowitz was an effect on leukocytes, since whole blood was present during his respiration studies. Fulton and Spooner[115] found no trace of cytochrome oxidase activity, while Ryley[263] found that addition of cytochrome c stimulated oxidation of paraphenlyenediamine or succinic acid by T. vivax extracts.

Extracts of T. vivax oxidized α-glycerophosphate only slightly more rapidly than succinate or DPNH,[124] whereas the species of the brucei group, in which glycerophosphate oxidase is believed to play a major role in electron transfer, showed much higher rates of glycerophosphate oxidation (see below). Thus, as in T. cruzi and T. congolense, the mechanism of electron transfer in the bloodstream form of T. vivax remains unknown.

In the presence of glucose, the rate of oxygen consumption of T. vivax bloodstream forms was about 800–2800 $\mu$l/mg N/hr and the rate of glucose consumption 3–18 mg/mgN/hr [86,263]. These rates resemble those of members of the brucei group, and are higher than those usually found among the lewisi group. The variability depends largely on the state of development of the infection in the host; trypanosomes from early infections with low parasitemia showed the highest rates. Strains carried in rats by direct blood inoculation did not differ significantly from sheep strains transmitted via the insect vector.[86]

Acetic, pyruvic, and lactic acids, glycerol and $CO_2$ were major products of aerobic glucose metabolism; anaerobiosis markedly increased glycerol and lactic acid production and decreased formation of acetic acid, pyruvic acid and $CO_2$. Traces of citrate, but no succinate, were found among the metabolic products.[263]

## Trypanosoma congolense (Group III)

On the basis of cyanide sensitivity and a number of other characteristics, the congolense group of trypanosomes has been considered to fall between the lewisi group and the brucei group in characteristics of respiratory metabolism.[315, 316, 317] T. congolense is the only member of this group whose respiration has been studied.

Respiration of the bloodstream form of T. congolense has been reported to be somewhat cyanide sensitive, less so than that of members of the lewisi group.[263, 315, 316, 317] Fulton and Spooner,[115] on the other hand, found respiration to be insensitive to cyanide, and suggested that reports of cyanide sensitivity were due to contamination of trypanosome preparations with white blood cells. Respiration was not inhibited by carbon monoxide, but was somewhat inhibited by azide.[115] Spectroscopic studies gave no evidence for the presence of any of the cytochromes.[115, 263]

Fulton and Spooner[115] obtained no evidence for the presence of cytochrome oxidase activity, while Ryley[263] found that oxidation of succinic acid and paraphenylene diamine by cell extracts was increased by addition of cytochrome c. No such stimulation of succinate oxidation by cytochrome c was found by Grant et al.,[124] however. Homogenates of T. congolense were capable of reducing exogenous cytochrome c.[115]

Thus, while some of the results are puzzling, it seems likely that the cytochrome system either is entirely missing or of very minor importance in the bloodstream form of *T. congolense*, which resembles the brucei group in this respect.

The mechanism of electron transfer in the bloodstream form of *T. congolense* remains problematical. While it is possible that the α-glycerophosphate oxidate system believed to serve this purpose in members of the brucei group (see below) is present, extracts of *T. congolense* oxidized DPNH and α-glycerophosphate at approximately equal rates.[124] while in the brucei group, glycerophosphate oxidation was several-fold more rapid than DPNH oxidation.

The culture form of *T. congolense*, on the other hand, was rather markedly cyanide sensitive,[320] and by analogy with other species (see below), it seems likely that the cytochrome system may be important for electron transfer in the culture form.

During glucose metabolism, the rates of oxygen consumption by bloodstream forms of *T. congolense* (about 1400 µl/mg N/hr) and glucose consumption (about 5 mg/mg N/hr) at 37° were similar to those of the brucei group, and somewhat higher than those of the lewisi group.[6] Ryley[263] found a considerably lower rate of $O_2$ consumption, which he tentatively attributes to the fact that his experiments were performed in salt solution in contrast to the serum used by other workers. The RQ for glucose metabolism was about 1.0.

In serum or whole blood and at low $CO_2$ tension, Agosin and von Brand[6] found that utilization of one mole of glucose by bloodstream forms of *T. congolense* resulted in the consumption of 2.4 moles of $O_2$, and the production of 2.4 moles of $CO_2$ and 1.3 moles of acetic acid, plus a much smaller amount of pyruvate. These end products accounted for all the glucose consumed. In Ringer-bicarbonate solution, with 5% $CO_2$, Ryley[263] found 0.5 moles $O_2$ consumed, and production of 0.50 moles $CO_2$, 0.36 moles glycerol, 1.00 moles acetic acid, 0.49 moles succinic acid, and traces of lactic acid. The production of succinic acid at high $CO_2$ tensions, but not at low tensions, supports the hypothesis (discussed in connection with *T. cruzi*) that succinic acid is synthesized by way of $CO_2$ fixation. The differences in $O_2$ consumption and $CO_2$ production reported by the two groups of investigators may be an effect of serum, as mentioned above.

Anaerobically, in Ringer-bicarbonate, there was a slight *consumption* of $CO_2$, increased production of glycerol and succinic acid, and production of pyruvic acid.[263]

The bloodstream form of *T. congolense* thus resembled *T. cruzi* and *T. lewisi* in producing large amounts of $CO_2$, succinic acid and acetic acid as endproducts of glucose metabolism, and differed markedly from the bloodstream forms of the brucei group (see below) in this respect. In the anaerobic production of glycerol, presumably as a mechanism for reoxidizing reduced DPN, however, it resembled the brucei group.

The cultural form (in the supernatant phase of diphasic blood agar medium, at low $CO_2$ tensions) consumed $O_2$ and glucose only one-half to one-third as rapidly as the bloodstream form. This difference can probably be accounted for by the fact that the culture forms were studied at 30°C, and the bloodstream forms at 37°C. The respiratory quotient was again, near 1.0. $CO_2$, pyruvate and acetate were the major aerobic end products, with smaller amounts of lactate, succinate, and glycerol also being formed. Anaerobically, no $CO_2$ was produced, while production of acetate and succinate was greatly increased.[320]

Respiration of the culture form of *T. congolense* was moderately, but distinctly, inhibited by fluoroacetate and malonate,[320] indicating that the reactions of the Krebs cycle play some part in respiration. The small magnitude of the effect may be due, in part, to low permeability.

Whether or not the reports of moderate cyanide sensitivity of the blood-stream form are correct, it seems clear that *T. congolense* and *T. vivax* are actually intermediate between the lewisi and brucei groups in many respects. The lack of measurable cytochrome pigments in the bloodstream form, and the anaerobic production of glycerol, link them with the brucei group, while the production from glucose of $CO_2$, acetate, succinate, and lactate are typical of the lewisi group. In *T. congolense* we see, in milder degree, the differences between bloodstream and culture forms which appear much more sharply in organisms of the brucei group.

## Trypanosoma rhodesiense (Group IV), Sub-group ii

The bloodstream forms of trypanosomes of Group IV (brucei group) have been found to differ from those in the lewisi group by the complete absence of cytochrome pigments and consequent insensitivity of respiration to cyanide, by producing almost no $CO_2$ during glucose utilization (RQ *ca.* O), and by the production of pyruvic acid and glycerol as almost the sole products of glucose degradation. In addition, the brucei group appeared to be more sensitive to sulfhydryl group inhibitors, more dependent on exogenous carbohydrates for survival and motility, and to utilize sugar at a somewhat more rapid rate. The cultural forms of the members of the brucei group, on the other hand, tended to resemble the lewisi group in these respects. As has been mentioned above, the congolense and vivax groups are intermediate in many respects between the extremes represented by the lewisi and brucei groups.

On the basis of characteristics other than respiratory metabolism, the brucei group has been divided into three subgroups, members of two of which have been subject to considerable metabolic study. Present information, however, does not indicate any consistent metabolic differences between these subgroups.

Trypanosomes of the brucei group have been found to be much more dependent on exogenous carbohydrate for maintenance of motility, respi-

ration, and survival than members of the lewisi group.[263] In the case of
*T. rhodesiense*, Tobie *et al.*[304] found little or no ammonia production during
cultivation in media with low sugar concentrations, in contrast to findings
with *T. cruzi.*[321] This suggests that *T. rhodesiense* did not oxidize protein or
amino acids from the serum-containing medium. However, although trypanosomes in the low sugar media utilized less glucose, growth was not limited,
but reached the same levels as in high-sugar media.


## ENZYMATIC PATHWAYS

The respiration of the culture form of *T. rhodesiense* was cyanide-sensitive,
and cytochrome a, but not cytochrome c was detected spectroscopically in
this form. Homogenates did not couple oxidation of reduced DPN to reduction of cytochrome c. These facts suggest the presence of a cytochrome
system different from the "classical" system shown in Fig. 2 in which cytochrome c is an essential intermediate.[264] In addition, there was evidence for
an alternative electron transfer system, insensitive to cyanide and to antimycin A, in the culture form.[124]

In contrast, the bloodstream form was insensitive to cyanide, and showed
no spectroscopic evidence of cytochrome pigments; all attempts to demonstrate a cytochrome system in the bloodstream form have given negative
or equivocal results.[115, 124, 263, 264] Instead, electron transfer in the bloodstream form seems to be via the glycerophosphate oxidase system discussed
below.

Of the enzymes of the EMP glycolysis pathway, hexokinase, glycerokinase,
aldolase, $\alpha$-glycerophosphate dehydrogenase, and lactic dehydrogenase have
been demonstrated in both the bloodstream and culture forms. Of the HMP
enzymes, TPN-linked glucose-6-phosphate dehydrogenase was found in
both forms while 6-phosphogluconic acid dehydrogenase was apparently
absent.[264] In agreement with these results, tracer studies indicated that
carbohydrate breakdown in the bloodstream form was via the EMP route
rather than the HMP shunt.[121]

Of the enzymes related to the Krebs cycle, aconitase, TPN-linked isocitric dehydrogenase, fumarase, DPN-linked malic dehydrogenase, TPN-
linked "malic enzyme", and oxalacetic decarboxylase were found in both
culture and blood forms.[264] Mechanisms for the oxidation of succinate
were also detected in both forms, although the activity in the bloodstream
form was very low.[124] Pyruvate oxidase was found only in the culture
form.[264]


## BLOODSTREAM FORM

There is considerable evidence that in the bloodstream form of *T. rhode-*
*siense*, electron transfer is carried out by the coupling of an L $\alpha$-glycerophos-

phate oxidase (I) with a DPN-linked L $\alpha$-glycerophosphate dehydrogenase (II).

$$\text{glycerophosphate} + \tfrac{1}{2}O_2 \rightarrow \text{dihydroxyacetone phosphate} + H_2O \qquad (I)$$

dihydroxyacetone phosphate + DPNH + $H^+$ → glycerophosphate + $DPN^+$ + $H_2O$ $\qquad$ (II)

$$DPNH + H^+ + \tfrac{1}{2}O_2 \rightarrow DPN^+ + H_2O \qquad (III)$$

The sum (III) of these coupled reactions utilizes oxygen to reoxidize DPN reduced during oxidation of respiratory substrates. In support of this scheme, it has been found that in the bloodstream forms of *T. rhodesiense* and other members of the brucei group (but not in the culture forms, or the bloodstream forms of the other three groups), the activities of glycerophosphate oxidase and dehydrogenase were much higher than those for oxidation of succinate and DPNH, and that the oxidation of DPNH by dialysed cell free preparations was greatly stimulated by the addition of catalytic amounts of dihydroxyacetone phosphate or glycerophosphate, as would be predicted on the basis of reactions I and II above. The rate of oxygen consumption by cell-free preparations of the glycerophosphate oxidase was considerably lower than the respiratory rate of intact cells, but this discrepency may be due to inactivation of the oxidase during the preparation of the extracts.[122, 123, 124]

As has been mentioned, *T. rhodesiense* showed almost no respiration in the absence of exogenous substrates. Glucose, fructose, mannose and glycerol caused marked stimulation of respiration, and promoted survival and motility. A considerable variety of other carbohydrates were not utilized. Aerobically, when both glucose and glycerol were present, both were consumed by bloodstream forms, each at about half the rate at which it would be used in the absence of the other substrate. Glycerol was not utilized anaerobically, but the presence of glycerol markedly inhibited anaerobic glucose consumption.[264] The nature of this glycerol-glucose competition is unknown.

Grant and Fulton[121] studied the metabolism of $^{14}C$-labeled glucose by the bloodstream form of *T. rhodesiense*. Aerobically, in the presence of serum and $CO_2$, 83 per cent of the radiocarbon was recovered as pyruvic acid, and 9 per cent as glycerol, with only traces of succinate and $CO_2$ being formed. Only about 1.5 per cent of the glucose carbon was incorporated into cellular material. Thus, the aerobic metabolism of this species appears to be an almost strict conversion of glucose to pyruvic acid:

$$\text{glucose} + O_2 \rightarrow 2 \text{ pyruvate} + 2H_2O.$$

Ryley[263, 264] found a somewhat higher glycerol formation, and traces of lactic, succinic, and citric acids. In all cases however, the great majority of the glucose carbon appeared as pyruvate.

Anaerobically, pyruvate and glycerol were formed in approximately equal amounts, and accounted for essentially all the glucose carbon.[121, 263, 264] The large anaerobic $CO_2$ fixation found in members of the lewisi group and in the culture form of *T. rhodesiense* was absent in the bloodstream form; instead, there was small net production of $CO_2$.[263, 264]

The distribution of the several carbon atoms of glucose among the pyruvate carbon atoms was found to be consistent with conversion of glucose to pyruvate via EMP glycolysis pathway, while the absence of any appreciable production of $CO_2$ from glucose appears to eliminate the HMP shunt or direct oxidation pathways.[121] Small amounts of glucose carbon were found in alanine, aspartic acid, glycine and serine (but not in glutamic acid), and in

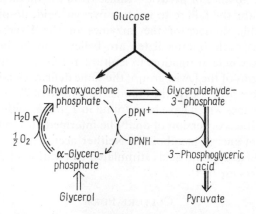

FIG. 4. Role of the $\alpha$-glycerophosphate oxidase system in the metabolism of trypanosomes of the brucei group. The main aerobic pathway of glucose metabolism is in heavy arrows, that of glycerol in double arrows, and the catalytic glycerophosphate cycle in broken arrows.

the glycerol and glycerophosphate (but not the fatty acid) portion of lipids. With labeled acetate as the substrate, radioactivity was found in fatty acids, but little or none in pyruvate or $CO_2$. With radioactive bicarbonate, some small amounts of radiocarbon were found in the carboxyl groups of succinate, practically none in pyruvate.[121]

The essentially quantitative conversion of glucose to pyruvate aerobically and to equimolar quantities of pyruvate and glycerol anaerobically can be accounted for by the operation of the EMP glycolysis pathway coupled with the L $\alpha$-glycerophosphate oxidase system, as shown in Fig. 4. In the presence of oxygen, the triose phosphates derived from glucose are oxidized quantitatively to pyruvate, with dihydroxyacetone phosphate and glycerophosphate acting catalytically, via the glycerophosphate oxidase system, to transfer electrons from reduced from DPN to oxygen. The same system can account for aerobic oxidation of glycerol to pyruvic acid. Anaerobically oxidation of one molecule of triose phosphate to pyruvate is coupled with reduction of a second molecule to glycerol (via glycerophosphate).

It has been suggested above that in *T. cruzi* and related species, formation of succinate as an end-product of glucose metabolism results from the carboxylation of pyruvate to form a four-carbon, dicarboxylic acid. The formation of small amounts of succinate and aspartic acid from glucose, and appearance of bicarbonate carbon in the carboxyl groups of succinate indicate that this process occurs to a very slight degree in *T. rhodesiense*, while the small amounts of these products, and the failure to detect appreciable $CO_2$ fixation, emphasize the relative unimportance of this pathway in the bloodstream form of *T. rhodesiense*.

The apparent absence of pyruvic oxidase from the bloodstream form[264] would account for the failure to oxidize pyruvic acid, despite the presence of a considerable number of the enzymes of the Krebs cycle.[264, 333] Since the Krebs cycle intermediates are believed to be involved in $CO_2$ fixation and succinate formation in culture forms generally, and in the bloodstream forms of the lewisi group, the same deficiency might account for the failure of these processes in the bloodstream form of *T. rhodesiense*. Those Krebs cycle enzymes which have been found in *T. rhodesiense* are presumably involved in the interconversion of anabolic intermediates, rather than in the main pathway of energy metabolism. Neither acetate, nor any of the Krebs cycle acids or related amino acids stimulated respiration of the bloodstream form of *T. rhodesiense*.[264]

## CULTURE FORM

As mentioned above, respiration of the culture form of *T. rhodesiense* has been found to be markedly cyanide sensitive, and cytochrome pigments, although not cytochrome c, have been detected in these forms. Glycerophosphate oxidation by cell extracts was slower than oxidation of succinate or DPN, indicating that the glycerophosphate oxidase system could account for only a fraction of the electron transfer activity. Such extracts oxidized DPN rapidly at the expense of $O_2$ even in the presence of cyanide and antimycin A, so that some non-cytochrome electron transfer system seems also to have been present.[124, 264]

As in the blood form, endogenous respiration was extremely small. The same sugars which stimulated respiration of the blood form also stimulated that of the culture form. In the case of the culture form, however, glycerol was consumed anaerobically as well as aerobically, and in mixtures of glucose and glycerol, glycerol was consumed to the near exclusion of glucose, both aerobically and anaerobically. There was significant stimulation of respiration by a number of Krebs cycle acids, especially at low pH, but not by acetate, pyruvate, lactate, or ethanol.[264]

The products of carbohydrate metabolism by the culture form differed notably from those of the blood form. In long term experiments, $CO_2$

production accounted for a large proportion of the glucose or glycerol carbon consumed; acetate and succinate, but no pyruvate or glycerol, were also formed. In shorter experiments, more acid and less $CO_2$ were produced, suggesting that partially oxidized products first accumulated and were later oxidized to $CO_2$.[264]

Anaerobically, succinate was the major product, and appreciable amounts of acetate were also produced, but no pyruvate or glycerol. Large amounts of $CO_2$ were fixed during anaerobic glucose or glycerol consumption, and these substrates were not consumed unless $CO_2$ was present.[264]

These differences between bloodstream and culture forms are typical of those found among the trypanosomes in general, especially those of the brucei group. In *T. rhodesiense*, the presence of pyruvate oxidase in the culture, but not in the blood form seems adequate to account for many of these differences. In the culture form, the activity of this enzyme would permit the pyruvate formed via the EMP cycle to enter the Krebs cycle and be oxidized nearly to completion, while lack of the enzyme would cause pyruvate to accumulate. Inability to carry on further breakdown of pyruvate would prevent anaerobic fermentation of glycerol by the blood form, for lack of an electron acceptor, while in the culture form, redox balance could be maintained by reduction of pyruvate to the levels of succinate or acetate. The importance of glycerol as an anaerobic product in the blood form seems to reflect the importance of the glycerophosphate oxidase system and the inability to degrade pyruvate, while the reverse situation results in the anaerobic formation of succinate and acetate in the culture form. No precise explanation can be given at present for the $CO_2$-dependence of anaerobic metabolism in the culture form, though it is possible that the $CO_2$ is required for the generation of electron acceptors.

In all of these characteristics, the culture form of *T. rhodesiense*, and of other members of the brucei group (see below) showed a closer resemblance to the members of the lewisi group than did the bloodstream forms.

### Trypanosoma gambiense (Group IV), Sub-group ii

*T. gambiense* and *T. rhodesiense* seem to be very similar in their respiratory characteristics.

The bloodstream form of *T. gambiense*, like that of *T. rhodesiense*, was insensitive to cyanide, azide, and carbon monoxide, and showed no evidence of the presence of cytochromes.[115, 263] Instead, the glycerophosphate oxidase system described for *T. rhodesiense* appeared to be the major pathway of electron transfer.[124]

In sharp contrast, respiration of the culture form of *T. gambiense* was markedly sensitive to cyanide and carbon monoxide, and the carbon monoxide inhibition was reversed by light. There was spectroscopic evidence for the presence of cytochromes a and b, (but not cytochrome c) and oxidation of glycerophosphate and succinate (but not DPNH) by cell extracts was distinctly reduced by cyanide and antimycin A. The relative rates of oxidation of glycerophosphate, succinate, and DPNH by such extracts indicate that glycerophosphate oxidase was not the main pathway of electron transfer in the cultural form.[115, 124]

Aerobically, bloodstream forms converted glucose to pyruvate in almost quantitative agreement with the equation:

$$\text{glucose} + O_2 \rightarrow 2\,\text{pyruvic acid} + 2\,H_2O$$

and with almost no formation of $CO_2$ or other end products. Metabolic rates were higher in blood than in serum, but the nature of the products was similar in both cases. Arsenic-resistant strains were generally similar to the normal strain, but showed somewhat reduced metabolic rates, and greater resistance to arsenicals and nitrofurans.[263, 322, 333] Anaerobically, *ca.* 1 mole of pyruvate and 1 mole of glycerol were produced for each mole of glucose utilized.[263]

In the culture form, on the other hand, aerobic utilization of glucose resulted in formation of 0.83 moles of acetic acid, 0.33 moles of succinic acid, 0.20 moles of pyruvic acid, and 0.17 moles of lactic acid, per mole of glucose, altogether accounting for some 72 per cent of the glucose carbon utilized.[263] In a separate experiment, the RQ was found to be close to 1.0, indicating a considerable $CO_2$ production, which probably accounts for much of the carbon not accounted for by the organic acids. The rate of oxygen consumption (per cell) of the culture form was about one-tenth that of the bloodstream form,[323] a difference too great to be accounted for solely on the basis of the difference in incubation temperature (29° *vs.* 37°C).

### Trypanosoma hippicum (Group IV), Sub-group iii

The bloodstream form of *T. hippicum* was found to be markedly dependent on exogenous carbohydrate for survival; no respiration occured in glucose-free saline medium, and equilibration without glucose for as little as five minutes often caused irreversible loss of respiratory activity.[134]

Rates of oxygen consumption were found to be proportional to glucose concentration up to about 0.003 M, and independent of glucose concentrations above this point. Maximum respiratory rates (38°C) were of the order of 1000 $\mu$l $O_2$/mg N/hr in saline and 1400 $\mu$l/mg N/hr in plasma. Glycerol supported oxygen consumption at a rate nearly 1.5 times that with glucose; $\alpha$- and $\beta$-glycerophosphate and glyceraldehyde supported respiration, but at lesser rates than glucose. Glycogen, hexose phosphates, lactate, pyruvate, and a variety of Krebs cycle acids caused no appreciable effect on respiration, either in the presence or absence of glucose. Respiration was almost entirely insensitive to cyanide and azide; concentrations of 0.01 M or greater being necessary to produce even minor (and almost certainly nonspecific) inhibition.[134]

Aerobically, glucose and glycerol were oxidized almost quantitatively to pyruvate, with consumption of the theoretical amounts of $O_2$. Anaerobically, one mole of pyruvate and one mole of glycerol were formed per mole of glucose oxidized.[134] The carbon balance was thus identical with that found in *T. rhodesiense* and *T. gambiense*.

Of the enzymes of the EMP glycolysis pathway, hexokinase, aldolase, and DPN-linked triose phosphate dehydrogenase could be demonstrated, while lactic dehydrogenase could not. Evidence was found for a glycerol kinase, which would permit oxidation of glycerol *via* the pathways shown in Figure 4, above, and for dehydrogenases acting on glycerol, and on $\alpha$ and $\beta$-glycerophosphates. The presence of glucose-6-phosphate dehydrogenase was questionable. Analysis of the cells revealed the presence of most of the phosphorylated intermediates of the EMP pathway.[134] These results are strong evidence for the operation of the EMP pathway in *T. hippicum*, and are in agreement with the findings for *T. rhodesiense*.

Attempts to demonstrate cytochrome oxidase, succinic dehydrogenase, and malic dehydrogenase gave negative results.[134] The lack of succinic dehydrogenase activity is rather surprising, in view of the positive evidence for succinic acid oxidation in other members of the brucei group.[124] The negative results may have been due to the use of assay procedures designed specifically for dehydrogenases leading into the cytochrome system.

### Trypanosoma brucei (Group IV), Sub-group ii, Trypanosoma evansi, Trypanosoma equinum, Trypanosoma equiperdum (Group IV), Sub-group iii

Insofar as these four species have been studied, their respiratory metabolism appears to be essentially similar to that of *T. rhodensiense* and the other members of the brucei group.[5, 62, 115, 124, 195, 198, 210, 251, 263, 302, 303]

In *T. evansi*, Marshall[198] made the interesting observation that cyanide, although having little effect on oxygen consumption, decreased the pyruvic acid formation from the usual 2 moles/mole glucose to 1 mole/mole glucose.

### Leishmania donovani

Much less is known concerning the respiratory metabolism of the leishmanias than about that of the trypanosomes. The intracellular habitat of the mammalian phase of *Leishmania* creates special difficulties in obtaining sufficient experimental material.

Respiration of the intracellular form of *L. donovani* was found to be cyanide sensitive and weakly sensitive to azide,[113] suggesting a relationship to the lewisi-cruzi group of trypanosomes. The culture form was distinctly more sensitive than the intracellular form, however.[60, 113] Inhibition by iodoacetate suggests the importance of glycolysis, while inhibition by fluoro-acetate, but not by malonate, may indicate that part but not all of the Krebs cycle is functional.[60, 113]

The endogenous respiratory rate of culture forms of *L. donovani* has been reported as 35–70 $\mu$l $O_2$/mg N/hr at 37°C,[60] 69–115 $\mu$l/mg N/hr at 30°C,[318] and as about 0.06 $\mu$l/million cells/hr at 25°C.[113] The rate decreased with increasing culture age, and was sensitive to pH, ion concentration, and other experimental variables. The RQ was about 0.8–0.9. The nature of the endogenous substrate was uncertain, but a polysaccharide containing glucose, galactose, and arabinose was found in the cells.

Respiratory rates of the intracellular Leishman-Donovan bodies were similar; the RQ was 0.55–0.69.[113]

Glucose, fructose, mannose, galactose, and ribose have been reported to stimulate respiration, while maltose, lactose, and a number of polysaccharides cause little or no increase.[56, 60, 113] Chatterjee and Ghosh[60] found marked stimulation with sucrose, and demonstrated invertase activity in *L. donovani* extracts,[59] while Fulton and Joyner[113] found little stimulation by sucrose. There is similar disagreement in the case of glycerol. The most stimulatory sugars more than doubled the respiratory rate of culture forms. Glucose metabolism of Leishman-Donovan bodies was considerably slower, only about half again the endogenous rate.

Culture forms consumed about 1.5 moles $O_2$ and produced about 1.5 moles $CO_2$ per mole of glucose consumed.[60] Other products of aerobic glucose metabolism included large amounts of succinate, and smaller amounts of acetate and pyruvate; ethanol, glycerol, lactate and a number of other organic acids were sought but not detected.[56, 77, 113]

Anaerobically, glucose was fermented, with the formation of 1.5–1.7 equivalents of acid per mole of glucose. No $CO_2$ or pyruvate were formed; the acid produced was mostly succinic. There was no Pasteur effect; the rate of glucose consumption was the same anaerobically as aerobically.

Chatterjee and Ghosh[60] found that malate, $\alpha$-ketoglutarate and pyruvate stimulated respiration of culture forms, while lactate, acetate, and other Krebs cycle acids did not. Fulton and Joyner[113] found no stimulation with pyruvate. Von Brand and Agosin[318] found stimulation by many Krebs cycle acids, especially at low pH. Pyruvate was consumed, though it caused little increase in respiratory rate. Malonate inhibited respiration on all the acids, and endogenous respiration. Glutamine, glutamate, asparagine, and aspartate markedly increased $O_2$ consumption.[60] A number of transaminases were found in *L. donovani*.[58]

## Leishmania enriettii

The culture form of *L. enriettii* was found to have an endogenous respiratory rate of 36 $\mu$l $O_2$/mg N/hr at 30°C. Glucose increased this rate to about 250 $\mu$l/mg N/hr. Fructose, mannose, galactose, several disaccharides, glycerol, and glucosamine also stimulated respiration. Pyruvate and many of the Krebs cycle acids were stimulatory, especially at low pH, while none of several amino acids tested caused stimulation. Respiration was markedly sensitive to cyanide and iodoacetate, and somewhat reduced by fluoro-acetate.[341, 347, 348, 349]

## Strigomonas oncopelti

*Strigomonas oncopelti* is a trypanosomid parasitic in the milkweed plant, and is considered to be more closely related to the "primitive" insect try-panosomids than to the members of the genus *Trypanosoma*.

Spectroscopic studies of *S. oncopelti* indicated the presense of cytochromes a, b, and c. Marked sensitivity of respiration to cyanide, azide, and carbon monoxide, and reversal of carbon monoxide inhibition by light supported the belief that electron transfer occurs via the cytochrome system.[115, 263] Low cytochrome oxidase activity has been reported; the weakness of activity may have resulted from technical difficulties.[115] Oxidation of succinate and glycerophosphate by cell-free extracts was inhibited by cyanide and anti-mycin A, as would be expected if the cytochrome system were operative. Oxidation of DPNH was, however, insensitive to these reagents, suggesting the possibility of an alternative electron transfer pathway. The rate of oxida-tion of L $\alpha$-glycerophosphate was too low for the glycerophosphate oxidase system (discussed in connection with *T. rhodensiense*) to account for any major part of the electron transfer process.[124]

No maltase, amylase, or phosphorylase activity could be demonstrated in *S. oncopelti*, a finding consistent with the apparent lack of endogenous poly-saccharide reserves (see below). Of the enzymes of the EMP glycolysis pathway, there was direct or presumptive evidence for hexokinase, phospho-glucomutase, ketoisomerase, aldolase and DPN-linked phosphoglyceralde-hyde dehydrogenase, and there seems no reason to doubt that this is the major pathway of glucose breakdown.[261]

Among the enzymes related to the Krebs cycle, evidence exists for the presence of pyruvic carboxylase, ethanol dehydrogenase, lactic dehydro-genase, succinic dehydrogenase, fumarase, and malic dehydrogenase.[115, 124, 261] Since carbohydrate oxidation was notably incomplete (see below) further study is desirable to determine whether or not the entire enzymatic mechanism of the Krebs cycle is present. Failure of malonate to inhibit respiration of intact cells (pH 7.3) may indicate that the cycle is inoperative, or may result from permeability difficulties.[261]

*S. oncopelti* remained motile and consumed oxygen at an appreciable rate (146 $\mu$l/mg N/hr) in the absence of exogenous carbohydrate, resembling trypanosomes of the lewisi group, and differing from the other trypanosomes in this respect. The RQ of this endogenous respiration was about 0.9. The low and somewhat questionable glycogen content of the cells, plus lack of endogenous acid production, make it unlikely that the endogenous substrate was carbohydrate. Anaerobically, on the other hand, metabolism and motility were dependent on the presence of exogenous carbohydrate.[261]

Suitable carbohydrates (glucose, fructose, or mannose) stimulated respiration by 150–300 per cent, while lactose, sucrose, maltose, galactose, and glycerol produced much less stimulation.[261] The RQ of glucose metabolism ranged from 1.0 in cells from old cultures to 2.4 in cells harvested during rapid growth. Carbon balance experiments in $CO_2$-bicarbonate media indicated that oxidation of glucose resulted in consumption of 0.38 moles of $O_2$ and production of 0.95 moles $CO_2$, 0.91 moles ethanol, 0.32 moles glycerol, 0.22 moles succinic acid, 0.28 moles pyruvic acid, and traces of lactic, acetic and citric acids, per mole of glucose. In the absence of $CO_2$, glucose utilization and succinate production were decreased. The products accounted for 5.61 out of 6 glucose carbon atoms.[261, 263]

The pattern and variety of end products produced from glucose generally resembled that found in the culture forms of the mammalian trypanosomes, and in the bloodstream forms of the lewisi group. *S. oncopelti* differed from all these, however, in producing large amounts of ethanol and glycerol, but only traces of acetic acid, and in having an RQ considerably greater than 1.0. The high RQ was probably associated with ethanol production, since conversion of pyruvate to ethanol results in release of a molecule of $CO_2$, without any corresponding increase in oxygen consumption. As discussed in connection with *T. cruzi*, production of succinate probably results from carboxylation of pyruvic acid to produce a 4-carbon dicarboxylic acid. Anaerobically, production of $CO_2$, ethanol, and glycerol was reduced by about half, and production of succinic acid approximately doubled.[261, 263]

Ethanol, lactate, succinate, and $\alpha$-ketoglutarate, aspartic acid, asparagine, glutamic acid, glutamine and alanine stimulated respiration to varying degrees.[261] Oxidation of these compounds suggests that many, at least, of the part reactions of the Krebs cycle occur in *S. oncopelti*, and again raises the problem of the causes for accumulation of incompletely oxidized products of carbohydrate metabolism, a general characteristic of the Trypanosomidae so far studied. The failure of citrate, pyruvate, and butyrate to stimulate respiration, and the slight inhibition of respiration with acetate and propionate[261] cannot be interpreted until more is known about the permeability of *S. oncopelti* to these substances. The oxidation of several amino acids is consistent with the suggestion (discussed in connection with *T. cruzi*) that protein may be the substrate of endogenous metabolism.

Development of chemically defined media for *S. oncopelti*[216, 217] opens the possibility of parallel studies on respiratory metabolism and growth.

## Crithidia fasciculata

Of the presumably primitive trypanosomids, whose entire life cycle is confined to invertebrate hosts, only *Crithidia fasciculata*, a parasite of mosquitoes, has been the subject of studies of respiratory metabolism. It is of especial interest, morever, because it is one of the very few trypanosomids whose nutritional requirements have been studied in chemically defined media.[79, 217, 218, 219, 220, 221]

Very little evidence is available relating to the electron transfer pathway in *C. fasciculata*. Succinic dehydrogenase from *C. fasciculata* reduced exogenous cytochrome c, and weak cytochrome c oxidase activity has been detected in extracts.[149, 281]

Of the enzymes of the EMP glycolysis pathway, hexokinase, enolase, and alcohol dehydrogenase have been detected in *C. fasciculata*. No phosphohexokinase, aldolase, or lactic dehydrogenase activities were found, but these negative results may have been due to technical difficulties. Of the HMP shunt enzymes, glucose-6-phosphate dehydrogenase was present.[267]

Of the enzymes related to the Krebs cycle, aconitase, TPN-linked isocitric dehydrogenase, succinic dehydrogenase, DPN-linked malic dehydrogenase, and fumarase, as well as pyruvic oxidase, acetic thiokinase, and succinate cleaving enzyme, have been demonstrated.[149, 281]

The organisms survived 12 hrs or more in the absence of exogenous carbohydrate. The endogenous oxygen consumption averaged 122–135 $\mu$l $O_2$/mg N/hr at 25°C in saline media without $CO_2$, and the RQ was 0.85. Ammonia nitrogen increased during endogenous metabolism, while total nitrogen, carbohydrate, and lipid remained constant, suggesting that proteins were the major endogenous substrates. This ammonia production did not occur in the presence of utilizable sugars.[73]

Glucose, glycerol, dihydroxyacetone, and other sugars stimulated respiration. Hydrolysis of sucrose, maltose, and cellobiose was shown with cell extracts.[73]

Aerobically, respiration on glucose was at about five times the endogenous rate. The RQ was 1.06 (considered to be significantly greater than 1.00) and, per mole of glucose, about 2.6 moles of $O_2$ were consumed and 2.7 moles of $CO_2$, 0.6 moles of succinate, 0.4 moles of ethanol, and 0.04 moles of pyruvate were produced. The products accounted for all the glucose carbon utilized indicating that none of the glucose was assimilated.[73]

Anaerobic glucose metabolism produced (per mole glucose) about 0.96 moles ethanol, 0.38 moles succinic acid, 0.38 moles $CO_2$, and 0.33 moles lactic acid, accounting for about 80 per cent of the glucose carbon.[267] Glycerol, acetic and pyruvic acids were not found. *C. fasciculata* appeared to differ from *Strigomonas oncopelti* in producing larger amounts of ethanol, smaller amounts of succinate, and little or no glycerol and pyruvic acid. Some of these differences, particularly the small amounts of succinic acid produced, may have resulted from the fact that *C. fasciculata* was studied in the absence and *S. oncopelti* in the presence of $CO_2$-bicarbonate.

None of the Krebs cycle acids caused clear-cut stimulation of respiration at pH 7.4, (although possible slight stimulation was found with oxalacetic and isocitric acids), but α-ketoglutarate and pyruvate stimulated respiration of starved cells at pH 3.0. Glutamine, glutamic acid, asparagine, and perhaps aspartic acid and alanine stimulated respiration at pH 7.4.[149] A considerable number of the lower alcohols stimulated respiration.[73]

In general, *C. fasciculata* (like *S. oncopelti*) differed from the cultural forms of the mammalian trypanosomes in the production of ethanol as a major product of glucose metabolism. The range of end products formed from glucose appeared to be somewhat more restricted in *C. fasciculata* than in *S. oncopelti*.

Although studies of the nutritional requirements of *C. fasciculata* (cited above) have concentrated more on requirements for vitamins and other trace nutrients than on bulk carbon and energy sources, they indicate that sorbitol and sucrose can substitute for glucose. Sucrose was less effective than glucose at temperatures above 30°C; a mixture of glutamate, succinate, and lactate partially counteracted the effects of increased temperature.[75, 221]

## Summary of Trypanosomes

A notable feature of the respiratory metabolism of the Trypanosomidae is the degree to which differences in metabolism have been found to parallel the supposed phylogenetic relationship within the group. Beginning with the presumably primitive insect flagellates like *Crithidia*, a steady narrowing and specialization of the metabolic patterns progresses throught the culture (insect?) stages of mammalian parasites, the bloodstream trypanosomes of the lewisi, vivax, and congolense groups, and culminates in the bloodstream forms of the brucei group. (The precise position of the leishmanias in this scheme remains uncertain until the respiration of the intracellular stages is more fully characterized; present indications suggest affinities to the lewisi trypanosomes.) If the culture forms of the mammalian parasites are considered as "embryonic recapitulations", this scheme corresponds in great detail with the evolution of the group as reconstructed from other evidence. This agreement is especially striking, because attempts to identify similar biochemical correlations with phylogenesis in other groups have given disappointing results, at least in the realm of respiratory metabolism.

It seems rather peculiar that this evolutionary trend should be in the direction of less complete oxidation of substrates, despite the fact that it is associated with the adaptation to life in blood, an oxygen-rich environment. As a result, less useful energy is derived per molecule of substrate, and the efficiency of energy transformation is still further decreased by the substitution of the non-phosphorylative glycerophosphate oxidase system for the oxidative phosphorylation carried out by the cytochrome system. Perhaps, in a substrate-rich environment like blood, energetic efficiency is relatively unimportant, but even so, it is hard to see why an inefficient system should have a selective advantage over a more efficient one.

It is also noteworthy that glucose carbon does not appear to be assimilated by the trypanosomes; hence glucose and similar substrates serve as energy sources, but not as carbon sources, in marked contrast to the situation in the phytoflagellates, trichomonads (see below) and several other groups. Thus, in *T. rhodensiense*, less than 1 per cent of the carbon of radioactive glucose was incorporated into the cells,[121] and carbon balance studies with *C. fasciculata*[73] and with bloodstream forms of many species of trypanosomes of the brucei group[263] have indicated that all of the glucose carbon appears in catabolic end products. Carbon recoveries with culture forms, members of the lewisi and congolense groups, and *S. oncopelti* have been less complete, but it is more likely that the lack of quantitative recovery was due to the greater number of end products formed than that it indicates assimilation. It would seem, therefore, that carbohydrate metabolism in the trypanosomes serves solely as a source of energy, and that synthesis of cellular material requires preformed precursors from the environment. The complex amino acid and vitamin requirements of cultured trypanosomids[75] are consistent with such a radical separation of energy metabolism from synthetic pathways. The trichomonads, however, have shown equally complex nutritional requirements, yet have been found to assimilate glucose carbon readily (see below). The inability to store carbohydrate as polysaccharide reserves[334] probably accounts in large part for the rapid deterioration of brucei-group trypanosomes in substrate-free media.

### TRICHOMONADIDAE

The trichomonads are zooflagellates parasitic chiefly in the digestive and reproductive tracts of animals. Like that of the trypanosomids, the respiratory metabolism of the trichomonads is characterized by incomplete oxidations, even when oxygen is readily available. Unlike the trypanosomids, however, the trichomonads appear to be adapted to oxygen deficient environments, as indicated by their preference for anaerobic and strongly reducing growth media.[191] Anaerobic, rather than aerobic, fermentation should therefore probably be considered the typical form of energy metabolism in these organisms.

Correlation of the various studies of trichomonad metabolism is complicated by taxonomic difficulties. Except in the case of pedigreed laboratory strains, it is frequently uncertain whether the findings of different investigators relate to the same or to different species.

#### Trichomonas vaginalis

*T. vaginalis*, a parasite of the human reproductive tract, has been reported to consume $0.54$–$0.95$ $\mu l$ $O_2$/million cells/hr in the absence of exogenous substrate, and $1.62$–$2.65$ $\mu l$/million cells/hr when glucose was provided.[181,

9*

[243, 341] On a per cell basis, these rates are of the same general order as those found in the trypanosomes. The trichomonad cells are, however, considerably larger[262] than those of the trypanosomes, so that on a dry weight basis, the respiratory rate of the trichomonads would probably be less than that of the trypanosomes by a factor of 5 to 10.

The oxygen consumption was found to be entirely insensitive to cyanide and azide,[224, 243] and hence is almost certainly not mediated by a cytochrome system. Ninomiya and Suzuoki[224] found that the rate of $O_2$ consumption was inversely related to $O_2$ tension over the range of 5 to 100 per cent oxygen. Peroxide inhibited respiration, and little or no catalase was present. These findings are consistent with the suggestion[16] that transfer of electrons to oxygen resulted in the formation of peroxide, accounting for toxic effects of oxygen.

All the enzymes of the EMP glycolytic pathway except phosphorylase and alcohol dehydrogenase have been demonstrated in *T. vaginalis*,[16, 17, 328, 339, 340] and many of the phosphorylated intermediates of the pathway have been demonstrated in cell extracts.[340] Of the HMP shunt, TPN-linked glucose-6-phosphate dehydrogenase and phosphoribose isomerase have been demonstrated.[329] and there was tracer evidence that this shunt pathway may be important in $CO_2$ fixation (see below).

Of the enzymes related to the Krebs cycle, only malic dehydrogenase and "malic enzyme" have been demonstrated,[17, 328, 341] while provisional tests for isocitric and succinic dehydrogenases were negative.[341] The insensitivity of respiration to malonate, fluoroacetate, or parapyruvate, even when pyruvate was the substrate, and the failure of any of the Krebs cycle intermediates to stimulate respiration, suggested that the Krebs cycle *per se* was not involved in respiratory metabolism.[224, 341]

Kunitake *et al*[180] found conversion of $C^{14}$-glucose to aspartic acid, glutamic acid and proline, and conversion of small amounts of the 2- and 3-carbons of succinic acid to $CO_2$, reactions which they suggest are best explained by at least a low level of Krebs cycle activity.

Of 30-odd carbohydrates and related compounds, only glucose and such glucose polymers as maltose, dextrin, soluble starch and glycogen gave good growth; fructose and galactose appeared to permit slight growth, while the remaining compounds were not utilized.[310] Glucose and maltose caused marked stimulation of respiration.[224] Aerobic metabolism of glucose resulted in production of large amounts of $CO_2$ and acid. Approximately one mole of $CO_2$ and one-half mole of acid were produced per mole of $O_2$ consumed, giving an RQ of about 1.0.[243] The acid produced aerobically has seemingly not been identified, nor has the possibility of aerobic $H_2$ production (which would appear in manometric experiments as a reduced consumption of $O_2$) been ruled out.

Anaerobically, glucose metabolism resulted in the formation of $CO_2$, acid, and a "gas other than $CO_2$" which a variety of evidence indicates was $H_2$.[224, 243] With carefully standardized cultures, the rate of $CO_2$ production was approximately the same anaerobically as aerobically; about 1.25 equivalents of acid and 0.5 moles of "$H_2$" were produced per mole of $CO_2$. The ratios of products were found, however, to vary greatly, depending upon the strain of organism, the age of the inoculum and culture, the culture medium, etc. These variations were extremely marked; in certain cases, almost no gas was produced.[243] This variability of metabolic products, which seems considerably greater than has been found with other protozoa, adds to the difficulty in comparing the results of various workers.

Among the acids produced anaerobically, lactic acid has been identified as accounting for some 30–50 per cent of the total acid production. Malic acid[329] and small amounts of pyruvic acid[181] have been detected in media after growth. From the results of studies on T. foetus (see below), it seems likely that the unidentified acids produced may include succinic and acetic.

Anaerobic gas production was inhibited by cyanide and carbon monoxide, and the carbon monoxide inhibition was reversed by light. This effect was presumably on $H_2$ production, which in other organisms has been found to depend on a heavy metal catalyst.[243]

T. vaginalis, unlike several other trichomonads, has been found to utilize lactic, malic and pyruvic acids, with the consumption of oxygen (aerobically) and the production of $CO_2$ (anaerobically).[224, 341] The mechanism of these oxidations is entirely unknown. Evidence has already been presented for the deficiency or absence of the Krebs cycle in this species; oxidation of pyruvic acid-2-[14]C resulted in the formation of a labeled product which was not identical with any of the Krebs cycle acids, or related amino acids.

Cultures of T. vaginalis were found to fix considerable amounts of radioactive $CO_2$,[181] most of which could be recovered as radioactive lactic acid in the medium.[329] The radioactivity was found entirely in the carboxyl position of lactic acid. On the basis of this distribution of [14]C, it was suggested that $CO_2$ fixation occurred by addition to ribulose diphosphate (as in photosynthetic $CO_2$ fixation), and the product was then cleaved to produce C-1-labeled phosphoglyceric acid, which, in turn, was converted to lactate. The presence of several enzymes involved in pentose formation via the HMP shunt (see above) is consistent with this scheme.

### Trichomonas foetus

T. foetus, a trichomonad parasitic in the reproductive tract of cattle, has been studied by a number of investigators with somewhat discrepant results.

Ryley[261] found no spectroscopic evidence for any of the cytochromes in T. foetus, while Suzuoki and Suzuoki[300] found spectral bands similar to those of cytochrome b, but no trace of cytochrome a or c. Extracts possessed no cytochrome oxidase activity,[261] and respiration was insensitive to cyanide and azide.[89, 91, 185, 261, 300] Thus, it seems clear that the cytochrome system is not a major pathway of electron transfer.

Doran[89] found that oxygen consumption on glucose (though not endogenous oxygen consumption) was distinctly inhibited in an atmosphere of 100 per cent oxygen, while Ninomiya and Suzuoki[224] found no such inhibition. In the case of *T. vaginalis*, which possessed little or no catalase, it was suggested that such oxygen toxicity was the result of a peroxide-forming transfer of electrons to oxygen. *T. foetus*, however, was found to possess considerable catalase;[89, 224, 261] nevertheless peroxide impaired the motility of *T. foetus*.[261]

Amylase, maltase, and phosphorylase were found in *T. foetus*, as would be expected from its possession of glycogen reserves.[194, 261]

Of the EMP glycolysis enzymes, there was direct or presumptive evidence for hexokinase, phosphoglucomutase, phosphohexoisomerase, phosphofructokinase, aldolase, DPN-linked phosphoglyceraldehyde dehydrogenase, phosphoglyceromutase, and enolase.[185, 261] Respiration was relatively sensitive to iodoacetate. Of the HMP shunt enzymes, only TPN-linked glucose-6-phosphate dehydrogenase, and of the enzymes related to the Krebs cycle, only "malic enzyme" (catalysing addition of $CO_2$ to pyruvate to form malate) have been demonstrated.[185] Malonate did not inhibit respiration.[89, 300]

Rates of endogenous oxygen consumption in the range of $100–200 \ \mu l/10^8$ cells/hr have been reported,[89, 91, 261] and there were apparently some minor differences between strains.[91] The endogenous RQ varied with the buffer used, averaging about 0.9 in tris-maleate buffer and about 1.2 in phosphate, both at pH 6.4.[185] Intracellular glycogen was consumed during endogenous metabolism,[261] producing acid and gas. There is disagreement between the results of various workers as to the nature of the acids produced. Ryley[261] found 1.70 molecules of acetic acid, 0.44 molecules of succinic acid, and less than 0.05 moles of lactate produced per glucose unit of glycogen. No pyruvic acid, formic acid, ethanol, or glycerol could be detected; all the acid produced and approximately† 85 per cent of the glycogen carbon were accounted for. Doran,[91] on the other hand, found that in four different strains of *T. foetus*, some 30–50 per cent of the endogenous acid production was lactic acid.

Anaerobically, endogenous metabolism involves glycogen utilization, and production of $H_2$ and succinic and acetic acids. In the presence of 5 per cent $CO_2$, the rate of glycogen consumption and of succinate production were markedly increased, and $CO_2$ fixation occurred. In the absence of $CO_2$, acetate was the major acid produced, and considerable amounts of

---

† The degree of recovery was uncertain because of inability to correct for possible $CO_2$ production or fixation.

$CO_2$ were given off.[261] These results suggest that succinic acid was produced by condensation of $CO_2$ and pyruvate, perhaps by way of the "malic enzyme". It should be noted, however, that evidence was found for an entirely different mode of $CO_2$ fixation in *T. vaginalis*. As with aerobic metabolism, Doran[89] found lactic acid to compose about 40 per cent of the endogenous acid production, while Ryley[261] found only traces of lactic acid.

In the presence of glucose, rates of oxygen consumption were about 1.5 to 2.0 times the endogenous rates. A considerable variety of other carbohydrates stimulated respiration to varying degrees.[89, 91, 185, 261, 300] There is by no means complete agreement as to which carbohydrates are stimulatory, or concerning their relative effectiveness. In part, these differences may result from differences in the experimental conditions and the criteria for recognizing significant stimulation. In addition, there appear to be genuine differences between strains of *T. foetus*, since Doran[91] found differences among four strains studied under comparable conditions. Doran[91] found approximately 40 per cent of the acid produced during glucose utilization to be lactic acid.

Under anaerobic conditions, glucose and other carbohydrates stimulated production of acid, $CO_2$, and $H_2$, although not to equal degrees.[89, 91, 300] Again, different workers obtained distinctly different results as to the nature of the acids produced. Suzuoki and Suzuoki[300] found that succinate accounted for more than 70 per cent of the acid, with only minor amounts of lactate and pyruvate, while Doran[89, 91] found that about 40 per cent of the acid was lactic.

During utilization of exogenous glucose, the glycogen stores of the cells increased considerably. Under aerobic conditions, this increase was equivalent to about 40–50 per cent of all the glucose consumed; anaerobic glycogen formation was less, but still appreciable. With maltose, a slowly utilized substrate, the glycogen stores decreased, but to a lesser degree than in the absence of substrate.[261] As Ryley[261] has pointed out, none of the attempts to study carbon balance of glucose utilization have taken into account the probability of simultaneous synthesis or utilization of glycogen reserves. Until the complications inherent in this situation (see discussion of a comparable problem with *Euglena*) have been resolved, all such carbon balance studies involve great uncertainties.

A number of longer term, growth-culture experiments have supplemented the information obtained by briefer metabolic studies. Once again, different investigators find different proportions of acid end products. Suzuoki and Suzuoki[299] found 83 per cent of the acid in culture vessels to be succinic, while lactic and pyruvic together accounted for less than 10 per cent. Lindblom,[185] on the other hand, found some 57 per cent succinic, 11 per cent lactic, and 12 per cent pyruvic. Suzuoki and Suzuoki[299] analysed the gas accumulating in closed culture vessels, and showed the presence of large amounts of $H_2$ and traces of methane, in addition to $O_2$, $CO_2$, and $N_2$. These analyses are the primary reason for identifying the "gas other than $CO_2$" in manometric experiments as $H_2$.

There is some disagreement, also, as to the ability of T. foetus to utilize lactate, pyruvate and other acids and amino acids related to the Krebs cycle. Suzuoki and Suzuoki[300] found little or no stimulation of respiration by such compounds, and Lindblom[185] found an actual depression of respiration in most cases. Ryley[261] obtained slight stimulation by lactate, succinate, and a number of amino acids and lower fatty acids, but not by pyruvate, while Doran[89, 91] found small but significant stimulation of respiration with both lactate and pyruvate. Suzuoki and Suzuoki[300] found that pyruvate stimulated anaerobic gas production, Doran[89, 91] found such stimulation with both lactate and pyruvate, while Lindblom[185] found little or no stimulation with either acid.

The source of metabolic $H_2$, and the significance of $H_2$ production in the over-all metabolic scheme, require clarification. Formate has been found to stimulate $H_2$ production[185, 300] and both formic dehydrogenase and hydrogenase activities have been demonstrated,[185] suggesting that $H_2$ may be formed from formate via the "hydrogenlyase" reaction,

$$HCOOH \rightarrow CO_2 + H_2$$

which is believed to be the sum of the reactions catalysed by these two enzymes. Formate (plus acetate) might be derived from pyruvate by reactions known to occur in $H_2$-producing bacteria. Whether this mechanism is the main or sole $H_2$ producing process in trichomonads is still unknown.

The wide differences among the results of various investigators concerning several aspects of the metabolism of T. foetus are striking, and somewhat difficult to explain. There is no evidence that the discrepancies result from erroneous methods. Strain differences almost certainly exist,[91] and apparently no two investigators have worked with the same strains. But the differences among the four strains studied by Doran were relatively minor, compared with the range of differences reported in the literature. It seems more probable that the major differences result from differences in growth and manometric media and procedures. The extreme sensitivity to such factors found in T. vaginalis[243] and T. foetus[185] suggest that relatively minor, and perhaps unrecognized differences in techniques might produce large differences in results.

## Trichomonas suis and other Trichomonads of Swine

Doran[89] and Lindblom[185] have studied the metabolism of different strains of trichomonads from the cecum or intestine of swine. While there is some taxonomic uncertainty, both are probably strains of T. suis. In the general properties of respiratory metabolism (cyanide insensitivity, utilization of carbohydrates, with the production of acid products, anaerobic production of $H_2$, enzymatic activities, etc.) these organisms were very similar to T. foetus. Some differences between the two species in metabolic rates, and in the effects of individual substrates and metabolic inhibitors were noted, but these were relatively minor (particularly in comparison with range of variation reported for T. foetus itself), and in many cases the differences reported by the two workers were in opposite directions.

The same workers also studied (different strains of) trichomonads from the nasal passages of swine. The nasal trichomonads were found to differ in some respects from both the cecal trichomonads of swine and from T. foetus, but again, the differences were no greater than those reported in various studies of T. foetus.

Doran[90] also studied a small trichomonad, believed on morphological grounds to be different from T. suis, from the cecum of swine. Again, considering the apparent variability within single species, the differences between this organism and other swine trichomonads are not striking.

Cross-infection studies have suggested that the various swine trichomonads may be variant forms of the same species, which may, in turn, be identical with T. foetus, while morphological criteria have suggested specific differences among the various forms (see Doran[89, 90] for discussion). For the present at least, it seems unlikely that comparisons of respiratory metabolism will contribute more than minor and supplementary evidence toward a solution of this taxonomic problem.

## Other Trichomonads

T. gallinarum appears to conform in general to the metabolic pattern found in T. foetus and the swine trichomonads, again with certain rather minor differences. The most marked of these differences appear to be a greater ability to oxidize pyruvate, formate, and malate, presence of "malic enzyme" and markedly higher activities of malic dehydrogenase and hydrogenase.[185]

T. gallinae has been reported to lack catalase, and its glycogen showed somewhat different properties from that of T. foetus.[194, 261]

Data on other trichomonads may be found in papers by Read[242] and Willems et al.[322] Information concerning T. termopsidis, a trichomonad symbiotic in termites, is reviewed below, in connection with other termite flagellates.

Despite the confusing variability in the results of studies of trichomonad metabolism it is clear that the respiratory metabolism of this group shows a distinctive pattern, different from that of any other group of protozoa so far studied.

Like that of the Trypanosomidae, the main respiratory metabolism of the trichomonads appears to be fermentative, with the formation of incompletely oxidized products even under aerobic conditions. The electron transfer system is almost certainly not a cytochrome system, but whether it corresponds to any of the non-cytochrome systems found in bloodstream forms of trypanosomes is uncertain. The preference for anaerobic or semi-anaerobic growth conditions, and the tendency for respiration to decrease with increasing oxygen tension (even at $O_2$ tensions below that of air) indicate that anaerobic processes may be the "normal" sources of metabolic energy, even though experimental rates of oxygen consumption are relatively high.

All present evidence points to the absence of a functional Krebs cycle, although a few individual enzymes from this cycle have been reported in some species. Oxidation of pyruvate, when it occurs, is apparently by some mechanism other than the Krebs cycle. Nevertheless, a systematic study of the distribution of Krebs cycle enzymes in several species of trichomonads would be valuable.

There is strong evidence for the presence of the EMP glycolysis pathway in several trichomonads, and a lesser amount of evidence for the HMP shunt, but no real evidence as to which of these is the major route for carbohydrate breakdown. The nature of the acid end products of carbohydrate breakdown appears to be highly variable, even within a single species. Thus, in both *T. vaginalis* and *T. foetus*, reports vary from large amounts of succinic acid with only traces of lactic to results indicating that 50 per cent or more of the acid produced is lactic. Production of lesser, but significant amounts of acetic and pyruvic acids also has been reported. Since tracer studies suggest that lactic acid is produced by $CO_2$ fixation to intermediates of the HMP shunt, while other evidence suggests that succinic acid arises from $CO_2$ fixation to pyruvate, variations in the nature of the end products may indicate changes in the relative importance of the EMP and HMP pathways, perhaps in response to culture ages, differences in media, or other environmental variables. In any event, most studies point to the ability to fix considerable amounts of $CO_2$.

Hydrogen production is a well-established characteristic of the anaerobic metabolism of trichomonads, although one might wish for more frequent demonstration that the "gas other than $CO_2$" in manometric experiments is actually $H_2$. The question of whether $H_2$ production occurs in the presence of $O_2$ remains unanswered; this is particularly unfortunate because any appreciable $H_2$ production would cause an undetected error in manometric measurements of $O_2$ consumption.

In the possession of glycogen reserves, which increase during utilization of exogenous carbohydrates and decrease during incubation in the absence of substrate, the trichomonads differ markedly from the trypanosomes. While the trypanosomes appear to utilize exogenous carbohydrate solely as a fuel for energy production, the trichomonads seem to carry out a "fermentative assimilation" process, analogous to the oxidative assimilation which is typical of the phytoflagellates and numerous other microorganisms. This ability to assimilate an appreciable fraction of carbohydrates which are simultaneously being utilized as energy sources is not, in the trichomonads, correlated with a general ability to synthesize protoplasmic constituents solely from a single carbon source; the semi-defined media which have been developed for trichomonads indicate elaborate requirements for specific amino acids, purines, vitamins, lipids, sterols, and miscellaneous "growth factors", some of which remain unidentified.[191, 266, 290]

## TERMITE FLAGELLATES

The intestines of termites and wood roaches contain symbiotic flagellates of the orders Trichomonadida, Polymastigida and Hypermastigida, which are essential for digestion of the cellulose which forms a major portion of the food of these insects. The flagellates have been found to contain cellulase and cellobiase, while the intestines of defaunated insects did not.[305] Hungate[146] has calculated that most of the oxidative metabolism of the intact termite results from oxidation of the fermentation products of the protozoa. The termite flagellates are anaerobes, and extremely sensitive to oxygen toxicity.[145, 306] Attempts to culture the flagellates axenically have so far been unsuccessful, although survival and limited growth *in vitro* have been attained.[127, 306]

Most experimental studies, therefore, have been done on mixed populations obtained directly from termites. Hungate[147, 148] has reviewed the metabolism of these organisms.

Cellulose supported growth of *Trichomonas termopsidis*,[306] and was fermented by mixed populations of flagellates.[127, 145, 146] Cellobiose stimulated fermentation to about the same extent, while glucose was used at a lower rate.[127] Starch, dextrin, glycogen, inulin, or cellobiose could not replace cellulose in supporting growth of *T. termopsidis*.[306]

In manometric experiments, cellulose was fermented with the production of $CO_2$, $H_2$, and acid; acetic acid accounted for about 85 per cent of the total acid production. No indications were found of the formation of ethanol, glycerol, formate, or acetylmethyl carbinol, nor of the release of free glucose during cellulose utilization.[145, 146] Trager,[306] however, found evidence that a soluble material, fermentable by bacteria, was released by *T. termopsidis*.

Hungate[146] found evidence for two types of fermentation from (mixed) flagellate populations. One type yielded, per cellulose hexose unit, 0.4 $CO_2$, 0.4 $H_2$ and 2.2 acid, while the other yielded 1.4 $CO_2$, 2.4 $H_2$, and 1.4 acid. Which type of fermentation was found appeared to depend on the colony from which the termites originated, perhaps because of differences in the flagellate fauna of the various colonies.

9a*

## OPALINA

N. W. Hunter[151, 152] has used cytochemical methods to study the enzymes of *Opalina carolinensis*. Of the glycolytic enzymes, aldolase, $\alpha$-glycerophosphate dehydrogenase and lactic dehydrogenase were found in the cytoplasm. Cytochrome oxidase, "citric dehydrogenase", glutamic dehydrogenase, succinic dehydrogenase, fumarase, and malic dehydrogenase were localized in the mitochondria.

## CILIATES

Aside from the enormous literature on *Tetrahymena*, information on the respiratory metabolism of the ciliates is, for the most part, scanty and piecemeal.[280] It is difficult, therefore, to generalize concerning the metabolism of the ciliates as a group. Insofar as *Tetrahymena* may be considered typical, the ciliates appear to be among the most "animal-like" of the protozoa so far studied. The similarity of the nutritional requirements of *Tetrahymena* to those of multicellular animals has frequently been emphasized. The main outlines of energy metabolism, EMP glycolysis and the Krebs cycle aerobically, and acid fermentation under anaerobic conditions, likewise resemble those found in higher metazoa. However, the presence of appreciable amounts of acetic and succinic acids among the fermentation products, the presence of the enzymes of the glyoxylate cycle, and the apparent peculiarities in the electron transfer system indicate that similarities to metazoa should not be taken too much for granted.

The much smaller amount of data on *Paramecium* suggest that this genus resembles *Tetrahymena* in many respects. Studies of the anaerobic rumen ciliates, on the other hand, indicate similarities to the symbiotic zooflagellates. In neither case, however, is sufficient information available to permit such comparisons to be made with confidence. Concerning other ciliates, even less can be said.

### Tetrahymena

Because it is one of the few ciliates which grows readily and heavily in pure culture, and because its nutritional requirements have been identified and chemically-defined media devised, *Tetrahymena pyriformis*† has been the subject of numerous metabolic studies, probably more than have been performed on any other single protozoan species. A considerable number of strains exist, and strain differences in respiratory physiology have been described. Most of such differences seem to be minor, and in many cases are

† *T. pyriformis* has, in the past, been called *T. geleii*, *Glaucoma pyriformis*, *Leucophrys pyriformis*, *Colpidium campylum*, and probably other names as well. Corliss[70, 71, 72] has discussed the species and strain designations from both taxonomic and historical viewpoints.

obscured or confused by differences in experimental techniques. No attempt will be made, therefore, to differentiate between the various strains in the discussion that follows. The physiology of *Tetrahymena* has been ably reviewed by Kidder and Dewey[172] and by Seaman.[280]

*T. pyriformis* is capable of phagotrophic feeding, but will also grow on an entirely liquid medium, obtaining all its nutrients from dissolved materials. The presence of oxygen was found to be required for growth,[232] but the cells survived periods of several days under anaerobic conditions.[260, 301]

## ELECTRON TRANSFER

The information available concerning the nature of the electron transfer system in *T. pyriformis* is confusing and frequently contradictory, but the weight of the evidence suggests that the classical cytochrome system typical of mammalian tissues, if present at all, is not the main pathway of electron transfer in this organism.

Studies with inhibitors of the cytochrome system have given widely varying results. Baker and Baumberger[19, 20] found that carbon monoxide inhibited respiration at low $O_2$ tensions, while Ryley[260] found no inhibition with a somewhat lower carbon monoxide tension. Studies of cyanide inhibition have given widely varying results; inhibitions ranging from zero to 80 per cent have been reported with $10^{-3}$ M cyanide.[20, 133, 202, 204, 260] Much of this variability probably reflects strain differences, since McCashland et al.,[204] in a comparison of seven strains under similar experimental conditions, found degrees of inhibition covering essentially the same range. A number of workers have reported that inhibition was greater in the presence that in the absence of glucose, and probably other differences in experimental technique also affect the results. McCashland[202] found that growth in the presence of increasing concentrations of cyanide resulted in a decreased sensitivity to cyanide, and that the degree of sensitivity of either normal or adapted cells was affected by changes in the medium. Even where cyanide sensitivity was readily demonstrable, however, there was a question as to whether inhibition resulted from the classical action of cyanide on cytochrome oxidase. The concentrations of cyanide required to produce marked inhibition were generally somewhat higher than is usually found with cytochrome oxidase. Moreover, studies with cell-free *Tetrahymena* preparations (see below) have indicated cyanide sensitivity of $O_2$ consumption in systems where classical cytochrome oxidase activity cannot be detected.

Results of attempts to demonstrate individual components of the cytochrome system in *Tetrahymena* have likewise given confusing and inconsistant results. Using spectroscopic methods, Baker and Baumberger[20] reported the presence of cytochromes c, b, a, and $a_2$, of which $a_2$ is not a component of the mammalian cytochrome system. Seaman[269] presented a value for the cytochrome c content. Baker[19] found that *Tetrahymena* grown on *Streptococcus lactis*, a bacterium which lacks cytochromes, had a lower cytochrome c content than organisms grown on *E. coli* or yeast autolysate. Ryley[260] reported weak absorption bands corresponding to cytochromes a, b, and c, and a strong band corresponding to cytochrome e.† Møller and Prescott[209] reported strong bands in the region of 552 mμ, near the cytochrome e region. Since the "cytochrome e" absorption peak at 552–555 mμ is very close to that of cytochrome c (550 mμ), it is probable that some of the earlier reports of cytochrome c actually refer to this peak. Tests for cytochrome c oxidase activity have given contradictory results. Ryley[260] and Eichel[93, 95] were unable to detect any cytochrome c oxidase in *Tetrahymena* preparations, while Seaman[278] found relatively high activity in several strains. The disparate results cannot be due to strain differences, since the GL strain was studied by all three workers. Seaman[278] has shown that cytochrome c oxidase is lost or inactivated during some procedures for preparing homogenates and extracts, but Eichel[95] obtained negative results after a serious attempt to duplicate Seaman's preparatory procedure. (In a later publication, Eichel[97] reports finding very slight cytochrome c oxidase activity in certain preparations.)

There is general agreement that *Tetrahymena* extracts are capable of transferring electrons from succinate[93, 273, 274, 278] or DPNH[95] to mammalian cytochrome c (succinic-cytochrome c reductase and DPN-cytochrome c reductase activities). There is, however, strong reason to doubt that cytochrome c is an intermediate in the normal pathway of electron transfer from either substrate to oxygen. In both cases, electron transfer to oxygen was more rapid than transfer to cytochrome c, which could hardly be the case if cytochrome c were an intermediate in transfer to oxygen. Moreover, these preparations showed no cytochrome c oxidase activity; hence no mechanism was available by which electrons transferred to cytochrome c could be passed on to oxygen. Reduction of cytochrome c, therefore, appears to be a side reaction, comparable to the reduction of such dyes as indophenol or methylene blue. In support of this view, cytochrome c reductase activity in *Tetrahymena* differed markedly from that in mammalian preparations in its sensitivity to antimycin A and in other properties, again suggesting that the reaction was not identical with the normal electron transfer reactions in the mammalian cytochrome system.‡[93, 95, 96] Cytochrome c reductase activity has been demonstrated in bacteria which totally lack cytochrome c, so that the presence of such activity is not, *per se*, evidence for the presence of a classical cytochrome system.

---

† Absorption bands due to hemoglobin are also present.[171] The function of hemoglobin in ciliate metabolism remains unknown.

‡ It should be noted that these conclusions are largely independent of whether cytochrome c oxidase is actually present in *Tetrahymena*. Even if the presence of the classical cytochrome system should be demonstrated, the behavior of these preparations indicates the presence of a very active alternative to the classical pathway.

The nature of the alternative pathway is unknown. Similarities between the succinate and DPNH oxidizing systems[95, 96, 98] suggest that transfer from these two substrates occurs via a common pathway, and as would be expected, the DPN-linked oxidation of glutamate and $\beta$-hydroxybutyrate shows similar properties.[98] The cyanide and azide sensitivity of these systems,[95, 96] and the presence of cytochrome e and perhaps other unusual cytochromes suggest that a cytochrome system (perhaps based on cytochrome e) other than the classical mammalian type may be involved. Inhibition by atabrine, and reversal of this inhibition by flavin mononucleotide suggest that a flavin enzyme may be involved at some step other than the substrate-level dehydrogenase.[94] The system was found to be largely localized in particles (presumably mitochondria) sedimented by moderate centrifugation.[95] Oxidase activity of homogenates was very unstable, but could be stabilized by succinate, blood serum, and a heat stable, diffusible constituent of crude serum albumin.[98, 278] Electron transfer may be coupled to ATP synthesis, as in the case of the classical cytochrome system; the measured efficiency of phosphorylation by the *Tetrahymena* system was low, but this is thought due to the presence of an "uncoupling agent"† in the preparations rather than to intrinsic inefficiency.

Transfer of electrons from L-lactic acid by *Tetrahymena* preparations occurred via a system differing from both that for succinate and DPNH and the classical cytochrome system. The lactate oxidase was insensitive to cyanide and other inhibitors of the succinate and DPNH system, showed a different distribution after centrifugal fractionation, and did not seem to be coupled to ATP synthesis. Transfer of electrons to $O_2$ resulted in the formation of hydrogen peroxide, rather than water (though catalase in the extracts ordinarily broke down the peroxide as rapidly as it was formed). Since such peroxide formation is characteristic of flavin oxidases, the lactic acid oxidase of *Tetrahymena* is believed to belong to this group.[101, 102, 103]

The presence of alternative pathways for electron transfer does not, of course, exclude the possibility that the classical cytochrome system may also be present. The reports of cytochrome c oxidase activity (discussed above), the finding of Seaman[272, 286] that cytochrome c was required for optimal rates of oxidation of several substrates (including succinate and lactate), and the reports of spectroscopic evidence for the presence of at least traces of cytochrome c suggest the possible presence of such a system.

Nishi and Scherbaum[224a, 224b] report changes in levels of DPN, DPNH, TPN, DPNH oxidase activity and oxidative phosphorylation during sychronized cell division in *Tetrahymena*.

---

† This agent, which inhibits electron transfer and uncouples phosphorylation in both *Tetrahymena* and mammalian systems, appears to result from enzyme-catalysed breakdown of phospholipids in the Tetrahymena extracts.[92, 97, 99, 101]

## ENZYMATIC PATHWAYS

There is strong and convincing evidence for the presence of the EMP glycolysis pathway in *T. pyriformis*. The presence of most of the individual enzymes of this pathway has been demonstrated,[260, 272] as have the over-all conversions of hexose (glucose, fructose, mannose, or galactose) to phosphoglyceric acid,[271] and of fructose diphosphate to lactate.[260]

Of the enzymes of the HMP shunt, TPN-linked glucose-6-phosphate dehydrogenase and TPN-linked 6-phosphogluconic acid dehydrogenase have been demonstrated.[272] There is also evidence for direct non-phosphorylative oxidation of glucose.[271, 272] There appears to be no direct evidence concerning the relative importance of the EMP and HMP pathways in glucose utilization by intact cells.†

Of the Krebs cycle enzymes, pyruvic oxidase[279, 301, 277] "acetate activating enzyme,"[280] aconitase,[100] TPN-linked isocitric dehydrogenase,[272] $\alpha$-ketoglutaric oxidase,[277] succinic dehydrogenase[93, 260, 272] (see also the discussion of the electron transfer system above), fumarase,[100] and DPN-linked malic dehydrogenase[272] have been demonstrated in *T. pyriformis*. As with many other protozoa, attempts to demonstrate the functioning of the complete cycle were complicated by limitations of cellular permeability.[285] Since, however, *Tetrahymena* has been shown to oxidize most of the acids of the Krebs cycle, since malonate inhibited acetate and pyruvate metabolism with accumulation of succinate, and this inhibition was reversed by fumarate and other dicarboxylic acids,[268, 270] and since citrate accumulated in *Tetrahymena* poisoned with fluoroacetate,[280] there seems no question but that the cycle is present, and functions in the classical fashion.

DPN-linked $\beta$-hydroxybutyric acid dehydrogenase, which serves as a connecting link between fatty acid oxidation and the Krebs cycle, and glutamic acid dehydrogenase, which plays a somewhat similar role in amino acid metabolism, were present.[98, 272] The "succinate cleaving enzyme", which catalyses the reaction,

$$\text{Succinate} + \text{DPNH} + 2\,\text{Coenzyme A} + 2\text{ATP} + \text{H}^+$$
$$\rightleftharpoons 2\,\text{Acetyl Coenzyme A} + 2\text{ADP} + \text{DPN}^+ + 2\text{P}_i$$

was first demonstrated in *Tetrahymena* preparations.[282, 286]

The "key enzymes" of the glyoxylate cycle, isocitrate lyase and malate synthase, have been found in *T. pyriformis*.[139, 139a, 247] The two enzymes were independently inducible and repressible, and their relative activities within the cell varied greatly.[139a] In cells for which acetate is a major carbon and energy source, the glyoxylate cycle seems to operate in conversion of acetate to carbohydrate, but the presence of the enzymes in cells incapable

---

† The lack of $CO_2$ production during anaerobic carbohydrate utilization[260, 301] would argue against a major role for the HMP pathway, were it not that an unknown degree of $CO_2$ fixation occurs under these conditions. Ryley[260] found that glucose actually does increase anaerobic $CO_2$ production under low $CO_2$ tensions.

of glyconeogenesis from acetate, and in several intracellular locations (see below) suggests that they may have other functions besides their role in the glyoxylate cycle.

## ENDOGENOUS RESPIRATION

When incubated at approximately 25°C in the absence of exogenous substrate, *T. pyriformis* consumes $O_2$ at a rate which has been reported to range from 10–40 μl/mg dry wt/hr[20, 132, 203, 226, 234]† The rate varied with age of culture, concentration of cells in the incubation vessels, and other factors. Raising the temperature to 37°C approximately doubled the rate.[260] The rate of endogenous metabolism has been reported to remain practically unchanged for at least 5 hr in the absence of substrate,[260] and respiratory rates within the normal range have been reported for cells after 12 hr in inorganic media.[268, 270] Baker,[19] however, reports a decrease of nearly 50 per cent in the respiratory rate during the first 5 hr in the absence of substrate. Despite the fact that the cells contained reserves of glycogen equivalent to 14–23 per cent of their dry weight,[193, 260] glycogen utilization was sufficient to account for only about one-tenth of the endogenous oxygen consumption. This fact, plus the RQ of 0.85, suggests that lipids, proteins, or both, are the major substrates of aerobic endogenous metabolism.[260]

Anaerobically, the situation was somewhat different; Thomas,[301] found the rate of anaerobic acid production to decline rapidly by as much as 60 per cent during the first few hours of incubation. By the end of 5 hr, the rate had become relatively stable. After 24 hr, the cells began to die; death was prevented by the presence of glucose. No metabolic $CO_2$ production could be detected, and there was net fixation of $CO_2$ in the presence of bicarbonate buffers. Lactic, succinic, and acetic acids were the only fermentation products found, and accounted for essentially all the organic carbon recovered from the medium. The relative amounts of these products varied; in general, lactic acid was the major product in phosphate buffer while the three compounds were produced in roughly equal amounts in bicarbonate buffer. In all cases, the nature and proportions of products produced were similar to those found in the presence of glucose (see below), suggesting that carbohydrate was the major endogenous substrate. Ryley,[260] demonstrated net utilization of cellular glycogen during anaerobic, endogenous metabolism. In $CO_2$-bicarbonate systems, disappearance of glycogen resulted (per glycogen glucose unit) in the assimilation of 0.34–0.41 molecules of $CO_2$ and formation of 0.94 molecules of succinic acid, 0.47 of lactic acid, 0.32 of acetic acid, and a trace of ethanol. No pyruvic acid was found. The products accounted for 91 per cent of the carbon of the glycogen and $CO_2$ which disappeared. This carbon balance again strongly suggests that in the absence of $O_2$, glycogen is the major endogenous substrate. In contrast to the

† Several of these values have been recalculated on the assumption that 1 mg N equals 9 mg dry weight or 6 × 10⁵ cells.[260, 272] As with other protozoa, however, the size and weight of the cells varies with age and growth conditions.[226]

results of Thomas, Ryley found metabolic $CO_2$ production in $CO_2$-free buffer systems.

## SUBSTRATE UTILIZATION

Considering the extent to which the enzymology of carbohydrate metabolism has been studied in *Tetrahymena*, there is surprisingly little information available concerning the role of carbohydrate metabolism in the economy of the intact organism. It is known that carbohydrate is not required for growth, though it produces moderate stimulation of growth of *Tetrahymena* in otherwise-adequate media.[172] In the absence of carbohydrate, the amino acids in the medium presumably served as carbon and energy sources. When present, however, a number of hexoses and polysaccharides were utilized, as indicated by acid production.† Dextrin, glycogen and starch supported considerably better growth than did glucose.[252]

Loefer[187] measured the consumption of glucose by growing *Tetrahymena* cultures, and calculated that 0.2–0.4 mg glucose were consumed per million cells per hour. If this glucose were completely oxidized (which is unlikely, in view of the possibility of assimilation, and of acid production in deep culture), this rate of utilization would result in an $O_2$ consumption of some 200 μl/million cells/hr, as compared with a respiration rate of 400–700 μl on peptone growth media.[226, 234] Comparisons between growth conditions, where $O_2$ may often be limiting, and manometric experiments are of questionable significance, however. Baker[19] found no removal of glucose from the medium and no stimulation of respiration by glucose in the absence of other substrates. In the presence of yeast autolysate, appreciable glucose consumption occurred. The rate of glucose consumption decreased with increasing age of the culture, reaching zero during the stationary phase of the growth curve. Cells grown in the presence of glucose consumed much less glucose when transferred to fresh, glucose-containing media than did cells grown without glucose; since the total $O_2$ consumption of the cells grown without glucose was sufficient to oxidize only about 10 per cent of the glucose consumed, it was suggested that the extra sugar used by these cells was stored as carbohydrate reserves. Ryley[260] found that addition of glucose to inorganic media stimulated the respiration of *Tetrahymena* only about 10 per cent above the endogenous rate. Glucose utilization was demonstrated by analysis of the medium; the extra $O_2$ consumed was sufficient to oxidize less than one-tenth of the glucose consumed. As Ryley pointed out, these data might indicate either that consumption of glucose partially inhibited oxidation of endogenous glycogen or other substrates, or that a large fraction of the glucose was assimilated rather than oxidized (assimilation of 90 per

---

† There are, however, considerable differences between strains in rates of glucose consumption, and at least one strain does not utilize glucose at all under such conditions (R. W. Hanson, personal communication). Acid production presumably results from oxygen depletion in deep culture vessels, since acid does not accumulate during carbohydrate metabolism in well-aerated media.[252]

cent or more of glucose at expense of oxidation of the remainder is energetically possible, and has been shown to occur in some algae[82]). Hogg and Wagner[140] found that glycogen synthesis accounted for all the glucose consumed aerobically. It is improbable that aerobic fermentation contributed to these results, since the usual fermentation products of *Tetrahymena* caused equal or greater stimulation of respiration than did glucose.

Since the peptones used in routine culture of *Tetrahymena* supported respiration at more than double the endogenous rate,[226, 234] the slight effect of glucose on respiration suggests that carbohydrate plays a distinctly secondary role in the respiratory metabolism during normal aerobic growth.

Anaerobically, glucose caused a relatively greater stimulation of respiration, increasing the rate of $CO_2$ production about 33 per cent above the endogenous rate,[260] and caused a marked increase in acid production.[301] The acids produced, lactic, acetic, and succinic, were the same as those produced endogenously, and the proportions varied in the same way, depending on whether phosphate or bicarbonate buffer was used. The proportion of lactic acid produced tended to increase, however, as increasing amounts of glucose were consumed. The amount of extra acid produced was, nevertheless, not sufficient to account for more than about 40–65 per cent of the glucose consumed. This discrepancy may indicate that a considerable portion of the glucose carbon was assimilated, or that the presence of glucose decreased the rate of fermentation of cellular glycogen, or both. Only systematic studies with isotopic tracers could distinguish between these alternatives.

Tracer studies[192, 312] indicated that most of the assimilated $CO_2$ was in the terminal carbons of succinic acid, strongly suggesting that $CO_2$ fixation and succinate formation occurred by the carboxylation of pyruvate. This would explain the dependence of succinate formation on the presence of $CO_2$-bicarbonate, but not the similar dependence of acetate formation. Since lactate fermentation does not involve net oxidation or reduction, Thomas[301] has suggested that the oxidative production of acetate from pyruvate was required to furnish electrons for the reductive formation of succinate from pyruvate and $CO_2$. Oxidation-reduction balance by this mechanism, however, would require the formation of 2 moles of acetate per mole of succinate, while in fact, more succinate than acetate was produced. Seaman and Naschke[286] have suggested that reductive cleavage of succinate to acetate by the "succinate cleaving enzyme" serves as an electron-accepting mechanism coupled to simultaneous oxidative processes. This hypothesis would account for the dependence of acetate formation on conditions which permit formation of succinate, but there is no need for such an additional electron acceptor to support lactic acid fermentation. Perhaps the functioning of this system, in the presence of $CO_2$, permits the anaerobic utilization of proteins or fats, in addition to carbohydrates.

Acetate, propionate, butyrate, pyruvate, lactate, and several of the Krebs cycle acids have been reported to increase the respiration of intact *Tetrahymena* to varying degrees, up to twice the endogenous rate.[260, 268, 270, 285] The degrees of stimulation reported have been somewhat variable, and there is evidence that in many cases, permeability restrictions limited the rates of utilization of these substrates.[285]

In the case of acetate, it was found that the extra $O_2$ uptake was sufficient for complete oxidation of only 14 per cent of the acetate consumed. Cellular lipid and, to a much lesser extent, carbohydrate increased in a linear ratio to the amount of acetate consumed.[270] Glycogen synthesis from acetate has been shown to occur in cells grown on acetate. In the presence of glucose and acetate, glycogen was formed from acetate only after the glucose had been exhausted.[139] This glyconeogenesis from acetate was dependent on the presence of both glyoxylate cycle enzymes, isocitrate lyase and malate synthase. The presence of glucose markedly decreased the cellular level of malate synthase, while acetate increased the levels of both enzymes, though to different degrees.[139a] The intracellular distribution of the enzymes in cells capable of glyconeogenesis differed from that in cells which do not form glycogen from acetate; the differences were such as to suggest that for glyconeogenesis, both enzymes must be incorporated in a single intracellular particle.[139a] Tracer studies of acetate incorporation support the belief that conversion to glycogen was via the glyoxylate cycle.[139, 139a] Formation of glycogen from butyrate and other fatty acids, and from endogenous substrates, also occurred.[140]

Of nearly 40 amino acids tested, 9 stimulated respiration by amounts ranging from 10 to 50 per cent above the endogenous rate.[255] Of the commonly-occurring amino acids, those causing stimulation were L-phenylalanine, L-tyrosine, D- and L-cysteine, L-proline, L-isoleucine, and D- and L-leucine. Surprisingly, alanine, asparagine, glutamic acid, and glutamine, acids which are readily oxidized by most organisms, caused no stimulation. For lack of a better explanation, one is tempted to invoke permeability limitations to explain the failure of many amino acids to stimulate respiration.†

---

† The question of the cellular permeability of *Tetrahymena* is complicated by the occurrence of phagotrophy. It is unlikely that phagocytosis or pinocytosis occurs under the conditions of most respiration experiments, since Seaman[283, 284] found that no phagotrophy took place in synthetic media unless an inducer such as peptone was added. Even then, the amount of material ingested was far too small to account for the intake of such respiratory substrates as glucose or acetate. These considerations apply only to intake of dissolved nutrients; phagocytosis of bacteria or other particulate food would, of course, be a much more effective source of nutrients. In the present connection, it is interesting that 3,5-dinitrotyrosine, an analog of phenylalanine, was found to enter the cells more rapidly by diffusion than by phagotrophy.

Several of the amino acids essential for the growth of *Tetrahymena*[172] do not stimulate respiration. These compounds must certainly enter the cells. The amounts required for protein synthesis are probably much lower than those needed to produce respiratory stimulation, however, so that low permeability might account for these findings.

The stimulatory effects of individual amino acids were largely, though not strictly, additive.[255] Dipeptides containing one or more of the stimulatory amino acids also stimulated respiration.[254] Thus, the marked stimulation of respiration by peptone solutions[203, 226, 234] can probably be accounted for on the basis of the amino acid and peptide content of peptone. Utilization of peptides was associated with extracellular hydrolysis, but several of the peptides stimulated respiration more than did their constituent amino acids, suggesting that the intact peptides may have entered the cell and been utilized intracellularly. Net formation of glycogen from amino acids could not be demonstrated.[139, 140]

The very slight stimulation of respiration by glucose, as compared with peptone, combinations of amino acids, and lower fatty acids, the existence of strains which grow in peptone-glucose media without utilization of glucose, and the minor role of glycogen as a substrate for endogenous respiration all suggest that carbohydrate metabolism may play a distinctly secondary role in the aerobic energy metabolism of *Tetrahymena*, with amino acids and perhaps lipids serving as the major energy metabolites. Accumulation of ammonia during growth in peptone media likewise suggests utilization of amino acids as energy sources.[260] More thoroughgoing studies of the economy of intact cells are required, however, before it can be determined that this is actually the case.

Anaerobically, on the other hand, glycogen seems to be the major endogenous substrate. Since the formation of acid during growth in carbohydrate-containing media suggests that the oxygen supply is limiting under many growth conditions, it is possible that carbohydrate metabolism is an adjustment to near-anaerobic conditions in this case also. Acid does not appear to accumulate under well oxygenated conditions.[252] The seemingly greater importance of carbohydrate in the absence of oxygen may be due to the absence of fermentative pathways for amino acid and lipid catabolism. In any event, it seems likely that *Tetrahymena* will prove to be an interesting exception to the usual rule that carbohydrates are the most readily utilized energy sources, followed by fats, and finally amino acids and proteins.

## Paramecium

Information on the respiratory metabolism of *Paramecium* is surprisingly scanty. Early literature is included in Seaman's review.[280] *P. caudatum* at least, is apparently an obligate aerobe.[118]

Spectroscopic evidence has been presented for the presence of cytochromes a and c in *Paramecium* (Sato and Kimura, cited in[280]). There is general agreement that the respiration of *P. caudatum*,[68, 144, 229] *P. aurelia*,[229, 292] and *P. calkinsi*[37, 38] is somewhat sensitive to cyanide and azide. In general, however, the effects were obtained at concentrations of $10^{-3}$ to $10^{-2}$ M, which resulted in only about 50 per cent inhibition. Such results are subject to at least two alternative interpretations: that half or less of the respiration was carried on through a conventional cytochrome system, or that respiration was via some other system and was inhibited by nonspecific effects of high cyanide and azide concentrations. The significant inhibitions reported with lower concentrations of inhibitors[229, 292] support the former possibility, as does the light-reversible carbon monoxide inhibition of respiration.[68] Positive tests for cytochrome oxidase have been reported with *P. aurelia*,[292] *P. calkinsi*[37] and *P. putrinum*.[155] In view of the problems which have arisen in connection with the cytochrome system of *Tetrahymena* (see above), none of this evidence can be considered conclusive, and further studies of the electron transfer system in *Paramecium* would be welcome.

Geddes and Humphrey[118] showed anaerobic lactic acid production from hexose phosphate in extracts and intact cells of *P. caudatum*, suggesting the presence of the EMP glycolytic pathway. Hunter[155] obtained evidence for the glycolytic enzyme aldolase in *P. putrinum*.

Humphrey and Humphrey[144] found that malonate inhibited, and succinate stimulated the respiration of *P. caudatum* homogenates, suggesting the presence of the Krebs cycle.

The endogenous respiratory rate at 25°C of *P. caudatum* has been reported as 660 μl $O_2$/million cells/hr[68] and as 1500–4500 μl/million cells/hr;[229] that of *P. aurelia* as 450–1500 μl/million cells/hr[229] and 150–240 μl/million cells/hr.[292] The rates varied with the age, temperature[233] and nutritional status of the culture, and rates were different for "killer" and "sensitive" strains of *P. aurelia*. Little is known concerning the endogenous substrate, but in *P. caudatum* and *P. calkinsi*, ammonia liberation suggested that protein oxidation may account for a considerable part of the endogenous $O_2$ consumption.[38, 78]

In a complex medium, respiratory rates of single *P. caudatum* cells were found to vary widely, over a range equivalent to 200–2000 μl $O_2$/million cells/hr at 25°C.[266a] Glucose stimulated respiration of *P. caudatum* about 20 per cent above the endogenous rate;[229] glucose and acetate stimulated respiration of a "sensitive" strain of *P. aurelia* about 50 per cent, but had little or no effect on a "killer" strain.[292]

Addition of glucose, or especially starch, to *P. caudatum* decreased the rate of ammonia production, and resulted in production of unidentified organic acids.[78]

In a nearly-defined axenic growth medium,[169, 170, 207, 208] a carbon source such as acetate or pyruvate was required, in addition to the amino acids necessary for growth of *P. multimicronucleatum*. Glycogen, glucose, and fructose appeared to be less effective substitutes for acetate and pyruvate, while galactose, mannose, and glucose-1-phosphate seemed not to be used.[169]

## Symbiotic Rumen Ciliates

Large numbers of holotrich and oligotrich ciliates inhabit the rumens of sheep, cattle, and other ruminant mammals. Within the rumen, these protozoa participate, together with an extensive bacterial flora, in the conversion of cellulose, starch and other plant carbohydrates to lower fatty acids, which are then utilized by the mammalian host. In addition, since the rumen contents are digested in the more posterior parts of the host digestive system, the rumen flora and fauna provide a source of protein, vitamins, etc. different from those originally present in the food. Quantitative studies indicate that the protozoa play a significant part in these conversions.[126, 148, 228]

The rumen ciliates are obligate anaerobes, and many species have been shown to ingest bacteria,[128, 129, 130] as well as starch granules and cellulose fragments.[228] So far it has proved impossible to obtain any of these ciliates in permanent axenic culture, and most experimental studies have been performed on organisms isolated directly from rumen fluid. While surprisingly effective techniques have been developed for the isolation of particular species or groups of related species,[126] the majority of studies have been made on mixed populations, rather than single species. Interpretation of the results is further complicated by the possibility that the ciliates themselves perhaps contain symbiotic intracellular bacteria (see[129, 248]). The physiology of the rumen ciliates has been reviewed by Hungate[148] and Oxford.[228]

### RUMEN HOLOTRICHS

The holotrich ciliates of the rumen include members of the genera *Isotricha* and *Dasytricha*. *Isotricha* has been observed to ingest small starch grains, while *Dasytricha* apparently does not;[126, 298] most studies suggest that both genera depend for energy largely on soluble carbohydrates. The organisms are obligate anaerobes, whose metabolism is damaged by exposure to air.[135]

The cells have been found to contain extremely large reserves of a polysaccharide which has been shown to resemble amylopectin, the branched-chain component of starch.[108, 211] This starch was in the form of cytoplasmic granules, which disappeared during incubation in the absence of substrate;[135] granules were practically absent after 72–96 hr starvation.[128] Hydrogen, $CO_2$, and acid were produced during endogenous fermentation. For mixtures of *Isotricha prostoma* and *I. intestinalis*, the rates of fermentation were about (moles/million cells/hr): $H_2$, 0.35; $CO_2$, 0.28; acid, 0.38 for freshly isolated cells, decreasing 50–65 per cent after 24 hr starvation. For *Dasytricha*, the rates were much smaller, $H_2$, 0.02; $CO_2$, 0.02; and acid, 0.01. Per mg. of cell nitrogen, however, the rates were roughly equal for the two genera. The acids produced were mainly lactic, acetic, and butyric. Cellular nitrogen also disappeared during endogenous incubation.[126, 135]

Addition of any of several soluble carbohydrates stimulated fermentation rates as much as 5–10 fold,[126, 135, 136, 142] caused accumulation of polysaccharide reserves,[201, 227] and prolonged survival *in vitro*.[298] Of the monosaccharides, glucose and fructose were readily used by both dasytrichs and isotrichs, galactose by *Dasytricha* only,[142] while mannose, sorbose, xylose, and arabinose were not utilized. Of the oligosaccharides, sucrose and raffinose were used by both genera, cellobiose and maltose by *Dasytricha* only,[55, 142] while a variety of others were not used. The glucosides, amygdalin, salicin, arbutin, and aesculin were used. Among the polysaccharides, inulin, and plant and bacterial levans were used by both, and starch by *Isotricha* only (consistent with the observations that isotrichs ingest small starch grains while dasytrichs do not). Cellulose and glycogen did not prolong survival, nor oddly enough, did polysaccharide from the protozoa themselves either stimulate fermentation or prolong survival.[142, 298] Hexitols, hexose phosphates, lower fatty acids, and Krebs cycle acids had no effect on *in vitro* survival.[298] Studies of carbohydrase activities in cell extracts gave results generally consistent with the nutritional capabilities of intact cells.[143, 228]

Fermentation of glucose resulted in the formation of $CO_2$, $H_2$, lactic, acetic, and butyric acids, and traces of what was probably propionic acid.[126, 135] The proportions reported vary somewhat; in general, somewhat more $H_2$ was produced that $CO_2$, and on a molar basis more lactic acid was produced than either acetic or butyric. There seem to be no clear differences between isotrichs and dasytrichs in this respect. A large proportion of the glucose consumed (50–80%) was converted to intracellular reserves. From tracer experiments, Heald and Oxford[135] concluded that the breakdown of carbohydrate reserves continued during fermentation of exogenous glucose, and that there was dilution of the reserves by incorporation of the external substrate. This simultaneous synthesis and breakdown of reserve material during glucose utilization makes it difficult to obtain meaningful carbon balance data.

The fermentation products of *Dasytricha* on galactose resembled those on glucose, but a much smaller proportion of the galactose carbon was assimilated.[142]

The striking conversion of soluble sugar to storage polysaccharide by the rumen holotrichs was apparently unregulated; when supplied with large amounts of sugar, the organisms swelled and burst, seemingly as a result of excessive accumulations of intracellular polysaccharide.[298]

## RUMEN OLIGOTRICHS

The oligotrichs of the rumen include members of the genera *Diplodinium*, *Entodinium*, and *Metadinium*. Their metabolic behavior is markedly different from that of the holotrichs, and there appear to be significant generic and specific differences among the oligotrichs themselves, some of which will be pointed out below.

*Entodinium caudatum* remained active for 48 hr or more in the absence of substrate. During this time, the rate of gas production ($CO_2$ plus $H_2$) declined from about 400 to about 160 $\mu l/mg$ N/hr, and the starch content of the cells decreased 96 per cent.[2] These starch reserves, like those of the holotrichs, are probably amylopectin, since those of *Cycloposthium*, a related oligotrich from the horse cecum and intestine, were found to have this structure.[109]

The endogenous fermentation resulted in the formation of $H_2$, $CO_2$, acetic and butyric acids, and traces of formic and propionic acid. In contrast to the holotrichs, the oligotrichs produced only small amounts of lactic acid. The products listed account for most of the polysaccharide carbon which disappeared.[2]

Addition of glucose, maltose, or rice starch to *E. caudatum* after 24 hr starvation caused no stimulation of gas production during the first hour after substrate addition. Glucose, cellobiose, maltose, sucrose, and soluble starch were not removed from the medium. Rice starch granules were ingested, and (after several hours) caused some increase in the rate of gas production by starved cells, but did not restore the rate to that of unstarved organisms.[2] Gas production by *Diplodinium medium* was likewise not stimulated by glucose.[228]

*Diplodinium medium* ingested and digested cellulose, with concurrent deposition of starch reserves,[297] and has been found to contain cellulase.[147] Grains of rice and potato starch were used less effectively. The ability to use cellulose was lost after streptomycin treatment which did not kill the protozoa, and the suggestion was made that cellulose digestion might depend on intracellular bacterial symbionts.

*Entodinium* species were not observed to eat cellulose; some species ingested and used rice starch while others did not.[297] In *E. caudatum*, $\alpha$-amylase and maltase, enzymes of starch digestion, were the only carbohydrases found in appreciable amounts.[2]

Although the data are still somewhat scanty, they point to the probability that the rumen oligotrichs are unable to utilize dissolved carbohydrates (perhaps because of permeability restrictions?), and are dependent on particulate food for carbon and energy sources. Since even particulate starch was not readily fermented by *E. caudatum*, it may be that bacteria[129] form a major and essential portion of the diet of these organisms. *Diplodinium* is the only rumen ciliate so far implicated in the process of cellulose breakdown.

In contrast to the oligotrichs, the holotrichs utilized soluble carbohydrates readily, and apparently more easily than particulate materials. The marked ability of the holotrichs to utilize fructose-containing oligo- and polysaccharides (sucrose, raffinose, inulin, levans) may be an indication of their niche in the rumen ecology.

Mixed populations of sheep rumen protozoa have been reported to consume $H_2$.[85a]

## Other Ciliates

### BALANTIDIUM COLI

Although its normal environment in the mammalian gut must be almost anaerobic, *Balantidium coli* was found to have a rapid rate of oxygen consumption, 9000 μl $O_2$/million cells/hr at 37°C, and 4000 μl/million cells/hr at 28°C, in a complex growth medium. The RQ was 1.03. The respiration was markedly sensitive to iodoacetamide, malonate, fluoroacetate, and cyanide. All the data were consistent with carbohydrate oxidation via the usual EMP glycolysis-TCA cycle pathways.

Anaerobically, $CO_2$ was formed at about 2/3 the aerobic respiration rate. Anaerobic experiments in bicarbonate media indicated production of relatively small amounts of unidentified acid.[4]

### STYLONYCHIA PUSTULATA

Respiration of *Stylonychia pustulata* homogenates was stimulated by cytochrome c, succinate, fumarate, malonate, and oxalacetate. Oxidation of cytochrome c was inhibited by cyanide, that of succinate by malonate, and that of fumarate, by arsenite; all at low inhibitor concentrations. Cytochemical techniques indicated the presence of aldolase in the cytoplasm, and perhaps also in the mitochrondria, and of succinic, malic, lactic, and glutamic dehydrogenases, fumarase, and cytochrome oxidase in the mitochondria. Glycerophosphate dehydrogenase could not be detected.[153, 154]

Rice, corn and potato starches and glycogen disappeared on incubation with *Stylonychia* homogenates, but neither glucose nor maltose could be demonstrated among the products.[156]

### COLPODA CUCULLUS

Cytochrome c, citrate, α-ketoglutarate, succinate, fumarate, malate, oxalacetate, glutamate, and glycerophosphate have been reported to stimulate respiration of *Colpoda cucullus*. The results are somewhat difficult to interpret, because of the use with intact cells of reaction mixtures designed for homogenates. Cyanide did not immediately inhibit oxidation of cytochrome c, but caused marked inhibition after about 20 minutes. Malonate inhibited succinate oxidation.[158] Cytochemical staining indicated the presence of aldolase in the cytoplasm and cytochrome oxidase in the mitochondria.[157]

Single cells of *Bresslaua insidiatrix* have been reported to consume oxygen at rates equivalent to 80–400 μl/million cells/hr.[266a] Cysts respired at a much lower rate; the rate decreased during encystment and increased during excystment.

## SARCODINA

The scanty information available concerning the respiratory metabolism of the Sarcodina is almost entirely limited to three groups of amebas; small soil amebas of the *Acanthamoeba-Mayorella-Hartmannella* group, the giant amebas *Chaos chaos* and *Amoeba proteus*, and the endoparasite, *Entamoeba histolytica*. Balamuth and Thompson[23] have written a valuable review of amebal metabolism. Other Sarcodina, including such major groups as the Heliozoida, Radiolarida, Foraminiferida, and Mycetozoida remain virtually unstudied.

### Acanthamoeba castellanii and similar spp.

Small soil amebas, referred to the genera *Acanthamoeba*, *Mayorella*, and *Hartmannella*, have been isolated and maintained in axenic culture, and have been the subjects of a number of studies of respiratory metabolism. Studies with several different species within this group have given similar, though not completely identical results. *Hartmannella*, at least seems to be an obligate aerobe, since the organisms died in an $H_2$-$CO_2$ atmosphere.[25]

Respiration of *Mayorella palestinensis*[250] and *Acanthamoeba* sp.[223] was sensitive to cyanide, but the degree of inhibition was so low as to suggest either that the usual cytochrome system was not involved, or that a large fraction of the total respiration occurred via cyanide-insensitive pathways. Azide inhibition resembled cyanide inhibition in this respect.[250] It may be recalled that similar findings with *Tetrahymena* apparently resulted from the presence of an electron transfer system different from the classical cytochrome system.

Relatively little is known concerning the enzymatic pathways of respiratory metabolism in these organisms; Neff *et al.*[223] obtained evidence for the presence of lactic, succinic, and $\beta$-glycerophosphate dehydrogenases in *Acanthamoeba* sp.

The endogenous respiratory rate of *M. palestinensis* was found to be about $90 \mu l$ $O_2$/mg N/hr, or 10 $\mu l$ $O_2$/million cells/hr at 27°C.[249] That of *Acanthamoeba* sp. was very similar, 120 $\mu l$ $O_2$/mg N/hr at 28°C.[223] In both cases the initial RQ was about 0.85; in *Acanthamoeba*, the RQ declined to 0.75 as endogenous metabolism continued. Such RQ values suggest the oxidation of substrates more reduced than carbohydrate, but must be interpreted with caution because of the distinct possibility that incompletely oxidized metabolic products, of unknown composition, were excreted. Anaerobically, *Acanthamoeba* produced $CO_2$ at about the same rate as under aerobic conditions.[223] Stores of fat, but not of glycogen, could be detected in *Acanthamoeba*,[223] again suggesting that the endogenous substrate is not carbohydrate in nature.

Starvation for 24 hr decreased the endogenous respiratory rate of *M. palestinensis* somewhat.[249] The respiration was relatively insensitive to pH over a considerable range. Oxygen tensions above 5% $O_2$ supported maximum respiration; at 1–3% $O_2$, oxygen consumption was decreased about one-half.

The role of glucose in the metabolism of these amebas is somewhat of an enigma. Addition of glucose, or some alternative carbon source, greatly increased growth of all strains in peptone media, although several strains appeared capable of some growth in peptone alone.[3, 25, 55, 248] Early attempts to demonstrate disappearance of glucose from the medium gave negative results[53] or indicated extremely low rates of utilization.[223] Band,[25] however, found appreciable consumption of [14]C-labeled glucose by Hartmannella rhysodes. He showed that in this species, the difficulty in demonstrating glucose consumption by analysis of the medium resulted from the excretion of materials reacting like glucose with the ordinary reagents for carbohydrate determination; glucose disappearance could be demonstrated readily by the use of the highly specific glucose oxidase method.

During growth on [14]C-glucose, radioactive carbon appeared in cellular material, in $CO_2$, and in products excreted into the medium. Seventy-six percent of the $CO_2$ produced under these conditions was derived from glucose, showing that glucose was a major respiratory substrate.[25]

A considerable variety of other hexoses and hexose oligosaccharides have been shown to replace glucose in supporting growth of Mayorella[248] and Acanthamoeba[223] while sorbose, most pentoses, sugar alcohols, powdered starch, and cellulose were ineffective.[222, 223] Glycerol, acetate, and lactate also supported growth of Acanthamoeba[3, 25, 223] and the growth rate on acetate was as great or greater than on glucose. The concentration of glucose required for maximum rates of growth of Acanthamoeba and Hartmannella was much higher than would be needed to fulfil the carbon and energy requirements of growth;[3, 25] as Band[25] has suggested, this concentration dependence may indicate that cellular permeability was the factor limiting the rate of sugar metabolism. Growth on acetate was much less dependent on substrate concentration.[3] Uptake of acetate from the medium, accompanied by fat synthesis, has been demonstrated in Acanthamoeba sp.[223]

Considering the apparent importance of sugars in the metabolism of these amebas, it is surprising that glucose caused no appreciable stimulation of respiration above the endogenous rate in Mayorella[249, 250] or Acanthamoeba,[223] even after starvation or other treatments intended to enhance glucose consumption. In this respect, the behavior of the amebas recalls that of Euglena gracilis var. bacillaris. Reich,[250] however, found a small but consistent stimulation by glucose in cyanide- or azide-poisoned Mayorella. It may be that glucose utilization interfered with the oxidation of endogenous substrates by mechanisms similar to those indicated in Fig. 3, B and C, in such a way that the utilization of glucose resulted in no change in the total metabolic rate. The results with cyanide-poisoned cells would be explained if the reserve oxidation process were slightly more cyanide-sensitive than the oxidation pathways for glucose. Studies combining respirometric and tracer techniques would provide a test of this hypothesis.

Several soil amebas, particularly *Acanthamoeba castellanii*, showed considerable growth in peptone media without the addition of sugar, acetate, or other carbon sources.[25, 55] Peptone was found to cause a 15 per cent increase in the respiratory rate of *Mayorella palestinensis*,[249] suggesting that peptides and amino acids may serve as energy sources for these species. Respiration of another species of *Acanthamoeba*, in contrast, was not stimulated by peptone or by individual amino acids.[223] Cailleau[55] studied the changes in nitrogenous materials during growth of *A. castellanii* in peptone media, and found evidence of considerable breakdown of protein to lower molecular weight nitrogen compounds. Very little ammonia was produced, in contrast to what would be expected if amino acids were being used as energy sources. Considerable quantities of unidentified nitrogen compounds were found, which might correspond to alternative end products (urea?) of amino acid degradation. Neff *et al.*,[223] on the other hand, found qualitative evidence of ammonia formation during growth of their *Acanthamoeba* sp. on peptone-containing media.

## Amoeba proteus and Chaos chaos

The respiratory metabolism of the giant amebas, *Amoeba proteus* and *Chaos chaos* (*C. carolinensis, Pelomyxa carolinensis*) is of especial interest because of their frequent use as experimental organisms in cellular physiology. Data, however, are scanty, probably because of the difficulty of obtaining the organisms in sufficient numbers for convenient study.

Oxygen consumption of *C. chaos* was extremely cyanide sensitive; cyanide concentrations of $10^{-7}$ M or greater caused 50–70 per cent inhibition, while concentrations as low as $10^{-9}$ M had some effect.[231, 235] Still lower concentrations stimulated growth and respiration. Direct assays for cytochrome oxidase, however, gave negative results.[10] Respiration of *A. proteus* was inhibited about 50 per cent by $10^{-3}$ M cyanide.[67] From spectroscopic evidence, it has been suggested that the electron transfer system in *A. proteus* and *C. chaos* may be based on cytochrome e rather than cytochrome c.[209] A similar suggestion has been discussed with regard to *Tetrahymena*.

The respiratory rate of *A. proteus* was given by Clark[67] as about 1400 μl $O_2$/million cells/hr (temperature not specified), while Brachet[46] found a much lower value, about 300 μl/million cells/hr, at 23°C. The respiratory rate of the much larger *C. chaos* was 1500–16,000 μl/million cells/hr at 25°C.[230, 266a] It is questionable whether these rates should be considered "endogenous," since both species usually contain numerous food vacuoles which persist and contain food for long periods after feeding has ceased. As would be expected, well fed *C. chaos* consumed more $O_2$, and starved organisms less, than "normal" cells. The respiratory rate increased with temperature up to 35°C, with a $Q_{10}$ of *ca.* 1.9.[230] Glycogen was present in *A. proteus*, and decreased markedly during the first three days of starvation.

It would appear that the usual pathways of carbohydrate oxidation are present in *Chaos*. Borner and Mattenheimer[39] studied the respiratory enzymes of *C. chaos*, using micromethods which permitted use of as few as two amebas. Of the enzymes related to the EMP pathway, they found hexokinase, hexosephosphate isomerase, aldolase, DPN-linked phosphoglyceraldehyde dehydrogenase, phosphoglycerate kinase, enolase, and "pyruvate kinase." Of the HMP enzymes, glucose-6-phosphate dehydrogenase was detected, and of the Krebs cycle and related enzymes, isocitric dehydrogenase, fumarase, DPN-linked malic dehydrogenase, and "malic enzyme." Andresen *et al.*[10] found succinic dehydrogenase in this species. Centrifugal displacement indicated that the succinic dehydrogenase was localized in particulate structures, presumably mitochondria. Enolase, but not hexokinase, has been detected in *A. proteus*.[46]

*C. chaos* took up little $^{14}$C-labeled glucose from the medium unless phagocytosis or pinocytosis was induced (Glucose itself was not an effective inducer of pinocytosis[57]). Thus, the cells are probably relatively impermeable to sugar, and depend upon food vacuole formation for their nutrition. Of the glucose carbon consumed, 10–15 per cent was retained in the cells for 400 hr or more. Sixty to 80 per cent of the carbon released was $CO_2$, while the rest was in a form which did not diffuse from the medium to NaOH.

## Entamoeba histolytica

Of the parasitic amebas, *Entamoeba histolytica* (synonym, *Endamoeba histolytica*) is the only species whose respiratory metabolism has been seriously investigated. The normal environment of this species is anaerobic, and the organisms are probably obligate anaerobes.[23, 287] Lack of techniques for axenic culture has greatly handicapped study of *E. histolytica*, and the recent reports of media which permit pure culture of this[88] and other[87] parasitic amebas should be a considerable aid to future research.

As would be expected in an anaerobe, cytochrome pigments have not been detected in *E. histolytica*.[137] Cyanide and azide caused some inhibition of growth, but at concentrations where non-specific effects were to be expected.[345] The succinic dehydrogenase of *E. histolytica* could, however, be coupled with exogenous cytochrome c.[276]

Of the glycolytic enzymes, hexokinase is almost certainly present, though difficult to demonstrate. Phosphohexoseisomerase, phosphohexokinase, and aldolase were demonstrated.[137, 178, 179] Glyceraldehyde phosphate dehydrogenase activity appeared to be present[179] but not coupled to DPN reduction,[137] a most unusual situation. Homogenates converted fructose diphosphate to pyruvate, and decarboxylated pyruvate to acetaldehyde and $CO_2$. Production of $CO_2$ from glucose or from hexose diphosphate appeared to be coupled in some fashion with production of $H_2S$ from sulf-hydryl compounds such as cysteine, since each process was stimulatory to the other. The mechanism of the coupling is unknown, but may be associated with the atypical glyceraldehyde phosphate dehydrogenase.[179]

Of the enzymes of the HMP cycle, TPN-linked glucose-6-phosphate de-hydrogenase was present, while no TPN- or DPN-linked 6-phosphogluconic dehydrogenase could be detected.[137] It seems probable that the shunt is absent in this species, and that glucose-6-phosphate dehydrogenase functions as part of the Entner-Doudoroff pathway described below.

Extracts of *E. histolytica* were shown to cleave 6-phosphogluconate to triose phosphate plus pyruvate, suggesting the operation of the Entner-Doudoroff sequence of reactions:

$$6\text{-phosphogluconate} \rightarrow 2\text{-keto-3-deoxy-6-phosphogluconate}$$
$$\rightarrow \text{glyceraldehyde-3-phosphate} + \text{pyruvate.}$$

Isotope distribution studies[104] confirmed the presence of this pathway, and indicated that it is of considerable quantitative importance. This finding is of especial interest, because *E. histolytica* is the only animal cell proven to carry out these reactions, previously known from bacteria.

Of the Krebs cycle enzymes, only succinic dehydrogenase[276] has been found in *E. histolytica*. Keto acids other than pyruvate were not attacked,[179] and fluoroacetate was completely without effect on growth.[345]

Glucose, a variety of other hexoses and hexose oligosaccharides, and several pentoses stimulated $CO_2$ production by washed cells of *E. histoly-tica*.[179] Glucose-$^{14}$C was converted to cellular materials, including gly-cogen, to $CO_2$, and to lactate.[32, 104, 106] Isotope distribution studies indi-cated that the lactate formed was derived via the Entner-Doudoroff pathway and EMP glycolysis, while the HMP shunt was inactive.[104]

## General Discussion, Sarcodina

Data on the respiration of the free-living amebas are still too scanty to provide a clear picture of the metabolism of these organisms. Except for electron transfer, such information as is available gives no direct evi-dence of the presence of unorthodox metabolic pathways, but raises a number of questions. What are the carbohydrate-like products excreted by the *Acanthamoeba* group during glucose utilization? And why is there no stimulation of respiration by carbon and energy sources essential for vigo-rous growth? In both the small and the giant amebas, there are strong indications of restricted permeability to respiratory substrates.

Studies of *Entamoeba histolytica* indicate that the metabolism of this organism is very different from that of the free-living amebas, and perhaps from all other protozoa. The presence of the Entner-Doudoroff pathway is unique among the protozoa thus far studied (except possibly *Trypanosoma cruzi*), and the mechanisms leading from phosphoglyceraldehyde to pyruvate appear to differ from those described in any other organisms.

The gaps in our knowledge of both types of ameba are large and important, while the metabolism of other groups of Sarcodina is virtually unknown. In view of the evidence for multiple derivation of the Sarcodina from the flagellates, comparative studies of intermediate forms would be of particular interest.

## SPOROZOA

The malaria parasites, genus *Plasmodium*, are the only sporozoa whose respiratory metabolism has been studied in any detail. Such studies, moreover, have been confined almost entirely to the erythrocytic phase of the life cycle. We are dealing, therefore, with an intracellular parasite living in an environment (vertebrate erythrocytes) rich in oxygen and other nutrients.

The intracellular habitat of Plasmodium spp. poses considerable difficulty in the study of their metabolism as distinct from that of the host cells. One approach to this problem has been to compare the metabolism of parasitized blood, or erythrocytes, to that of uninfected controls. There are several objections to this procedure. The presence of the parasites is by no means the only difference between normal and malarial blood; for example, in *P. berghei* infections the parasitemia was often relatively low, while the reticulocyte level was so greatly increased that the metabolic changes due to reticulocytosis were at least as great as those due to the presence of the parasites.[289] In chickens, frequent bleeding, intended to mimic the destruction of erythrocytes produced by infection, caused very significant increases in the rate of erythrocyte respiration even before reticulocytes appeared.[291] Even if this were not the case, the presence of the parasite would almost certainly be expected to change the metabolism of the host cell. It has sometimes been suggested that the parasite may "take over" a portion of the host cell metabolism for its own purposes, so that the functional unit of respiration is the parasitized erythrocyte, rather than the parasite itself (though studies on isolated parasites do not appear to support this extreme view).

A second approach to the problem has been the study of parasites freed from the host cells by physical, chemical, or immunochemical lysis. Such procedures avoid the difficulties of correction for host cell metabolism, but involve the danger of injury to the protozoon, particularly where nonspecific lysins like saponin are used. The fact that such isolated parasites have been shown to survive for several days, and to undergo some degree of normal development *in vitro*[307, 308, 309] suggests that such injury may be minimal. Such results also encourage the hope that continued axenic culture of *Plasmodium* cells may eventually be achieved, eliminating most of the problems just discussed.

The respiratory metabolism of *Plasmodium* has been reviewed by Fulton[112] and by McKee.[206] So far, there has been no evidence for important metabolic differences among the various species; nevertheless, it seems safest to discuss the species separately.

## Plasmodium gallinaceum

Relatively little is known concerning the electron transfer system in *P. gallinaceum*, or indeed, in any other species of malarial parasite. The respiration was cyanide sensitive, and cyanide increased lactate accumulation,[197] suggesting that a cytochrome system may be involved.

Of the enzymes of the EMP glycolysis pathway, Speck and Evans[294] presented direct or indirect evidence for the presence of hexokinase, hexose phosphate isomerase, aldolase, DPN-linked glyceraldehyde phosphate dehydrogenase, and DPN-linked lactic dehydrogenase. Marshall[197] found most of the phosphorylated intermediates of glycolysis in parasitized erythrocytes. The extensive conversion of glucose to lactate (see below), and the much greater inhibition by iodoacetate of glucose metabolism than of lactate metabolism[197] suggest that EMP glycolysis is the major pathway of carbohydrate degradation. No evidence seems to be available concerning the HMP shunt.

Oxidation of pyruvate, lactate, and a variety of Krebs cycle acids;[197, 291, 295] catalytic stimulation of pyruvate metabolism by Krebs cycle acids; and the inhibition of pyruvate, lactate, and glucose metabolism by malonate, with accumulation of succinate[295] indicated that the TCA cycle is probably the major oxidative pathway for these substrates. Many of the acids stimulated respiration of free parasites much more than that of parasitized erythrocytes,[295] suggesting that the permeability of the erythrocyte may limit the availability of these substrates to the protozoon.

The respiratory rate of washed, parasitized red cells† was 40–50 per cent of that of similar cells suspended in serum or in glucose-containing media,[197, 291, 295] and the respiratory rate fell rapidly with time.[291] The nature of the endogenous substrate is unknown. Dasgupta[85] found no cytochemical evidence for the presence of glycogen in *P. gallinaceum*, *P. cynomolgi* or *Hepatocystis kochi*, though glycogen was detected in *Hepatozoon, Theileria*, and *Babesia* species. Marshall[197] found lactate production during endogenous metabolism of parasitized erythrocytes, while Speck *et al.* found no lactate accumulation with free parasites.[295] With the free parasites, the endogenous respiration had an RQ of 0.9 and was inhibited by malonate. The absence of glucose increased the rate of formation of ammonia,[214] suggesting that protein was oxidized under these conditions.

---

† In experiments with *P. gallinaceum*, respiration of parasitized blood is (per erythrocyte) 10 or more times that of normal blood, leaving little doubt that most of the respiration of parasitized blood may be attributed to the protozoon.

Addition of glucose, lactate, or pyruvate to washed parasitized erythro-cytes increased the respiratory rate to 2–4 times the endogenous rate.[197,214, 291, 295] The rate of respiration increased with glucose concentration up to about 1.6 mg glucose per ml,[197] and the stimulation due to glucose was sufficient, or nearly sufficient, to account for the difference between the respiratory rates in serum and in saline solutions.[197, 291] During the early stages of glucose consumption, a large fraction of the glucose was converted to lactic acid, and a smaller portion oxidized to $CO_2$. Then, as the glucose was used up, lactate oxidation continued until the accumulated lactate had been consumed.[291] The rates of $O_2$ consumption on glucose, lactate and pyruvate were similar, and the increased rate of respiration due to glucose continued after all the glucose had been used, until the accumulated lactate had been exhausted. Thus, it appears that lactate oxidation via the TCA cycle cannot keep up with glycolysis. As would be expected under these circumstances, the reported proportions of oxygen consumed and lactic acid produced per glucose molecule vary considerably with experimental conditions.

Production of lactate and $CO_2$ accounted for only about 60–90 per cent of carbon of the glucose utilized.[291] While small amounts of pyruvate and succinate were found among the products, these were not sufficient to account for the missing carbon, and it was stated that no evidence was obtained that the missing carbon was used for polysaccharide synthesis.

Under anaerobic conditions, lactate was the only detected product of glucose metabolism, and accounted for about 90 per cent of the glucose carbon. In the absence of oxygen, the lactate was not further degraded. The presence of $CO_2$ appeared to have no effect on this lactic acid fermentation; attempts to detect $CO_2$ fixation gave inconsistent results.[291]

Speck et al.[295] studied the carbohydrate metabolism of parasites freed from host erythrocytes by treatment with hemolytic antiserum. Rates of respiration and of pyruvate consumption of the free parasites were increased by a mixture of coenzymes and related cofactors, suggesting that the para-sites rely on the host cells for supply or retention of these substances. Rates of respiration of the free parasites were usually between 30 and 60 per cent of those of parasitized erythrocytes, and declined after about an hour.

Glucose, lactate, pyruvate, and most of the acids of the Krebs TCA cycle stimulated respiration of the free parasites. Glucose consumption by the free parasities was as rapid as that of the parasitized erythrocytes, but a larger fraction was converted to lactate, and a smaller fraction oxidized, in the free parasites. Parasitized erythrocytes oxidized pyruvate almost entirely to $CO_2$, while in the free parasites, a small but appreciable proportion of the pyruvate was converted to acetate. These three products accounted for about 80–85 per cent of the pyruvate carbon in both cases.[295] It would appear, therefore, that the enzymatic machinery for both glycolytic and oxidative metabolism of carbohydrate was present in the parasites themselves, though the oxidative processes seem to have been damaged somewhat when the parasites were released from the host cell.

There is considerable difficulty in expressing the rates of respiratory metabolism of malarial parasites in terms comparable with those used for other protozoa. Rates are often expressed in terms of the number of parasitized cells, with a correction for the respiration of the unparasitized erythrocytes also present in the preparations. Some erythrocytes, however, contain more than one parasite, and individual parasites vary greatly in size during the course of the reproduction cycle. Silverman et al.[291] found that the respiratory rate was correlated more closely with the total surface area of the parasites than with the number of parasites. In the presence of glucose, this rate was 7 $\mu$l $O_2/10^9$ sq. microns surface/hr at 40°C. Assuming that this rate was essentially constant throughout the life cycle, this would amount to about 0.007 $\mu$l/million cells/hr for the smallest forms (average area 1 sq. micron) to about 0.33 $\mu$l/million cells/hr for the largest forms (average area 48 sq. microns). Manwell and Feigelson[196] found a rate of glucose consumption of 0.03 mg/$10^9$ sq. microns/hr, a value considerably higher than that reported by Silverman et al.

Marshall[197] found no stimulation of respiration of parasitized erythrocytes by tyrosine, glutamate, or aspartate. Moulder and Evans[214] found production of amino nitrogen during glucose metabolism by P. gallinaceum. The total amount of nitrogenous end products was about the same in the presence as in the absence of glucose, but amino nitrogen was the major product in the presence of glucose, while ammonia production was greater when glucose was absent. Anaerobiosis markedly decreased the amount of amino nitrogen released, and prevented the increase in ammonia production when glucose was absent. The results are consistent with the view that proteins are degraded to amino acids in the presence of glucose, and that in the absence of glucose, these amino acids are further oxidized as an energy source. The apparent dependence of the rate of protein hydrolysis on the presence of oxygen remains unexplained.

The observation that malarial parasites and other haemosporidians ingest the contents of erythrocytes by phagocytosis[256, 257, 258] indicates that protein (hemoglobin, in particular) is readily available to the parasites. The high rates of glucose consumption, and the release (in the presence of glucose) of amino compounds rather than ammonia, suggest that when carbohydrate is available, protein metabolism may serve chiefly as a source of amino acids for growth, rather than as an energy source.

### Plasmodium berghei

The ability of P. berghei to parasitize common laboratory rodents makes it a particularly convenient experimental organism. Against these advantages must be weighed the experimental difficulties arising from a relatively

low degree of parasitemia, and a frequently high reticulocyte level in parasitized blood.[288, 289]

The respiration of parasitized reticulocytes was more than twice that of
normal reticulocytes, and the percentage inhibition of both types of cells
by $10^{-4}$ M cyanide was about equal, suggesting that a cytochrome system
was functional in both the host cell and parasite.[114]

Hexokinase has been detected in *P. berghei*, and partially characterized.[110]

In parasites freed from host cells with specific antiserum, isotope distribution studies of the conversion of glucose to lactate were consistent with
the belief that EMP glycolysis was the major pathway of glucose degradation. Some anomalous labeling suggested that about 2 per cent of the total
glucose breakdown might have occurred via the HMP shunt.[44] In the same
studies, only about 2 per cent of the glucose carbon appeared as $CO_2$, while
most of the remainder was recovered as organic acids and hexose phosphates.
Thus, the Krebs cycle appears to play a minor role, at most, in the metabolism of free parasites. The malonate sensitivity of respiration of parasitized
reticulocytes, therefore, should perhaps be attributed to the host cells.

Glucose did not stimulate the respiration of parasitized reticulocytes, yet
glucose, when present, was consumed. The rate of glucose consumption was
greater in parasitized than in control cells.[114] Thus, it appears that glucose
utilization "spares" the consumption of endogenous substrates (see p. 212,
above). With free parasites, quite different results were obtained; almost no
respiration was found in the absence of glucose. It would appear, therefore,
that the "endogenous" substrate was supplied to the parasite by the host cell.

There is reason to believe that this endogenous substrate was not glucose,
since the presence of the host cell increased the respiratory rate of the
parasites several-fold, while rates of glucose consumption and lactate consumption and lactate production were little changed.[43] More detailed
analysis of the interrelations between host cell and parasite are necessary,
however, before such findings can be interpreted with confidence. The
"endogenous" RQ of both parasitized and control cells was near 1.0.[114]

In the presence of glucose and serum, parasitized reticulocytes consumed 0.065–0.088 μl $O_2$/million cells/hr at 38°C, as compared with about
half this rate for uninfected reticulocytes.[114] Oxygen consumption rates
of free parasites were, however, only 25–30 per cent of the difference between parasitized and control reticulocytes.[43] As was mentioned above,
this difference has been attributed to provision of oxidizable substrates to
the parasite by the host cell. Glucose consumption of the free parasites was,
on the other hand, some 70–80 per cent of that calculated for the intracellular
parasites.[43]

When labeled glucose was consumed by free parasites, about 70 per cent
of the carbon was recovered in the form of lactic acid, while much smaller
amounts were found in acetic, pyruvic, and succinic acids and only very

small amounts in $CO_2$. Rather marked accumulation of hexose phosphate occurred, amounting to 6–7 per cent of the glucose carbon consumed. This suggests that phosphofructokinase, or some nearby step, was the rate-limiting step in glycolysis. The products and intermediates identified accounted for about 90 per cent of the glucose carbon.[44] This pattern is apparently typical of short-term experiments; after about an hour, the rate of glucose utilization decreased, and no additional lactate was produced.[43]

The yield of lactate per glucose molecule was much lower in normal reticulocytes than in free parasites, and the values for parasitized reticulocytes were essentially identical to the sum of the values for each type of cell alone.[43]

## Plasmodium knowlesi

The glucose consumption and respiration of monkey erythrocytes infected with *P. knowlesi* were much greater than those of normal erythrocytes. The respiration of parasitized erythrocytes was cyanide- and carbon monoxide-sensitive.[205, 330] Rates of oxygen consumption were greatest in an atmosphere of 5% $O_2$, decreasing slightly with increasing $O_2$ tension up to 100% $O_2$, and were decreased to about half in 0.37% $O_2$.[11, 205]

Addition of extra glucose to parasitized blood did not stimulate respiration above that in blood alone,[330] but glucose, lactate, and glycerol stimulated the respiration of washed parasitized cells markedly. As in *P. gallinaceum*, conversion of glucose to lactate occured much more rapidly than further oxidation of the lactate; lactate therefore accumulated during glucose metabolism, and continued to be consumed after the glucose had been exhausted.[24, 205, 330] The oxygen consumed during utilization of lactate was only about one-third of the amount required for complete oxidation of the lactate,[205] suggesting either the formation of incompletely oxidized endproducts or assimilation of some of the lactate carbon.

Respiration of washed parasitized erythrocytes was stimulated slightly by amino acids, but not by acetate or succinate.[205]

*In vitro* cultivation of parasitized erythrocytes appeared to reduce the respiration of the parasites markedly, without much change in the rates of glucose or lactate consumption.[24]

## Other Species of Plasmodium

Bovarnick *et al.*[41, 42] have studied the metabolism of the duck parasite, *P. lophurae*. Respiration of parasitized erythrocytes was 3–10 times that of normal controls. Parasites freed from the host cells by saponin treatment showed respiratory rates up to 70 per cent of those of the parasitized cells. Respiration was cyanide sensitive.

Glucose, lactate, or pyruvate caused a 10-fold increase in the respiratory rate of free parasites, while succinate, fumarate, AMP, or ATP caused 2–3-fold increase. The increase due to adenosine phosphates was presumably catalytic.

The endogenous metabolism decreased almost to zero within 90 minutes; the decrease was prevented by the presence of substrates, AMP, or ATP. When glucose was added after a period of incubation without substrate, the respiratory rate increased only slowly. The lag could be prevented by the addition of succinate, fumarate, or AMP with the glucose. The labile phosphate content of the parasites was found to decrease during incubation without substrate; partial recovery occurred after the addition of substrate.

Sherman[287a] partially characterized the DPN-linked lactic dehydrogenase of *P. lophurae* and showed that it differed from the corresponding enzyme of the host erythrocytes.

Velick[313] studied the relation of respiratory metabolism to developmental stage, using a strain of *P. cathemerium* with a highly synchronous life cycle. The respiratory rate was found to increase during growth and division, from 0.1–0.2 $\mu$l $O_2$/million parasites/hr in newly infected cells to about ten times this rate in schizonts. If the approximately 50-fold increase in surface area reported by Silverman *et al.*[291] in *P. gallinaceum* also holds true for *P. cathemerium*, these results would indicate that the respiratory rate per unit area decreases during growth and division.

Warren and Manwell[327] found the rate of glucose consumption of *P. relictum* to be about 1.8 mg/parasite/hr for an "average" parasite with 39 sq. microns surface.

## General Discussion, Plasmodium

In summary, the respiratory metabolism of malarial parasites appears to depend largely on glucose as an energy source. Fermentation of glucose to lactic acid, via the EMP route, was far more rapid than was the further oxidation of lactate; in the glucose-rich environment of the bloodstream, therefore, fermentation probably accounts for a large proportion of the glucose consumption. The Krebs TCA cycle appears to be present in *P. gallinaceum* but not in *P. berghei*. Where present, this system probably accounts for the further oxidation of lactate.

Such limited evidence as is available suggests that little glucose carbon is assimilated, and that carbohydrate reserves are lacking. Raw materials for synthesis of cellular constituents must presumably be derived preformed from the host cell or plasma. Conversely, it would appear that the proteins, etc., derived from the host are not used as energy sources except in the absence of carbohydrate. These complex relationships deserve much further investigation, however, before firm conclusions can be drawn.

### TOXOPLASMA GONDII

*T. gondii* is an intracellular parasite of mammals and birds whose taxonomic position is so questionable that it is uncertain whether it should be considered a protozoon. Fulton and Spooner[116] have made a valuable study of its respiratory metabolism.

Oxygen consumption was cyanide sensitive, and cytochromes a, b, and c were detected spectroscopically. Hexokinase was present, and glucose and fructose phosphates were oxidized by extracts, and in some cases by intact cells. These facts, plus extensive lactic acid production by intact cells, leave little doubt that the EMP pathway is functional. The production of considerable amounts of $CO_2$ from glucose might be accounted for either by the HMP shunt or the Krebs cycle; present information does not appear to be sufficient to distinguish between these alternatives.

No respiration was detected in the absence of exogenous substrate. It would appear either that no reserve substrates are available, or that such reserves as may exist are consumed by mechanisms which do not require oxygen.

Glucose permitted respiration with a $Q_{O_2}$ of about 30 and an RQ of 0.83 to 1.14. Several other carbohydrates, including hexoses, hexose disaccharides, glycogen and ribose, stimulated respiration to lesser degrees. Glycerol, glutamine, pyruvate, and $\alpha$-ketoglutarate stimulated respiration, while lactate and several Krebs cycle intermediates did not. Glucose-6-phosphate and fructose diphosphate stimulated respiration; fructose-1-phosphate did not.

Approximately 3 moles of $O_2$ were consumed for each mole of glucose consumed. $CO_2$ production accounted for about half the carbon of the glucose, and lactate production for about 30–40 per cent; small amounts of acetic, propionic, butyric, and valeric acid were detected. Anaerobically, lactate accounted for more than half of the glucose carbon.

Clearly, as in many parasitic forms, fermentation was quantitatively important even under aerobic conditions. Rapid oxidation of glutamine, and respiratory stimulation by pyruvate and $\alpha$-ketoglutarate suggest the presence of at least portions of the TCA cycle. Otherwise, the pattern of substrate utilization is not readily interpreted in terms of metabolic pathways, and is more suggestive of limited cellular permeability. Glycogen and the hexose phosphates, which were utilized, would not be expected to penetrate cell membranes readily, however.

## SUMMARY AND DISCUSSION

From the foregoing survey, it is apparent that the protozoa can no longer be considered among the neglected stepchildren of metabolic research. Species of *Tetrahymena*, the trypanosomes, and *Euglena* are well on their way to rank among the most thoroughly examined objects in the study of respiratory metabolism, ranking only slightly behind certain vertebrate tissues, yeast, and bacteria in this regard. And while there are glaring gaps in our knowledge, including major groups on which work has hardly begun, the same could be said for most other phyla. This being the case, it is appropriate to take stock of the present position.

The most impressive accomplishments, so far, have been in the area of what might be called descriptive biochemistry, the identification of the substrates, enzymatic pathways, and products of respiratory metabolism in individual species or groups of protozoa. These accomplishments should not be minimized; such characterization has as much theoretical and practical significance to the protozoologist as comparable descriptions of morphology, nutritional requirements, life cycles, and the like. Insofar as it involves identification, in the protozoa, of respiratory mechanisms already known in other organisms, such information is of primary interest only to the specialist in protozoology.

Of far more general interest would be the discovery of new or unexpected respiratory mechanisms in the protozoa. So far, such discoveries have been relatively few. The $\alpha$-glycerophosphate electron transfer process in the trypanosomes, and the unexpected presence of the Entner-Doudoroff pathway in *Entamoeba histolytica*, are the best documented cases. In addition, there is strong suggestive evidence for other "new" electron transfer mechanisms in the trypanosomes, amebas, and *Tetrahymena*, and for an unusual process of phosphoglyceraldehyde oxidation in *Entamoeba histolytica*. One may reasonably expect that further new or variant mechanisms will become apparent as the "classical" pathways are studied in more detail in a greater variety of protozoa, since most such discoveries are made by a process of eliminating the expected explanations. Studies of hydrogen production in the rumen and termite flagellates, trichomonads, and entamoebas may give insight into new mechanisms of fermentative oxidation-reduction balance.

Where respiratory metabolism is concerned, the early, and probably naïve, expectations of "comparative biochemistry" have not, for the most part, been fulfilled. The strong correlation between the metabolic characteristics of the trypanosomes and the characteristics more frequently used for taxonomic purposes is encouraging, but is so far a more or less isolated case. In general, the simple cataloging and comparison of the distribution of enzymes or enzyme systems does not seem to provide any clear-cut picture of evolutionary relationships. To cite a specific instance, the known enzymatic differences between *Tetrahymena* and the nonphotosynthetic euglenoids appear rather trivial when compared with the marked differences in morphology, nutrition, and ecology of the two species. Apparently the main enzymatic pathways of energy metabolism tend to be conserved during evolution, and where certain pathways are nonfunctional (as, for example, the Krebs cycle in trypanosomes, trichomonads, and *Entamoeba*), their distribution seems to reflect ecological parallelism more than phylogenetic relationship.

The very real differences in energy metabolism between phylogenetic groups appear to involve the more subtle mechanisms by which the enzymatic reactions are regulated and integrated into the biochemistry of the intact cell. The marked, and often highly specific permeability limitations which restrict substrate utilization in the phytoflagellates (and probably also protect these cells from high concentrations of potentially toxic organic compounds) fall in this category, and seem to explain many of the peculiarities of the group. The pathways of aerobic glycolysis in the trichomonads and in the trypanosomes appear to be very similar. Yet the trichomonads form and utilize extensive glycogen reserves, while the trypanosomes do not, and the proportions of various fermentation products in any given species of trypanosome appear to be fairly stereotyped, while these proportions vary greatly in the trichomonads. What is the origin of these differences? Are they somehow related to the probable differences in the electron transfer system of the two groups, and if so, what is the nature of the relationship? Why, for that matter, should the normally-anaerobic trichomonads possess a system capable of transferring electrons to oxygen? Do the same enzymes perform some other function in the absence of oxygen? Is there any synthesis of ATP coupled to electron transfer through this system?

If this sort of question is important to an understanding of the evolution of energy metabolism among the protozoa, it is equally important in a far more general context. We know a great deal about the nature of the metabolic machinery within cells, and about the processes this machinery carries out, whereas we know almost nothing about the controls which regulate and integrate this machinery so that the cell as a whole functions as a harmonious, homeostatic unit. This area of "metabolic regulation" is virtually unexplored, not only in the protozoa, but in all types of living things. The analysis of such control mechanisms, in any type of cell whatsoever, would be of the greatest interest, not only for the specific information it revealed, but as a source of techniques and principles which could be applied to similar investigations of other organisms.

Reasons were presented in the introduction of this chapter for believing that protozoan cells may have particular advantages for experimental investigation of such problems, and in the cases of *Euglena*, the trypanosomes, and *Tetrahymena*, at least, enough background information is available so that such questions are beginning to emerge; the investigator who chooses to work with these organisms need not feel handicapped in comparison with those studying more conventional materials.

Successful exploitation of this area of research calls for a kind of approach which has been relatively rare till now, a kind of organism-oriented biochemistry in which the tools and knowledge of the (usually enzyme-oriented) biochemist are applied intensively to a single type of cell, with an attempt to correlate information at all levels, from the characterization of isolated enyzmes to the effects of environment on the input-output economics of the intact cell. It will require more scientists who are willing to become specialists in the biochemistry of (say) *Tetrahymena* in the same sense that others are specialists in the biochemistry of carbohydrates or the taxonomy of ciliates. It is worth noting that a large fraction of our best present informa-

10a RP

tion on protozoan metabolism has originated from persons who might be described in such terms. To the extent that precedent can be trusted, respect and affection for the experimental organism as such appear to be rewarded by accomplishment.

## ACKNOWLEDGEMENTS

The author is greatly indebted to the numerous persons who responded to his requests for reprints, references, and information regarding work in progress, and who answered his written or oral queries. Special thanks are offered to Dr. A. H. Roush for reading and criticizing a portion of the manuscript, and to Dr. Barry W. Wilson for helpful discussions of several issues considered in the chapter.

TABLE I. BALANCE SHEET FOR EXPONENTIAL GROWTH OF CHILOMONAS PARAMECIUM WITH ACETATE AS SOLE CARBON AND ENERGY SOURCE. GENERATION TIME WAS 5.5 HR. QUANTITIES OF METABOLITES ARE THE AMOUNTS CONSUMED OR PRODUCED BY A MILLION CELLS IN ONE HOUR, COMPILED FROM DATA OF HUTCHENS ET AL.[162]

|  | μgm | μgm-atoms carbon |
|---|---|---|
| Acetate consumed | 125 | 5.00 |
| Ammonia consumed | 3.4 | |
| Oxygen consumed | 70 | |
| Starch produced | 22 | 0.82 |
| Protein produced | 21 | 0.88 |
| Fat produced | 6 | 0.40 |
| Total carbon assimilated | | 2.10 |
| $CO_2$ produced | 107 | 2.32 |
| Total carbon accounted for | | 4.42 (88%) |

TABLE II. CLASSIFICATION OF THE TRYPANOSOMES ACCORDING TO HOARE[138]

Section A
  Group I (lewisi)
    T. theileri
    T. lewisi
    T. cruzi
Section B
  Group II (vivax)
    T. vivax
    T. uniforme
  Group III (congolense)
    T. congolense
    T. dimorphon
    T. simiae

Group IV (brucei)
  Subgroup i (suis)
    T. suis
  Subgroup ii (brucei)
    T. brucei
    T. rhodesiense
    T. gambiense
  Subgroup iii (evansi)
    T. evansi
    T. equinum
    T. equiperdum

## REFERENCES

1. AARONSON, S., and BAKER, H. (1959) A comparative biochemical study of two species of *Ochromonas*. *J. Protozool.* **6**, 282–284.
2. ABOU AKKADA, A. R., and HOWARD, B. H. (1960) The biochemistry of rumen protozoa. 3. The carbohydrate metabolism of *Entodinium*. *Biochem. J.* **76**, 445–451.
3. ADAM, K. M. G. (1959) The growth of *Acanthamoeba* species in a chemically defined medium. *J. Gen. Microbiol.* **21**, 519–529.
4. AGOSIN, M., and VON BRAND, T. (1953) Studies on the respiratory metabolism of *Balantidium coli*. *J. Infect. Diseases* **93**, 101–106.
5. AGOSIN, M., and VON BRAND, T. (1954) The effect of puromycin on the carbohydrate metabolism of *Trypanosoma equiperdum*. *Antibiot. Chemotherapy* **4**, 624–632.
6. AGOSIN, M., and VON BRAND, T. (1954) Studies on the carbohydrate metabolism of *Trypanosoma congolense*. *Exptl. Parasitol.* **3**, 517–524.
7. AGOSIN, M., and VON BRAND, T. (1955) Characterization and intracellular distribution of the succinic dehydrogenase of *Trypanosoma cruzi*. *Exptl. Parasitol.* **4**, 548–563.
8. AGOSIN, M., and WEINBACH, E. C. (1956) Partial purification and characterization of the *iso*citric dehydrogenase of *Trypanosoma cruzi*. *Biochim. Biophys. Acta* **21**, 117–126.
9. ALBAUM, H. G., SCHATZ, A., HUTNER, S. H., and HIRSHFIELD, A. (1950) Phosphorylated compounds in *Euglena*. *Arch. Biochem. Biophys.* **29**, 210–218.
10. ANDRESEN, N., ENGEL, FR., and HOLTER, H. (1951) Succinic dehydrogenase and cytochrome oxidase in *Chaos chaos*. *Compt. Rend. Trav. Lab. Carlsberg, Ser. Chim.* **27**, 408–420.
11. ANFINSEN, C. B., GEIMAN, Q. M., MCKEE, R. W., ORMSBEE, R. A., and BALL, E. G. (1946) Studies on malarial parasites. VIII. Factors affecting the growth of *Plasmodium knowlesi in vitro*. *J. Exptl. Med.* **84**, 607–621.
12. ARCHIBALD, A. R., HIRST, E. L., MANNERS, D. J., and RYLEY, J. F. (1960) Metabolism of the protozoa. Part VIII. The molecular structure of a starch-type polysaccharide from *Chilomonas paramecium*. *J. Chem. Soc.* pp. 556–560.
13. ARCHIBALD, A. R., MANNERS, D. J., and RYLEY, J. F. (1958) Structure of a reserve polysaccharide (leucosin) from *Ochromonas malhamensis*. *Chem. Ind. (London)*, pp. 1516–1517.
14. BAERNSTEIN, H. D. (1953) The enzyme systems of the culture form of *Trypanosoma cruzi*. *Ann. N.Y. Acad. Sci.* **56**, 982–984.
15. BAERNSTEIN, H. D. (1953) Malic dehydrogenase and related enzymes in the culture form of *Trypanosoma cruzi*. *Exptl. Parasitol.* **2**, 380–396.
16. BAERNSTEIN, H. D. (1955) Aldolase in *Trichomonas vaginalis*. *Exptl. Parasitol.* **4**, 323–334.
17. BAERNSTEIN, H. D. (1959) Lactic dehydrogenase in *Trichomonas vaginalis*. *J. Parasitol.* **45**, 491–498.
18. BAERNSTEIN, H. D., and REES, C. W. (1952) Aldolase in the culture form of *Trypanosoma cruzi*. *Exptl. Parasitol.* **1**, 215–228.
19. BAKER, E. G. S. (1942) The growth and metabolism of a ciliate protozoan, *Tetrahymena geleii*. Thesis, Stanford University.
20. BAKER, E. G. S., and BAUMBERGER, J. P. (1941) The respiratory rate and the cytochrome content of a ciliated protozoan (*Tetrahymena geleii*). *J. Cellular Comp. Physiol.* **17**, 285–303.
21. BAKER, H., HUTNER, S. H., and SOBOTKA, H. (1955) Nutritional factors in thermophily: a comparative study of bacilli and *Euglena*. *Ann. N.Y. Acad. Sci.* **62**, 349–376.
22. BALAMUTH, W. (1958) Utilization of glucose by *Entamoeba invadens* in actively growing cultures. *J. Protozool.* **5** (Suppl.), 16 (abst.).
23. BALAMUTH, W., and THOMPSON, P. E. (1955) Comparative studies on amoebae and amoebicides. *In Biochemistry and Physiology of Protozoa* (HUTNER, S. H., and LWOFF, A., eds.), Vol. II, pp. 277–345 Academic Press, New York.

10a*

24. BALL, E. G., MCKEE, R. W., ANFINSEN, C. B., CRUZ, W. O., and GEIMAN, Q. M. (1948) Studies on malarial parasites. IX. Chemical and metabolic changes during growth and multiplication *in vivo* and *in vitro*. *J. Biol. Chem.* **175**, 547–571.

25. BAND, R. N. (1959) Nutritional and related biological studies on the free-living soil amoeba *Hartmannella rhysodes*. *J. Gen. Microbiol.* **21**, 80–95.

26. BARKER, S. A., BEBBINGTON A., and BOURNE, E. J. (1953) The mode of action of the Q-enzyme of *Polytomella coeca*. *J. Chem. Soc.* pp. 4051–4057.

27. BARKER, S. A., and BOURNE, E. J. (1955) Composition and synthesis of the starch of *Polytomella coeca. In Biochemistry and Physiology of Protozoa* (HUTNER, S. H., and LWOFF, A., eds.), Vol. II. pp. 45–56. Academic Press, New York.

28. BARRY, S. C. (1962) Utilization of glucose by *Astasia longa*. *J. Protozool.* **9**, 395–400.

29. BASH-LEWINSON, D., and GROSSOWICZ, N. (1957) Transaminases in *Trypanosoma cruzi. Bull. Res. Council Israel Sect. E.* **6**, 91–92.

30. BEBBINGTON, A., BOURNE, E. J., STACEY, M., and WILKINSON, I. A. (1952) The Q-enzyme of *Polytomella coeca*. *J. Chem. Soc.* pp. 240–245.

31. BEBBINGTON, A., BOURNE, E. J., and WILKINSON, I. A. (1952) The conversion of amylose to amylopectin by the Q-enzyme of *Polytomella coeca*. *J. Chem. Soc.* pp. 246–253.

32. BECKER, C. E., and GEIMAN, Q. M., (1955) Utilization of glucose by two strains of *Entamoeba histolytica. Exptl. Parasitol.* **4**, 493–501.

33. BELSKY, M. M., and SCHULTZ, J. (1962) Partial characterization of hexokinase from *Euglena gracilis* var. *bacillaris*. *J. Protozool.* **9**, 195–200.

34. BEVINGTON, J. C., BOURNE, E. J., and TURTON, C. N. (1953) Chemical degradation of $^{14}$C-glucose and its application to $^{14}$C starch from *Polytomella coeca*. *Chem. Ind.* (*London*) pp. 1390–1391.

35. BEVINGTON, J. C., BOURNE, E. J., and WILKINSON, I. A. (1950) A microbiological method for the preparation of $^{14}$C-labeled starch from sodium acetate. *Chem. Ind.* (*London*) pp. 691–692.

36. BLUM, J. J., PODOLSKY, B., and HUTCHENS, J. O. (1951) Heat production in *Chilomonas. J. Cellular Comp. Physiol.* **37**, 403–426.

37. BOELL, E. J. (1945) Respiratory enzymes in *Paramecium*. I. Cytochrome oxidase. *Proc. Nat. Acad. Sci. U.S.* **31**, 396–402.

38. BOELL, E. J. (1946) The effect of azide on *Paramecium calkinsi*. *Biol. Bull.* **91**, 238–239 (abst.).

39. BORNER, K., and MATTENHEIMER, H. (1959) Nachweis von Enzymen der Glycolyse und des Tricarbonsäurecyclus in Amöben (*Chaos chaos* L.) *Biochim. Biophys. Acta* **34**, 592–593.

40. BOURNE, E. J., STACEY, M., and WILKINSON, I. A. (1950) The composition of the polysaccharide synthesized by *Polytomella coeca*. *J. Chem. Soc.* pp. 2694–2698.

41. BOVARNICK, M. R., LINDSAY, A., and HELLERMAN, L. (1946) Metabolism of the malarial parasite with reference particularly to the action of antimalarial agents. I. Preparation and properties of *Plasmodium lophurae* separated from the red cells of duck blood. *J. Biol. Chem.* **163**, 523–533.

42. BOVARNICK, M. R., LINDSAY, A., and HELLERMAN, L. (1946) Metabolism of the malarial parasite, with reference particularly to the action of antimalarial agents. II. Atabrine (Quinacrine) inhibition of glucose oxidation in parasites partially depleted of substrate. Reversal by adenylic acid. *J. Biol. Chem.* **163**, 535–551.

43. BOWMAN, I. B. R., GRANT, P. T., and KERMACK, W. O. (1960) The metabolism of *Plasmodium berghei*, the malarial parasite of rodents. I. The preparation of the erythrocytic form of *P. berghei* separated from the host cell. *Exptl. Parasitol.* **9**, 131–136.

44. BOWMAN, I. B. R., GRANT, P. T., KERMACK, W. O., and OGSTON, D. (1961) Metabolism of *Plasmodium berghei*, the malarial parasite of rodents. 2. An effect of mepacrine on the metabolism of glucose by the parasite separated from its host cell. *Biochem. J.* **78**, 472–478.

45. Bowman, I. B. R., Von Brand, T., and Tobie, E. J. (1960) The cultivation and metabolism of trypanosomes in the presence of trehalose with observations on trehalase in blood serum. *Exptl. Parasitol.* **10**, 274–283.

46. Brachet, J. (1955) Recherches sur les interactions biochimiques entre le noyeau et le cytoplasme chez les organisms unicellulaires. I. *Amoeba proteus. Biochim. Biophys. Acta* **18**, 247–268.

47. Brawerman, G., and Konigsberg, N. (1960) On the formation of the TPN requiring glyceraldehyde-3-phosphate dehydrogenase during the production of chloroplasts in *Euglena gracilis. Biochim. Biophys. Acta* **43**, 374–381.

48. Buetow, D. E. (1961) Variation of the respiration of protozoan cells with length of centrifuging. *Anal. Biochem.* **2**, 242–247.

49. Buetow, D. E. (1961) Ethanol stimulation of oxidative metabolism in *Euglena gracilis. Nature* **190**, 1196.

50. Buetow, D. E., and Blum, J. J. (1961) Biochemical changes during acetate deprivation and repletion in *Euglena.* Absts. of Papers Presented at the First Annual Meeting of the American Society for Cell Biology, p. 23 (abst.).

51. Buetow, D. E., and Levedahl, B. H. (1960) Relations between steroid molecular structure and cell growth. *Arch. Biochem. Biophys.* **86**, 34–41.

52. Buetow, D. E., and Levedahl, B. H. (1961) The action of testosterone at the cell level. Testosterone stimulation of the respiration of *Euglena gracilis. Arch. Biochem. Biophys.* **94**, 358–363.

53. Cailleau, R. (1933) Culture *d'Acanthamoeba* en milieu liquide. *Compt. Rend. Soc. Biol.* **113**, 990–992.

54. Cailleau, R. (1933) Culture *d'Acanthamoeba* sur milieu peptoné. Action sur les glucides. *Compt. Rend. Soc. Biol.* **114**, 474–476.

55. Cailleau, R. (1934) Utilisation de milieux liquides par *Acanthamoeba castellanii. Compt. Rend. Soc. Biol.* **116**, 721–723.

56. Chang, S. L. (1948) Studies on haemoflagellates. IV. Observations concerning some biochemical activities in culture, and respiration in three species of leishmanias and *Trypanosoma cruzi. J. Infect. Diseases* **82**, 109–118.

57. Chapman-Andresen, C., and Holter, H. (1955) Studies on the ingestion of [14]C glucose by pinocytosis in the amoeba *Chaos chaos. Exptl. Cell. Res. Suppl.* **3**, 52–63.

58. Chatterjee, A. N., and Ghosh, J. J. (1957) Transaminases of *Leishmania donovani*, the causative organism of kala-azar. *Nature* **180**, 1425.

59. Chatterjee, A. N., and Ghosh, J. J. (1958) Metabolism of sucrose by *Leishmania donovani. Ann. Biochem. Exptl. Med.* (Calcutta) **18**, 69–76.

60. Chatterjee, A. N., and Ghosh, J. J. (1959) Studies on the metabolism of *Leishmania donovani*, the causative agent for kala-azar. *Ann. Biochem. Exptl. Med.* (Calcutta)**19**, 37–50.

61. Chatterjee, A. N., and Ghosh, J. J. (1960) $CO_2$ assimilation by *Leishmania donovani. Nature* **185**, 322.

62. Chen, G., and Geiling, E. M. K. (1946) Glycolysis in *Trypanosoma equiperdum. Proc. Soc. Exptl. Biol. Med.* **63**, 486–487.

63. Cheniae, G. M. (1962) Fatty acid synthesis by extracts of *Euglena. Plant Physiol.* **37** (Suppl.). lx–lxi (abst.).

63a. Cirillo, V. P. (1951) The utilization of various organic nitrogen compounds for the growth of *Chilomonas paramecium. Proceedings of the American Society of Protozoologists.* **2**, 19 (abst.).

64. Cirillo, V. P. (1955) Induction and inhibition of adaptive enzyme synthesis in a phytoflagellate. *Proc. Soc. Exptl. Biol. Med.* **88**, 352–354.

65. Cirillo, V. P. (1956) Induced enzyme synthesis in the phytoflagellate, *Polytoma. J. Protozool.* **3**, 69–74.

66. CIRILLO, V. P. (1957) Long-term adaptation to fatty acids by the phytoflagellate, *Polytoma uvella*. *J. Protozool.* **4**, 60–62.
67. CLARK, A. M. (1942) Some effects of removing the nucleus from *Amoeba*. *Australian J. Exptl. Biol. Med. Sci.* **20**, 241–247.
68. CLARK, A. M. (1945) The effect of cyanide and carbon monoxide on the oxygen consumption of *Paramoecium caudatum*. *Australian J. Exptl. Biol. Med. Sci.* **23**, 317–321.
69. CLARKE, A. E., and STONE, B. A. (1960) Structure of the paramylon from *Euglena gracilis*. *Biochem. Biophys. Acta* **44**, 161–163.
70. CORLISS, J. O. (1952) Comparative studies on holotrichous ciliates of the *Colpidium-Glaucoma-Leucophrys-Tetrahymena* group. I. General consideration and history of strains in pure culture. *Trans. Am. Microscop. Soc.* **71**, 159–184.
71. CORLISS, J. O. (1953) Comparative studies on holotrichous ciliates in the *Colpidium-Glaucoma-Leucophrys-Tetrahymena* group. II. Morphology, life cycles, and systematic status of strains in pure culture. *Parasitology* **43**, 49–87.
72. CORLISS, J. O. (1954) The literature on *Tetrahymena*: its history, growth, and recent trends. *J. Protozool.* **1**, 156–169.
73. COSGROVE, W. B. (1959) Utilization of carbohydrates by the mosquito flagellate *Crithidia fasciculata*. *Can. J. Microbiol.* **5**, 573–578.
74. COSGROVE, W. B., and SWANSON, B. K. (1952) Growth of *Chilomonas paramecium* in simple organic media. *Physiol. Zool.* **25**, 287–292.
75. COWPERTHWAITE, J., WEBER, M. M., PACKER, L., and HUTNER, S. H. (1953) Nutrition of *Herpetomonas* (*Strigomonas*) *culicidarum*. *Ann. N.Y. Acad. Sci.* **56**, 972–981.
76. CRAMER, M., and MYERS, J. (1952) Growth and photosynthetic characteristics of *Euglena gracilis*. *Arch. Mikrobiol.* **17**, 384–402.
77. CROWTHER, S., FULTON, J. D., and JOYNER, L. P. (1954) The metabolism of *Leishmania donovani* in culture. *Biochem. J.* **56**, 182–185.
78. CUNNINGHAM, B., and KIRK, P. L. (1941) The chemical metabolism of *Paramecium caudatum*. *J. Cellular Comp. Physiol.* **18**, 299–316.
79. DANFORTH, W. F. (1952) Oxidative metabolism of *Euglena*. Thesis, University of California, Los Angeles.
80. DANFORTH, W. (1953) Oxidative metabolism of *Euglena*. *Arch. Biochem. Biophys.* **46**, 164–173.
81. DANFORTH, W. F. (1961) Oxidative assimilation of acetate by *Euglena*. Carbon balance and effects of ethanol. *J. Protozool.* **8**, 152–158.
82. DANFORTH, W. F. (1962) Substrate assimilation and heterotrophy. In *Physiology and Biochemistry of Algae* (LEWIN, R. A., ed.), pp. 99–123. Academic Press, New York.
83. DANFORTH, W. F., and WILSON, B. W. (1957) Adaptive changes in the acetate metabolism of *Euglena*. *J. Protozool.* **4**, 52–55.
84. DANFORTH, W. F., and WILSON, B. W. (1961) The endogenous metabolism of *Euglena gracilis*. *J. Gen. Microbiol.* **24**, 95–105.
85. DASGUPTA, B. (1960) Lipides in different stages of the life cycle of malaria parasites and some other protozoa. *Parasitology* **50**, 501–508.
85a. DEMEYER, D., and HENDERICK, H. (1964) Investigation on the carbon dioxide reducing capacity of rumen bacteria and protozoa. *Arch. Intern. Physiol. Biochem.* **72**, 1–8.
86. DESOWITZ, R. S. (1956) Observations on the metabolism of *Trypanosoma vivax*. *Exp. Parasitol.* **5**, 250–259.
87. DIAMOND, L. S. (1960) The axenic culture of two reptilian parasites, *Entamoeba terrapinae* Sanders and Cleveland, 1930, and *Entamoeba invadens* Rodhain, 1934. *J. Parasitol.* **46**, 484.
88. DIAMOND, L. (1961) Axenic cultivation of *Entamoeba histolytica*. *Science* **134**, 336–337.
89. DORAN, D. J. (1957) Studies on trichomonads. I. The metabolism of *Trichomonas foetus* and trichomonads from the nasal cavity and cecum of swine. *J. Protozool.* **4**, 182–190.

90. DORAN, D. J. (1958) Studies on trichomonads. II. The metabolism of a *Trichomonas batrachorum*-type flagellate from the cecum of swine. *J. Protozool.* **5**, 89–93.

91. DORAN, D. J. (1959) Studies on trichomonads. III. Inhibition, acid production, and substrate utilization by 4 strains of *Tritrichomonas foetus*. *J. Protozool.* **6**, 177–182.

92. EDWIN, E. E., and GREEN, J. (1960) Reversal by $\alpha$-tocopherol and other substances of succinoxidase inhibition produced by a *Tetrahymena pyriformis* preparation. *Arch. Biochem. Biophys.* **87**, 337–338.

93. EICHEL, H. J. (1954) Studies on the oxidation of succinic acid by cell-free homogenates of *Tetrahymena pyriformis* S and W. *J. Biol. Chem.* **206**, 159–169.

94. EICHEL, H. J. (1956) Effects of atabrine and flavin mononucleotide on oxidation of succinic acid by *Tetrahymena pyriformis*. *Biochim. Biophys. Acta* **22**, 571–573.

95. EICHEL, H. J. (1956) Respiratory enzyme studies in *Tetrahymena pyriformis*. II. Reduced diphosphopyridine nucleotide oxidase and reduced diphosphopyridine nucleotide cytochrome c reductase. *J. Biol. Chem.* **222**, 121–136.

96. EICHEL, H. J. (1956) Respiratory enzyme studies in *Tetrahymena pyriformis*. III. Some properties of reduced diphosphopyridine nucleotide oxidase. *J. Biol. Chem.* **222**, 137–144.

97. EICHEL, H. J. (1959) A mammalian and protozoan electron-transport inhibitor in *Tetrahymena pyriformis*. *Arch. Biochem. Biophys.* **34**, 589–591.

98. EICHEL, H. J. (1959) Respiratory enzyme studies in *Tetrahymena pyriformis*. 4. Stabilization of electron transport components. *Biochem. J.* **71**, 106–118.

99. EICHEL, H. J. (1960) Electron-transport and phosphorylation inhibitor in *Tetrahymena* and evidence for its formation by a phospholipase. *Biochim. Biophys. Acta* **43**, 364–366.

100. EICHEL, H. J. (1961) Localization of fumarase and aconitase in *T. pyriformis* fractions. *J. Protozool.* **8** (Suppl.), 16 (abst.).

101. EICHEL, H. J. (1961) Respiratory enzyme studies in the ciliated protozoan, *Tetrahymena pyriformis*. *Symposia Genetica et Biologica Italica* **8**, 381–417.

102. EICHEL, H. J., and REM, L. T. (1959) Lactic oxidase of *Tetrahymena pyriformis*. *Arch. Biochem. Biophys.* **82**, 484–485.

103. EICHEL, H. J., and REM, L. T. (1959) Lactic oxidase of *Tetrahymena pyriformis*: the over-all reaction. *Biochim. Biophys. Acta* **35**, 571–573.

104. ENTNER, N. (1958) On the pathway of carbohydrate metabolism in *Entamoeba histolytica*. *J. Parasitol.* **44**, 638.

105. ENTNER, N., and ANDERSON, H. H. (1954) Lactic and succinic acid formation by *Endamoeba histolytica in vitro*. *Exptl. Parasitol.* **3**, 234–239.

106. ENTNER, N., and HALL, N. C. (1955) Some aspects of carbohydrate metabolism of *Endamoeba histolytica*. *Exptl. Parasitol.* **4**, 92–99.

107. EPPLEY, R. W. (1962) Light-induced acetate incorporation in *Chlamydomonas mundana* Geroff. *Plant Physiol.* **37** (Suppl.). lix–lx (abst.).

107a. ESHLEMAN, J. N., and DANFORTH, W. F. (1964) Some characteristics of ethanol metabolism in *Euglena gracilis* var. *bacillaris*. *J. Protozool.* **11**, 394–399.

108. FORSYTH, G., and HIRST, E. L. (1953) Protozoal polysaccharides. Structure of the polysaccharide produced by the holotrich ciliates present in sheep's rumen. *J. Chem. Soc.* pp. 2132–2135.

109. FORSYTH, G., HIRST, E. L., and OXFORD, A. E. (1953) Protozoal polysaccharides. Structure of a polysaccharide produced by *Cycloposthium*. *J. Chem. Soc.* pp. 2030–2033.

110. FRASER, D. M., and KERMACK, W. O. (1957) The inhibitory action of some antimalarial drugs and related compounds on the hexokinase of yeast and of *Plasmodium berghei*. *Brit. J. Pharmacol.* **12**, 16–23.

111. FULLER. R. C., and GIBBS, M. (1959) Intracellular and phylogenetic distribution of ribulose-1,5-diphosphate carboxylase and D-glyceraldehyde-3-phosphate dehydrogenases. *Plant Physiol.* **34**, 324–329.

112. FULTON, J. D. (1951) The metabolism of malaria parasites. *Brit. Med. Bull.* **8**, 22–27.
113. FULTON, J. D., and JOYNER, L. P. (1949) Studies on protozoa. Part I. The metabolism of Leishman-Donovan bodies and flagellates of *Leishmania donovani. Trans. Roy. Soc. Trop. Med. Hyg.* **43**, 273–286.
114. FULTON, J. D., and SPOONER, D. F. (1956) The *in vitro* respiratory metabolism of erythrocytic forms of *Plasmodium berghei. Exptl. Parasitol.* **5**, 59–78.
115. FULTON, J. D., and SPOONER, D. F. (1959) Terminal respiration in certain mammalian trypanosomes. *Exptl. Parasitol.* **8**, 137–162.
116. FULTON, J. D., and SPOONER, D. F. (1960) Metabolic studies on *Toxoplasma gondii. Exptl. Parasitol.* **9**, 293–301.
116a. GALE, E. F. (1951) Organic nitrogen. *In Bacterial Physiology* (WERKMAN, C. H., and WILSON, P. W., eds.), pp. 428–466. Academic Press, New York.
117. GAUSE, G. F., KOCHETKOVA, G. V., and VLADIMIROVA, G. V. (1959) Action of anti-cancer substances upon the biochemical mutants of microorganisms with impaired oxidation. *Doklady Akad. Nauk. SSSR* **124**, 674–677. Translation by DEPORTE, P. V., Cancer Chemotherapy Repts. **4**, 48–51.
118. GEDDES, M., and HUMPHREY, G. F. (1951) Glycolysis in *Paramecium caudatum. Australian J. Exptl. Biol. Med. Sci.* **29**, 187–193.
119. GEE, R. W., SALTMAN, P., and EPPLEY, R. (1962) Pathways of acetate metabolism in *Chlamydomonas mundana* Geroff. *Plant Physiol.* **37** (Suppl.): lix (abst.).
120. GOJDICS, M. (1953) *The Genus Euglena* p. 24. University of Wisconsin Press, Madison.
121. GRANT, P. T., and FULTON, J. D. (1957) The catabolism of glucose by strains of *Trypanosoma rhodesiense. Biochem. J.* **66**, 242–250.
122. GRANT, P. T., and SARGENT, J. R. (1960) Properties of L-α-glycerophosphate oxidase and its role in the respiration of *Trypanosoma rhodesiense. Biochem. J.* **76**, 229–237.
123. GRANT, P. T., and SARGENT, J. R. (1961) L-α-glycerophosphate dehydrogenase, a component of an oxidase system in *Trypanosoma rhodesiense. Biochem. J.* **81**, 206–214.
124. GRANT, P. T., SARGENT, J. R., and RYLEY, J. F. (1961) Respiratory systems in the Trypanosomidae. *Biochem. J.* **81**, 200–206.
125. GROSS, J. A., and WOLKEN, J. J. (1960) Two c-type cytochromes from light- and dark-grown *Euglena. Science* **132**, 357–358.
126. GUTIERREZ, J. (1955) Experiments on the culture and physiology of holotrichs from the bovine rumen. *Biochem. J.* **60**, 516–522.
127. GUTIERREZ, J. (1956) Metabolism of cellulose-digesting, symbiotic flagellates of the genus *Trichonympha* from the termite *Zootermopsis. J. Protozool.* **3**, 39–42.
128. GUTIERREZ, J. (1958) Observations on bacterial feeding by the rumen ciliate *Isotricha prostoma. J. Protozool.* **5**, 122–126.
129. GUTIERREZ, J., and DAVIS, R. E. (1959) Bacterial ingestion by the rumen ciliates *Entodinium* and *Diplodinium. J. Protozool.* **6**, 222–226.
130. GUTIERREZ, J., and HUNGATE, R. E. (1957) Interrelationship between certain bacteria and the rumen ciliate *Dasytricha ruminantium. Science* **126**, 511.
131. HAIGH, W. G., and BEEVERS, H. (1962) Acetate metabolism in algae. *Plant Physiol.* **37**, (Suppl.) lx (abst.).
132. HALL, R. H. (1938) The oxygen consumption of *Colpidium campylum. Biol. Bull.* **75**, 395–408.
133. HALL, R. H. (1941) The effect of cyanide on oxygen consumption of *Colpidium campylum. Physiol. Zool.* **14**, 193–208.
134. HARVEY, S. C. (1947) The carbohydrate metabolism of *Trypanosoma hippicum. J. Biol. Chem.* **179**, 435–453.
135. HEALD, P. J., and OXFORD, A. E. (1953) Fermentation of soluble sugars by anaerobic holotrich ciliate protozoa of the genera *Isotricha* and *Dasytricha. Biochem. J.* **53**, 506–512.

136. HEALD, P. J., OXFORD, A. E., and SUGDEN, B. (1952) A convenient method for preparing massive suspensions of virtually bacteria-free ciliate protozoa of the genera *Isotricha* and *Dasytricha* for manometric studies. *Nature* **169**, 1055–1056.

137. HILKER, D. M., and WHITE, A. G. C. (1959) Carbohydrate metabolism of *Endamoeba histolytica*. *Exptl. Parasitol.* **8**, 534–548.

138. HOARE, C. A. (1957) The classification of trypanosomes of veterinary and medical importance. *Vet. Rev. Annotations* **3**, 1–3.

139. HOGG, J. F. (1959) Glycogen synthesis from fatty acids in *Tetrahymena*. *Fed. Proc.* **18**, 247 (abst.).

139a. HOGG, J. F., and KORNBERG, H. L. (1962) The metabolism of $C_2$ compounds in micro-organisms. 9. Role of the glyoxylate cycle in protozoal glyconeogenesis. *Biochem. J.* **86**, 462–468.

140. HOGG, J. F., and WAGNER, C. (1956) The glycogen metabolism of *Tetrahymena pyriformis*. *Fed. Proc.* **15**, 275 (abst.).

141. HOLZ, G. G., Jr. (1954) The oxidative metabolism of the cryptomonad flagellate, *Chilomonas paramecium*. *J. Protozool.* **1**, 114–120.

142. HOWARD, B. H. (1959) The biochemistry of rumen protozoa. 1. Carbohydrate fermentation by *Dasytricha* and *Isotricha*. *Biochem. J.* **71**, 671–675.

143. HOWARD, B. H. (1959) The biochemistry of rumen protoza. 2. Some carbohydrases in cell-free extracts of *Dasytricha* and *Isotricha*. *Biochem. J.* **71**, 675–680.

144. HUMPHREY, B. A., and HUMPHREY, G. F. (1948) Studies on the respiration of *Paramecium caudatum*. *J. Exptl. Biol.* **25**, 123–134.

145. HUNGATE, R. E. (1939) Experiments on the nutrition of *Zootermopsis*. III. The anaerobic carbohydrate dissimilation by the intestinal protozoa. *Ecology* **20**, 230–245.

146. HUNGATE, R. E. (1943) Quantitative analyses of the cellulose fermentation by termite protozoa. *Ann. Entomol. Soc. Am.* **36**, 730–739.

147. HUNGATE, R. E. (1946) The symbiotic utilization of cellulose. *J. Elisha Mitchell Sci. Soc.* **62**, 9–24.

148. HUNGATE, R. E. (1955) Mutualistic intestinal protozoa. *In Biochemistry and Physiology of Protozoa* (HUTNER, S. H., and LWOFF, A., eds.), Vol. II, pp. 159–199. Academic Press, New York.

149. HUNTER, F. R. (1960) Aerobic metabolism of *Crithidia fasciculata*. *Exptl. Parasitol.* **9**, 271–280.

150. HUNTER, F. R., and LEE, J. W. (1962) On the metabolism of *Astasia longa* Jahn. *J. Protozool.* **9**, 74–78.

151. HUNTER, N. W. (1955) Histochemical demonstration of some anaerobic dehydrogenases in *Opalina carolinensis* Metcalf. *Physiol. Zool.* **28**, 302–307.

152. HUNTER, N. W. (1957) Intracellular localization of some hydrolases, and iron and copper porphyrin enzymes of *Opalina carolinensis*. *Trans. Am. Microscop. Soc.* **76**, 36–45.

153. HUNTER, N. W. (1958) Enzyme systems in *Stylonychia pustulata*. I. Cytochemical studies on the oxidation of the dicarboxylic acid substrates. *Physiol. Zool.* **31**, 23–27.

154. HUNTER, N. W. (1959) Enzyme systems of *Stylonychia pustulata*. II. Miscellaneous systems (hydrases, hydrolases, and dehydrogenases). *J. Protozool.* **6**, 100–104.

155. HUNTER, N. W. (1959) Enzyme patterns in *Paramecium putrinum* Claparède and Lachmann. *Trans. Am. Microscop. Soc.* **78**, 363–370.

156. HUNTER, N. W. (1960) Enzyme systems in *Stylonychia pustulata*. III. Hydrolysis of starches and glycogen. *Physiol. Zool.* **33**, 64–67.

157. HUNTER, N. W. (1961) Enzyme systems of *Colpoda cucullus*. II. Intracellular activity of some enzymes as determined by histochemistry. *Trans. Am. Microscop. Soc.* **80**, 38–43.

158. HUNTER, N. W., and HUNTER, F. R. (1957) Enzyme systems of *Colpoda cucullus*. I. Oxidation of certain Krebs cycle intermediates. *J. Cellular Comp. Physiol.* **50**, 341–346.

159. HURLBERT, R. E., and RITTENBERG, S. C. (1962) Glucose metabolism of *Euglena gracilis* var. *bacillaris*; growth and enzymatic studies. *J. Protozool.* **9**, 170–182.

160. HUTCHENS, J. O. (1940) The need of *Chilomonas paramecium* for iron. *J. Cellular Comp. Physiol.* **16**, 265–267.

161. HUTCHENS, J. O. (1951) Machine efficiency of assimilative processes. *Fed. Proc.* **10**, 622–628.

162. HUTCHENS, J. O., PODOLSKY, B., and MORALES, M. F. (1948) Studies on the kinetics and energetics of carbon and nitrogen metabolism of *Chilomonas paramecium*. *J. Cellular Comp. Physiol.* **32**, 117–141.

163. HUTNER, S. H., BACH, M. K., and ROSS, G. I. M. (1956) A sugar-containing basal medium for vitamin $B_{12}$ assay with *Euglena*; application to body fluids. *J. Protozool.* **3**, 101–112.

164. HUTNER, S. H., and PROVASOLI, L. (1951) The phytoflagellates. *In Biochemistry and Physiology of Protozoa* (LWOFF, A., ed.) Vol. I, pp. 27–128. Academic Press, New York.

165. HUTNER, S. H., and PROVASOLI, L. (1955) Comparative biochemistry of flagellates. *In Biochemistry and Physiology of Protozoa* (HUTNER, S. H., and LWOFF, A., eds.), Vol. II, pp. 17–43. Academic Press, New York.

166. HUTNER, S. H., PROVASOLI, L., and FILFUS, J. (1953) Nutrition of some phagotrophic fresh-water chrysomonads. *Ann. N.Y. Acad. Sci.* **56**, 852–862.

167. JACOBS, M. H. (1940) Some aspects of cell permeability to weak electrolytes. *Cold Spring Harbor Symp. Quant. Biol.* **8**, 30–39.

167a. JAHN, T. L. 1936. Effect of aeration and lack of $CO_2$ on growth of bacteria-free cultures of protozoa. *Proc. Soc. Exptl. Biol. Med.* **33**, 494–498.

168. JAHN, T. L. (1941) Respiratory metabolism. *In Protozoa in Biological Research* (CALKINS, G. N., and SUMMERS, F. M., eds.), pp. 352–403. Columbia University Press, New York.

169. JOHNSON, W. H., and MILLER, C. A. (1956) A further analysis of the nutrition of *Paramecium*. *J. Protozool.* **3**, 221–226.

170. JOHNSON, W. H., and MILLER, C. A. (1957) The nitrogen requirements of *Paramecium multimicronucleatum*. *Physiol. Zool.* **30**, 106–113.

171. KEILIN, D., and RYLEY, J. F. (1953) Haemoglobin in protozoa. *Nature* **172**, 451.

172. KIDDER, G. W., and DEWEY, V. C. (1951) The biochemistry of ciliates in pure culture. *In Biochemistry and Physiology of Protozoa* (LWOFF, A., ed.), Vol. I, pp. 324–400. Academic Press, New York.

173. KORNBERG, H. L. (1959) Aspects of terminal respiration in microorganisms. *Ann. Rev. Microbiol.* **13**, 49–78.

174. KORNBERG, H. L., and EDSDEN, S. R. (1961) The metabolism of 2-carbon compounds by microorganisms. *Advan. Enzymol.* **23**, 401–470.

175. KORNBERG, H. L., and KREBS, H. A. (1957) Synthesis of cell constituents from $C_2$-units by a modified tricarboxylic acid cycle. *Nature* **179**, 988–991.

176. KREBS, H. A., and KORNBERG, H. L. (1957) Energy transformations in living matter. *Ergeb. Physiol. Biol. Chem. Exp. Pharmacol.* **49**, 212–298.

177. KREGER, D. R., and MEEUSE, B. J. D. (1952) X-ray diagrams of *Euglena*-paramylon, of the acid-insoluble glucan of yeast cell walls, and of laminarin. *Biochim. Biophys. Acta* **9**, 699–700.

178. KUN, E., and BRADIN, J. L., Jr. (1953) The role of sulfur in the metabolism of *Endamoeba histolytica*. *Biochim. Biophys. Acta* **11**, 312–313.

179. KUN, E., BRADIN, J. L, Jr., and DECHARY, J. M. (1956) Correlation between $CO_2$ and $H_2S$ production by *Endamoeba histolytica*. *Biochim. Biophys. Acta.* **19**, 153–159.

180. KUNITAKE, G., STITT, C., and SALTMAN, P. (1962) Terminal respiration in *Trichomonas vaginalis*. *J. Protozool.* **9**, 371–373.

181. KUPFERBERG, A. B., SINGHER, H. O., LAMPSON, G., LEVY, L., and ROMANO, A. A. (1953) Studies on the metabolism of *Trichomonas vaginalis*. *Ann. N.Y. Acad. Sci.* **56**, 1006–1015.

182. LELOIR, L. F. (1960/61) The biosynthesis of glycogen, starch and other polysaccharides. *Harvey Lectures Ser.* **56**, 23–43.
183. LEWIN, J. C. (1950) Obligate autotrophy in *Chlamydomonas moewusii* Geroff. *Science* **112**, 652–653.
184. LEWIN, R. A. (1954) The utilization of acetate by wild-type and mutant *Chlamydomonas dysosmos. J. Gen. Microbiol.* **11**, 459–471.
185. LINDBLOM, G. P. (1961) Carbohydrate metabolism of trichmonads: growth, respiration and enzyme activity in four species. *J. Protozool.* **8**, 139–150.
186. LITTLE, P. A., OLESON, J. J., and WILLIAMS, J. H. (1951) Growth studies on *Polytomella agilis. Proc. Soc. Exptl. Biol. Med.* **78**, 510–513.
187. LOEFER, J. B. (1938) Utilization of dextrose by *Colpidium, Glaucoma, Chilomonas*, and *Chlorogonium* in bacteria-free cultures. *J. Exptl. Zool.* **79**, 167–183.
188. LWOFF, A. (1951) Introduction to biochemistry of protozoa. In *Biochemistry and Physiology of Protozoa* (LWOFF, A., ed.), Vol. I, pp. 1–26. Academic Press, New York.
189. LWOFF, A., IONESCO, H., and GUTMANN, A. (1949) Métabolisme de l'amidon chez un flagellé sans chlorophylle incapable d'utiliser le glucose. *Compt. Rend.* **228**, 342–344.
190. LWOFF, A., IONESCO, H., and GUTMANN, A. (1950) Synthèse et utilisation de l'amidon chez un flagellé incapable d'utiliser les sucres. *Biochim. Biophys. Acta* **4**, 270–275.
191. LWOFF, M. (1951) The nutrition of parasitic flagellates (Trypanosomidae, Trichomonadinae). In *Biochemistry and Physiology of Protozoa* (LWOFF, A., ed.), Vol. I, pp. 129–176. Academic Press, New York.
192. LYNCH, V. H., and CALVIN, M. (1952) Carbon dioxide fixation by microorganisms. *J. Bacteriol.* **63**, 525–531.
193. MANNERS, D. J., and RYLEY, J. F. (1952) Studies on the metabolism of the protozoa. 2. The glycogen of the ciliate *Tetrahymena pyriformis* (*Glaucoma piriformis*). *Biochem. J.* **52**, 480–482.
194. MANNERS, D. J., and RYLEY, J. F. (1955) Studies on the metabolism of the protozoa. 6. The glycogens of the parasitic flagellates *Trichomonas foetus* and *Trichomonas gallinae. Biochem. J.* **59**, 369–372.
195. MANNOZZI-TORINI, M. (1940) Alcune osservazioni sopra il metabolismo del *Trypanosoma evansi. Arch. Sci. Biol.* (*Bologna*) **26**, 565–580.
196. MANWELL, R. D., and FEIGELSON, P. (1949) Glycolysis in *Plasmodium gallinaceum. Proc. Soc. Exptl. Biol. Med.* **70**, 578–582.
197. MARSHALL, P. B. (1948) The glucose metabolism of *Plasmodium gallinaceum*, and the action of antimalarial agents. *Brit. J. Pharmacol.* **3**, 1–7.
198. MARSHALL, P. B. (1948) The glucose metabolism of *Trypanosoma evansi* and the action of trypanocides. *Brit. J. Pharmacol.* **3**, 8–14.
199. MARZULLO, G., and DANFORTH, W. F. (1964) Kinetic studies of the oxidative assimilation of acetate by a non-photosynthetic strain of *Euglena gracilis. J. Gen. Microbiol.* **34**, 9–20.
200. MARZULLO, G., and DANFORTH, W. F. (1964) Composition of ethanol insoluble assimilatory products of oxidative assimilation of acetate by *Euglena gracilis. J. Gen. Microbiol.* **34**, 21–29.
201. MASSON, F. M., and OXFORD, E. A. (1951) The action of the ciliates of the sheep's rumen upon various water-soluble carbohydrates, including polysaccharides. *J. Gen. Microbiol.* **5**, 664–672.
202. McCASHLAND, B. W. (1956) Adaptation by *Tetrahymena pyriformis* to potassium cyanide. II. Adaptation against respiratory inhibition. *J. Protozool.* **3**, 131–135.
203. McCASHLAND, B. W., and KRONSCHNABEL, J. M. (1962) Exogenous factors affecting respiration in *Tetrahymena pyriformis. J. Protozool.* **9**, 276–279.
204. McCASHLAND, B. W., MARCH, W. R., and KRONSCHNABEL, J. M. (1957) Variations in the inhibitory effect of KCN upon growth and respiration in seven strains of *Tetrahymena. Growth* **21**, 21–27.

205. McGee, R. W., Ormsbee, R. A., Anfinsen, C. B., Geiman, Q. M., and Ball, E. G. (1946) Studies on malarial parasites. VI. The chemistry and metabolism of normal and parasitized (*P. knowlesi*) monkey blood. *J. Exptl. Med.* **84**, 569–582.

206. McKee, R. W. (1951) Biochemistry of *Plasmodium* and the influence of antimalarials. *In Biochemistry and Physiology pf Protozoa* (Lwoff, A., ed.), Vol. I, pp. 252–322. Academic Press, New York.

207. Miller, C. A., and Johnson, W. H. (1957) A purine and pyrimidine requirement for *Paramecium multimicronucleatum. J. Protozool.* **4**, 200–204.

208. Miller, C. A., and Johnson, W. H. (1960) Nutrition of *Paramecium*: a fatty acid requirement. *J. Protozool.* **7**, 297–301.

209. Møller, K. M., and Prescott, D. M. (1955) Observations on the cytochromes of *Amoeba proteus, Chaos chaos*, and *Tetrahymena geleii. Exptl. Cell Res.* **9**, 373–377.

210. Moraczewski, S. A., and Kelsey, F. E. (1948) Distribution and rate of metabolism of phosphorous compounds in *Trypanosoma equiperdum. J. Infect. Diseases* **82**, 45–51.

211. Mould, D. L., and Thomas, G. J. (1958) The enzymatic degradation of starch by holotrich protozoa from sheep rumen. *Biochem. J.* **69**, 327–337.

212. Moulder, J. W. (1948) The oxidative metabolism of *Trypanosoma lewisi* in a phosphate saline medium. *J. Infect. Diseases* **83**, 33–41.

213. Moulder, J. W. (1948) Changes in the glucose metabolism of *Trypanosoma lewisi* during the course of infection in the rat. *J. Infect. Diseases* **83**, 42–49.

214. Moulder, J. W., and Evans, E. A. (1946) The biochemistry of the malaria parasite. VI. Studies on the nitrogen metabolism of the malaria parasite. *J. Biol. Chem.* **164**, 145–157.

215. Myers, J., and Graham, J. R. (1956) The role of photosynthesis in the physiology of *Ochromonas. J. Cellular Comp. Physiol.* **47**, 397–414.

216. Nathan, H. A. (1958) Purine biosynthesis by the trypanosomid flagellate, *Strigomonas oncopelti. J. Protozool.* **5**, 194–195.

217. Nathan, H. A., Baker, H., and Frank, O. (1960) Influence of pteridines on the production of vitamin $B_{12}$ by trypanosomid flagellates. *Nature* **188**, 35.

218. Nathan, H. A., and Cowperthwaite, J. (1955) "Crithidia factor"—a new member of the folic acid group of vitamins. *J. Protozool.* **2**, 37–42.

219. Nathan, H. A., and Funk, H. B. (1959) Relationships between pteridines and other heterocycles (purines, riboflavin, and vitamin $B_{12}$). *Am. J. Clin. Nutr.* **7**, 375–384.

220. Nathan, H. A., Hutner, S. H., and Levin, H. L. (1956) Independent requirements for "crithidia factor" and folic acid in a trypanosomid flagellate. *Nature* **178**, 741–742.

221. Nathan, H. A., Hutner, S. H., and Levin, H. L. (1958) Assay of pteridines with *Crithidia fasciculata. J. Protozool.* **5**, 134–138.

222. Neff, R. J. (1957) Purification, axenic cultivation, description of a soil amoeba, *Acanthamoeba* sp. *J. Protozool.* **4**, 176–182.

223. Neff, R. J., Neff, R. H., and Taylor, R. E. (1958) The nutrition and metabolism of a soil amoeba, *Acanthamoeba* sp. *Physiol. Zool.* **31**, 73–91.

224. Ninomiya, H., and Suzuoki–Z. (1952) The metabolism of *Trichomonas vaginalis* with comparative aspects of trichomonads. *J. Biochem.* (*Tokyo*) **39**, 321–331.

224a. Nishi, A., and Scherbaum, O. H. (1962) Levels of pyridine nucleotides and DPNH oxidase activity in growing and stationary protozoan cultures. *Biochim. Biophys. Acta* **65**, 411–418.

224b. Nishi, A., and Scherbaum, O. H. (1962) Oxidative phosphorylation in synchronized cultures of *Tetrahymena pyriformis. Biochim. Biophys. Acta* **65**, 419–424.

225. Nishimura, M. (1959) A new hematin compound isolated from *Euglena gracilis. J. Biochem.* (*Tokyo*) **46**, 219–223.

226. Ormsbee, R. A. (1942) The normal growth and respiration of *Tetrahymena geleii. Biol. Bull.* **82**, 423–437.

227. OXFORD, A. E. (1951) The conversion of certain soluble sugars to a glucosan by holotrich ciliates in the rumen of sheep. *J. Gen. Microbiol.* **5**, 83–90.

228. OXFORD, A. E. (1955) The rumen ciliate protozoa: their chemical composition, metabolism, requirements for maintenance and culture, and physiological significance for the host. *Exptl. Parasitol.* **4**, 569–605.

229. PACE, D. M. (1945) The effect of cyanide on respiration in *Paramecium caudatum* and *Paramecium aurelia. Biol. Bull.* **89**, 76–83.

230. PACE, D. M., and BELDA, W. H. (1944) The effect of food content and temperature on respiration in *Pelomyxa carolinensis* Wilson. *Biol. Bull.* **86**, 147–153.

231. PACE, D. M., and BELDA, W. H. (1944) The effects of potassium cyanide, potassium arsenite, and ethyl urethane on respiration in *Pelomyxa carolinensis. Biol. Bull.* **87**, 138–144.

232. PACE, D. M., and IRELAND, R. L. (1945) The effects of oxygen, carbon dioxide, and pressure on growth in *Chilomonas paramecium* and *Tetrahymena geleii* Furgason. *J. Gen. Physiol.* **28**, 547–557.

233. PACE, D. M., and KIMURA, K. K. (1944) The effect of temperature on respiration in *Paramecium aurelia* and *Paramecium bursaria. J. Cellular Comp. Physiol.* **24**, 173–183.

234. PACE, D. M., and LYMAN, E. D. (1947) Oxygen consumption and carbon dioxide elimination of *Tetrahymena geleii* Furgason. *Biol. Bull.* **92**, 210–216.

235. PACE, D. M., and McCASHLAND, B. W. (1951) Effects of low concentration of cyanide on growth and respiration of *Pelomyxa carolinensis* Wilson. *Proc. Soc. Exptl. Biol. Med.* **76**, 165–168.

236. PADILLA, G. M., and BUETOW, D. E. (1959) Effects of starvation on the streptomycin-bleached flagellate, *Euglena gracilis* var. *bacillaris. J. Protozool.* **6** (Suppl.), 29 (abst.).

237. PADILLA, G. M., and JAMES, T. W. (1957) Determination of oxygen uptake by the colorless flagellate, *Astasia longa*, in the presence and absence of carbon dioxide. *J. Protozool.* **4** (Suppl.), 8 (abst.).

237a. PRICE, C. A. (1961) A zinc-dependent lactate dehydrogenase in *Euglena gracilis. Biochem. J.* **82**, 61–66.

238. PRINGSHEIM, E. G. (1955) Kleine Mitteilungen über Flagellaten und Algen. II. *Euglena gracilis* var. *saccharophila* n. var. und eine vereinfachte Nährlösung zur Vitamin-$B_{12}$-Bestimmung. *Arch. Mikrobiol.* **21**, 414–419.

239. PRINGSHEIM, E. G. (1955) Kleine Mitteilungen über Flagellaten und Algen. Über *Ochromonas danica* n. sp. und andere Arten der Gattung. *Arch. Mikrobiol.* **23**, 181–192.

240. RAHN, O. (1941) Protozoa need $CO_2$ for growth. *Growth* **5**, 197–199.

241. RAW, I. (1959) Some aspects of carbohydrate metabolism of cultural forms of *Trypanosoma cruzi. Rev. Inst. Med. Trop. São Paulo* **1**, 192–194.

242. READ, C. P. (1955) Comparative studies on the physiology of trichomonad flagellates. *J. Parasitol.* **41** (Suppl.), 16 (abst.).

243. READ, C. P., and ROTHMAN, A. H. (1955) Preliminary notes on the metabolism of *Trichomonas vaginalis. Am. J. Hyg.* **61**, 249–260.

244. REAZIN, G. H., Jr. (1954) On the dark metabolism of a golden-brown alga, *Ochromonas malhamensis. Am. J. Botany* **41**, 771–777.

245. REAZIN, G. H., Jr. (1956) The metabolism of glucose by the alga *Ochromonas malhamensis. Plant Physiol.* **31**, 299–303.

246. REEVES, H. C., KADIS, S., and AJL, S. (1962) Enzymes of the glyoxylate by-pass in *Euglena gracilis. Biochim. Biophys. Acta* **57**, 403–404.

247. REEVES, H., PAPA, M., SEAMAN, G., and AJL, S. (1961) Malate synthetase and isocitratase in *Tetrahymena pyriformis. J. Bacteriol.* **81**, 154–155.

248. REICH, K. (1935) The cultivation of a sterile amoeba on media without solid food. *J. Exptl. Zool.* **69**, 497–500.

249. REICH, K. (1948) Studies on the respiration of an amoeba *Mayorella palestinensis. Physiol. Zool.* **21**, 390–412.

250. REICH, K. (1955) The effects of cyanide and azide on respiration of the amoeba, *Mayorella palestinensis*. *Physiol. Zool.* **28**, 145–150.
251. REINER, L., SMYTHE, C. V., and PEDLOW, J. T. (1936) On the glucose metabolism of trypanosomes (*Trypanosoma equiperdum* and *Trypanosoma lewisi*). *J. Biol. Chem.* **113**, 75–88.
252. REYNOLDS, H., and WRAGG, J. B. (1962) Effect of type of carbohydrate on growth and protein synthesis by *Tetrahymena pyriformis*. *J. Protozool.* **9**, 214–222.
253. ROGINE DE FEKETE, M. A., LELOIR, L. F., and CARDINI, C. E. (1960) Mechanism of starch biosynthesis. *Nature* **187**, 918–919.
254. ROTH, J. S., and EICHEL, H. J. (1961) Studies on the metabolism of L-phenylalanine by *Tetrahymena pyriformis* W. *J. Protozool.* **8**, 69–71.
255. ROTH, J. S., EICHEL, H. J., and GINTER, E. (1954) The oxidation of amino acids by *Tetrahymena geleii* W. *Arch. Biochem. Biophys.* **48**, 112–119.
256. RUDZINSKA, M. A., and TRAGER, W. (1957) Intracellular phagotrophy by malaria parasites: an electron microscope study of *Plasmodium lophurae*. *J. Protozool.* **4**, 190–199.
257. RUDZINSKA, M. A., and TRAGER, W. (1959) Phagotrophy and two new structures in the malaria parasite *Plasmodium berghei*. *J. Biophys. Biochem. Cytol.* **6**, 103–112.
258. RUDZINSKA, M. A., and TRAGER, W. (1962) Intracellular phagotrophy in *Babesia rodhaini* as revealed by electron microscopy. *J. Protozool.* **9**, 279–288.
259. RYLEY, J. F. (1951) Studies on the metabolism of protozoa. 1. The metabolism of the parasitic flagellate, *Trypanosoma lewisi*. *Biochem. J.* **49**, 577–585.
260. RYLEY, J. F. (1952) Studies on the metabolism of the protozoa. 3. Metabolism of the ciliate, *Tetrahymena pyriformis* (*Glaucoma pyriformis*). *Biochem. J.* **52**, 483–492.
261. RYLEY, J. F. (1955) Studies on the metabolism of the protozoa. 4. Metabolism of the parasitic flagellate *Strigomonas oncopelti*. *Biochem. J.* **59**, 353–361.
262. RYLEY, J. F. (1955) Studies on the metabolism of the protozoa. 5. Metabolism of the parasitic flagellate *Trichomonas foetus*. *Biochem. J.* **59**, 361–369.
263. RYLEY, J. F. (1956) Studies on the metabolism of the protozoa. 7. Comparative carbohydrate metabolism of eleven species of trypanosomes. *Biochem. J.* **62**, 215–222.
264. RYLEY, J. F. (1962) Studies on the metabolism of protozoa. 9. Comparative metabolism of blood-stream and culture forms of *Trypanosoma rhodesiense*. *Biochem. J.* **85**, 211–223.
265. SAGER, R., and GRANICK, S. (1953) Nutritional studies with *Chlamydomonas reinhardi*. *Ann. N.Y. Acad. Sci.* **56**, 831–838.
266. SANDERS, M. (1957) Replacement of serum for *in vitro* cultivation of *Tritrichomonas foetus*. *J. Protozool.* **4**, 118–119.
266a. SCHOLANDER, P. F., CLAFF, C. L., and SVEINSSON, S. L. (1952) Respiratory studies of single cells. II. Observations on the oxygen consumption in single protozoans. *Biol. Bull.* **102**, 178–184.
267. SCHWARTZ, J. B. (1961) Anaerobic metabolism of *Crithidia fasciculata*. *J. Protozool.* **8**, 9–12.
268. SEAMAN, G. R. (1949) The presence of the tricarboxylic acid cycle in the ciliate *Colpidium campylum*. *Biol. Bull.* **96**, 257–262.
269. SEAMAN, G. R. (1949) Cytochrome c, diphosphopyridine nucleotide, glutathione, and adenosine triphosphate content of the ciliate *Colpidium campylum*. *J. Cellular Comp. Physiol.* **33**, 1–3.
270. SEAMAN, G. R. (1950) Utilization of acetate by *Tetrahymena geleii* (S). *J. Biol. Chem.* **186**, 97–104.
271. SEAMAN, G. R. (1951) Enzyme systems in *Tetrahymena geleii* S. III. Aerobic utilization of hexoses. *J. Biol. Chem.* **191**, 439–446.
272. SEAMAN, G. R. (1951) Enzyme systems in *Tetrahymena geleii* S. I. Anaerobic dehydrogenases concerned with carbohydrate oxidation. *J. Gen. Physiol.* **34**, 775–783.

273. SEAMAN, G. R. (1952) Enzyme systems in *Tetrahymena geleii* S. IV. Combination of arsonoacetate with carboxyl affinity points on the succinic dehydrogenase. *Arch. Biochem. Biophys.* **35**, 132–139.

274. SEAMAN, G. R. (1952) Inhibition of the succinic dehydrogenase of *Tetrahymena geleii* S. by a phosphono-substituted succinate analog. *Arch. Biochem. Biophys.* **39**, 241–243.

275. SEAMAN, G. R. (1953) The succinic dehydrogenase of *Trypanosoma cruzi. Exptl. Parasitol.* **2**, 236–241.

276. SEAMAN, G. R. (1953) Inhibition of succinic dehydrogenase of parasitic protozoans by an arseno and phosphono analog of succinic acid. *Exptl. Parasitol.* **2**, 366–373.

277. SEAMAN, G. R. (1953) Effect of thioctic acid on the incorporation of carbon dioxide into pyruvate. *J. Bacteriol.* **65**, 744–745.

278. SEAMAN, G. R. (1954) Enzyme systems in *Tetrahymena*. V. Comparison of succinic oxidase activity in different strains. *Arch. Biochem. Biophys.* **48**, 424–430.

279. SEAMAN, G. R. (1954) Pyruvate oxidation by extracts of *Tetrahymena pyriformis. J. Gen. Microbiol.* **11**, 300–306.

280. SEAMAN, G. R. (1955) Metabolism of free-living ciliates. *In Biochemistry and Physiology of Protozoa* (HUTNER, S. H. and LWOFF, A., eds.), Vol. II, pp. 91–158. Academic Press, New York.

281. SEAMAN, G. R. (1956) Succinate metabolism of hemoflagellates. *Exptl. Parasitol.* **5**, 138–148.

282. SEAMAN, G. R. (1957) Preparation and properties of the succinate cleaving enzyme. *J. Biol. Chem.* **228**, 149–161.

283. SEAMAN, G. R. (1961) Some aspects of phagotrophy in *Tetrahymena. J. Protozool.* **8**, 204–212.

284. SEAMAN, G. R. (1962) Two techniques applicable for the study of phagotrophy in ciliates. *J. Protozool.* **9**, 335.

285. SEAMAN, G. R., and HOULIHAN, R. K. (1950) *Trans*-1,2-cyclopentanedicarboxylic acid, a succinic acid analog affecting the permeability of the cell membrane. *Arch. Biochem. Biophys.* **26**, 436–441.

286. SEAMAN, G. R., and NASCHKE, M. D. (1955) Reversible cleavage of succinate by extracts of *Tetrahymena. J. Biol. Chem.* **217**, 1–12.

287. SHAFFER, J. G. (1953) Factors affecting the propagation of *Endamoeba histolytica in vitro* in the S–F medium and in tissue bearing substrate. *Ann. N.Y. Acad. Sci.* **56**, 1033–1047.

287a. SHERMAN, I. W. (1961) Molecular heterogeneity of lactic dehydrogenase in avian malaria (*Plasmodium lophurae*). *J. Exptl. Med.* **114**, 1049–1062.

288. SHERWOOD JONES, E., MAEGRAITH, B. G., and GIBSON, Q. H. (1953) Pathological processes in disease. IV. Oxidations in the rat reticulocyte, a host cell of *Plasmodium berghei. Ann. Trop. Med. Parasitol.* **47**, 431–437.

289. SHERWOOD JONES, E., MAEGRAITH, B. G., and SCULTHORPE, H. H. (1951) Pathological processes in disease. IV. The oxygen uptake of blood from albino rats infected with *Plasmodium berghei. Ann. Trop. Med. Parasitol.* **45**, 244–252.

290. SHORB, M. S., and LUND, P. G. (1959) Requirement of trichomonads for unidentified growth factors, saturated and unsaturated fatty acids. *J. Protozool.* **6**, 122–130.

291. SILVERMAN, M., CEITHAML, J., TALIAFERRO, L. G., and EVANS, E. A., Jr. (1944) The *in vitro* metabolism of *Plasmodium gallinaceum. J. Infect. Diseases* **75**, 212–230.

292. SIMONSON, D. H., and VAN WAGENDONK, W. J. (1952) Respiratory studies on *Paramecium aurelia*, variety 4, killers and sensitives. *Biochim. Biophys. Acta* **9**, 515–527.

293. SMILLIE, R. M. (1960) Alkaline C-1 fructose-1,6-diphosphatase. Evidence for its participation in photosynthesis. *Nature* **187**, 1024–1025.

294. SPECK, J. F., and EVANS, E. A., Jr. (1945) The biochemistry of the malaria parasite. II. Glycolysis in cell-free preparations of the malaria parasite. *J. Biol. Chem.* **159**, 71–81.

295. SPECK, J. F., MOULDER, J. W., and EVANS, E. A., Jr. (1946) The biochemistry of the malarial parasite. V. Mechanism of pyruvate oxidation in the malaria parasite. *J. Biol. Chem.* **164**, 119–144.

296. STROSS, R. G. (1960) Growth response of *Chlamydomonas* and *Haematococcus* to the volatile fatty acids. *Can. J. Microbiol.* **6**, 611–617.

297. SUGDEN, B. (1953) The cultivation and metabolism of oligotrich protozoa from the sheep's rumen. *J. Gen. Microbiol.* **9**, 44–53.

298. SUGDEN, B., and OXFORD, A. E. (1952) Some cultural studies with holotrich ciliate protozoa of the sheep's rumen. *J. Gen. Microbiol.* **7**, 145–153.

299. SUZUOKI-Z., and SUZUOKI-T. (1951) Hydrogen evolution by *Trichomonas foetus*. *Nature* **168**, 610.

300. SUZUOKI-Z., and SUZUOKI-T. (1951) Carbohydrate metabolism of *Trichomonas foetus*. *J. Biochem.* (Tokyo) **38**, 237–254.

301. THOMAS, J. O. (1942) The anaerobic carbohydrate metabolism of *Tetrahymena geleii*. Thesis, Stanford University.

302. THURSTON, J. P. (1958) The oxygen uptake of *Trypanosoma lewisi* and *Trypanosoma equiperdum*, with especial reference to oxygen consumption in the presence of amino acids. *Parasitology* **48**, 149–164.

303. THURSTON, J. P. (1958) The effect of some metabolic inhibitors on the oxygen uptake of *Trypanosoma lewisi* and *Trypanosoma equiperdum*. *Parasitology* **48**. 165–183.

304. TOBIE, E. J., VON BRAND, T., and MEHLMAN, B. (1950) Cultural and physiological observations on *Trypanosoma rhodesiense* and *Trypanosoma gambiense*. *J. Parasitol.* **36**, 48–54.

304a. TOUSTER, O. (1962) Carbohydrate metabolism. *Ann. Rev. Biochem.* **31**, 407–450.

305. TRAGER, W. (1932) A cellulase from the symbiotic intestinal flagellates of the roach, *Cryptocercus punctulatus*. *Biochem. J.* **26**, 1762–1771.

306. TRAGER, W. (1934) The cultivation of a cellulose-digesting flagellate; *Trichomonas termopsidis* and of certain other termite protozoa. *Biol. Bull.* **66**, 182–190.

307. TRAGER, W. (1950) Studies on the extracellular cultivation of an intracellular parasite (avian malaria). I. Development of the organisms in erythrocyte extract, and the favoring effect of adenosine triphosphate. *J. Exptl. Med.* **92**, 349–366.

308. TRAGER, W. (1952) Studies on the extracellular cultivation of an intracellular parasite (avian malaria). II. The effects of malate and coenzyme A concentrates. *J. Exptl. Med.* **96**, 465–476.

309. TRAGER, W. (1953) Further studies on the extracellular cultivation of an avian malaria parasite. *Ann. N.Y. Acad. Sci.* **56**, 1074–1080.

310. TRUSSELL, R. E., and JOHNSON, G. (1941) Physiology of a pure culture of *Trichomonas vaginalis*. III. Fermentation of carbohydrates and related compounds. *Proc. Soc. Exptl. Biol. Med.* **47**, 176–178.

311. UKELES, R. (1953) Effect of pantothenate on growth of *Chilomonas* in the presence of propionate. *Proceedings of the Society of Protozoologists.* **4**, 19 (abst.).

312. VAN NIEL, C. B., THOMAS, J. O., RUBEN, S., and KAMEN, M. (1942) Radioactive carbon as an indicator of carbon dioxide fixation. IX. The assimilation of carbon dioxide by protozoa. *Proc. Nat. Acad. Sci. U.S.* **28**, 157–161.

313. VELICK, S. F. (1942) The respiratory metabolism of the malarial parasite, *P. cathemerium*, during its developmental cycle. *Am. J. Hyg.* **35**, 152–161.

314. VISHNIAC, W., and REAZIN, G. H. (1957) Photoreduction in *Ochromonas malhamensis*. *In Research in Photosynthesis* (GAFFRON, H., BROWN, A. H., FRENCH, C. S., LIVINGSTON, R., RABINOVITCH, E. I., STREHLER, B. L., and TOLBERT, N. E., eds.), pp. 239–242. Interscience, New York.

315. VON BRAND, T. (1951) Metabolism of Trypanosomidae and Bodonidae. *In Biochemistry and Physiology of Protozoa* (LWOFF, A., ed.), Vol. I. pp. 178–234. Academic Press, New York.

316. VON BRAND, T. (1956) Beziehungen zwischen Stoffwechsel und taxonomischer Einteilung der Säugetiertrypanosomen. *Zool. Anz.* **157**, 119–123.

317. VON BRAND, T. (1960) Der Stoffwechsel der Trypanosomen. *Ergeb. Biol.* **22**, 30–46.

317a. VON BRAND, T. (1963) Der Kohlenhydratstoffwechsel der Protozoen. *Ergeb. Mikrobiol. Immunitätsforsch. u. Exptl. Therap.* **36**, 1–58.

318. VON BRAND, T., and AGOSIN, M. (1955) The utilization of Krebs cycle intermediates by the culture forms of *Trypanosoma cruzi* and *Leishmania donovani. J. Infect. Diseases* **97**, 274–279.

319. VON BRAND, T., MCMAHON, P., TOBIE, E. J., THOMPSON, M. J., and MOSETTIG, E. (1959) The chemical composition of culture form of *Trypanosoma cruzi. Exptl. Parasitol.* **8**, 171–181.

320. VON BRAND, T., and TOBIE, E. J. (1959) Observations on the metabolism of the culture form of *Trypanosoma congolense. J. Parasitol.* **45**, 204–208.

321. VON BRAND, T., TOBIE, E. J., KISSLING, R. E., and ADAMS, G. (1949) Physiological and pathological observations on four strains of *Trypanosoma cruzi. J. Infect. Diseases* **85**, 5–16.

322. VON BRAND, T., TOBIE, E. J., MEHLMAN, B., and WEINBACH, E. C. (1953) Observations on the metabolism of normal and arsenic-resistant *Trypanosoma gambiense. J. Cellular Comp. Physiol.* **41**, 1–22.

323. VON BRAND, T., WEINBACH, E. C., and TOBIE, E. J. (1955) Comparative studies on the metabolism of the culture form and the bloodstream form of *Trypanosoma gambiense. J. Cellular Comp. Physiol.* **45**, 421–434.

324. VON DACH, H. (1942) Respiration of a colorless flagellate, *Astasia klebsii. Biol. Bull.* **82**, 356–371.

325. VON DACH, H. (1953) Effects of some intermediary metabolites on rate of $O_2$ consumption of a colorless euglenoid flagellate, *Astasia klebsii. Fed. Proc.* **12**, 149 (abst.).

326. WARREN, L. G. (1960) Metabolism of *Schizotrypanum cruzi* Chagas. I. Effect of culture age and substrate on respiratory rate. *J. Parasitol.* **46**, 529–539.

327. WARREN, L., and MANWELL, R. D. (1954) Rate of glucose consumption by malarial blood. *Exptl. Parasitol.* **3**, 16–24.

328. WELLERSON, R., Jr., and KUPFERBERG, A. B. (1962) On glycolysis in *Trichomonas vaginalis. J. Protozool.* **9**, 418–424.

329. WELLERSON, R., Jr., DOSCHER, G. E., and KUPFERBERG, A. B. (1960) Carbon dioxide fixation in *Trichomonas vaginalis. Biochem. J.* **75**, 562–565.

330. WENDEL, W. B. (1943) Respiratory and carbohydrate metabolism of malaria parasites (*Plasmodium knowlesi*). *J. Biol. Chem.* **148**, 21–34.

331. WETHERELL, D. F. (1958) Obligate phototrophy in *Chlamydomonas eugametos. Physiol. Plantarum* **11**, 260–274.

332. WILLEMS, R., MASSART, L., and PEETERS, G. (1942) Über den Kohlenhydratstoffwechsel von *Trichomonas hepatica. Naturwissenschaften* **30**, 169–170.

333. WILLIAMSON, J. (1953) Observations on the dehydrogenase activity of normal and drug-resistant strains of *Trypanosoma rhodesiense. Exptl. Parasitol.* **2**, 348–357.

334. WILLIAMSON, J., and DESOWITZ, R. S. (1961) The chemical composition of trypanosomes. I. Protein, amino acid and sugar analysis. *Exptl. Parasitol.* **11**, 161–175.

335. WILSON, B. W. (1962) Controlled growth and the regulation of the metabolism of the flagellates *Astasia* and *Euglena*. Thesis, University of California, Los Angeles.

335a. WILSON, B. W. (1963) The oxidative assimilation of acetate by *Astasia longa* and the regulation of cell respiration. *J. Cellular Comp. Physiol.* **62**, 49–56.

336. WILSON, B. W., BUETOW, D. E., JAHN, T. L., and LEVEDAHL, B. H. (1959) A differential effect of pH on cell growth and respiration. *Exptl. Cell Res.* **18**, 454–465.

337. WILSON, B. W., and DANFORTH, W. F. (1958) The extent of acetate and ethanol oxidation by *Euglena gracilis. J. Gen. Microbiol.* **18**, 535–542.

337a. WILSON, B. W., and JAMES, T. W. (1963) The respiration and growth of synchronized populations of the cell *Astasia longa. Exptl. Cell Res.* **32**, 305–319.
338. WINGO, W. J., and CAMERON, L. E. (1952) Effect of thyroxin upon growth and oxygen uptake of *Tetrahymena geleii* (Y). *Texas Rept. Biol. Med.* **10**, 1075–1083.
339. WIRTSCHAFTER, S. K. (1954) Evidence for the existence of the enzymes hexokinase and aldolase in the protozoan parasite, *Trichomonas vaginalis. J. Parasitol.* **40**, 360–362.
340. WIRTSCHAFTER, S., and JAHN, T. L. (1956) The metabolism of *Trichomonas vaginalis*: the glycolytic pathway. *J. Protozool.* **3**, 83–85.
341. WIRTSCHAFTER, S., SALTMAN, P., and JAHN, T. L. (1956) The metabolism of *Trichomonas vaginalis*: the oxidative pathway. *J. Protozool.* **3**, 86–88.
342. WISE, D. L. (1955) Carbon sources for *Polytomella caeca. J. Protozool.* **2**, 156–158.
343. WISE, D. L. (1959) Carbon nutrition and metabolism of *Polytomella caeca. J. Protozool.* **6**, 19–23.
344. WISE, D. L. (1961) Absorption of acid nutrients by an acetate flagellate. *J. Protozool.* **8** (Suppl.), 8–9 (abst.).
345. YANG, W. C. T. (1959) Effect of several metabolic inhibitors on the survival and growth of *Entamoeba histolytica. Am. J. Trop. Med. Hyg.* **8**, 575–579.
346. ZELEDÓN, R. (1960) Comparative physiological studies on four species of hemoflagellates in culture. I. Endogenous respiration and respiration in the presence of glucose. *J. Protozool.* **7**, 146–150.
347. ZELEDÓN, R. (1960) Comparative physiological studies on four species of hemoflagellates in culture. II. Effect of carbohydrates and related substances and some amino compounds on the respiration. *J. Parasitol.* **46**, 541–551.
348. ZELEDÓN, R. (1960) Comparative physiological studies on four species of hemoflagellates in culture. III. Effect of the Krebs' cycle intermediates on the respiration. *Rev. Biol. Trop. Univ. Costa Rica* **8**, 25–33.
349. ZELEDÓN, R. (1960) Comparative physiological studies on four species of hemoflagellates in culture. IV. Effect of metabolic inhibitors on the respiration. *Rev. Biol. Trop. Univ. Costa Rica* **8**, 181–195.

# CONTRACTILE VACUOLES, IONIC REGULATION, AND EXCRETION

J. A. KITCHING

*School of Biological Sciences*
*University of East Anglia*
*Norwich, Great Britain*

# CONTENTS

# INTRODUCTION

During the last five years improved methods of cutting and preparing sections for electron microscopy have been applied to the study of the contractile vacuoles of Protozoa; morphology has at last caught up with physiology in this field of enquiry. The chemical study of the vacuolar contents has scarcely begun, in spite of the prospect of a striking advance in knowledge once the difficulties associated with the minute size of the contractile vacuole have been overcome. However, the ultimate objective must be a study at the molecular level, where morphology will merge with biochemistry and structure with function.

This chapter is not a comprehensive review. It is merely an attempt to discuss aspects of current interest in research on contractile vacuoles. Much early work will be passed over, as it has already been reviewed extensively.[28, 37, 44]

# FINE STRUCTURE IN RELATION TO VACUOLAR MECHANISM

In some Protozoa contractile vacuoles arise by the fusion of smaller contributory vacuoles; in others they are fed by a system of canals. How does the water get into the contributory vacuoles or canals? Some clue to the solution of this problem may be given by the differentiation of the cytoplasm around contractile vacuoles. This differentiation is perceptible even in amoebae, which have "roving" contractile vacuoles, but is more strongly marked in Protozoa with fixed contractile vacuoles. In a dividing *Didinum nasutum* buds of differentiated material move out from the original contractile vacuole to the place where the new ones arise. Early accounts of structural elements associated with contractile vacuoles have been or soon will be superseded, for some of these elements are barely visible by light microscopy and others are beyond the limits of resolution by that technique. Comprehensive investigations by electron microscopy have been made on *Amoeba*, *Paramecium*, and *Tetrahymena*, and these will be described in some detail. Important information is also available about the locally differentiated cytoplasm in peritrichs and about the structure of the discharge canal of various other Ciliophora.

In electron micrographs the membrane surrounding the contractile vacuole of *Amoeba proteus*, like a cell membrane, appears as a double line.[64] There is no sign of any fibres in it in recent electron micrographs of osmium-

fixed material. Material fixed in other ways and examined as flattened fragments show a fairly coarse fibrillar network,[3, 55] but the fixation is un-
convincing. A weak birefringence, positive with respect to the tangent,
could indicate a fibrillar structure in the vacuolar wall.[3, 81] Cytochemical
tests have suggested that polysaccharide material forms an inner layer
(adjacent to the lumen). The vacuolar wall thus has clear resemblances to
the surface membrane of the body, and in that sense the vacuolar fluid is
already physiologically external.

The contractile vacuole of *Amoeba* (and related forms) is surrounded by
a region of numerous small vesicles, and outside these by a single layer of
mitochondria[30, 54, 64, 68] (Figs. 1 and 2). Occasional vesicles are seen to

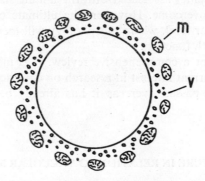

FIG. 1. Diagram of the contractile vacuole of *Amoeba proteus*, surrounded by
small vacuoles (v) and a layer of mitochondria (m). From Mercer.[64]

be in open continuity with the contractile vacuole, and it is reasonable to
assume that vesicles are continually forming around the contractile vacuole
and discharging into it.

Only observations of the living animal can give a continuous and reliable
series of stages of the complicated vacuolar apparatus of *Paramecium*.
Unfortunately *Paramecium* moves too fast (as seen with the microscope) and
rotates as it swims. Methods used to slow *Paramecium* may distort the
working of the vacuolar apparatus, and this is certainly true of the application of pressure by means of the cover glass. Electronic flash photography
might add some useful information.

An outstandingly important study with the electron microscope has
recently been carried out on *Paramecium* by Schneider.[83] Figure 6, taken
from Schneider's paper, summarizes present knowledge of the structure of
the contractile vacuole of *P. caudatum* and *P. aurelia*. The nephridial (or
radial) canals are surrounded by a "nephridioplasm" comparable with the
"spongiome" of *Campanella* (see below). This nephridioplasm, which blackens
on impregnation with osmium tetroxide,[26] is shown in Schneider's electron

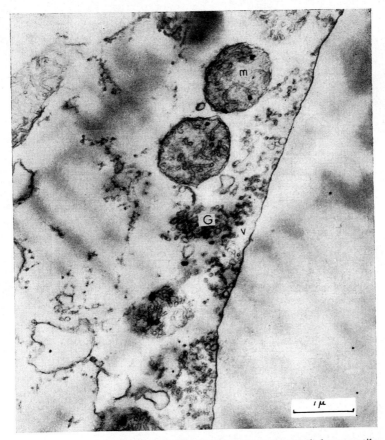

FIG. 2. Electron micrograph showing the edge of a well extended contractile vacuole of *Amoeba proteus*. The empty vacuole appears in the clear area to the right and is bounded by a membrane similar to the external plasma membrane. A layer of mitochondria (m) completely surrounds the vacuole. The space between the vacuole membrane and the mitochondria is crowded with vast numbers of small vesicles (v) which are probably transporting water to the main vacuole. The cluster of vacuoles at G is probably of a different type. From Mercer.[64]

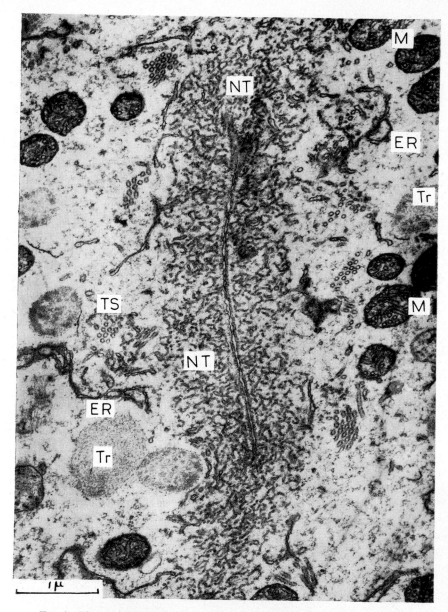

FIG. 3. Electron micrograph through longitudinal section of nephridial canal (= radial canal) of *Paramecium caudatum*. The nephridial canal is in systole, and is surrounded by nephridial tubules (NT). Tubular structures (TS) lie in bundles in an outer zone. Membranes of the endoplasmic reticulum (ER) lead into the nephridioplasm. M, Mitochondria; Tr, trichocyst. From Schneider.[83]

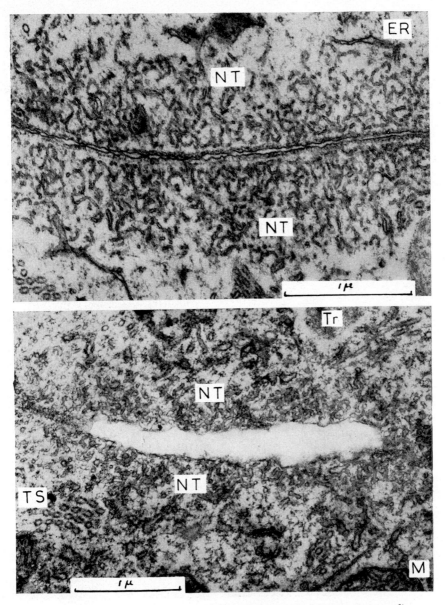

Fig. 4. Electron micrograph of the nephridial canal of *Paramecium aurelia* in systole (above) and in diastole (below). During systole of the canal the mouths of the nephridial tubules (NT) are shut off from the nephridial canal; during diastole of the canal they open into it. ER, endoplasmic reticulum; TS, tubular structures; M, mitochondrion; Tr, trichocyst. From Schneider.[83]

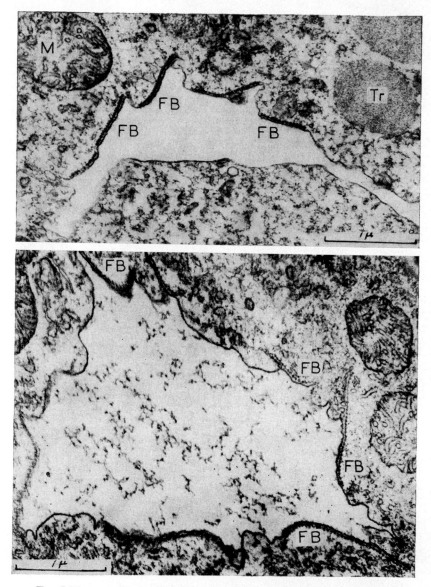

FIG. 5. Electron micrograph of the contractile vacuole of *Paramecium aurelia* in systole (above, longitudinal section) and in diastole (below, tangential section). FB, fibrillar bundles lying in the walls of the vacuole, presumably contractile; M, mitochondria; Tr, trichocyst. From Schneider.[83]

micrographs to consist of a network of fine tubules, about 20 mμ in diameter when fully distended (Figs. 3 and 4). These nephridial tubules communicate with tubular components of the endoplasmic reticulum, which according to

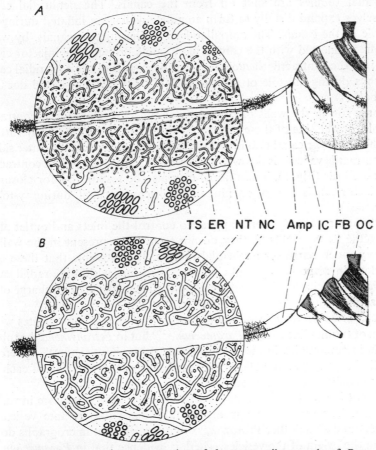

TS  ER  NT  NC   Amp  IC  FB  OC

FIG. 6. Diagrammatic representation of the contractile vacuole of *Paramecium*. A, nephridial canal in systole, contractile vacuole in diastole. B, nephridial canal in diastole, contractile vacuole in systole. Tubular membranes of the endoplasmic reticulum (ER) lead up to the edge of the nephridioplasm and make a direct connexion with the nephridial tubules (NT). During systole of the nephridial canal the connection of the nephridial tubules with the nephridial canal is interrupted, whereas during diastole of the canal the mouths of the nephridial tubules open into the nephridial canal. Outside the zone of the nephridial tubules lie tubular structures (TS) arranged in bundles. The nephridial canals pass into the ampullae (Amp) which communicate with the contractile vacuole through the injector canals (IC). Contractile fibrillar elements (FB), which begin at the level of the ampullae, pass over the injector canal to the contractile vacuole, where they run spirally as a broad band to the outlet canal (OC), which they likewise enclose spirally. From Schneider.[83]

Schneider permeates the whole cytoplasm of the *Paramecium*. Distally the nephridial tubules lead to the nephridial canals, but open into these only while these are in diastole; during systole of the nephridial canals the nephridial tubules are shut off from the canals. The nephridial canals themselves expand distally to form ampullae which are inflated during late diastole of the canals. The ampullae lead to the injector canals, by which they are connected with the contractile vacuole proper. The injector canals open into the contractile vacuole only during systole of the nephridial canals and thus during diastole of the vacuole[28, 34, 83] so that liquid does not flow back.

Fibrils run in the walls of the ampullae, injector canals, and contractile vacuole, on the side of these structures which lies toward the body surface; and the discharge canal also is enclosed in fibrils. At systole the outer side of the contractile vacuole is thrown into folds, probably owing to the contraction of these fibrils (Fig. 5). These fibrils may also be responsible for closure of the injector canals and for opening of the discharge canal, during systole of the vacuole.

Although contractile fibrils appear to control the inlets and outlet of the contractile vacuole proper, they do not seem to be present in the walls of the very much narrower nephridial tubules. It is possible that these open and close in response to small changes of pressure within the radial canals and that these changes in turn depend on the local effects of discharge of the contractile vacuole.

The contractile vacuole of *Tetrahymena pyriformis* communicates with a system of tubules like that of *Paramecium*,[20] but in *Tetrahymena* the tubules remain in communication with the vacuole throughout the cycle. There are two discharge pores, and 200 or more fibres run from the wall of each discharge canal to the vacuolar surface.

It is not known how the water is separated from the cytoplasm in various Protozoa. The separation appears to take place into minute vesicles in *Amoeba*, and some other Protozoa,[66] but the electron micrographs do not explain the origin of the vesicles. There is evidence that in *Paramecium* and *Tetrahymena* the nephridial tubules connect with endoplasmic reticulum, which may provide the water. A similar system of tubules, forming a "spongiome" (= nephridioplasm) around the contractile vacuole of peritrich ciliates, has been described by Fauré-Fremiet and his colleagues.[22, 23] The tubules are of two kinds, 15–20 mμ and about 50 mμ in diameter, the latter with rodlets in their surface.[9] In *Zoothamnium* spp. the larger tubules are grouped in bundles and communicate with the smaller ones by a plexus of small canals. The spongiome is said to communicate with the endoplasmic reticulum. A local cytoplasmic differentiation is indicated in electron micrographs of *Tokophrya*,[77] and an investigation of the soil amoeba *Acanthamoeba* sp. has also shown a system of tubules opening into a duct which leads into the contractile vacuole.[91] Water separation thus appears to occur over large areas of intracytoplasmic surface, and the morphological complexity is probably sufficient to support either excretion or the resorption of select substances or both. Whether in fact these processes take place must ultimately be determined by physiological investigation; it is clear that this morphological complexity has some physiological significance. Thus the problem of the origin of the vacuolar fluid has been pushed back to an earlier stage in vacuolar development, but remains otherwise much where it has stood for twenty years or more: osmosis, phase separation, secretion and resorption may all play their parts. The biochemical mechanisms have yet to be unravelled.

Fibres are found in the region of the discharge canal or pore in various Protozoa with fixed contractile vacuoles. In *Tokophrya*[77] and *Metaradiophrya*[73] fibres radiate from the discharge canal to the vacuolar walls. There is little doubt that similar fibres will be described in many other Protozoa, and it is probable that these vacuolar fibres are contractile. They are optically hollow and of about the same diameter as other tubular fibres of uncertain function found in various Protozoa. The association of ciliary basal bodies with contractile vacuoles in *Stentor*[94] and *Tokophrya*[77] may be fortuitous, or it might indicate that basal bodies are required for the manufacture of the fibres.

It is interesting that in various Protozoa the length of the vacuolar cycle and the ultimate diameter of the contractile vacuole are both affected in the appropriate direction by a change in the osmotic pressure of the medium. Thus the vacuole does not discharge at a fixed volume nor after a fixed interval of time. This complex form of control is more easily understood if we suppose that the vacuole has an inherent rhythmicity which is however itself affected by vacuolar size or by some related variable such as the strain which might be imposed by vacuolar distension on a system of fibres.[49] Moreover, in organisms such as *Paramecium* with more than one contractile vacuole, each acts independently, maintaining its own rhythm and emptying only when a certain size has been attained.

## OSMOTIC AND IONIC REGULATION

### Preliminary Discussion

Contractile vacuoles are found in almost all freshwater Protozoa; the dinoflagellates are an exception, but their pustule system of vacuoles permanently open to the outside may correspond to contractile vacuoles. Contractile vacuoles are found in some marine and parasitic Protozoa, but not in all. In general they are missing from marine Rhizopoda, from most parasitic Rhizopoda, and from Sporozoa, but they are found in a number of marine and parasitic ciliates and in some marine flagellates. This distribution has led to the supposition that contractile vacuoles perform an osmoregulatory function which is unnecessary in marine and endoparasitic habitats. This supposition must be examined critically.

All freshwater animals which have been sufficiently investigated have an osmotic pressure of the cells and body fluids above that of the external freshwater. This excess of osmotic pressure is due to various inorganic salts which are maintained at a higher concentration than outside and to organic substances in solution, including proteins and amino acids, which do not in practice escape. The evidence for freshwater Protozoa is scanty, but such of it as there is accords with the view that their internal osmotic pressure exceeds that outside.

It must not however be supposed that marine Protozoa require no osmoregulation. There is abundant evidence that Protozoa are distinctly permeable to certain of the ions of seawater, including no doubt $Na^+$ and $Cl^-$ (see below). Owing to the presence of indiffusible organic ions within the cell, the penetrating ions will be subject to a Donnan distribution which in itself will result in an excess osmotic pressure within the cell. To this must be added any osmotic pressure due to other solutes. In the absence of some active form of osmoregulation, the body of a marine protozoon would swell until the excess osmotic pressure (ever diminishing but never attaining zero) was counterbalanced by tension at the body surface.

The high proportion of potassium to sodium within Protozoa (discussed below) recalls the similar situation in many other cells. The low internal concentration of sodium is most easily explained in terms of the "sodium pump". The existence of such a device has been overwhelmingly substantiated by the work of Ussing on frog skin and of Hodgkin and his colleagues on squid axons. It seems reasonable to use this hypothesis for other less well investigated cells including Protozoa. The potentiality of the sodium pump as a means of lowering the internal osmotic pressure depends on the concentration of sodium in the external medium. This potentiality is therefore considerable in seawater but very small and probably of no consequence in freshwater. Thus contractile vacuoles appear to be unnecessary for marine Protozoa and their presence in certain marine flagellates and ciliates might even lead to the suspicion that these may have had freshwater ancestors.

A more detailed discussion follows of the present status of certain topics about which assumptions have been made in this section. The distribution of ions between Protozoa and their outside media probably involves other regulating mechanisms besides the sodium pump.

## Internal Osmotic Pressure of Protozoa

Few attempts have been made to measure the internal osmotic pressure of Protozoa directly, and most indirect estimates are open to criticism.

*Amoeba proteus* was found by Mast and Fowler[63] to shrink in concentrations of various non-electrolytes down to and including 0.005 M, so that they concluded that the osmotic pressure of the cytoplasm is extremely low. A slow shrinkage of *Pelomyxa carolinensis* even without added solute was ascribed by Belda[4] to the effect of starvation, and after correcting Belda's results for this, Løvtrup and Pigón[57] deduced from his experiments that the normal internal osmotic pressure is equal to that of a 0.08 M solution of non-electrolyte. From the vapour pressure exerted by boiled or frozen amoebae they obtained a value of 0.107 M non-electrolyte, but this estimate is open to the objection that additional material may have gone into solution

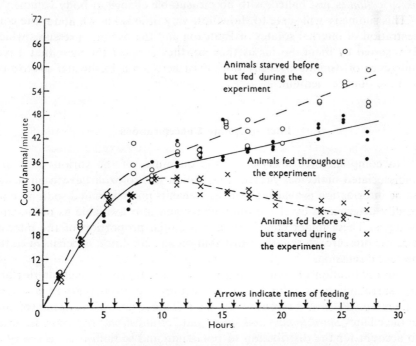

FIG. 7. The effect of feeding and starvation on the uptake of $^{42}$K by *Spirostomum ambiguum*. From Carter.[11]

as a result of the cytolysis. Schmidt-Nielsen and Schrauger[82] have obtained similar results (see p. 329) by freezing point determinations.

Gelfan[29] found the conductivity of the cytoplasm of various ciliates to be equal to that of a 0.035–0.06 M solution of KCl, but non-electrolytes are excluded by this method. Picken[72] estimated the vapour pressure of *Spirostomum* protoplasm as equal to that of about 0.025 M NaCl, but cytolysis may have affected his results.

After inactivating the contractile vacuole with cyanide, Kitching[36] found that a freshwater peritrich just failed to swell in 0.05 M sucrose, and he

11*

concluded that this concentration represented its internal osmotic pressure. Similarly a marine peritrich poisoned with dilute cyanide failed to swell in seawater, with which it was presumed to be isotonic, but swelled in diluted seawater even more than it did when the contractile vacuole was working.[35] The obvious conclusion may well be correct, but is open to the criticism that cyanide may have led to the accumulation of incomplete breakdown products of larger molecules, and thus to a rise of internal osmotic pressure. The best indirect estimate of internal osmotic pressure is probably provided by the fact that in 0.04–0.05 M sucrose the contractile vacuole of the suctorian *Discophrya collini* is just halted, with no measurable change of body volume.[42]

This summary will serve to show how very little is known about the concentration of internal solutes of Protozoa and the osmotic pressures which are exerted by them. So far as they go, they support the view that a real difference of osmotic pressure does exist between a freshwater protozoon and the outside medium.

## Internal Solute Concentrations

No comprehensive analyses of the quantities of the various ions and undissociated molecules present in solution in Protozoa have been made. Some information is available for the elements potassium and sodium, both readily determined by flame photometry and also available as radioactive isotopes. These might contribute a substantial proportion of the internal osmotic pressure, so that their distribution and condition is pertinent to the present discussion.

The distribution of sodium and potassium between the cell interior and the surrounding medium has been investigated in the larger amoebae (*A. proteus, Pelomyxa carolinensis*), in a soil amoeba *Acanthamoeba* sp., and in the ciliates *Spirostomum ambiguum* and *Tetrahymena pyriformis*. In order to account for the distribution of potassium and sodium it is necessary to know how much of these elements exists in ionized form and how much is either unionized or "bound". We also need to know the potential difference at the body surface before we can say which ions are distributed passively and which are likely to be the subject of active transport to replace losses by leakage. Information about the distribution of chloride and other anions between cells and medium would also be helpful. Unfortunately not enough is yet known about any one species to provide a comprehensive description of ionic distribution.

*Pelomyxa carolinensis*, grown in Pringsheim solution, was found to have a water content of about 90% w/w, the wet weight being determined by the use of a diver balance; slightly lower values (81–87%) were obtained by a less reliable method involving the use of heavy water.[76] The internal potassium concentration was estimated by Riddle[75] as $34.5 \pm 5.0$ mM/l, and by

Chapman-Andresen and Dick[13] as 32–37 mM/l. The internal sodium concentration either did not exceed that outside (Riddle, unpublished observations) or may have been slightly lower (as given by Chapman-Andresen and Dick). The membrane potential, as found by Riddle, is 67–100 mV and averages 86.5 mV negative inside. This is too low to hold the potassium in equilibrium, so that it is necessary to invoke some supplementary hypothesis, e.g. that the measured potential falls short of the actual owing to leakage, or that some of the potassium is unionized, or that there is an active uptake of potassium. As the potential difference disappears at an external potassium concentration approximately equal to that inside, Riddle concluded that all the internal potassium is ionized and exerts its normal activity and that potassium is actively transported inwards to compensate for that which leaks out. Even so, if the existing membrane potential is to be attributed to the concentration ratio of an ion, then for some ion that ratio must be over 10. The high membrane potential is already well substantiated for *Pelomyxa carolinensis*[97] and for *A. proteus*,[6, 89, 90] and there is every indication from Riddle's work that the responsible ion is potassium. The distribution of sodium is discussed in a later section.

The minute *Acanthamoeba* sp., grown in a nutrient medium of rather high osmotic pressure, was studied by Klein.[51, 52] Analyses of centrifuged pellets of amoebae, after due allowance for extracellular space, gave water 80 per cent, sodium 32 mM/l, potassium 57 mM/l. This gives a ratio of 8 to 1 for potassium concentration against that of the "amoeba-suspending medium" used for washing the amoebae and at least 30 to 1 against that of the normal culture medium. In studies of the uptake of $K^{42}$ Klein found that the internal specific activity never reached anywhere near that outside; he concluded that only about 40 per cent of the potassium was exchangeable. This result is surprising; it emphasises the need for similar combined studies by conventional analysis and by radioactivity with other biological materials.

The ciliate *Spirostomum ambiguum*, cultured in an artificial freshwater adjusted with respect to sodium or potassium concentration, was equilibrated by Carter[11] with an otherwise similar medium containing radioactive potassium or sodium or bromide; the internal levels of exchangeable potassium, sodium and halide were determined. Even on the assumption that the whole cell volume is water the internal concentration of potassium was over 10 times that outside. Internal sodium concentrations were of the same order as those outside at normal low external concentrations, and slightly lower than outside at a higher external concentration of 4 mM/l. The sum of the internal concentrations of sodium, potassium, and halide about equalled the total concentration of outside solutes, and, in fact, exceeded it for the lowest external concentration. It is unlikely that all the other internal anions exert negligible osmotic pressure, and there are probably substantial quantities of unionized material in solution. Nevertheless we do not known whether some of the internal potassium may not be "bound" and so osmotically inactive. It is particularly interesting that the level of exchanged potassium was higher in fed than in starved *Spirostomum*. Although feeding might enhance the activity of a mechanism of active transport, it seems likely that in any case it leads to an increase in the concentration of anions or anionic groups capable of attracting potassium.

Direct analyses have been made of the sodium and potassium and chloride contents of *Tetrahymena pyriformis* by flame photometry.[2, 19] In the investigation by Dunham and Child,[19] the cells were packed by centrifuging and allowance was made for dead space. The cells contained about 80 per cent of water, and after allowance for this the potassium concentration of cells grown in the "normal" proteose peptone medium amounted to about 8 times, and the sodium concentration to less than half of that in the medium. According to Andrus and Giese,[2] in *Tetrahymena* grown in a 10 per cent artificial sea-water medium the ratios were 10 times for potassium and times 1/12 for sodium. The sum of concentrations of potassium and sodium was slightly higher[19] or substantially lower[2] in the cells than in the medium. However, the media used for *Tetrahymena* contained considerably more sodium than a normal freshwater. Unfortunately no information is available for *Tetrahymena* adapted to more dilute media.

### Permeability to Inorganic Salts

The uptake and outwash of radioactive potassium and sodium and bromide in the ciliate *Spirostomum ambiguum* was studied by Carter.[11] Uptake and loss of potassium followed the course expected of a cell with a single internal compartment, with a half equilibration time of 2–3 hr. Outwash of sodium could be analysed into a fast and a very much slower component, with a half equilibration time of about 3 minutes for the former.

The potassium or sodium contents of *Tetrahymena pyriformis*, as measured by flame photometry, rises substantially with a substantial rise in the external concentration of potassium or sodium (Dunham and Child[19]). Around and below the normal level of external potassium concentration, internal changes in potassium are slow. On the other hand there is a limited rapid loss of sodium in response to dilution of sodium outside. As in *Spirostomum*, there appears to be a fast sodium compartment, but this might be outside the cell barrier. As shown by the use of isotopes, about 90 per cent of the potassium and sodium of *Tetrahymena* living in the standard medium are exchangeable.

Studies on the exchange of isotopes of sodium and potassium or bromide have been carried out on *Acanthamoeba* (Klein,[51, 52]) and *Pelomyxa carolinensis* (Chapman-Andresen and Dick,[13]) and demonstrate a fairly considerable flux. All such studies with isotopes are open to the theoretical interpretation that part or all of the exchange could take place by "exchange diffusion". The demonstration of permeability in *Tetrahymena* by net chemical change is unequivocal in this respect.

Observations of changes in body volume and rate of output of the contractile vacuole accord with the view that NaCl passes through the cell surface fairly readily. They are discussed in a later section.

## Active Transport of Ions

The concentration of sodium within amoebae, *Spirostomum*, and *Tetrahymena* is much lower than that of potassium. It is unlikely that substantially all the potassium is "bound". It is also unlikely that the fluxes of sodium and potassium already reported are mediated solely by exchange diffusion. In the long run this cannot be true for potassium as growing and multiplying Protozoa must accumulate this ion; and the direct permeation of potassium and sodium has been demonstrated in *Tetrahymena*.

In view of the potential difference, positive outside, which is normally maintained across the cell surface of Protozoa, and of their evident permeability to sodium, it seems necessary to conclude that sodium is pumped out actively. This conclusion is supported, for *Tetrahymena*, by the observation of Andrus and Giese[2] that cooling leads to an entry of sodium and loss of potassium, which is reversed on restoration of a normal temperature, as is erythrocytes. The high internal concentration of potassium can be explained in several ways: in terms of a Donnan distribution coupled with sodium extrusion, by a failure to ionize, by preferential adsorption at a system of structurally arranged negative sites, or by a potassium pump. Given the fact of an outwardly operating sodium pump, it would be expected that potassium would become concentrated within the cell sufficiently to neutralize electrically a substantial share of the excess negative charges due to organic acids, proteins, etc., unable to escape from the cell. Under these conditions the ratio of concentrations of potassium ions, in to out, would be counterbalanced by an appropriate potential difference. As already suggested in the case of *P. carolinensis*, the observed potential difference may be too small. It may therefore prove necessary to supplement or replace this hypothesis. Supplementation with a potassium pump is one attractive alternative. The potential difference would then depend on a combination of ionic ratios and permeabilities, towards which potassium would contribute predominantly. There is evidence that in *Tetrahymena* the uptake of a large part of the potassium is linked with sodium extrusion, presumably through a carrier in the membrane.[2] It can be assumed that ion-pumping mechanisms are present in all Protozoa. The possibility of potassium binding requires much further investigation.

It is possible that contractile vacuoles take part in the expulsion of sodium. The extensive intracellular surfaces of the water-collecting contributory vacuoles, tubules, or ducts could perhaps carry out this function. Chapman-Andresen and Dick[13] have published some very preliminary results on

*P. carolinensis* which might support this view, but much more work is needed.

## Permeability to Water

There is abundant evidence that Protozoa swell or shrink osmotically when the concentration of the external medium is changed. *Amoeba proteus*[63] and *Pelomyxa carolinensis*[4] shrank in non-electrolyte solutions at a rate indicating a permeability of 0.026 and 0.02 $\mu^3/\mu^2$/atm/min. The rate of swelling of *Vorticella marina* on transfer to diluted seawater indicated a permeability of about 0.1 $\mu^3/\mu^2$/atm/min at 14–17°C, with a considerable increase at higher temperatures.[40] Studies of the permeation of $H_2O$ and of $D_2O$ by means of the Cartesian diver have given an estimate of the diffusion constant of these substances across the cell membrane.[57] This estimate was then converted to give a permeability constant of 0.011 $\mu^3/\mu^2$/atm/min. An estimate[36] of 0.125–0.25 $\mu^3/\mu^2$/atm/min for *Carchesium aselli* is based on the rate of vacuolar output, and depends on certain conclusions discussed in the next section. All these estimates are possibly subject to some error arising from the assumption that the only barrier to penetration is at the cell surface.[18] Internal membranes might delay equilibration.

## Sources of Water for Evacuation

Addition to the water content of the body could take place by metabolic production of water, by food vacuoles or pinocytosis, and by osmotic uptake through the body surface. The rate of oxygen consumption of *Paramecium caudatum*[67] is only sufficient to account for less than 1 per cent of the rate of vacuolar output, so that metabolic water can be ignored,[47] probably generally. Uptake of food vacuoles is approximately sufficient to account for the whole of the output of the contractile vacuole in certain marine Peritricha, but of less than 10 per cent in freshwater Peritricha. In *Paramecium*,[61] and in *Vorticella similis*,[62] the water expelled on the discharge of spent food vacuoles approximately equals that taken in with food. In general it seems likely that water taken in with food is not an important contributor to water expelled by the contractile vacuole, although an increase in vacuolar output during feeding has been reported for Ophryoscolecidae[60] and for Suctorida.[43, 78] Some Protozoa with no mouth (Astomatida) or with only intermittent feeding (Suctorida) have active contractile vacuoles. It is difficult to test the suggestion that in some Protozoa the membrane of the oesophogeal sac is specially permeable and is an important site for the osmotic uptake of water. Pinocytosis is not reported in ciliates and seems to occur only on suitable stimulation in Rhizopoda. In view of all these considerations it seems likely that in most freshwater Protozoa the bulk of the water expelled by the contractile vacuole enters through the general body surface by osmosis.

## Effects of External Osmotic Pressure

Under normal conditions of a steady state, the rate of gain of water by a protozoon, comprising water taken up in food vacuoles, water entering by osmosis, and water formed metabolically, must equal the rate of loss, comprising discharge by contractile vacuoles and in spent food vacuoles.[37] As already pointed out, metabolic water and in many cases the uptake and loss of water in food vacuoles are negligible, so that we are left with a state of balance in which water taken up osmotically is baled out by the contractile vacuole. The rate of uptake of water by osmosis is approximately determined by the "permeability" ($k$) to water, the area ($A$) of the membrane, and the difference between the osmotic pressures of the liquid inside ($P_i$) and outside ($P_o$) the organism:

$$\begin{array}{l}\text{Rate of vacuolar} \quad \text{Rate of osmotic} \\ \text{output} \qquad\qquad = \text{uptake of water} = kA\,(P_i - P_o).\end{array}$$

Although it has been suggested by Mast[61] that entry of water by osmosis into *Paramecium* is restricted to the oesophageal sac, there is no substantial evidence in favour of this view. In any case, $k$ represents the effective permeability through the effectively permeable area $A$.

If the osmotic pressure of the external medium is increased by the addition of a non-penetrating solute, this increase should decrease the rate of entry of water. With perfect osmoregulation the rate of output of the contractile vacuole should instantly be decreased to correspond, so that a new steady state would be set up with the body volume unchanged. At the opposite extreme, if the contractile vacuole has no capacity to adjust its rate of output in accordance with needs, it might be expected to continue operating in spite of the decreased rate of osmotic uptake of water by the body, so that the body would shrink until (in an extreme example) the osmotic pressure of the aqueous phase of the cytoplasm was raised sufficiently to restore the osmotic influx to the original level. As will be seen below, Protozoa differ in the extent of their approach to ideal regulation.

In the suctorian *Discophrya collini* (formerly *D. piriformis*) addition of sucrose to the freshwater medium rapidly reduces the rate of output of the contractile vacuole to a new steady level; on return to the normal medium the normal rate of output is restored. A concentration of about 0.05 M sucrose is just sufficient to reduce the vacuolar output to zero, and at any higher concentration there is also a shrinkage of the body. At substantially higher concentrations (e.g. 0.14 M) the body shrinks greatly; therefore it cannot be supposed that a shrinkage of the body at the lower concentrations has been masked by large quantities of non-aqueous material. Up to a concentration of about 0.05 M sucrose the rate of vacuolar output declines in direct proportion to the external concentration. Thus within the limitations of the methods used for measurement, the contractile vacuole of *Discophrya collini* behaves as would be expected of a perfect osmoregulatory device.[42] The extent to which in fact it falls short of perfection will be discussed in a later section.

In the peritrich *Carchesium aselli* the rate of vacuolar output is also depressed by the addition of sucrose to the external medium. Some slight vacuolar activity persists at an external concentration of 0.05 M sucrose, even though the body is slightly shrunk.[41] Kamada[33] reported some persistence of vacuolar activity in *Paramecium* shrunk in a hypertonic solution of NaCl. When *Pelomyxa carolinensis* was treated with 0.1 M mannitol the contractile vacuoles continued operating for 80 minutes, even though the body was shrinking all the time.[4]

A number of investigators have used solutions of substances which in the course of time appeared to penetrate the surface of the body in substantial quantity. For instance, Kamada[33] reported that the vacuolar output of *Paramecium* sp. was at first drastically reduced in 0.025 M NaCl but that in the course of an hour or two it recovered almost to its original level. This was confirmed by Frisch.[25] Similar results have also been obtained by Seravin,[85, 86] with solutions of single salts, and the same explanation probably applies. Marine peritrich ciliates undergo a drastic swelling and increase in vacuolar output on transfer to dilute seawater, but these increases are not maintained; it is reasonable to suppose that the increased vacuolar output depends on an increased body volume, and that both decline again with escape of salts.[35] The minute freshwater amoeba *A. lacearata* was grown by Hopkins[32] in cultures made up with various concentrations of seawater. It swelled or shrank with change of concentration, but the body soon returned to its normal volume again as though salts had crossed the membrane. The rate of vacuolar output increased or decreased with the initial swelling or shrinkage of the body, but the results were somewhat irregular over this important transition period. However, the vacuolar output did show an inverse relationship with concentration of the medium even after full adaptation to it. Hopkins regarded these observations as an indication that the contractile vacuole is not osmoregulatory, basing this conclusion on the supposition that no substantial difference of osmotic pressure appears to exist between the amoebae and their medium. The observations are important although this conclusion is not valid. The effect of a low concentration of a non-penetrating solute should be investigated. I have little doubt that it would lead to a persisting reduction in output, as with *Discophrya*. When *Discophrya* was transferred to dilute solutions of ethylene glycol, which normally penetrates cell membranes with moderate but not excessive speed, there was at first a depression or cessation of vacuolar function, followed by a recovery which presumably reflects the entry of the solute. On return to the ordinary freshwater medium there was an immediate drastic rise in rate of vacuolar output, which subsequently declined to normal. It may be presumed that the very high output was associated with an abnormally large difference of osmotic pressure across the body surface owing to the presence of ethylene glycol within the body. An abnormally high output was also maintained for a short time after *Discophrya* cultured in 10 per cent seawater had been transferred to tap water.[42]

More information is needed about the rates of vacuolar output of Protozoa under natural conditions, and especially about the comparative rates for freshwater and marine Protozoa. In an interesting study of Protozoa from brine pools of a wide range of salinity, Gayewskaya[27] found that some species possess numerous non-contracting vacuoles, some have no vacuoles at all, and some maintain a very slow frequency of vacuolar contraction. A low frequency in saline media is also reported by Ermakof for many species.[21] Chadwick[12] has found an inverse relation between rate of vacuolar output and the salinity of the habitat for *Vorticella utriculus* living in brackish rock-pools.

## Effects of Temperature

The frequency of vacuolar discharge increases with increasing temperature within reasonable biological limits, as shown in various ciliates (Smyth,[87] for *Stylonychia*, with earlier references). In view of the fact that in ciliates the vacuolar frequency probably depends on the rate of separation of water and on an inherent rhythmicity of the discharge mechanism, both of which are likely to be affected by temperature, interpretation of temperature coefficients of vacuolar frequency is difficult.

The rate of output of the contractile vacuole of *Carchesium aselli* was increased by increase of temperature within reasonable biological limits, with a $Q_{10}$ of 2.5–3.2. Except after extreme treatment, the rate of vacuolar output returned to normal when a normal room temperature (15°C) was restored and the body volume did not at any time show any measurable change.[40]

The effect of temperature on rate of vacuolar output could be interpreted either in terms of a change in the internal osmotic pressure of the organism, which might change with temperature either because of metabolic changes or because of changes in ionization of proteins, or in terms of a change in the permeability of the cell surface to water. It was found[41] that a slightly hypertonic solution of sucrose (0.06 M) was just as effective in stopping the contractile vacuole of *Carchesium aselli* at 30°C as at 15°C, whereas if the osmotic pressure of the cytoplasm had been increased to three-fold or more, as would be required to explain the results on this hypothesis, the vacuolar output should not have been reduced by as much as 50 per cent. On the other hand when the marine peritrich *Vorticella marina* was placed in dilute seawater (25%), it swelled more quickly at higher temperatures, with a $Q_{10}$ of very roughly 2.5–3.2. It is therefore reasonable to ascribe the effect

11a*

of temperature on the contractile vacuole of *Carchesium aselli* to changes in the permeability of the cell membrane, to which the contractile vacuole quite quickly responds.

The contractile vacuole of *Discophrya* responds rather more slowly to changes of condition, and thus permits a more detailed examination of the immediate effects of a change of temperature.[45] On a sharp rise of temperature from below 15°C the current vacuolar cycle was terminated by systole sooner than would normally have been expected. The vacuolar output was then greatly reduced, and often no vacuoles were visible for several minutes During this period the body often became smoother in outline, as though taking up water from the medium. Finally vacuolar activity was resumed and proceeded at a higher level of frequency and rate of output than at the initial temperature. Clearly the rise of temperature caused an immediate acceleration of the rhythmic process which leads to contraction, but at the same time depressed water separation. Ultimately the separation of water was resumed, perhaps in response to the increased hydration of the cytoplasm.

## Effects of Heavy Water ($D_2O$)

Heavy water has been used in permeability studies as a tracer for ordinary water, and from time to time the validity of this procedure has been questioned. Løvtrup and Pigón[57] failed to find any difference between the Fick's diffusion constants of $H_2O$, $D_2O$, and $H_2O^{18}$ across the surface of *Pelomyxa carolinensis* in experiments with a Cartesian diver. Differences in permeability to $H_2O$ and $D_2O$ have been found with erythrocytes [8, 69] but not with *Arbacia* eggs.[58] Apart from a possible difference in ability to pass through cell membranes, deuterium oxide undoubtedly has a toxic effect on cells when present in high concentrations. It seems likely that substitution of deuterium for hydrogen in enzymes and substrates will interfere with the rates of metabolic reactions.

When *Discophrya collini* was irrigated with mixtures of $D_2O$ and $H_2O$ (made up with 5% or more of $D_2O$) the rate of vacuolar output was temporarily reduced, but later reverted to normal.[50] In mixtures made up from 25 per cent or more $D_2O$ there was a temporary shrinkage of the body and a temporary stoppage of the contractile vacuole. On return to ordinary water there was a greater than normal rate of vacuolar output, which soon subsided to normal. These results are very similar to those obtained with ethylene glycol, already described, and we must conclude that $D_2O$ and DHO penetrate into the cell less readily than $H_2O$. The results obtained could be interpreted on the assumption that the diffusion constant for water crossing the cell membrane is 10 per cent lower for $D_2O$ than for $H_2O$. Alternatively, they might indicate a lower fugacity for $D_2O$ and DHO than for $H_2O$.

## Regulation of Vacuolar Output

When *Disocophrya collini* grown in 10 per cent seawater was transferred to tap water, there was a small increase in body volume, rendered conspicuous by the filling up of irregularities of the pellicle, but these reappeared later as the vacuolar output subsided to its final level. Similarly, in response to a sharp rise in temperature, there was a slight temporary swelling of the

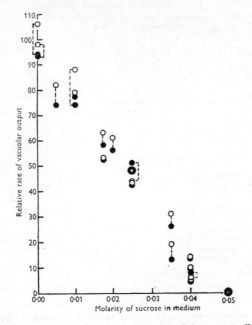

FIG. 8. The relation between the rate of output of the contractile vacuole of *Discophrya collini* (= *D. piriformis*) and the concentration of sucrose in the medium. ○ the rate of vacuolar output in sucrose solution expressed as a percentage of the original rate in tap water; ● the rate of vacuolar output in sucrose solution expressed as a percentage of the final rate in tap water. The two percentages calculated for each experiment are joined by a broken line where necessary. A thick circle indicates that the two percentages are the same. There are two coincident pairs at 0.05 M-sucrose. From Kitching.[42]

body, as shown by the disappearance of kinks in the body surface, before the rate of vacuolar output increased. It is possible that the increase in vacuolar output and the slight swelling result independently, but it is also possible that the increase of body volume mediates the increased output.

The response of the contractile vacuole of *Discophrya collini* to a slight increase in the external osmotic pressure, as brought about by the addition of sucrose to the external medium, is not immediate but occurs with a significant lag. Provided that the osmotic pressure of the external medium remains below that of the cytoplasm, shrinkage can only be due to the activity of the contractile vacuole; insofar as this fails to reduce its output to the level required for perfect osmoregulation, the body will shrink. It appears (Fig. 8) that within the limits of·error the rate of output after attainment of a steady state conforms with the requirements of perfect osmoregulation. Nevertheless, the delay in adjustment to the new level does represent a

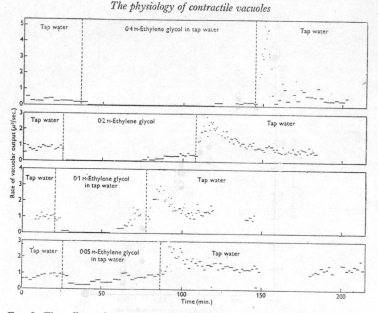

FIG. 9. The effect of treatment with a solution of ethylene glycol, and of return to Bristol tap water, on the rate of output of the contractile vacuole of *Discophrya collini*. From Kitching.[42]

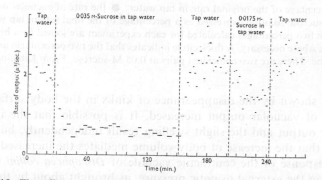

FIG. 10. The effect of treatment with a solution of sucrose on the rate of output of the contractile vacuole of *Discophrya collini*. From Kitching.[42]

shrinkage in body volume, which can be estimated (Fig. 13) from the record of vacuolar output. On this basis the shrinkage of the body which is necessary just to halt the contractile vacuole of *Discophrya collini* is about $1^1/_2$ per cent. The existence of a significant "unstirred layer"[16] on the surface the organism would reduce this value.

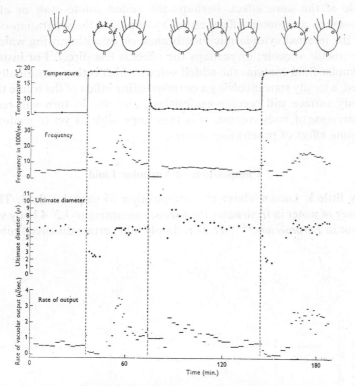

FIG. 11. Effects of sudden changes of temperature on the vacuolar cycle of *Discophrya collini*. From Kitching.[45]

In accordance with this hypothesis, *Pelomyxa carolinensis* has a less sensitive osmoregulatory mechanism in that a greater shrinkage is necessary to stop the contractile vacuole. The same is probably true of *Paramecium*. In marine peritrichs a considerable swelling of the body must take place before there is any substantial increase in rate of vacuolar output.[35] In *Crithidia fasciculata* suspended in sodium chloride solution, the rate of vacuolar output increased much more than the body volume with decreased concentration of the solute.[14]

The mechanism by which water is separated remains entirely unknown. Presumably in *Amoeba* the membranes of the small vesicles which surround the vacuole are important. It is possible that in ciliates the water comes from the channels of the endoplasmic reticulum.

There is evidence that not only in a small amoeba[32] but also in *Disco-phrya*[42] the rate of vacuolar output is depressed by the presence of extra salt within the cytoplasm, and ethylene glycol appears to act in the same way. The relatively small response of the contractile vacuoles of marine peritrichs to seawater in the range 100 to 75 per cent is probably another example of the same effect. Perhaps the added solute—salt or ethylene glycol—exerts an osmotic effect, either by opposing the separation of water across the internal cytoplasmic membranes, or by withdrawing water from the contractile vacuole; or perhaps the effect is less direct. For instance, if the vacuolar fluid contains the added solute, which is thus continually being expelled, a steady state involving a corresponding influx of the solute through the body surface will become established, and this in turn will require a slight decrease of body volume. It is thus impossible as yet to evaluate this interesting effect of penetrating solutes.

### Composition of Vacuolar Fluid

Very little is known about the composition of vacuolar fluid. The high turn-over of water in freshwater Protozoa, amounting to 1.3–4 body volumes per hour in *Paramecium*,[44] seems to imply that certain dissolved substances

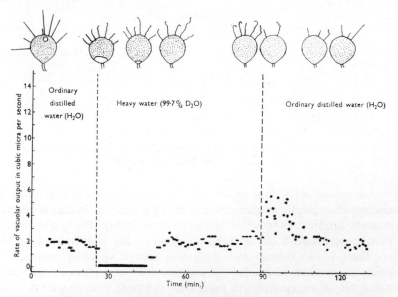

FIG. 12. Effects of $D_2O$ (99.7 per cent) on the rate of output of the contractile vacuole of *Discophrya collini*. Note the single high point at 14.7 $\mu^3$/sec shortly after return to ordinary water. Changes in general appearance are shown above. The unstippled area adjacent to the stalk, which appears on transfer to heavy water, is a region of the body which has collapsed and is very thin. From Kitching and Padfield.[50]

must be separated from the vacuolar fluid and retained. This separation could be effected osmotically if sufficient of some other substance or substances was in some way passed into the vacuole so as to raise the osmotic pressure of the vacuolar fluid to a level at discharge not less than that of the cytoplasm. However, doubt has been expressed as to whether sufficient of a suitable excretory substance could be produced to effect osmotic separation at the required rate. Alternatively, an active "secretory" process may be involved. This might consist either of the active secretion of water into the vacuolar apparatus, or, more plausibly,[47] of the separation into it of water

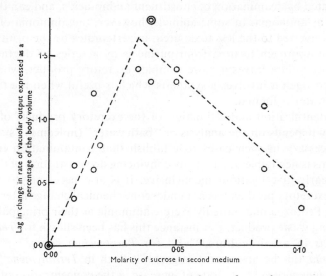

FIG. 13. The relation of the lag in change of rate of vacuolar output, expressed as a percentage of the body volume, and the concentration of sucrose to which *Discophrya collini* was transferred from tap water. From Kitching.[42]

with various dissolved substances and the active withdrawal of certain valuable solutes.

The freezing point of liquid withdrawn from the contractile vacuole of *Amoeba proteus* has now been determined with the Ramsay freezing point apparatus by Schmidt-Nielsen and Schrauger,[82] and compared with that of samples of protoplasm. The results correspond to an osmolality averaging $32 \times 10^{-3}$ for the vacuolar fluid, $101 \times 10^{-3}$ for the protoplasm, and $8 \times 10^{-3}$ for the medium. The variation was not unduly great and the differences are very significant indeed. Provided that the value for cytoplasm was not elevated by the treatment, the results support the view that active transport is involved in the production of the vacuolar fluid of *Amoeba*.

## EXCRETION OF NITROGEN

### Excretion of Dissolved Substances

Waste nitrogen is produced in living organisms by the degradation of nucleic acids and proteins. The stages of breakdown of uric acid by various animals through allantoin, allantoic acid, and urea to ammonia have been tabulated and discussed by Florkin and Duchateau[24] in a well-known review. Each step in the degradation is mediated by its particular enzyme, and the stage of degradation attained depends on the range of enzymes available in the organism in question. In the breakdown of protein, nitrogen is separated by deamination of constituent amino-acids, and can thus appear directly as ammonia. In some animals, however, the ammonia of deamination is converted to the less toxic urea, in vertebrates by the ornithine cycle. Thus the approach to urea from purine is by a series of degradations of which any failure leaves a more complex excretory product, whereas from amino-nitrogen it involves a synthesis which is useful when the turnover of solvent water is limited.

The identification and estimation of the excretory products of Protozoa normally depends on the analysis of "bath water" (in Ramsay's[74] phrase). It is necessary in such cases to establish that contamination from other organisms is negligible. Lack of any convincing demonstration of this renders certain early investigations inconclusive. It is also necessary to make sure that an excretory product has not undergone chemical change after excretion.

Many Protozoa undoubtedly excrete ammonia as their principal nitrogen-containing waste product. For instance this has been shown for *Tetrahymena pyriformis* in axenic culture,[59, 65] for *Paramecium* spp.,[15, 88] and for *Leishmania* (in the absence of sugar).[79] Both in *Tetrahymena*[65] and in *Paramecium aurelia*[88] the rate of increase in the concentration of ammonia in the culture remained constant throughout the rapid increase of population, but no doubt some ammonia escaped.

Excretion of urea by ciliates has been claimed and disputed. Weatherby[92, 93] reported the excretion of urea by washed *Paramecium* and *Spirostomum*. No urea could be detected in cultures of *Tetrahymena* by Lwoff and Roukhelman[59] although urea which was added was recovered satisfactorily. However, Nardone and Wilber[65] reported that in a culture of *Tetrahymena* the urea concentration rose in two days from zero to 1·8 mg per ml—a concentration regarded by Dewey, Heinrich and Kidder[17] as impossibly high—and then fell again to zero. According to Seaman[84] *Tetrahymena* possesses the enzymes of the ornithine cycle and synthesizes urea from ammonia but then splits it again to ammonia by means of a pH-sensitive urease. The functional significance of this biochemical manoeuvre to a primitively aquatic animal is not clear, although it is possible that the inactivation of ammonia could be beneficial to a population living in a confined space. The results of Dewey, Heinrich, and Kidder[17] directly contradict those of Seaman: no urea could be found in the culture, nor could any urease activity be detected, by a very sensitive method, in cultures or homogenates of *Tetrahymena*. Arginine is essential to *Tetrahymena* for growth. If *Tetrahymena* can operate the ornithine cycle, citrulline and ornithine should each be capable of replacing arginine; but in fact they cannot. It appears that they can enter the body, since in the presence of arginine they are beneficial. Very little citrulline and arginine were synthesized in homogenates. This work of Dewey, Heinrich, and Kidder was well controlled and it is difficult not to accept it. No urea could be found by Soldo and Wagtendonk[88] in cultures of *Paramecium aurelia*, actively growing or otherwise, and no urease could be found in cell extracts.

Very little is known about the excretion of nucleotide nitrogen by Protozoa. Soldo and Wagtendonk[88] have reported the excretion of hypoxanthine by *Paramecium aurelia*, and the same has recently been reported[53] for *Tetrahymena pyriformis*. This invites the speculation that substances less able than urea to penetrate cell surfaces may be excreted by contractile vacuoles. It seems possible that the acquisition of a contractile vacuole as an osmoregulatory device might permit the loss of the enzymes mediating the terminal stages of nucleotide degradation. This might necessitate the retention of contractile vacuoles by secondarily marine *Protozoa*.

## Excretory Granules

The well known crystals of *Amoeba*, sometimes observed in vacuoles and sometimes free in the cytoplasm, have been identified by Griffin[31] as carbonyl diurea (triuret). The crystals are of two kinds, truncated bipyramids, which are nearly isotropic, and strongly birefringent plates. *Amoeba dubia* possesses both kinds, the proportions depending on the food.[10] *A. proteus* possesses only bipyramids, but on recrystallization these are converted to plates. Synthetic triuret crystallizes as plates. Carlstrom and Max Møller[10] point out that it is not absolutely certain that the bipyramids are triuret rather than some closely related precursor, but they believe that they are triuret with some impurity which leads to the different crystal form.

Crystals are abundant in the carnivorous amoebae *A. proteus*, *A. dubia*, and *Pelomyxa carolinensis*, but absent in the herbivorous *Pelomyxa palustris*. However, it is not known whether they result from deamination of degraded protein or from the breakdown of nucleic acids, or both. In spite of extensive observations, reviewed by Andresen,[1] nothing is known about their fate. It is stated that although crystals and other inclusions may coalesce and ultimately be defecated by starved amoeba, the defecation of crystal vacuoles is abnormal. However, in the small rhizopod *Cochliopodium bilimbosum*, which feeds on bacteria and does not have too many crystals, Bernheimer[5] has reported on occasional passage of single crystals into "excretion vacuoles" (presumably contractile vacuoles), which in due course discharge to the outside. The crystals are described as bipyramidal, as in *Amoeba proteus*.

Granules of unknown composition are found in various other Protozoa. References are given by Wichterman.[96] Granules in *Spirostomum* are known to consist of calcium phosphate in the form of apatite.[70, 71] Schewiakoff[80] reported that crystals dissolve in the neighbourhood of the contractile vacuoles in *Paramecium*, and MacLennan[60] considered that contributory vacuoles originated from granules, possibly excretory, in *Ophryoscolecidae*; these conclusions require further examination. Numerous crystals were found by Wichterman[95] in a race of *Paramecium bursaria* free of zoochlorellae, although green specimens had no crystals. Green specimens kept in the dark for 25 days developed crystals. The dependence on type of nutrition recalls the distribution in species of *Amoeba*. It would be interesting to know more about these crystals.

## Vacuolar Activity and Metabolism

The activity of the contractile vacuole is brought to a halt in an atmosphere devoid of oxygen, rapidly in peritrich ciliates,[39] more gradually in *Paramecium*.[38] Cyanide drastically reduces vacuolar activity in peritrichs but is much less effective in *Paramecium*; this probably merely reflects differences in general metabolism. Hydrostatic pressures of 5000 to 6000 psi (340–408 atm) also inhibit vacuolar activity in *Paramecium* and in *Discophrya*.[46, 48] In all these cases it is possible that the production of some excretory product necessary for vacuolar activity has been inhibited, but it is more likely that the energy source for vacuolar activity has been cut off. The greatly increased vacuolar activity of *Discophrya* during feeding[43, 78] might be associated with an increased rate of disposal of waste products.

## ACKNOWLEDGMENTS

Figures 1 and 2 are reproduced from the paper by Dr. E. H. Mercer in the *Proceedings of the Royal Society*; Figures 3–6 from the paper by Prof. L. Schneider in the *Journal of Protozoology*; Figure 7 from the paper by Dr. L. Carter in the *Journal of Experimental Biology*, and Figures 8–13 from papers by Kitching in the *Journal of Experimental Biology*. I am grateful to the other authors and to the Council of the Royal Society, to the Editor of the *Journal of Protozoology*, and to the Company of Biologists Ltd., for permission to reproduce the figures. I am indebted to Dr. R. S. Lynch for her helpful criticism of the manuscript.

## REFERENCES

1. ANDRESEN, N. (1956) Cytological investigations on the giant amoeba *Chaos chaos* L. C.R.Lab. Carlsberg **29**, 435–555.
2. ANDRUS, W. DE W., and GIESE, A. C. (1963) Mechanisms of sodium and potassium regulation in *Tetrahymena pyriformis* strain W. *J. Cell Comp. Physiol.* **61**, 17–30.
3. BAIRATI, A., and LEHMANN, F. E. (1956) Structural and chemical properties of the contractile vacuole of *Amoeba proteus. Protoplasma* **45**, 525–539.
4. BELDA, W. H. (1943) Permeability to water in *Pelomyxa carolinensis.* III. The permeability constant for water in *Pelomyxa carolinensis. Salesianum* **38**, 17–24.
5. BERNHEIMER, A. Q. (1938) Fate of crystals in Amoebas. *Arch. Protistenk.* **90**, 365–368.
6. BINGLEY, M. S., and THOMPSON, C. M. (1962) Bioelectric potentials in relation to movements in amoebae. *J. Theoret. Biol.* **2**, 16–32.
7. BRAND, T. VON (1957) Metabolism of Trypanosomidae and Bodonidae; in *Biochemistry and Physiology of Protozoa* ed. LWOFF, A. Academic Press Inc., Vol. 1, pp. 177–234.
8. BROOKS, S. C. (1935) The permeability of erythrocytes to deuterium oxide (heavy water). *J. Cell. Comp. Physiol.* **7**, 163–171.
9. CARASSO, N., FAURÉ-FREMIET, E., and FAVARD, P. (1962) Ultrastructure de l'appareil excréteur chez quelques ciliés péritriches. *J. Microscopie* **1**, 445–468.
10. CARLSTROM, D., and MAX MØLLER, K. (1961) Further observations of the native and recrystallized crystals of the amoeba *Amoeba proteus. Exp. Cell Res.* **24**, 393–404.
11. CARTER, L. (1957) Ionic regulation in the ciliate *Spirostomum ambiguum. J. Exp. Biol.* **34**, 71–84.
12. CHADWICK, A. (1960) Studies on the relationship between the salinity and the activity of the contractile vacuoles of two species of Protozoa found in the rock-pools near Tvärminne. *Soc. Sci. Fenn. Comm. Biol.* **23**, No. 4, 15 pp.
13. CHAPMAN-ANDRESEN, C., and DICK, D. A. T. (1962) Sodium and bromine fluxes in the amoeba *Chaos chaos* L. *C.R. Lab., Carlsberg* **32**, 445–469.
14. COSGROVE, W. B., and KESSEL, R. G. (1958) The activity of the contractile vacuole of *Crithidia fasciculata. J. Protozool.* **5**, 296–298.
15. CUNNINGHAM, B., and KIRK, P. (1941) The chemical metabolism of *Paramecium caudatum. J. Cell. Comp. Physiol.* **18**, 299–316.
16. DAINTY, J. (1963) Water relations of plant cells. Advances in Botanical Research **1**, 279–326.
17. DEWEY, V. C., HEINRICH, M. R., and KIDDER, G. W. (1957) Evidence for the absence of the urea cycle in *Tetrahymena. J. Protozool.* **4**, 211–219.
18. DICK, D. A. T. (1959) Osmotic properties of living cells. *Internat. Rev. Cytol.* **8**, 388–448.
19. DUNHAM, P. B., and CHILD, F. M. (1961) Ion regulation in *Tetrahymena. Biol. Bull. Woods Hole* **121**, 129–140.
20. ELLIOTT, A. M., and BAK, I. J. (1964) The contractile vacuole and related structures in *Tetrahymena pyriformis. J. Protozool.* **11**, 250–261.
21. ERMAKOV, N. (1937) Some observations on the physiology of organisms from brine pools (in Russian). *Acad. Sci. Ukraine, Med. J.* **7**, 565–572.
22. FAURÉ-FREMIET, E., FAVARD, P., and CARASSO, N. (1962) Étude au microscope électronique des ultrastructures d'*Epistylis anastatica* (Cilié Péritricha). *J. Microscopie* **1**, 287–312.
23. FAURÉ-FREMIET, E., and ROUILLER, C. (1959) Le cortex de la vacuole contractile et son ultrastructure chez les Ciliés. *J. Protozool.* **6**, 29–37.
24. FLORKIN, M., and DUCHATEAU, G. (1943) Les formes du système enzymatique d'uricolyse et l'évolution du catabolism purique chez les animaux. *Arch. int. Physiol.* **53**, 267–307.

25. FRISCH, J. A. (1939) The experimental adaptation of *Paramecium* to seawater. *Arch. Protistenk.* **93**, 38–71.
26. GATENBY, J. B., DALTON, A. J., and FELIX, M. D. (1955) The contractile vacuole of Parazoa and Protozoa, and the Golgi apparatus. *Nature* **176**, 301–302.
27. GAYEWSKAYA, N. S. (1924) On the question of the function of pulsating and non-pulsating vacuoles of saltwater infusoria (English summary). *Russk. gidrobiol. Zh.* **3**, 239–252.
28. GELEI, J. (1935) A véglények kiválasztószerve alkati, fejlödestani és élettani szempont-bol. *Math. term. Közl.* **37**, 1–128.
29. GELFAN, S. (1928) The electrical conductivity of protoplasm. *Protoplasma* **4**, 192–200.
30. GREIDER, M. B., KOSTIR, W. J., and FRAJOLA, W. J. (1958) Electron microscopy of *Amoeba proteus. J. Protozool.* **5**, 139–146.
31. GRIFFIN, J. L. (1960) The isolation, characterization, and identification of the crystalline inclusions of the large free-living amoebae. *J. Biophys. Biochem. Cytol.* **7**, 227–234.
32. HOPKINS, D. L. (1946) The contractile vacuole and the adjustment to changing concentration in freshwater amoeba. *Biol. Bull. Woods Hole* **90**, 158–176.
33. KAMADA, T. (1935) Contractile vacuole of *Paramecium. J. Fac. Sci., Tokyo Univ.* **4**, 49–62.
34. KING, R. L. (1935) The contractile vacuole of *Paramecium multimicronucleata. T. Morph.* **58**, 555–571.
35. KITCHING, J. A. (1936) The physiology of contractile vacuoles. II. The control of body volume in marine Peritricha. *J. Exp. Biol.* **13**, 11–27.
36. KITCHING, J. A. (1938) The physiology of contractile vacuoles. III. The water balance of freshwater Peritricha. *J. Exp. Biol.* **15**, 143–151.
37. KITCHING, J. A. (1938) Contractile vacuoles. *Biol. Rev.* **13**, 403–444.
38. KITCHING, J. A. (1939) The effects of a lack of oxygen and of low oxygen tensions on *Paramecium. Biol. Bull. Woods Hole* **77**, 339–353.
39. KITCHING, J. A. (1939) On the activity of Protozoa at low oxygen tensions. *J. cell. comp. Physiol.* **14**, 227–236.
40. KITCHING, J. A. (1948) The physiology of contractile vacuoles. V. The effects of short-term variations of temperature on a freshwater peritrich ciliate. *J. Exp. Biol.* **25**, 406–420.
41. KITCHING, J. A. (1948) The physiology of contractile vacuoles. VI. Temperature and osmotic stress. *J. Exp. Biol.* **25**, 421–436.
42. KITCHING, J. A. (1951) The physiology of contractile vacuoles. VII. Osmotic relations in a suctorian, with special reference to the mechanism of control of vacuolar output. *J. Exp. Biol.* **28**, 203–214.
43. KITCHING, J. A. (1952) The physiology of contractile vacuoles. VIII. The water relations of the suctorian *Podophrya* during feeding. *J. Exp. Biol.* **29**, 363–371.
44. KITCHING, J. A. (1952) Contractile vacuoles. *Symp. Soc. Exp. Biol.* **6**, 145–165.
45. KITCHING, J. A. (1954) The physiology of contractile vacuoles. IX. Effects of sudden changes in temperature on the contractile vacuole of a suctorian; with a discussion of the mechanism of contraction. *J. Exp. Biol.* **31**, 68–75.
46. KITCHING, J. A. (1954) The physiology of contractile vacuoles. X. Effects of high hydrostatic pressure on the contractile vacuole of a suctorian. *J. Exp. Biol.* **31**, 76–83.
47. KITCHING, J. A. (1956) Contractile vacuoles of Protozoa. Protoplasmatologia III D 4a. Ed. HEILBRUNN, L. V., and WEBER, F.; Springer-Verlag, Vienna.
48. KITCHING, J. A. (1957) Effects of high hydrostatic pressures on the activity of flagellates and ciliates. *J. exp. Biol.* **34**, 494–510.
49. KITCHING, J. A. (1961) The physiological basis of behaviour in the Protozoa. pp. 60–78 in *The Cell and the Organism*, ed. RAMSAY, J. A., and WIGGLESWORTH, V. B., Cambridge University Press, 350 pp.

50. KITCHING, J. A., and PADFIELD, J. E. (1960) The physiology of contractile vacuoles. XI. Effects of heavy water on the water balance of a suctorian. *J. Exp. Biol.* **37**, 73–82.

51. KLEIN, R. L. (1959) Transmembrane flux of $K^{42}$ in *Acanthamoeba* sp. *J. cell. comp. Physiol.* **53**, 241–258.

52. KLEIN, R. L. (1961) Homeostatic mechanisms for cation regulation in *Acanthamoeba* sp. *Exp. Cell Res.* **25**, 571–584.

53. LEBOY, P. S., CLIVE, S. G., and CONNER, R. L. (1964) Phosphate, purines and pyrimidines as excretory products of *Tetrahymena*. *J. Protozool.* **11**, 217–222.

54. LEHMANN, F. E. (1959) Der Feinbau der Organoide von *Amoeba proteus* und seine Beeinflussung durch verschiedene Fixierstoffe. *Ergebn. Biol.* **21**, 88–127.

55. LEHMANN, F. E., MANNI, E., and BAIRATI, A. (1956) Der Feinbau von Plasmalemma und kontraktiler Vakuole bei *Amoeba proteus* in Schnitt- und Fragmentpräparaten. *Rev. Suisse Zool.* **63**, 246–255.

56. LLOYD, F. E. (1928) The contractile vacuole. Biol. Rev. **3**, 329–358.

57. LØVTRUP, S., and PIGÓN, A. (1951) Diffusion and active transport of water in the amoeba *Chaos chaos* L. *C.R. Lab.*, *Carlsberg* **28**, 1–36.

58. LUCKÉ, B., and HARVEY, E. N. (1935) The permeability of living cells to heavy water (deuterium oxide). *J. Cell. Comp. Physiol.* **7**, 153–162.

59. LWOFF, A., and ROUKHELMAN, N. (1926) Variations de quelques formes d'azote dans une culture pure d'infusoires. *C.R. Acad. Sci.*, *Paris* **183**, 156–158.

60. MACLENNAN, R. J. (1933) The pulsatory cycle of the contractile vacuole in the Ophryoscolecidae, ciliates from the stomach of cattle. *Univ. Calif. Publ. Zool.* **39**, 205–250.

61. MAST, S. O. (1947) The food-vacuole in *Paramecium*. *Biol. Bull. Woods Hole* **92**, 31–72.

62. MAST, S. O., and BOWEN, W. J. (1944) The food-vacuole in the Peritricha, with special reference to the hydrogen-ion concentration of its contents and of the cytoplasm. *Biol. Bull. Woods Hole* **87**, 188–222.

63. MAST, S. O., and FOWLER, C. (1935) Permeability of *Amoeba proteus* to water. *J. Cell. Comp. Physiol.* **6**, 151–167.

64. MERCER, E. H. (1959) An electron microscopic study of *Amoeba proteus*. *Proc. Roy. Soc. B.* **150**, 216–232.

65. NARDON, R. M., and WILBER, C. G. (1950) Nitrogenous excretion in *Colpidium campylum*. *Proc. Soc. Exp. Biol. N.Y.* **75**, 559–561.

66. NOIROT-TIMOTHÉE, C. (1960) Étude d'une famille de ciliés: les "Ophryoscolecidae". Structures et ultrastructures. *Ann. Sci. Nat.* **12**, 527–718.

67. PACE, D. M., and KIMURA, K. K. (1944) The effect of temperature on respiration in *Paramecium aurelia* and *Paramecium caudatum*. *J. Cell. Comp. Physiol.* **24**, 173–183.

68. PAPPAS, G. D., and BRANDT, P. W. (1958) The fine structure of the contractile vacuole in *Amoeba*. *J. Biophys. Biochem. Cytol.* **4**, 485–488.

69. PARPART, A. K. (1935) The permeability of the mammalian erythrocyte to deuterium oxide (heavy water). *J. Cell. Comp. Physiol.* **7**, 153–162.

70. PAUTARD, F. G. E. (1959) Hydroxyapatite as a developmental feature of *Spirostomum ambiguum*. *Biochem. Biophys. Acta* **35**, 33–46.

71. PAUTARD, F. G. E. (1960) Calcification in unicellular organisms. pp. 1–14 in "Calcification in Biological Systems", ed. SOGNNAES, R. F., *Amer. Ass. Adv. Sci.*, *Wash. D.C.* 1960.

72. PICKEN, L. E. R. (1936) A note on the mechanism of salt and water balance in the hetertrichous ciliate, *Spirostomum ambiguum*. *J. Exp. Biol.* **13**, 387–392.

73. PUYTORAC, P. DE. (1961) Complément à l'étude de l'ultrastructure des ciliés astomes du genre *Metaradiophrya* Hind 1935. *Arch. Anat. Microscop.* **50**, 35–58.

74. RAMSAY, J. A. (1961) The comparative physiology of renal function in invertebrates. pp. 158–174 in *The Cell and the Organism*. ed. RAMSAY, J. A., and WIGGLESWORTH, V. B., Cambridge University Press.

75. RIDDLE, J. (1962) Studies on the membrane potential of *Pelomyxa carolinensis*. *Exp. Cell. Res.* **26**, 158–167.
76. RIDDLE, J. (1962) Two methods for determining the water content of the giant amoeba *Pelomyxa carolinensis*. *Exp. Cell. Res.* **27**, 325–238.
77. RUDZINSKA, M. A. (1958) An electron microscope study of the contractile vacuole in *Tokophrya infusionum*. *J. Biophys. Biochem. Cytol.* **4**, 195–202.
78. RUDZINSKA, M. A., and CHAMBERS, R. (1951) The activity of the contractile vacuole in a suctorian (*Tokophrya infusionum*). *Biol. Bull. Woods Hole* **100**, 49–58.
79. SALLE, A. J., and SCHMIDT, C. L. A. (1928) The metabolism of *Leishmania tropica*. *J. Infect. Dis.* **43**, 378–384.
80. SCHEWIAKOFF, T. (1893) Über die Natur der sogenannten Exkretkörner der Infusorien. *Z. wiss. Zool.* **57**, 32–56.
81. SCHMIDT, W. J. (1939) Über die Doppelbrechung des Amöbenplasmas. *Protoplasma* **33**, 44–49.
82. SCHMIDT-NIELSEN, B., and SCHRAUGER, C. R. (1963) *Amoeba proteus*: studying the contractile vacuole by micropuncture. *Science* **139**, 606–607.
83. SCHNEIDER, L. (1960) Elektronenmikroskopische Untersuchungen über das Nephridialsystem von *Paramecium*. *J. Protozool.* **7**, 75–101.
84. SEAMAN, G. R. (1954) Enzyme systems in *Tetrahymena pyriformis* S. VI. Urea formation and breakdown. *J. Protozool.* **1**, 207–210.
85. SERAVIN, L. N. (1958) The changes of activity of the contractile vacuole of *Paramecium caudatum* dependent on environmental conditions. *Vestn. Leningrad. Univ.* **3**, 77–95.
86. SERAVIN, L. N. (1959) Changes in various functions of *Paramecium caudatum* in the course of adaptation to salt solutions. *Citologia, Moscow-Leningrad* **1**, 120–126.
87. SMYTH, J. D. (1942) The effect of temperature on the vacuolar frequency of *Stylonychia pustulata*. *Proc. Roy. Irish. Acad.* **48**, 25–41
88. SOLDO, A. T., and WAGTENDONK, W. J. VAN (1961) Nitrogen metabolism in *Paramecium aurelia*. *J. Protozool.* **8**, 41–55.
89. TELKES, M. (1931) Bioelectric measurements on amoebae. *Amer. J. Physiol.* **98**, 475–483.
90. UMRATH, K. (1956) Elektrische Messungen und Reizversuche an *Amoeba proteus*. *Protoplasma* **47**, 347–358.
91. VICKERMAN, K. (1962) Patterns of cellular organisation in limax amoebae. An electron microscope study. *Exp. Cell. Res.* **26**, 497–579.
92. WEATHERBY, J. H. (1927) The function of the contractile vacuole in *Paramecium caudatum*; with special reference to the excretion of nitrogenous compounds. *Biol. Bull. Woods Hole*, **52**, 208–218.
93. WEATHERBY, J. H. (1929) Excretion of nitrogenous substances in Protozoa. *Physiol. Zool.* **2**, 375–394.
94. WEISZ, P. B. (1951) An experimental analysis of morphogenesis in *Stentor coeruleus*. *J. Exp. Zool.* **116**, 231–237.
95. WICHTERMAN, R. (1948) The presence of optically active crystals in *Paramecium bursaria* and their relationship to symbiosis. *Anat. Rec.* **101**, 97–98.
96. WICHTERMAN, R. (1953) *The biology of Paramecium*. The Blakiston Company Inc., New York and Toronto, 527 pp.
97. WOLFSON, C. (1943) Potential difference measurements on *Chaos chaos*. *Physiol. Zool.* **16**, 93–100.

# NUTRITION AND GROWTH OF PROTOZOA

R. P. HALL

*Dept. of Biology*
*New York University*
*New York City, New York*

# CONTENTS

# NUTRITION

Protozoan diets must meet certain obvious needs. The diet must include raw materials for synthesis of the organic components of protoplasm, a supply of essential minerals, and also, for the majority of Protozoa, one or more vitamins or growth-factors which the organisms cannot synthesize. In addition, there must be an adequate dietary source of energy except for those Protozoa capable of converting the energy of light into chemical energy. Light is important for those species equipped with pigments functioning in photosynthesis and, in at least a number of such cases, can serve as the sole source of energy. However, chlorophyll-bearing flagellates vary in their relative dependence upon light. At temperatures of 20–32°C the growth rate of *Euglena gracilis* var. *bacillaris* has shown no significant correlation with light intensity. On the other hand, the growth of *Chlamydomonas moewusii* varied greatly with light intensity, failing at intensities below 15 ft-c.[178]

For all species which lack chromatophores, organic foods are the major sources of energy. Unlike certain bacteria, no typical protozoon can obtain all its needed energy by the oxidation of inorganic foods, although strain J of *Astasia longa* grows under conditions once thought to suggest such an energy source.[424, 427a] Other strains of the same species as well as related colorless Euglenida have failed to grow in the "minimal" medium,[426] and certain radiation-induced mutant strains of *A.longa* (strain J) also lack the ability to grow in this medium.[427] In general, the chemical and physical nature of favorable energy sources may vary from species to species, and perhaps to some extent from one environment to another.

## Methods of Feeding

Methods by which Protozoa obtain food from the surrounding medium vary. Saprozoic species utilize substances dissolved in the medium. Phagotrophic (or holozoic) types ingest other organisms or solid food of plant or animal origin, the usual type of diet varying more or less with the eater. Some Protozoa, such as *Ochromonas*,[368] combine both saprozoic and phagotrophic nutrition with the ability to carry on photosynthesis.

Phagotrophy in amoeboid organisms typically involves activity of pseudopodia, whereas non-amoeboid phagotrophs usually have a more or less permanent cytostome and cytopharynx for ingestion. This difference does

339

not mean that ingestion by an amoeboid organism is necessarily a simple process. In *Thecamoeba sphaeronucleolus*, for example, the tip of an extended pseudopodium adheres to the prey, such as a testate rhizopod. Next, the thick pellicle of the pseudopodium becomes softened, possibly being digested by cytoplasmic enzymes, and a "mouth" and "ingestive tube" are formed as a result of suction exerted by the endoplasm, now retreating toward the body proper. The prey is drawn down into the tube, ending finally in a food cup which is formed by invagination as the prey touches the cytoplasm. The captured organism is next engulfed in the cup, which soon becomes a food vacuole lined with invaginated plasma membrane. In the meantime, the pellicle formerly making up the tube becomes shriveled and soon shrinks to form a wrinkled mound on the body surface.[46]

An analogous mechanism is operative in the heliozoon, *Actinophrys sol*. A ciliate which makes firm contact with an axopodium is gradually carried to the surface of the body by cytoplasmic flow. When contact is made here, a membranous funnel grows out to enclose the prey in a food vacuole. A captured ciliate usually becomes inactive within a half hour and its pellicle then degenerates. In the meantime, the food vacuole is being drawn tightly to the body and finally becomes partly embedded in the outer cytoplasm of the captor.[270]

Ingestion by an amoeboid organism may also involve cutting food into morsels of suitable size, as in the various cases cited by Bovee.[46]

In phagotrophs with persistent mouths, a food vacuole typically is formed at the base of the cytopharynx as a bulbous enlargement which is eventually pinched off to form a vacuole in the endoplasm. Suctorian tentacles operate in similar fashion, a food vacuole being formed at the base of a feeding tentacle much as in a cytopharynx. In suctorian feeding[66, 212, 213] the extended tentacles must first adhere to the prey. This reaction apparently depends upon the presence of particular unidentified substances in the pellicle or cortex of ciliates, substances presumably absent in flagellates and amoebae. Thus, suctorian tentacles respond to "artificial ciliates" represented by bits of agar containing acetylcholine, reduced glutathione, peptone, $CaCl_2$ and $K_2HPO_4$ in particular concentrations, or to similar agar particles impregnated with a ciliate homogenate.[212] As noted in the outer zone of the tentacle in *Tokophrya infusionum*,[398] migratory elongated inclusions penetrate the plasma membrane at the tip and, upon contact with the prey, are probably ejected as a sort of nematocyst responsible for immobilization of the captive and dissolution of its pellicle.

In any event, digestion occurs within a food vacuole of a phagotroph and the products are then ready for assimilation. In addition to the types of enzymes usually assumed to participate in digestion, a high concentration of acid phosphatase activity has been noted in food vacuoles of *Tetrahymena pyriformis*, whereas non-phagocytic ciliates in a defined medium show no such concentration of the enzyme.[441]

Pinocytosis also has been described in such phagotrophic types as amoebae and ciliates. As described in various amoebae,[53, 54, 70, 327, 394] pinocytosis follows contact of the body surface with a certain substance and involves the formation of slender invaginations which are constricted to form pinocytosis vacuoles. These vacuoles contain materials which were dissolved in the external medium. Their formation is induced by such varied substances as proteins, salts and even toluidine blue. Many of these chemical inducers apparently do not penetrate the surface layer readily and presumably would not be taken up to a significant extent in the absence of pinocytosis. Pinocytosis also has been induced, or at least accelerated, in *Amoeba proteus* by exposure of the organisms to ultraviolet light.[387] In this amoeba, the process seems to be dependent upon aerobic respiration and is retarded by low temperatures.[108]

In a non-particulate medium, formation of ordinary food vacuoles in a phagotroph also may depend upon the presence of an inducer,[440] since *Tetrahymena pyriformis* shows very few such vacuoles in a defined medium. In fact, the essential difference between phagocytosis and pinocytosis may be more nearly quantitative than qualitative.

A sort of internal pinocytosis has been reported in *Glaucoma chattoni*.[210] Evaginations appear on the membrane of a food vacuole and apparently are pinched off to form small secondary vacuoles. A comparable "micropinocytosis" in which the products of digestion pass from food vacuoles into the cytoplasm also has been described in *Pelomyxa*.[394] Similar evaginations from the membrane of the cytopharynx, as well as from food vacuoles, have been described in *Paramecium aurelia*.[257]

Not much is known about the mechanisms of feeding in saprozoic Protozoa and the possible importance of pinocytosis in such organisms is yet to be determined. However, a few of the Protozoa formerly considered saprozoic have been found to feed by other methods as well. *Trypanosoma mega*, for example, possess a small cytostome and cytopharynx; pinocytosis vacuoles apparently are formed from the wall of the cytopharynx.[460] A similar cytostome has been reported in *Bodo*.[358] *Plasmodium lophurae* and *P. berghei*, which were formerly considered saprozoic organisms, ingest hemoglobin from the invaded corpuscles.[400, 401] The resulting food vacuole apparently represents the cavity of the "ring" stage in malarial parasites. *Babesia rodhaini*, which also ingests hemoglobin, seems to digest it completely so as to leave no residue of pigment ("hemozoin") like that seen in malarial parasites.[402] Incidentally, the absorption spectrum of the residual pigment in *P. lophurae* has been compared with that of hemoglobin.[445] Apparently analogous cases of phagocytic nutrition were observed earlier in a gregarine, *Monocystis banyulensis*, which ingests tissue cells of its host.[478] Ingestion, as noted in malarial parasites and *Babesia*, has been considered a type of pinocytosis, induced presumably by some constituent of the red corpuscle.[400, 402]

## Axenic Cultures in Research

The study of protozoan food requirements, aside from its intrinsic interest to protozoologists, has resulted in the development of reliable media for various species which are becoming increasingly useful in the study of protozoan metabolism and also as biochemical tools. *Euglena*, for example, has become the subject of a book detailing its virtues for such purposes.[513] The establishment of *killer* strains of *Paramecium aurelia* in axenic cultures should facilitate further investigation of their special properties.[455] Likewise, preliminary experiments with axenic cultures of Foraminifera[280] afford reason for hoping that a few of these Protozoa will soon be available as axenic material for research. Some of the slime-molds—e.g., *Physarum polycephalum*[107] and *Fuligo septica*[277]—have been established in pure cultures and such axenic material will broaden the scope of investigations on these organisms. The recent establishment of *Polysphondylium pallidum*[14a] in a defined medium also opens the way to intensive study of the acrasian group under precisely controlled conditions. Availability of such luminescent dinoflagellates as *Pyrodinium bahamense*[317] and *Gonyaulax scrippsae*[359a] in axenic cultures now affords material for detailed laboratory investigation of phosphorescent flagellates. A number of Protozoa are now available in axenic cultures[374] and their use in biochemical and pharmacological investigations has interested a growing number of workers.

The following are representative investigations in which Protozoa have been used either as subjects of study or as research tools: investigating the amino acid composition of Protozoa;[298, 421, 498, 515, 516] tracing amino acid metabolism;[112, 113, 347, 396, 397, 515] investigating modes of action and effects of antihistamines with such species as *Chlamydomonas pseudococcum* and *Euglena gracilis*,[179] *Chlorogonium tetragamum*,[242] and *Ochromonas malhamensis* and *Tetrahymena pyriformis*;[418] evaluating antimalarial drugs with *Crithidia fasciculata*;[339] preliminary screening of potential antitumor agents[228] and attempting to determine specific effects of such drugs;[5, 492] testing vitamin $B_{12}$ derivatives for possible inhibitory effects on *Euglena gracilis* and *Ochromonas malhamensis*;[25, 27] determining the points at which the anticonvulsant, primidone (Mysoline), affects folic acid metabolism in *Crithidia fasciculata*, *Euglena gracilis* and *Ochromonas malhamensis*;[22] with *Euglena gracilis*, *Ochromonas danica*, *O. malhamensis* and *Tetrahymena pyriformis*, tracing the inhibitory action of thalidomide to probable effects on oxidative mechanisms which can be counteracted by nicotinic acid (or nicotinamide, or NAD) added to the medium;[161] relating the effects of the tranquilizer, chlorpromazine, to alteration of membrane permeability in *Tetrahymena pyriformis*;[341] determining the effects of various drugs on pigment production in phytoflagellates;[1, 4, 8, 128, 179, 242, 375, 376, 392, 480] investigating effects of such anti-leukemic drugs as urethan, using the chrysomonad flagellate, *Poteriochromonas stipi-*

*tata*;[236, 237] investigating mode of action[329] and chemotherapeutic activity of drugs on *Trichomonas vaginalis*;[154, 415] evaluating effects of antibiotics and other substances on specific Protozoa by means of agar plate techniques;[425, 501] tracing biosynthesis of purines,[337] vitamin $B_{12}$[338] and thymine[237] in several species; considering effects of sex hormones at the cellular level;[59, 274] detecting inhibition of growth by certain steroids other than hormones;[81] testing hypocholesteremic agents with Protozoa;[6] determining the effects of purine antagonists;[110, 114, 166, 263], detecting effects of kinetin;[180, 181, 320, 389] by using radioactive materials, tracing uptake of minerals[452, 453] and of vitamin $B_{12}$;[479] evaluating nutrient values of foods;[126, 153, 357] detecting biochemical mutants in *Tetrahymena pyriformis*[140, 141] and *Chlamydomonas* spp.;[148, 287, 288] investigating serological types in *Tetrahymena*;[138, 296, 297] using *Tetrahymena pyriformis* for detecting effects of radiation on foods;[137] investigating various aspects of metabolism for which axenic material is particularly useful.[119, 120, 121, 273, 283, 291, 382, 403, 404, 405, 406, 407, 408, 438, 491, 496, 497, 507, 508, 509]

The determination of minimal food requirements has made possible the use of Protozoa in assay techniques:[192, 226] e.g., assay of biotin with *Ochromonas danica*,[23] assay of vitamin $B_{12}$ with *Euglena gracilis*[224, 234] and with *Ochromonas malhamensis*;[23, 28, 158] nicotinic acid with *Tetrahymena pyriformis*;[26] pantothenic acid with *T. pyriformis*;[24] pteridines with *Crithidia fasciculata*;[344] thiamine with *Ochromonas malhamensis*,[30] and thioctic acid with *Tetrahymena pyriformis*.[464] The establishment of *Acanthamoeba* sp.[10] and *Hartmannella rhysodes*[31, 32] in defined media has added two phagotrophic species to the list of potential assay organisms. Assays with Protozoa obviously can be applied to biochemical, clinical and oceanographic investigations.[231]

## Food Requirements

Under natural conditions, the nature of the protozoan diet varies widely in different organisms. Phototrophic species exposed to light may live mainly or completely on inorganic foods; typical heterotrophs must have organic sources of energy and building materials. The diet of phagotrophs often includes an assortment of other microorganisms. Such Protozoa as *Amoeba proteus* often seem to be opportunists, eating mainly what they can capture without obvious discrimination in regard to plant or animal kingdoms. However, amoebae apparently do have the ability to discriminate between useful food and something which is not useful, although the responsible mechanisms are not understood. Other types of phagotrophs may be predominately herbivorous, while others are mainly carnivorous or even completely so.

Under natural conditions, the diet of a carnivore sometimes includes a variety of other microorganisms, or even small Metazoa in some instances.

*Dileptus*, long known to feed on flagellates, ciliates and occasionally rotifers, has been found[56] to eat fragments of liver and such animals as small snails and planarian worms, cercariae or even *Hydra*, although overpowering *Hydra* requires attack by a pack of *Dileptus* rather than by a single individual. Nematodes and aquatic oligochaetes, if wounded, also are vulnerable, as are small clams if a piece of the shell is broken off. Almost equally impressive is the ingestion of *Paramecium multimicronucleatum* by *Didinium nasutum*, a feat said to require about a minute.[122]

In contrast to the catholic tastes of *Dileptus*, some carnivores have a restricted diet. For example, *Bresslaua insidiatrix*, *B. sicaria* and *B. vorax* thrive on *Colpoda duodenaria* but cannot grow on *Tetrahymena pyriformis*.[78] In addition, carnivores may suffer dietary deficiencies when their usual prey has not enjoyed a suitable diet. For instance, *Didinium nasutum* could not be maintained on *Paramecium aurelia* from certain monobacterial cultures, whereas *P. aurelia* from cultures containing natural mixtures of bacteria met the needs of the carnivores.[62]

Many ciliates are rather strictly herbivorous, feeding primarily on bacteria or small algae. Among these herbivores, microbial food seemingly suitable in size or other properties may differ considerably in nutritive value for a particular species, such as *Colpidium colpoda*.[61]

Growth of Protozoa in monoxenic cultures has frequently been useful as a source of research material maintained under fairly well controlled conditions—e.g., growth of *Dictyostelium discoideum* with *Aerobacter aerogenes*;[469] growth of *Entamoeba histolytica* with *Trypanosoma cruzi*;[355] growth of *Naegleria gruberi* with *Proteus Mirabilis*;[69] growth of *Bolivina* sp. with certain diatoms, although in this case a mixed flora proved more suitable than the single food organisms tested;[280] and various earlier examples cited by Van Wagtendonk.[488]

The identification of specific food requirements requires more or less extended investigations under carefully controlled conditions. The general problem may be complicated by the fact that food requirements sometimes vary with the strain, as in *Acrasis rosea*.[358] In *Tetrahymena pyriformis*[140, 141] some of these differences among strains are known to be inherited in Mendelian fashion. Determination of the minimal requirements of a freshly captured strain can involve a long series of tedious procedures, especially in the case of a heterotroph. Species of *Paramecium* have afforded excellent examples.[251, 252, 253, 290, 330, 331, 332] The first step, in any case, usually has been establishment of a clone culture in some medium which will support growth. From such cultures an axenic strain has next been established in a sterilizable medium. In the case of amoebae, migration on a sterile agar plate had been used by Neff,[345] extending earlier work of Oehler. In many other cases, the washing technique (serial transfers through a sterile medium, with or without added antibacterial agents) has produced the desired results. The sterilizable medium has often contained protein digests, a few salts, a fatty acid or sometimes a sugar, a few added vitamins, or other supplements believed to favor growth. Although some Protozoa, such as Euglenida, are tolerant to fairly wide variations in concentration of nutrients, certain other types may be much more fastidious, as pointed out by Provasoli[372] on the base of extensive experience with phytoflagellates. In any case, a satisfactory recipe results in a medium which is reproducible and is a dependable source of material for future investigation.

Once a crude medium suitable for the particular species has been developed, the aim becomes replacement of natural mixtures with known quantities of specific chemicals. Several or sometimes many such mixtures may be tried before the aim is realized—a chemically defined medium which supports good growth. Occasionally, a trace of some natural product, apparently not replaceable by a previously known growth-factor, has turned out to be necessary in approaching a chemically defined medium for a heterotroph. Perhaps the best known case is that of *Tetrahymena pyriformis*, the new requirement eventually being identified as α-lipoic, or thioctic, acid.[262, 430]

Once any such puzzle has been resolved, there remains only the problem of determining just which components of the chemically defined medium are actually essential to growth of the species. In one general method, the answers are sought through systematic deletions, in attempts to strip the original medium down to bare essentials. In these last stages the complications of sparing effects and quantitative interrelationships of various components of the medium must be considered, especially in the more complicated media for heterotrophs.[111, 448]

## CARBON SOURCES

Potential carbon sources for Protozoa range from $CO_2$ through various short-chain carbon compounds to some of the polysaccharides. For the typical photoautotroph growing in light, $CO_2$ is an adequate source. Heterotrophs need, in addition, some more complex carbon compound or compounds as a source of energy and for use in biosynthesis. That the relative importance of such carbon sources may vary with the species is suggested by reports that certain strains of *Astasia longa* can grow in an extremely low-carbon minimal medium which has failed to support other strains of the same species and of related colorless Euglenida.[424, 426] The suitability of any major carbon source for a heterotroph depends both upon the chemical nature of the substance and upon the ability of the organism to get the compound inside its body for use in metabolism.

Some of the chlorophyll-bearing dinoflagellates (various species of *Amphidinium, Exuviella, Gymnodinium, Gyrodinium, Peridinium*) are heterotrophic to a distinctly limited degree which varies with the genus. Certain organic carbon sources have doubled or tripled growth of *Gyrodinium* spp. when added to inorganic media but have not increased growth of several other tested species.[377]

Assimilation of $CO_2$ has been demonstrated in *Euglena gracilis*, in darkness as well as in light,[310] and at the other extreme of protozoan nutrition in *Trichomonas vaginalis*,[496] *Physarum polycephalum*[309] and *Tetrahymena pyriformis*.[309, 438, 472, 491] *E. gracilis* is interesting in that its pattern of $CO_2$-fixation in darkness is similar to that in light, in contrast to such algae as *Chlorella*. Deprivation of $CO_2$ seems to be relatively more detrimental to growth of *Chilomonas paramecium* than to that of *Tetrahymena pyriformis* in a peptone medium.[241]

Organic carbon sources vary considerably in their suitability for different Protozoa. *Chilomonas paramecium*[97, 202] can thrive on any one of several alcohols, fatty acids and certain other organic acids (such as lactic), but no carbohydrate has yet been shown to support its growth. No tested amino acid will serve as the sole source of energy and carbon for *C. paramecium*.[202] Under laboratory conditions, the ability to oxidize particular amino acids varies with the species, even in typical heterotrophs. In manometric tests, *Trypanosoma equiperdum* showed no oxygen uptake with an amino acid as the substrate, whereas *T. lewisi* oxidized both aspartic and glutamic acids and their amides.[473] The importance of suitable chemical structure is illustrated by the inhibition of growth produced in *C. paramecium* by various odd-number straight-chain alcohols and acids, even in the presence of a suitable carbon source.[97]

Phytoflagellates, for which acetate is typically very satisfactory, differ in their ability to utilize certain other carbon compounds. Thus, growth of *Chilomonas paramecium* is supported by caproic, caprylic, fumaric, $\alpha$-ketoglutaric or lactic acid, but $\alpha$-ketoglutarate is a poor carbon source for *Polytomella caeca* and the others fail to support growth of this species.[510, 511] However, homogenates of *P. caeca* are active for at least three of these unsatisfactory carbon sources, indicating that failure to take up a particular substrate can be responsible for some of the reported negative results in tests for utilization by intact organisms. The synthesis of adaptive enzymes also may be involved in the utilization of particular substrates to which a species has not been exposed recently; *Polytoma uvella*[72, 73, 74, 371] and *Euglena gracilis*[105] furnish examples. The former has shown adaptation to butyrate and caproate, while an ethanol-grown strain of *E. gracilis* has undergone adaptation to acetate upon transfer to this substrate. In addition, Lewin[288] noted that oxidation of acetate by wild-type *Chlamydomonas dysmosos* began immediately upon exposure to the substrate but assimilation began only after about 60 minutes, suggesting a sort of "assimilatory adaptation".

*Euglena gracilis* can assimilate acetate, mevalonate, $\beta$-hydroxy-$\beta$-methyl glutarate, $\beta$-dimethylaerylate, isovalerate, and several branched-chain derivatives. As determined with $C^{14}$-labeled substrates, each of these can be used in the synthesis of $\beta$-carotene,[459] but the status of most of them as major carbon sources is uncertain. Homogenates of a streptomycin-bleached strain were found to oxidize six acids of the citric acid cycle and to synthesize citric acid from oxalacetate.[103] Most intermediates of this cycle also can be oxidized by *Astasia longa* (strain J), although uptake is related to pH of the medium.[216]

Ethanol can be metabolized readily by *Euglena gracilis*[505] and the addition of alcohol to an acetate medium has increased the rate of assimilation but not the total consumption of acetate.[104] *Astasia longa*, in an alcohol medium, has shown a distinctly preferential synthesis of carbohydrates over lipids as compared with the acetate-grown strain.[60] Utilization of acetate by *E. gracilis* is slightly more efficient than utilization of alcohol—e.g., 42 per cent as compared with 39 per cent.[505] These data for *E. gracilis* are comparable with the 40 per cent oxidation of acetate (without added nitrogen source) reported earlier for *Chilomonas paramecium*.[40] Assimilation of methyl- and carboxyl-labeled acetate has been traced in *E. gracilis*.[104] The data (methyl-C contributing 70 per cent of the assimilated carbon) suggest passage of acetate into Krebs-cycle oxalacetate and assimilation of derived pyruvate. Tracer experiments[106] also have indicated that endogenous metabolism of *E. gracilis* continues during oxidation of exogenous substrates but that the assimilated substrate becomes mixed with and thus dilutes the endogenous reserves. The most recently deposited reserves are the first to be oxidized.

In the case of certain green flagellates which can be grown in darkness, acetate seems to be a good substitute for photosynthesis and proved to be the only one of several tested substrates which would support growth of *Chlamydomonas reinhardi* in darkness.[410] On the other hand, wild-type *C. dysmosos* has grown in darkness with acetate, pyruvate or lactate as the energy source in a mineral medium, but this ability to grow as a heterotroph can be lost as a result of mutation.[288] The chrysomonad, *Ochromonas malhamensis*, although able to use such compounds as acetate, butyrate, lactate and the like, also can digest starch[368] and utilize such other carbohydrates as glucose, levulose, galactose, sucrose and mannitol.

Carbohydrates as carbon sources are less widely used by Protozoa than are simpler materials. Polysaccharides other than starch are satisfactory for relatively few Protozoa, cited elsewhere,[186] and disaccharides are less commonly useful than monosaccharides. Although *Ochromonas*,[368] and perhaps closely related flagellates as well, can use both starch and simpler carbohydrates, this ability is not typical of the phytoflagellates. *Ochromonas* apparently represents a borderline case in which photosynthesis makes only a marginal contribution to nutrition. Chlorophyll *a* has been found, but not chlorophylls *b* and *c*, and there appears to be a net uptake of $CO_2$ only in the absence of utilizable organic carbon sources.[334] In other words,

12*

this chlorophyll-bearing flagellate seems to be more nearly a heterotroph than a phototroph. The Euglenida utilize exogenous carbohydrates poorly or not at all. Likewise, the phagotrophic *Oxyrrhis marina*, often considered a primitive dinoflagellate, apparently lacks the ability to use exogenous carbohydrates.[124] *Euglena gracilis* apparently produces no amylase, although laminarase activity has been reported in extracts of these flagellates.[151] Since laminarin seems to be similar to paramylum, such findings are not surprising. However, the exceptional *E. gracilis* var. *bacillaris* can use exogenous glucose[99, 217] and an appropriate hexokinase has been isolated from these flagellates.[37] A mutant strain of *Astasia longa* also can use glucose, showing uptake of the $C^{14}$-labeled sugar, but the parent stock lacks this ability.[35]

Outside the phytoflagellates, the ability to use a number of carbohydrates seems to be widespread, as pointed out elsewhere.[186] Such ability has been demonstrated by fermentation reactions, measurement of sugar consumption, stimulation of oxygen uptake by added carbohydrate, and the stimulation of growth in axenic cultures. However, it should be noted that acceleration of growth may be produced in some cases by carbohydrates which do not give positive fermentation tests.[134] Furthermore, comparative rates of fermentation may not correspond very well to the quantitative effects on growth.[382] In a more direct method for demonstrating uptake of sugars, $C^{14}$-glucose has been used with *Astasia longa*[35] and *Hartmannella rhysodes*.[31]

Differences in carbohydrate utilization have been noted among species in certain genera or families. For example, *Trichomonas gallinae* can utilize arabinose, fructose, galactose, glucose, maltose, sucrose, trehalose and turanose, as well as starch and glycogen, while *T. vaginalis* is unable to use arabinose, fructose, sucrose, and turanose.[382] Similar qualitative differences have been reported for strains of *Tetrahymena pyriformis*, as listed elsewhere.[186] Differences in fermentation rates also have been reported for various strains of *T. pyriformis*.[295] Adaptation to cyanide has an interesting effect on this ciliate: cyanide-adapted ciliates use glucose more rapidly than normal ones, although rate of oxidation and production of lactate are higher in the normals.[311] The ability to metabolize a specific carbohydrate may be quite restricted, even within a group of closely related species. For example, *Crithidia fasciculata* contains an enzyme which can oxidize sorbitol to fructose, but 23 related strains of insect parasites apparently lack this system.[95]

The mechanism of sugar uptake has been investigated in *Tetrahymena pyriformis* by Cirillo.[76] L-arabinose, a sugar which this ciliate does not metabolize, is not accumulated against a concentration difference. However, the process, which shows a high $Q_{10}$ and is competitively inhibited by glucose, is not simple diffusion but probably a "facilitated diffusion"[75] similar to that described by Cirillo in yeast. The experimental data apparently exclude pinocytosis as a significant mechanism in the uptake of sugar by *T. pyriformis*.

In addition to carbohydrates, simpler carbon sources also may be utilized by Protozoa other than phytoflagellates. For example, pyruvate and various TCA-acids can be used by malarial parasites,[434] Trypanosomidae[11, 18, 48, 49, 403, 435] and *Tetrahymena pyriformis*.[129, 432, 433, 437, 438] Pyruvate, acetate and lactate also stimulate respiration of X-irradiated *T. pyriformis*.[395] *Crithidia* (*Strigomonas*) *oncopelti*[405] uses lactic and succinic acids more readily than galactose and several disaccharides, while *Trichomonas foetus*[119] metabolizes lactic and pyruvic acids almost as readily as glucose. Here again, specific differences have been noted: *T. gallinae* oxidizes citric, fumaric, isocitric, $\beta$-hydroxybutyric, $\alpha$-ketoglutaric, malic and succinic acids; *T. vaginalis* has shown no activity for these intermediates of the tricarboxylic acid cycle.[382, 509]

In some cases, a sugar seems to be more satisfactory than simpler substances. For instance, acetate does not replace glucose as the principal energy source for *Crithidia* (*Strigomonas*) *oncopelti*. Yet acetate is assimilated and, in tests with $C^{14}$-acetate, labeled carbon appeared in such protoplasmic components as pyrimidines and amino acids.[347]

Utilization of complex carbohydrates is preceded necessarily by digestion which is carried out in food vacuoles in phagotrophic species or, in at least certain species, apparently outside the organism by means of extracellular enzymes. *Tetrahymena pyriformis* (cell-free homogenates) contains enzymes which digest starch and glycogen,[404] and the same is true for *Trichomonas foetus*.[406] Such a monosaccharide as glucose apparently is not necessarily a more satisfactory food than a polysaccharide. For example, population growth and size of *Tetrahymena pyriformis*, as well as amount of protein per ciliate, are greater with dextrin than with glucose.[386] If equivalent purity of the two carbohydrate preparations can be assumed, it would seem that the difference in molecular structure has a significance yet to be clarified.

Polysaccharides are synthesized by many Protozoa, if not all, and sometimes in rather large amounts. *Chilomonas paramecium* may store starch to the extent of about 20 per cent of its dry weight.[467] *Polytomella caeca* also synthesizes and stores large amounts of starch;[34, 36, 43] cell-free extracts of the flagellates can use glucose-1-phosphate but not glucose or disaccharides for this synthesis. The storage of other polysaccharides has not been investigated so thoroughly in phytoflagellates, although it appears that in the production of paramylum a pathway involving uridine is followed.[217] Synthesis of this polysaccharide in *Astasia longa* is believed to involve both the glyoxalate and tricarboxylic acid cycles.[216] Surprisingly, cellulose is synthesized by *Acanthamoeba* sp., although the polysaccharide has been detected only in the inner layer of the cyst wall.[346] A polysaccharide synthesized by *Crithidia fasciculata* is a galactan which apparently forms part of the pellicle rather than endoplasmic storage material.[96] Glycogen is stored in fairly large amounts by *Tetrahymena pyriformis*[322] and by *Trichomonas foetus* and *T. gallinae*.[323] In the case of *T. pyriformis* the stored glycogen enables the ciliates to remain motile for two or three days under anaerobic conditions, the carbohydrate being consumed gradually under anaerobiosis. Holotrichs (*Dasytricha, Isotricha*) from the sheep's rumen also store considerable amounts of polysaccharide as iodophilic cytoplasmic granules.[350] These protozoan glycogens are similar to but not identical with those of higher animals in chemical structure. Although the glycogens from *T. pyriformis* and rat liver both contain 13 glucose residues in each unit chain, the molecular weight of the ciliate glycogen is greater. Even two species of *Trichomonas* (*T. foetus, T. gallinae*) differ in molecular structure of their glycogens, a fact which might tend to support the validity of *Tritrichomonas* and *Trichomonas* as separate genera.

Products of carbohydrate dissimilation vary with the species. Carbohydrate metabolism of *Tetrahymena pyriformis*, unlike that of certain other Protozoa, is qualitatively comparable to that of mammalian tissues.[491] Enzymes of the Embden-Meyerhof pathway have been reported in a number of Protozoa: in such flagellates as *Crithidia* (*Strigomonas*) *oncopelti*,[405] *Trichomonas foetus*,[406] *T. vaginalis*,[19, 497, 508] several species of *Trypanosoma*;[18, 21, 165, 172, 194, 407, 443] in *Plasmodium gallinaceum*;[457] and in *Tetrahymena pyriformis*.[404, 429] In *Trypanosoma rhodesiense*, representing the "*brucei-evansi* group," L-$\alpha$-glycerophosphate dehydrogenase is linked to a particular hydrogen-transport system which is not sensitive to cyanide and contains no detectable cytochrome pigment.[173, 174, 175]

As might be expected, pyruvate has been detected frequently as a product of glucose dissimilation—e.g., in *Crithidia fasciculata*[94] and *C. oncopelti*,[405] in various species of *Trypanosoma*,[48] and in *Plasmodium knowlesi*.[499]

The products of pyruvate metabolism may vary from species to species, even within a single order or smaller taxonomic group. Among the Trypanosomidae, *Crithidia fasciculata* produces acetic, formic, lactic and succinic acids from pyruvate.[93] The accumulation of succinic acid in appreciable amounts seems to be correlated with the relatively slight succinic dehydrogenase activity reported for this flagellate.[215] The related flagellate, *C.* (*Strigomonas*) *oncopelti*, ferments glucose mainly to pyruvic and succinic acids, although small amounts of lactic acid, ethanol, glycerol and $CO_2$ have been reported.[405] For the same species, Clausen[79] has found acetate, succinate and probably lactate, plus some unidentified non-volatile acid, as products of glucose fermentation. Glucose is converted almost quantitatively into pyruvate by such trypanosomes as *T. hippicum*.[194] *T. lewisi*, on the other hand, produces formic, acetic, lactic and succinic acids, in addition to pyruvate,[403] much as does *C. fasciculata*. Under aerobic conditions, *T. congolense* produces mostly pyruvate and acetate from glucose, with traces of lactate, succinate and glycerol; anaerobically, the products are mostly pyruvate, acetate and succinate, with a small amount of glycerol.[52]

*T. cruzi* yields mainly acetic, citric and succinic acids, as well as some $CO_2$.[407]

Among the Trichomonadidae, *Trichomonas foetus* produces mostly acetate and succinate from glucose,[406] while in *T. vaginalis* under anaerobic conditions lactate is the major derivative of pyruvate.[20, 508] The production of malic acid and an unidentified additional organic acid also has been reported for the latter species.[495]

In *Plasmodium gallinaceum*, cell-free parasites oxidize pyruvate at a maximal rate only in the presence of dicarboxylic acids (e.g., succinate), thiamine (or else DPT), NAD, NADP, ATP and Mn, producing acetate in addition to $CO_2$ and $H_2O$.[458] According to Sherman,[444] the lactic de-hydrogenase of malarial parasites is characteristic of the species and is meta-bolically more efficient than the corresponding enzyme of the red corpuscle.

Observations on *Tetrahymena pyriformis* have indicated only acid products of hexose decomposition under anaerobic conditions.[472] The identified substances—acetic, lactic and succinic acids—were considered to be the only substances produced from sugars under the experimental conditions, since there was a net assimilation of $CO_2$. This anaerobic production of succinate by *T. pyriformis* apparently involves the breakdown of glycogen to hexose and carboxylation of phosphoenolpyruvate, followed by reduction of the product.[491]

## NITROGEN SOURCES

Potential sources of nitrogen for Protozoa include various inorganic and organic compounds, the suitability of which varies with the species. Of the potential inorganic sources, only nitrates and ammonium salts are known to meet the requirements of certain flagellates. Although few species have been tested adequately, there is as yet no real evidence that Protozoa can fix atmospheric nitrogen. An ammonium salt is suitable for many green and colorless flagellates, although concentrations must be considered carefully in constructing media for particularly sensitive phytoflagellates.[372] Under natural conditions, ammonium toxicity is usually negligible as an ecological factor, although this need not be the case in heavily polluted water with pronounced ammonification. Some of the green flagellates are known to use nitrates as the sole source of nitrogen.[372] With rare exceptions—e.g., *Polytoma ocellatum*[305] and apparently a very few strains of *Euglenida*, listed but not investigated by Provasoli[372]—colorless flagellates apparently cannot use a nitrate as the only nitrogen source. In this respect at least, a strain of *Euglena gracilis*[39] may resemble representative colorless phyto-flagellates, although this and several other species of *Euglena* can reduce ni-trate to nitrite.[185] This difference in ability to use nitrate presumably is related to the need for reduction during assimilation, although specific differences in enzymatic equipment are yet to be demonstrated for flagellates which can and those which cannot use nitrate as the sole source of nitrogen.

Although utilization of nitrite as the nitrogen source, rather than as an intermediate in assimilation of nitrate, has not been demonstrated in Protozoa, reduction of nitrite has been described in *Euglena gracilis* and the rate is doubled upon exposure to light, either aerobically or anaerobically; the reaction is stimulated also by addition to the medium of such reducing agents as malate and pyruvate.[235] It is not impossible that lack of evidence for utilization of nitrite may be attributable in part to tests of such salts at unfavorably high concentrations.

Organic sources of nitrogen, for Protozoa in general, range from single amino acids to natural proteins. The simplest organic source adequate for growth varies with the organism. A number of the phytoflagellates apparently can grow on a single amino acid, although suitability of particular amino acids apparently may vary with the species in a single genus, such as *Euglena*.[127] In tests of species of dinoflagellates belonging to the genera *Amphidinium, Exuviella, Gymnodinium, Gyrodinium* and *Peridinium*, an amino acid was in no case more satisfactory than a nitrate.[377] Certain other organic sources—urea, uric acid, xanthine—can be used by *Chlamydomonas reinhardi* but not by *Euglena gracilis*.[39] Factors responsible for such differences in utilization have not yet been investigated carefully, although "permeability" of the organism to different nitrogen compounds may be important. In *Chilomonas paramecium*[71, 77] any one of two amino acids and two amides supported growth comparable with that with ammonium nitrogen, while each of three purines supported moderately heavy growth. Other amino acids were of little or no value, and artificial mixtures were in no case better than a single suitable amino acid.[71] This lack of specificity would suggest that the organic sources which are satisfactory for such flagellates as *C. paramecium* are used primarily for production of the ammonia which is needed in biosynthesis. A typical heterotroph, on the other hand, has more restricted ability in biosynthesis and may specifically require certain amino acids which it cannot synthesize. Thus, the euglenoid flagellate, *Peranema trichophorum*, needs methionine and tryptophan.[230] The apparent requirements may be influenced by such things as differences in ability to take up particular amino acids from the medium. Glycine, for example, freely enters *Stentor coeruleus* but not *Amoeba proteus*, whose pellicle seems to be rather impermeable to this amino acid.[68] Uptake of glycine by the amoeba is increased ten-fold or more by adding a pinocytosis-inducer, such as plasma albumen, to the medium. The characteristic continuous feeding habit of *S. coeruleus* may have much the same effect.

There are good reasons for the usual assumption that a single amino acid is an inadequate nitrogen source for at least the majority of Protozoa outside the phytoflagellates. Presumably representative heterotrophs, such as *Tetrahymena pyriformis*[135, 262] and *Crithidia fasciculata*[98] require ten or more amino acids, while *Paramecium multimicronucleatum*[252] needs thirteen. *Leishmania tarentolae* needs an even longer list—at least 15 of the following: alanine, arginine, aspartate, glutamate, glycine, histidine, isoleucine, leucine, lysine, methionine, phenylalanine, proline, serine, threonine, tryptophan, tyrosine and valine.[475] Obviously, *Crithidia fasciculata* is less exacting than *L. tarentolae*, since it grows with only ten amino acids.[98, 265]

Although nitrogen sources more complex than synthetic mixtures of amino acids have been reported as requirements of *Colpidium campylum* and *Glaucoma* (*scintillans*) *chattoni*,[264] growth of the latter ciliate has been obtained in a mixture of twelve amino acids.[210] The amino acid requirements of *Hartmannella rhysodes* are intermediate in extent—arginine, isoleucine, leucine, lysine, methionine, threonine and valine.[32] However, an exception among typical heterotrophs has turned up in the observations of Newton[347] on *Crithidia* (*Strigomonas*) *oncopelti*, a trypanosomid flagellate for which methionine is the only essential amino acid in a defined minimal medium, and even methionine has been replaced by cystathionine, by homocysteine and formate, or by a mixture of cysteine, serine and threonine. This heterotrophic anomaly is perhaps attributable to the bacterial endosymbiote of *C. oncopelti*[167, 168] rather than to any extraordinary biosynthetic capabilities of the flagellate. Another peculiarity of *C. oncopelti* is the synthesis of lysine by a pathway involving $\alpha$, $\varepsilon$-diaminopimelic acid,[167] as in bacteria and green algae but not *Euglena*[486] and also in higher plants.[487]

Under natural conditions proteins form the major dietary sources of nitrogen for phagotrophic heterotrophs. Although extracellular digestion of proteins has been reported for certain Protozoa—e.g., *Leishmania tropica*,[411] *Euglena gracilis*[321]—which are not known to ingest solid food, there is no conclusive evidence that a natural protein can serve as the sole nitrogen source for such species or that the supposedly extracellular enzyme did not become so after disintegration of some of the organisms in cultures.

Phagotrophs ingesting other microorganisms presumably are equipped with the necessary protein-splitting enzymes. In *Tetrahymena pyriformis*, for example, gelatinase and caseinase activity have been known for many years.[131, 300] More recently, it has been found that this ciliate digests casein and fibrinogen readily but thrives on certain other proteins (e.g., egg albumin, soy bean proteins) only after they have been cooked or denatured in some other way.[484] The isolation and properties of a proteinase from *T. pyriformis* also have been described.[485] Proteinase activity and hydrolysis of hemoglobin were reported in malarial parasites[333] long before phagotrophy was described in these organisms.[400, 401] Mononucleate[201] and multinucleate amoebae likewise have been found to produce proteinases, as would be expected, but distinct quantitative differences have been observed in several species.[15] The proteinases of *Tetrahymena pyriformis* are active *in vitro* over the pH range, 2.2–9.6, with a maximum at about 6.0.[275, 276]

Similar enzymes of *Plasmodium gallinaceum* have a pH optimum of about 6.5.[333] Peptidases also have been reported in amoebae[201] and *Pelomyxa*,[15] as well as several species of ciliates. However, *Didinium nasutum*, according to Doyle and Patterson,[122] is unusual in that it probably takes over the dipeptidases of ingested *Paramecium multimicronucleatum* and uses the enzymes in digestion of its prey.

The starting point in synthesis of amino acids presumably is "activated" ammonia, which can be derived from ammonium salts, nitrates or suitable amino acids by particular species under laboratory conditions. For the flagellate, *Chilomonas paramecium*, certain amino acids and amides are as satisfactory as an ammonium salt,[71] although nitrate seems to be useless. For *Chlamydomonas reinhardi*, however, a nitrate is satisfactory in light,[410] and the same is true for various other green flagellates.[372] In fact, Provasoli has stressed the point that nitrate is sometimes preferable to an ammonium salt in cultures because uptake of the latter may lower the pH to an undesirable level in lightly buffered media. The relative usefulness of ammonium salts may vary with pH of the medium. McLaughlin[314] has found that below pH 7.0 ammonium salts are an excellent nitrogen source for chrysomonad flagellates; above pH 7.0, ammonium salts under laboratory conditions are more likely to be unfavorable for many marine and brackish water flagellates.[372]

The typical heterotroph which requires only certain amino acids as its dietary source obviously must synthesize its extra amino acids from one or more of those supplied in its medium. Biosynthetic ability may vary even among strains of a species, as in *Tetrahymena pyriformis*; in this ciliate, ability to synthesize serine is inherited as a recessive trait.[141] The general problem of substrates for biosynthesis has been considered in *Tetrahymena pyriformis* with a strain maintained in a defined medium containing eleven essential amino acids.[515] After incubation, both ciliates and culture fluid were analyzed for the eleven essential amino acids and seven non-essential ones. Five of the essential amino acids—arginine, methionine, serine, threonine and tryptophan, in descending order of utilization—were consumed extensively, presumably serving in part as nitrogen sources for synthesis of the non-essential amino acids recovered from the organisms and the culture fluid. By using dietary amino acids labeled with $C^{14}$, Newton[347] showed that exogenous glutamic or aspartic acid could be used by *Crithidia* (*Strigomonas*) *oncopelti* for synthesis of twelve amino acids; at the other extreme, arginine and leucine were assimilated mainly as such, with little or no interconversion. Acetate-$C^{14}$ also was traced into twelve amino acids. In *T. pyriformis*, oxidation of certain exogenous amino, acids—L-phenylalanine, L-tyrosine and, to a lesser degree, L-cysteine—has been reported.[397] Peptides containing phenylalanine and tyrosine produced greater stimulation of oxygen uptake than either of the component amino acids alone.[396]

Although few comparative data on amino acid content are available, species-specific differences in free amino acids have been noted for clones of

*Amoeba discoides, A. dubia* and *A. proteus*; in addition, two strains of *A. proteus* have shown consistent differences in alanine content.[195] A comparison of *Tetrahymena limacis* and strains of *T. pyriformis* also has shown some quantitative differences in amino acid content of extracts prepared from ciliates in axenic cultures.[298] Three other strains of *T. pyriformis* also have shown quantitative differences in amino acid content.[498] Mutant and wild type strains of *Chlamydomonas moewusii* were similar in their content of free amino acids, but differences in nucleotide-peptide components were noted.[346] Amino acid content also has been determined for isolated cilia of *T. pyriformis*[493] and flagella of *Chlamydomonas moewusii*,[255] as many as 16–18 amino acids being identified.

## PURINE AND PYRIMIDINE REQUIREMENTS

Protozoa differ among themselves in biosynthesis of nucleic acids. Some, such as typical phytoflagellates, can synthesize them from ordinary constituents of a simple medium. In fact, *Euglena gracilis* has been used as a manufacturing chemist in one laboratory to produce nucleic acids (particularly RNA) labeled in both base and pentose fractions.[391] *Ochromonas malhamensis*, although able to synthesize its needed purines from relatively simple precursors at temperatures below 35°,[232] can convert either dietary adenine or guanine into both nucleic acid bases and also can use 2,6-diaminopurine in the synthesis of both purines.[191]

Various Protozoa outside the phytoflagellate group need purines, or both purines and pyrimidines, as components of culture media. *Tetrahymena pyriformis* can convert dietary adenine into nucleic-acid adenine only[157] but can use dietary guanine for producing both NA-guanine and NA-adenine.[156] In other words, guanine is an absolute requirement of *T. pyriformis*.[262] The same is true for *Glaucoma chattoni*.[210, 262a] Guanylic acid is satisfactory for *Tetrahymena paravorax*[206] and for *T. corlissi*.[209] In contrast to *T. pyriformis*, a killer strain of *Paramecium aurelia* has synthesized NA-guanine and NA-adenine about equally well from exogenous adenine. However, after loss of kappa the ciliates used dietary adenine only half as efficiently for synthesis of NA-guanine as of adenine.[191] Another strain of *P. aurelia* can produce only NA-adenosine from dietary adenosine, although guanosine gives rise to both types of nucleic acid components.[456] *Paramecium multimicronucleatum* requires either guanosine or guanylic acid as a source of purines.[330] Under axenic conditions *in vitro* a derivative of adenine, methylthioadenosine, is about four times as effective a growth stimulant as adenosine for *Entamoeba histolytica*.[335]

Some heterotrophs are less exacting than others. *Crithidia fasciculata*, although apparently unable to synthesize the purine ring, can use the natural purines or their ribosides or nucleotides interchangeably.[7] Tests with radioactive precursors have indicated that *Trypanosoma cruzi* in cultures can synthesize adenine nucleotides slowly from glycine as one of the pre-

12a*

cursors and very rapidly from adenine, suggesting that the pathway from preformed purines is the preferential and natural one for *T. cruzi*.[152] Certain analogues, including 2,6-diaminopurine, also are satisfactory precursors in the case of *C. fasciculata*,[265] just as for *Ochromonas malhamensis*.[191] *C. oncopelti*, on the other hand, uses adenine specifically as a replacement for *p*-aminobenzoic acid.[357]

Synthesis of pyrimidines, for some Protozoa at least, seems to be less difficult than synthesis of purines. Such flagellates as *C. fasciculata*, which need an exogenous purine, can synthesize their pyrimidines from nonspecific dietary precursors, although from some more readily than from others. In *C. oncopelti*, $C^{14}$-glucose contributes carbon to all three pyrimidines as well as to adenine and guanine; acetic, aspartic and glutamic acids contribute carbon to the three pyrimidines only, glycine and serine only to the purines, while thymine seems to be useless as a precursor in biosynthesis of nucleic acids.[347] *Trypanosoma cruzi* can use orotic acid at a slow rate for synthesis of its pyrimidines, while uracil is an excellent precursor for all three NA-pyrimidines.[385] Representative ciliates require a pyrimidine. *Tetrahymena pyriformis*,[262] for example, can utilize either uracil (or uridine, or uridylic acid) or cytidine (or cytidylic acid). Although uptake of exogenous thymine occurs, a supplement of this pyrimidine alone is not adequate for growth, whereas labeled uracil used as the sole exogenous pyrimidine is converted into thymine, cytosine and uracil of nucleic acids.[198] Uracil also satisfies the pyrimidine requirements of *T. corlissi*,[209] *T. paravorax*[206] and *T. setifera*.[207] *Paramecium multimicronucleatum* needs either cytidylic or uridylic acid or one of the corresponding ribosides.[253] In apparent contrast to various ciliates, *Peranema trichophorum* grows best with both uracil and cytidylic acid as supplements.[466]

Little is known about the specific composition of nucleic acids in Protozoa. However, Jones and Thompson[254] have prepared and analyzed DNA from *Polytomella papillata* and *Tetrahymena pyriformis*. Although the usual basepairing relationships (adenine = thymine; guanine = cytosine) were determined, the ratio (adenine + thymine/guanine + cytosine) was 1.4 for *P. papillata* and 2.4 for the ciliate. Such data suggest that this ratio will be found to vary considerably in the group of Protozoa.

The effects of starvation on nucleic acid content have been traced in *Paramecium aurelia*. One generation on a starvation diet induced a significant decrease in macronuclear RNA but the DNA content showed no significant change.[269]

Exposure of nucleated and enucleate portions of *Amoeba proteus* to $C^{14}$-labeled uracil, orotic acid, adenine, or a mixture of all three has shown that synthesis of RNA depends upon presence of the nucleus.[365] These findings confirmed an earlier report[364] that uracil is taken up by enucleate amoebae but is not incorporated into RNA. Short exposures of *Euplotes eurystomus* to tritiated thymidine have made it possible to localize, in autoradiographs, the synthesis of DNA in the macronucleus and to trace its distribution during division of the macronucleus.[268]

## NITROGENOUS WASTES

Since the breakdown of amino acids in aerobic microorganisms usually leads to formation of ammonia as a major nitrogenous waste, this substance might be expected as an important excretory product in aerobic Protozoa. For example, in washed suspensions of *Paramecium caudatum* fed powdered fibrin, about 90 per cent of the waste nitrogen was eliminated as ammonia.[100] Early production of urea in axenic cultures has been reported for *Tetrahymena pyriformis*[336, 436, 439] but certain workers have concluded[109] that the activity of enzyme systems required for operation of the Krebs-Henseleit urea cycle is too low for functional significance of such a cycle in this ciliate. This urea cycle also seems to be inoperative in *Paramecium aurelia*.[456] Crystals stored in the cytoplasm of *Amoeba proteus* appear to be a tetragonal form of carbonyl diurea,[67] presumably an excretory product in this organism.

In addition to ammonia, various amino acids (glycine, glutamic acid, alanine, aspartic acid, tyrosine and cystine) are eliminated as waste products by *T. pyriformis*.[515] In the case of *P. aurelia*, ammonia (from deamination of amino acids), hypoxanthine (principal product of purines), dihydrouracil (possibly a product of pyrimidines), and traces of amino acids have been recognized as waste products, whereas negative results were obtained for urea, uric acid, allantoin, creatine and creatinine tests.[456]

Certain enzymes involved in catabolism of purines—adenase,[442] adenosine deaminase,[130] and guanase, uricase and xanthine oxidase[442]—have been reported in *Tetrahymena pyriformis*. Such enzymatic equipment could account for the appearance, in small amounts, of any such products as hypoxanthine, xanthine, uric acid, allantoin, urea and glyoxylic acid, as well as ammonia and carbon dioxide.

## MINERAL REQUIREMENTS

In addition to their other requirements, Protozoa obviously need minerals for growth. In at least certain cases, these requirements seem to be specific in the sense that substitutions are not possible. Investigation of such requirements can be tedious and sometimes frustrating, although now often facilitated to some degree by adding chelating agents to culture media.[188, 233, 378] In addition, the stress imposed by incubating cultures at relatively high temperatures tends to uncover metal requirements not so readily apparent at lower temperatures.[223] Investigations on heterotrophs can be particularly complicated because various components of the medium are often contaminated with trace metals and some of the components, certain amino acids in particular, are in themselves rather effective metal chelators. Such a medium might be considered a complex system in which various substances are competing with protozoan enzymes for particular metal ions. Even if the medium actually contains all the metals needed for growth, one of the essential metals might unite with some component of the medium to form a combination slightly more stable than its combination with its usual enzyme-substrate complex, leading to retarded growth of the organism. Addition of a specific metal ion to such an unfavorable medium may stimulate growth significantly and, within certain limits, the stimulation may be proportional to the amount of metal added. In such a case, it can still be difficult to decide whether the effect is a direct result of supplying a needed metal or an indirect effect in which the added metal merely displaces an essential one from its union with a component of the medium.

Failure of growth after omission of a particular metal also may be open to alternate explanations. The omitted metal may be essential to the organism under observation. Or the omitted metal, with a greater stability in complexes, may have been preventing combination of some truly essential metal with a component of the medium, thus leaving it available for the organisms in the culture medium.

In some cases uptake may depend upon concentration of a metal in the medium; in other cases, this is not the case. In *Acanthamoeba* sp. there seems to be an "active" intake of K against a concentration gradient, whereas the concentration of Na inside and outside the amoeba tends to be the same.[272] Regulation of Na and K in *Tetrahymena pyriformis* is upset by two hours of hypoxia and there is a partial loss of K.[16]

Chelating agents have been applied to the investigation of metal requirements. One approach has been that of removing some of the trace metal contaminants by treating components of the medium with chelating agents.[187, 188, 450] More extensive data have been obtained by adding chelators directly to the culture medium in order to maintain a sort of bound reserve supply. With appropriate concentrations of chelator and metals[378, 380] potentially toxic excesses of individual metals can be avoided while slow dissociation of complexes maintains in available form at least minimal amounts of metals essential to growth. This general procedure has been used with marked success in the development of culture media for some of the sensitive marine Protozoa and algae[378] and in the detection of specifically increased metal requirements when such organisms as *Euglena gracilis* and *Ochromonas malhamensis* are grown at unnaturally high temperatures.[225] Specific composition of the medium also may accentuate the requirement for a particular metal. For example, the presence of glucose augments the effect of magnesium on growth of *Tetrahymena pyriformis*.[450]

Aside from the influence on growth, morphological effects of minerals may be observed in some cases. For example, the exposure of *Stentor coeruleus* for brief periods to many different compounds in high concentrations induces shedding of the peristome, although the organelles of this region are later regenerated following return of the organism to a normal medium.[471]

It would be premature to attempt a complete list of minerals required by Protozoa as a group, but the available data for a variety of species suggest the following list of trace metals: calcium, cobalt, copper, iron, magnesium, manganese, molybdenum, phosphorus, potassium, silicon, sulfur, vanadium and zinc. It is not yet certain that all Protozoa need the entire list. Chlorophyll-bearing species may prove to have requirements slightly different from those of colorless types; differences among smaller groups also may occur in some cases. Species which build siliceous tests or skeletons obviously would need silicon in substantial amounts; other species might or might not need traces.

In addition to the apparent requirements of Protozoa, stimulatory effects on growth of one species or another, attributable to trace amounts of metals, have been reported for aluminium, barium, boron, iodine and sodium; for particular species, some members of this list may prove to be essential.

## Growth-factors

As components of chemically defined media, specific growth-factors (or vitamins) are required by a number of Protozoa but not by certain others. Since Protozoa probably do not differ very much among themselves with respect to the roles which vitamins play in their metabolism, it is generally assumed that such differences in requirements depend upon the extent to which particular species can synthesize the vitamins they need. Some of the green phytoflagellates, e.g., *Chlamydomonas moewusii*, among others,[373] can be grown in light in inorganic media without added vitamins and hence are ideal examples of photoautotrophs. For a few colorless phytomonads (e.g., *Polytoma obtusum*, *P. uvella*), the same type of medium is adequate for growth provided a source of energy, such as acetate, is added.[301, 306] These species are heterotrophic with respect to their source of energy but they can synthesize all their needed vitamins just as can the green autotrophs. On the other hand, a number of chlorophyll-bearing species, considered autotrophs in the days before axenic cultures, have turned out to require one or more vitamins and are thus auxotrophic rather than prototrophic.[372, 373, 377, 379, 380] Since these known auxotrophs are scattered among five different orders of phytoflagellates, the inability to synthesize particular vitamins apparently is common even among green flagellates. In fact, complete autotrophy may turn out to be the exception. Some of the older reports did not exclude all possible sources of contamination and thus might have missed such a requirement as that for vitamin $B_{12}$.[388]

### Thiamine

The thiamine requirement of Protozoa shows no clear correlation with the presence or absence of chlorophyll or with taxonomic relationships at the lower levels. For example, among the chlorophyll-bearing Cryptomonadida, *Cryptomonas ovata* and *Cyanophora paradoxa* need no thiamine for growth, while *Hemiselmis virescens* and *Rhodomonas lens* require the vitamin.[372, 373] A similar example is seen in Phytomonadida—thiamine or its thiazole moiety is needed by *Polytoma caudatum* and *P. ocellatum* but not by *P. obtusum* and *P. uvella*.[301] Comparable situations have turned up among the dinoflagellates.[373] At least a few of the chrysomonads cannot synthesize the vitamin. *Ochromonas malhamensis*, an excellent example, has been used in assays for thiamine in body fluids.[30]

Representative heterotrophs all require thiamine—e.g., *Crithidia fasciculata*,[265, 339] *C. oncopelti*,[347] *Leishmania tarentolae*,[475] among the flagellates; in the Sarcodina, *Acanthamoeba* sp.,[10] *Hartmannella rhysodes*,[31, 32] *Labyrinthula* spp.;[481] ciliates including *Glaucoma chattoni*,[210] *Paramecium aurelia*,[332] *P. multimicronucleatum*,[251] *Tetrahymena corlissi*,[209] *T. paravorax*,[206] *T. pyriformis*,[136, 262] *T. setifera*.[207]

The rigidity of the thiamine requirement has interested a few workers. As pointed out by Lwoff,[301] in reviewing work done in his laboratory, *Polytoma caudatum* and *P. ocellatum* can synthesize thiamine if supplied with its thiazole component, whereas *Polytomella caeca* and *Chilomonas paramecium* must have both thiazole and pyrimidine moieties. The peculiar "dinoflagellate," *Oxyrrhis marina*, resembles *Polytoma caudatum* in being able to substitute thiazole for its thiamine requirement.[124] In some cases, several different analogues are fairly good substitutes for the natural thiazole and pyrimidine in nutrition of several colorless phytoflagellates which can synthesize thiamine from these two precursors. One of the more recent examples is the observation that *C. paramecium* can synthesize thiamine from thiazole and 2-aminopyrimidine, as indicated by assays with thiamine-requiring *Lactobacillus fermentum*.[88] Such exacting heterotrophs as ciliates require the complete thiamine molecule.

The thiamine requirement of *Tetrahymena pyriformis* has had its ups and downs, however Thiamine was first reported as a requirement of this ciliate by Lwoff and Lwoff,[307] and the findings were subsequently confirmed with different strains of the species in other laboratories.[136, 262] There have also been reports that *T. pyriformis* can synthesize thiamine, at least under certain conditions. Such a conclusion was at one time supported by Kidder and Dewey,[258, 259, 260] and more recently by Seaman.[431] In the latter case, the conclusion was based upon standard methods of microbiological assay for thiamine; the obvious reservation is that some flaw in technique may have been overlooked. In the former instance, it would seem that too much faith was placed in the labels on bottles of commercial preparations.

## Riboflavin

Riboflavin, according to reported data, is required by fewer Protozoa than those needing thiamine. However, the list now incluces a phytoflagellate, *Peranema trichophorum*;[466] two Trypanosomidae: *Crithidia fascicu-*

*lata*[98, 265] and *Leishmania tarentolae*;[475] and certain ciliates: *Glaucoma chattoni*,[210] *Paramecium aurelia*,[332] *P. multimicronucleatum*,[251] *Tetrahymena corlissi*,[209] *T. paravorax*,[206] *T. pyriformis*,[136, 262] *T. setifera*.[207] The eventual establishment of such a requirement for many other heterotrophs is to be expected. Among the more obvious cases in which a riboflavin requirement may now be assumed are the trichomonad flagellates,[279, 447] media for certain species of which are now more or less completely defined.

Although the literature contains reports of biosynthesis by *T. pyriformis*,[261, 431] it is now generally believed that this species requires exogenous riboflavin for growth.

Contrary to the results observed in rats receiving little or no thiamine,[518] a diet very low in riboflavin has produced no significant change in susceptibility of these animals to *Trypanosoma cruzi*.[519]

## Pyridoxine

Pyridoxine or one of its derivatives (pyridoxamine or pyridoxal) is required by at least certain Protozoa. The best known case is that of *Tetrahymena pyriformis*,[136, 262] for which pyridoxamine is much more active than pyridoxine, while pyridoxal is intermediate in activity. The pyridoxine requirement of this species is inherited in Mendelian fashion as a dominant trait.[140] Other ciliates shown to require pyridoxine or one of its derivatives include *Glaucoma chattoni*,[210] *Tetrahymena corlissi*,[209] *T. paravorax*[206] and *T. setifera*.[207] Among the flagellates, *Crithidia fasciculata*[265, 339] requires pyridoxamine, while *Leishmania tarentolae* requires pyridoxal or pyridoxamine, the latter being replaceable by choline and pyridoxine.[475]

Imposition of a pyridoxine deficiency on rats has increased their susceptibility to experimental infection with *Trypanosoma cruzi*.[521]

## Pantothenate

Pantothenate is known to be a requirement for *Glaucoma chattoni*,[210] *Paramecium aurelia*,[332] *P. multimicronucleatum*,[251] *Tetrahymena corlissi*,[209] *T. paravorax*,[206] *T. pyriformis*[132, 136, 262] and *T. setifera*.[207] Although biosynthesis of pantothenate was at one time suspected in *T. pyriformis*,[261] the vitamin is now considered an absolute requirement for this species; in fact, *T. pyriformis* has been used for the assay of pantothenate in body fluids.[24]

Pantothenate also is required by certain flagellates—e.g., *Crithidia fasciculata*[339] and *Leishmania tarentolae*.[475] Although indirect evidence involving tests of inhibitory analogues and reversal by pantothenate, cited elsewhere,[186] suggests that malarial parasites and several species of *Trichomonas* also require pantothenate, the findings of Trager[474] indicate that *Plasmodium lophurae* needs coenzyme A rather than pantothenate alone.

Rats subjected to pantothenate deficiency develop experimental *Trypanosoma cruzi* infections more severe than those in controls on a normal diet.[520]

## Vitamin $B_{12}$

A requirement for vitamin $B_{12}$, first reported in *Euglena gracilis*, seems to be fairly common in phytoflagellates and is perhaps even more common than a thiamine requirement.[229, 230, 372, 373] Among the flagellates known to require this vitamin, there are not less than 10 species of Chrysomonadida, four Cryptomonadida, 14 Dinoflagellida, eight Euglenida and four Phytomonadida.[372, 124, 125] So far as published data go, nearly all Protozoa requiring $B_{12}$ are phytoflagellates, which share this requirement with such animals as man rather than with such protozoa as ciliates. However, *Acanthamoeba* sp. is an apparent exception in that it needs vitamin $B_{12}$ and thiamine, as do many phytoflagellates, but does not require various other vitamins essential for such phagotrophs as ciliates.[10] This amoeba is interesting also in that it builds an endocyst composed largely of cellulose.[346] *Hartmannella rhysodes* apparently differs from *Acanthamoeba* in requiring biotin as well as $B_{12}$ and thiamine.[32]

Uptake of vitamin $B_{12}$ by *E. gracilis* has been traced in relation to substrate concentration, pH of the medium, temperature and time of incubation by using $Co^{58}$-labeled material. At least 70 per cent of the intracellular cobalamin apparently was bound in the mitochondria and cell wall fractions of the flagellates after incubation with the labeled vitamin.[479] A $B_{12}$ deficiency in this species has resulted in a 12 per cent decrease in total nucleic acid content but no significant change in the DNA/RNA ratio.[454] In addition, the influence of $B_{12}$ (1.0–10,000 m$\mu$g/ml) on growth and size of *E. gracilis* has been traced by means of an automatic electronic device for sizing and counting. A very low $B_{12}$ concentration was correlated with gigantism and very slow fission. Higher concentrations increased rate of fission proportionately, and the average size was thus inversely proportional to concentration of the vitamin.[146]

The requirement of phytoflagellates for vitamin $B_{12}$ has been applied to assay techniques. *Euglena gracilis* was the first to be tested thoroughly,[234] and an improved medium for assays with this organism was described later.[224] This flagellate is sensitive to $B_{12}$ in concentrations as low as 0.05 m$\mu$g/100 ml, but it responds fairly well also to some of the "pseudo-vitamin $B_{12}$ compounds" which are not active for higher animals. Some of the marine phytoflagellates also respond to at least three analogues of cobalamin, and certain others are even less specific in their growth responses.[373] *Ochromonas malhamensis*, on the other hand, is much more specific, resembling higher animals such as man. As a result, this flagellate has been used extensively in bioassays.[28, 33, 158, 159] Up to a maximum, increasing concentration of $B_{12}$, which is correlated with increasing growth rate of *O. malhamensis*, is accompanied by increases in content of nicotinic acid, pantothenate and chlorophylls; on the other hand, stored carbohydrate shows little change, and both stored fat and free amino-N decrease with increasing growth rate.[160]

The $B_{12}$ requirement of another chrysomonad, *Prymnesium parvum*, cannot be met or spared by methionine, which can serve as the sole nitrogen source for this species. However, this amino acid does, in the presence of $B_{12}$, counteract the inhibition otherwise produced by certain analogues substituted at the benzimidazole part of the molecule. Interestingly, one of the tested analogues (FIII) can, in combination with methionine, replace cobalamin in supporting growth of *P. parvum*.[381]

The trypanosomid flagellate, *Crithidia fasciculata*, is not sensitive to cobalamin but does synthesize and show a growth response to "vitamin $B_{12}$ (Cr)," a less active factor which can replace cyanocobalamin for growth of *Ochromonas malhamensis*,[416] but with activity 1/100 as great. Another $B_{12}$-like compound, active for *Escherichia coli* and *Lactobacillus leichmannii* but not for *E. gracilis* or *O. malhamensis*, is synthesized by *Glaucoma chattoni* and by certain strains of *Tetrahymena corlissi* and *T. pyriformis*.[147]

The requirement for vitamin $B_{12}$ has been considered a likely factor influencing distribution and abundance of marine dinoflagellates and algae. Suboptimal concentrations of the vitamin, which is synthesized by a number of marine bacteria and some blue-green algae,[373] would be enough to support moderate (or "normal") populations of various flagellates and algae which require $B_{12}$. The minimal essential quantities are fantastically small, various species being sensitive to concentrations of $0.0001-0.005$ m$\mu$g/ml.[373] In fact, Droop[125] has pointed out that, on the basis of growth responses of *Monochrysis lutheri*, the limiting $B_{12}$ concentration for some planktonic microorganisms must be lower than any yet reported from sea water. Increases in concentration, such as those which may follow influx of fresh water from land drainage into bays or the extensive disintegration of seaweed, could be responsible to a significant degree for blooms of various organisms, as in the red tides occurring occasionally along the coasts of California, Peru, West Africa, and in the Gulf of Mexico and other areas. The probability that such factors as vitamins and trace metals are of prime importance in the development of blooms and red tides is strengthened by the finding that many different substrates (such as carbohydrates, alcohols, lipids, organic acids, amino acids) are of no apparent value to *Gymnodinium breve* as energy sources.[12]

### Biopterin (Crithidia factor)

Biopterin, first described as the *Crithidia* factor needed for growth of *C. fasciculata*,[340] proved to be an unconjugated pteridine, apparently 2-amino-4-hydroxy-6-dihydroxy-propylpteridine, although several related pteridines show more or less similar effects on growth. *C. fasciculata* requires both folic acid and such a 6-substituted pteridine.[55, 343]

In satisfactory media both *Ochromonas danica* and *O. malhamensis* synthesize *Crithidia* factor, and *C. fasciculata* apparently can do the same thing in a medium containing a substituted pyrimidine and a suitable sugar.[342] Biopterin stimulates the synthesis of vitamin $B_{12}$ by *Crithidia fasciculata* and also by *C. oncopelti* which does not require exogenous biopterin for growth. In the former species the available concentration of biopterin apparently determines whether or not the flagellates can synthesize vitamin $B_{12}$.[338]

A technique for assaying pteridines with *C. fasciculata* has been developed.[344] After the destruction of conjugated pteridines by acid hydrolysis, the method becomes specific for unconjugated pteridines with *Crithidia* factor activity. The method is sensitive to concentrations of 0.03 m$\mu$g/ml with biopterin as the standard.

## Folic Acid

The folic acid group includes several naturally occurring growth-factors (folic acid, its diglutamate and hexaglutamate, and folinic acid or the citrovorum factor). All members of the group contain *p*-aminobenzoic acid as a component of the pteroic acid moiety. A folic acid requirement has been reported for the trypanosomid flagellate, *Crithidia fasciculata*,[98, 265, 339] while the related *C. oncopelti* apparently needs only *p*-aminobenzoic acid.[347] Among the ciliates, folic acid is a known requirement of *Glaucoma chattoni*,[210] *Paramecium aurelia*,[332] *P. multimicronucleatum*,[251] *Tetrahymena corlissi*,[209] *T. paravorax*,[206] *T. pyriformis*[136, 262] and *T. setifera*.[207]

## Biotin

As a result of the difficulties in preparing biotin-free basal media, it has not been easy to establish a clear cut need for biotin in some of the heterotrophic Protozoa. In fact, biosynthesis of biotin by *T. pyriformis* was suggested at one time[261] as a result of such technical difficulties. However a need for biotin has since been demonstrated in *Ochromonas malhamensis*,[232] and it has been shown that this flagellate also can use bound biotin, represented by bacterial cells, added to a defined medium.[2] A new assay for biotin in body fluids and tissues involves *O. danica* as the assay organism.[23]

A biotin requirement has turned up also in *Oxyrrhis marina*[124] and in a few other more representative dinoflagellates.[372, 373] *Crithidia fasciculata* likewise has been shown to need biotin, earlier reports being confirmed with the use of the inhibitor, avidin.[265] The Sarcodina are represented by *Hartmannella rhysodes*,[32] a recent addition to the list of organisms requiring biotin. Among the ciliates, such a requirement has been reported recently for *Glaucoma chattoni*,[210] *Tetrahymena corlissi*,[209] *T. paravorax*[206] and *T. setifera*.[207]

## Nicotinic Acid

A requirement for nicotinic acid (or its amide) is known for several flagellates—*Crithidia fasciculata*,[265, 339] *C. oncopelti*,[347] *Leishmania tarentolae*[475]—and a few ciliates—*Glaucoma chattoni*,[210] *Paramecium aurelia*,[332] *P. multimicronucleatum*,[253] *Tetrahymena corlissi*,[209] *T. paravorax*,[206] *T. pyriformis*,[136, 262] *T. setifera*.[207]

Although it was believed at one time that *T. pyriformis* can grow without nicotinamide[261] and biosynthesis of the vitamin by this species has been reported more recently,[431] the present consensus is that *Tetrahymena* requires nicotinic acid or its amide. In fact, an assay technique for nicotinic acid in body fluids makes use of *T. pyriformis*.[26] The narrow specificity and high sensitivity of the method recommend it for clinical use.

## Thioctic Acid (α-lipoic acid, protogen)

Thioctic acid was first recognized in the concentrate stages as a requirement of *Tetrahymena pyriformis*[262]† and was later isolated as a purified substance ("protogen") free from other known growth-factors.[463] Later on, it became apparent that protogen is thioctic acid, or α-lipoic acid,[430] now known to be involved in the transfer of acyl groups to CoA in *T. pyriformis*.[432, 438] This growth-factor is now established as a requirement of *Glaucoma chattoni*,[210] *Tetrahymena corlissi*,[209] *T. paravorax*,[206] various strains of *T. pyriformis*,[262, 430] and *T. setifera*.[207]

## Lipid Requirements

Requirements for various lipids or their precursors have appeared in the investigation of various Protozoa.[227] Some species, and probably many, can synthesize all their metabolically important lipids; others cannot. The first group is represented by such flagellates as *Ochromonas danica* and *O. malhamensis*, which synthesize four "sulfolipids" and accumulate them bound to a large organic moiety which is not a carbohydrate.[183] *O. danica* also synthesizes arachidonic acid, a characteristic component of various lipids from animals.[182] Discovery of arachidonic acid and some of its precursors in *O. danica* should facilitate determination of the metabolic significance of this metabolite.

Certain other Protozoa have more restricted synthetic ability. *Trichomonas gallinae* and *T. gallinarum* are unable to synthesize certain saturated ($C_{14}$—$C_{18}$) and unsaturated ($C_{18}$—$C_{22}$) fatty acids.[447] Several trichomonads from poikilotherms—*Hypotrichomonas acosta*, *Monocercomonas colubrorum*, *Trichomonas batrachorum*, *Tritrichomonas augusta*—have analogous requirements which are satisfied by ascorbyl palmitate and TEM-4T, a

† Kidder and Dewey [262] have published an excellent summary of their earlier work on *T. pyriformis*; hence, reference has been made occasionally to this review rather than to the original papers.

semisynthetic fat.[279] In the presence of cholesterol, both linoleic and lino-lenic acids stimulate growth of *Trichomonas foetus*.[517] *Trypanosoma cruzi* requires stearic acid, which apparently can replace the serum require-ment.[41] The phagotrophic phytoflagellate, *Oxyrrhis marina*, needs a lipid obtained from lemon rind.[124]

Among the ciliates, a fatty acid such as oleic or stearic is needed by *Paramecium multimicronucleatum*.[331] In addition, growth of *Glaucoma chattoni* is stimulated by long-chain unsaturated acids,[210] while the sterol requirement of *Tetrahymena corlissi* is spared significantly by oleic acid.[209]

A sterol requirement has been attributed to a number of Protozoa.[308, 488] With trichomonad flagellates, the findings of Sanders,[417] Shorb and Lund,[447] Lee and Pierce,[278] and Lund and Shorb,[299] in partially to almost completely defined media, have paralleled earlier reports[64] for related species whose requirements may be satisfied by any one of several sterols (cholesterol, cholestanol, sitosterol, non-irradiated ergosterol, etc.). Cholesterol satisfies the sterol requirement of both *Trichomonas gallinae* and *Trichomonas* sp. For the former, cholesterol could not be replaced by 7-dehydrocholesterol, whereas *Trichomonas* sp. has utilized the substi-tute.[299] Although cholesterol, or else a closely similar substance, could be detected chromatographically in extracts of *Trichomonas foetus*, tests with acetate-1-$C^{14}$ have indicated synthesis of phospholipids but no ability to synthesize cholesterol.[184] The recovered cholesterol must have been derived from the culture medium. Cholesterol also has been recovered in significant quantities from *Trypanosoma cruzi*.[51]

Certain free-living Protozoa also need a sterol. The euglenoid flagellate, *Peranema trichophorum*, which needs cholesterol[466] is an example. Al-though *Euglena gracilis* shows no steroid requirement, ergosterol has been isolated from this species as well as from *Ochromonas danica*.[3, 462] Outside the flagellate group, a steroid (e.g., cholesterol, $\varDelta^4$-cholestenone, fucosterol, $\beta$-sitosterol) is required by several strains of the sarcodinid, *Labyrin-thula*.[482, 483] Although a biologically active sterol, $\varDelta^{22}$-stigmasten-3$\beta$-ol, forms about 0.3 per cent of the dry weight of the mycetozoan species, *Dictyostelium discoideum*,[196] this substance is produced from mevalonic acid during the "vegetative" phase of the cycle[248] and thus is not a dietary requirement.

Pathogenicity of a parasitic amoeba, *Entamoeba histolytica*, is enhanced by cholesterol, either added to a culture medium or fed to rats before or after intracaecal inoculation,[449] or given to experimentally inoculated guinea pigs showing hypercholesterolemia.[38]

Among the ciliates, a sterol requirement has been reported for *Parame-cium aurelia*[85, 86] and *P. multimicronucleatum*,[251] for both of which stigmasterol is one of the most active sterols tested. The genus *Tetrahymena* is represented by *T. corlissi*,[209] *T. paravorax*[206] and *T. setifera*.[207] Holz and his colleagues have uncovered an interesting situation in the sterol requirements of their ciliates. The requirements of all three species were satisfied by cholesterol. Zymosterol could replace cholesterol for *T. corlissi* and *T. paravorax* but *T. setifera* responded only to more immediate precursors such as demosterol or 7-dehydrocholesterol. Accordingly, it was suggested that *T. setifera* may have lost a biosynthetic mechanism common to the other ciliates.

In the case of *T. pyriformis*, which needs no exogenous sterol, stigmasterol has been found to antagonize certain growth inhibitors, producing partial reversal of inhibition by steroid hormones (cortisone, progesterone) and by colchicine,[84] and also to stimulate accumulation of phosphate, an effect which is produced also by cholesterol or by $\beta$-sitosterol.[83] Similarly, inhibition of growth by triparanol is prevented in several strains of *T. pyriformis* by certain sterols (cholesterol, $\beta$-sitosterol, $\Delta^7$-cholestenol and stigmasterol being the most effective) and also by oleic, palmitic or stearic acid; the last three were active only against low concentrations of inhibitor.[205]

## Alcohols

Although an alcoholic seems to be a rarity among Protozoa, *Tetrahymena setifera* is an apparent exception which must have ethyl or methyl alcohol, although at almost growth-factor levels.[207]

## Hematin

A requirement for hematin has been known for many years in various trypanosomid flagellates and was reported in detail in the investigations of Marguerite Lwoff, summarized in a brief review.[308] Although a similar requirement might be suspected for such blood parasites as *Plasmodium* and *Babesia*, adequate experimental data are lacking. Hematin presumably is involved in the synthesis of such equipment as cytochromes, catalase and peroxidase. In perhaps the majority of Protozoa, as represented by *Chilomonas paramecium*,[218] inorganic iron can be used for synthesis of these substances. It has been noted that, in the same type of medium, quantitative production of catalase varies from strain to strain of *Crithidia fasciculata* and among different species in this group of insect parasites.[500] In *Trypanosoma rhodesiense*, synthesis has been reported in culture flagellates but not in those taken from blood of a host.[164] Heme pigments, among which oxyhemoglobin is prominent, are synthesized by *Tetrahymena pyriformis*,[404] and protoporphyrin has been recovered from the medium in cultures incubated in darkness.[399] Peroxidase activity also is known in this ciliate.[275] However, neither heme nor protoporphyrin seems to be required by *T. pyriformis* or related ciliates.

## Protein Factors

Incompletely characterized protein factors have been reported as requirements of *Paramecium aurelia*,[470] *P. caudatum*[290] and *P. multimicro-*

*nucleatum*.[331] However, elimination of protein material from a medium for *P. caudatum* has been reported recently.[384a]

## Ecological Aspects of Nutrition and Metabolism

Protozoan nutrition obviously is related to protozoan ecology and, from the nutritional standpoint, there are many ecological niches. Habitats of free-living species range from relatively pure fresh and salt waters, which contain very little organic matter, to more or less extensively polluted waters containing appreciable quantities of organic material in various stages of decomposition. Certain species are normally terrestrial, some living in the films of moisture on particles in the soil, others thriving in or on decaying plant remains. A few hardy species live in moist sand along the seashore.[150] Endoparasites occur in various tissues and body fluids of their hosts. In such an assortment of local environments, the predominant types and the relative abundance of the major foods vary considerably. Both specific food requirements and methods of feeding are important factors influencing distribution of particular species. In relatively pure water, with insignificant organic contamination, saprozoic (osmotrophic) types find life rather difficult unless they are equipped with chlorophyll which takes the strain off the food supply as the basic source of energy. Environments of this general type are represented by the open oceans in which the organic content is quite low, a pound of beans representing a concentration equivalent to that of about 5 million gallons of water.[409] With their basal requirements often limited to an assortment of minerals, carbon dioxide and sometimes a vitamin or two, green osmotrophs can survive in waters low in organic materials. In such environments as oligotrophic lakes, the concentration of particular minerals, such as nitrates or phosphates, may even be a factor limiting density of populations.

Since chemoautotrophs are unknown among Protozoa, the absence of chlorophyll is correlated with the need for organic food as a source of energy. Hence, colorless osmotrophs would be expected to thrive only in environments supplying at least a minimum of useful organic material. Phagotrophs may be somewhat less rigidly restricted because they habitually ingest other organisms. So long as an environment can support green flagellates and algae, it should be satisfactory for at least a sparse population of herbivorous phagotrophs, although carnivores might find the hunting rather poor.

With an increase in the concentration of organic and inorganic materials, as in polluted waters, the possession of chorophyll no longer pays such a large premium. Colorless osmotrophs can thrive. Also, many of the green flagellates, which can use certain organic materials to advantage, multiply to densities never seen in less polluted waters. Herbivorous phagotrophs may find such environments very favorable and the life of a carnivore also becomes a relatively easy one. Freshwater lakes in sparsely settled areas rarely develop blooms but the pollution accompanying denser populations—e.g., fertilizers and animal wastes in drainage, with accumulation of organic materials and such minerals as phosphates and nitrates—often leads to blooms featuring, among the Protozoa, species of *Ceratium, Dinobryon, Gymnodinium* and *Synura* in particular.

Such blooms may cause a variety of harmful effects, including the smothering of susceptible aerobes or sometimes the death of higher animals when production of toxins is extensive.[367] Perhaps the most interesting of these toxins are the ones produced by certain marine dinoflagellates and the brackish water chrysomonad, *Prymnesium parvum*. The toxin of *Gonyaulax catenella* apparently is identical with the toxin found in California mussels (*Mytilus californiasus*) and is one of the most potent known toxins, the lethal intraperitoneal dose for a mouse being about 0.18 μg (or 9 μg/Kg body weight). Although the toxin decomposes in alkaline solution, it may undergo no appreciable loss of toxicity over a period of several months in an acid medium.[63] A more or less similar toxin from *Gymnodinium veneficum* has been related to death of fish during blooms, while the fluid from laboratory cultures produces toxic effects involving the nervous system of test animals.[9]

The toxin of *Prymnesium parvum*, "prymnesin", is a potent hemolysin. Partially purified preparations apparently represent a complex containing a lipid (perhaps a saponin) as well as proteins and polysaccharides.[522] Lethal effects on fish under laboratory conditions may be quite striking, with death after 3–30 minutes of exposure to the toxin.[314] Lethal activity for fish, the "ichthyotoxin" effect, requires a cofactor such as $CaCl_2$, $MgCl_2$, or streptomycin sulfate. Monovalent ions are less effective than divalent ones.[446, 522] Since tadpoles, but not frogs, are very susceptible, it is believed that the gill system is probably an important point of attack.[446] Toxin production in cultures is favored by relatively low salt concentrations (5 per cent seawater rather than higher concentrations) and by supplementary calcium.[384] Photoinactivation of *Prymnesium* ichthyotoxin has been reported for both visible light (400–510 mμ) and ultraviolet light (225 mμ), the effect being independent of the presence or absence of oxygen, the flagellates, or their pigment. It was concluded that the effect probably involves photochemical action on the toxin itself.[353] In addition, it has been found that constant illumination of cultures prevents production of ichthyotoxin by *P. parvum*.[383]

Less dramatic effects are produced by such metabolic products as carbohydrates and organic acids liberated by various other flagellates, including *Chlamydomonas* spp.[14, 193, 289] However, it has been suggested that such antibiotic effects as those evident between *Haematococcus* and *Chlamydomonas* involve the activity of unsaturated fatty acids eliminated into the medium.[370] Appreciable quantities of polysaccharides also may be produced. In at least one case the released polysaccharide believed to arise mostly from the superficial layer of the chlamydomonad theca, has amounted to about 100 mg/liter.[289] Certain marine dinoflagellates, such as *Katodinium dorsalisulcum*, also accumulate large amounts of polysaccharide in cultures. This carbohydrate of *K. dorsalisulcum* has shown antibiotic properties in tests with a number of marine bacteria.[319]

The soil as an environment is more or less comparable with waters polluted with organic matter, especially in the areas surrounding the roots of plants. The body of a host also falls into the same general category; endoparasites, in their natural hosts, obviously are living in environments which meet their nutritional needs.

Thorough understanding of protozoan relationships to their environments depends to a considerable extent upon accurate knowledge of the food requirements and biochemical activities of particular species, as well as the responses of Protozoa to physico-chemical factors in their environments. Much of this information must be obtained by bringing individual species into the laboratory, establishing them in pure cultures, and eventually growing them in chemically defined media.[123, 378, 379, 380] Detailed information on representative species would seem to be a logical foundation for analyzing the complex relationships within the flora and fauna of a lake or ocean. Laboratory investigations are supplying basic information on requirements for growth-factors[250, 372, 373, 377, 379] and for the various essential minerals and their relative concentrations in favorable media.[378, 379, 380] As pointed out above, laboratory investigations also have made possible the identification of organic materials eliminated into the medium. The importance of such varied information depends upon the basic position of the Protozoa and algae in the food chain which extends from inorganic and organic products of decay to the bodies of higher animals.

A special phase of protozoan ecology which also should gain from study of protozoan food requirements and biochemical activities is that of host-parasite relationships. There is still much to be learned about the activities of pathogenic and non-pathogenic Protozoa in their hosts, and the definitive answers to many obvious questions may depend to an important extent upon the study of parasitic species in chemically defined media.

Quantitative observations on the "zoochlorellae" content of coelenterate tissues under various conditions[523] and the isolation of axenic strains of presumably symbiotic dinoflagellates from their coelenterate hosts[315, 316] have pointed the way to more detailed investigation of the relationships between these "symbiotes" and their hosts, and also to carefully controlled morphological investigations of the flagellates (e.g.,[162]). Preliminary experiments with labeled carbon[171] indicate that, while there is some movement of products of photosynthesis from zooxanthellae to coral tissues, the rate is so slow that this contribution is probably unimportant in terms of gross nutrition of the host. Earlier findings, that the rate of calcium deposition is more rapid in corals equipped with zooxanthellae than in those without,[170] suggest that growth-factors may be the major contribution of these symbiotes. Protozoa also may benefit from symbiotes, as in the case of *Paramecium bursaria* in which the stimulatory effects of the symbiotic *Chlorella paramecii* are enhanced in light and in media containing very little particulate food.[257a]

In the case of parasitic Protozoa, findings can become interesting long before a defined medium for a particular species has been developed. Thus, Trager[476, 477] found that culture forms of *Trypanosoma vivax* became infective for vertebrate hosts after growth in *Glossina* tissue cultures with trehalose added to the medium, although incubation at 38°C for a day also seemed to be an essential factor. Observations of Weinman[494] on *T. rhodesiense* likewise have indicated that addition of trehalose to a medium for young culture strains restored their infectivity for vertebrates. On the other hand, Bowman, Von Brand and Tobie[47] failed to observe any increased infectivity after prolonged exposure of old strains of *T. gambiense* and *T. rhodesiense* to trehalose. Furthermore, neither species could utilize this sugar, which occurs in certain invertebrates but usually not in vertebrates.

Important progress toward defined media for parasites of the digestive tract is indicated by the relatively recent establishment of several trichomonad flagellates[115, 278, 279, 414, 417, 447] and species of *Entamoeba*[116, 117] in axenic cultures in steadily improving media. Replacement of serum has been possible in at least a few cases,[414, 417] and carbohydrates also have been replaced by a mixture of acetate, glycerol and glycerophosphate.[279] The development of methods for growing trichomonads on solid media[5, 17] has simplified procedures for establishment of clones[238, 413] and permits routine disc testing of chemotherapeutic drugs.[415]

## GROWTH OF PROTOZOA

### Growth of Individuals

As compared with available information on protozoan populations, relatively little was known about growth of individual Protozoa until rather recently. This is not surprising in view of the technical difficulties in tracing growth of isolated organisms under reasonably well controlled conditions. However, the introduction of methods for synchronizing fission of *Tetrahymena pyriformis*[420, 423] and more recently *T. vorax*[502] has made it possible to use mass cultures for investigating at least certain phases in the growth of individual Protozoa. Temperature cycling has arrested development of *T. pyriformis* at a specific point in the division cycle; essentially all of the treated ciliates have shown duplication of chromosomes, but also an archaic stomatogenous field of kinetosomes which persists for almost an hour after the last heat shock.[204, 208, 503] Morphological investigations also may be facilitated by these techniques for synchronization. For example, in synchronized populations of *T. pyriformis* macronuclear changes have been traced through two division cycles with electron and conventional microscopy.[145]

Growth of individual organisms has been traced carefully in a few laboratories, and the time required for nuclear and cytoplasmic division also has been determined for *T. pyriformis*.[58] By estimating dry weight with the scanning interference microscope and applying X-ray absorption techniques, growth of *Paramecium aurelia* has been traced under different conditions.[267] It was found that, with adequate food, increase in dry weight is exponential from fission to fission. In the same species, according to a later report,[514] the rates of synthesis of total protein and cytoplasmic RNA increase to a maximum just before fission. Growth of *Tetrahymena pyriformis* and growth of its macronucleus are linear between divisions, but the rates increase sharply during fission.[65] On the other hand, growth rate of *Amoeba proteus*, as measured with the Cartesian diver balance, decreased progressively from a maximum just after the last fission and then dropped to zero for about four hours preceding the next fission.[360] In this pre-fission period, the volume of the nucleus increased rapidly, while during fission itself there was no growth of the amoeba. The actual rate of growth was found to vary with the size of individual amoeba: an experimentally produced large specimen grew more slowly but showed a shorter generation time than average, while a smaller specimen grew more rapidly but needed a longer generation time.[361] In confirming earlier observations of Hartmann, Prescott[361] noted that periodic amputation of cytoplasm prevented fission and that the growth rate of such thwarted amoebae was slightly less than that of normal controls. Each operation caused a reversion of the organism to an earlier phase in its reproductive cycle.

An interesting daily periodicity in feeding activity has been noted in *Amoeba proteus*,[412] and this may be correlated with the individual growth curve as traced by Prescott.[361] During the first few hours of the cycle, amoebae fed *Tetrahymena pyriformis* ate voraciously; for the rest of the period they ate little or nothing. At the end of the 24-hour period, the amoebae became active again and began searching for food. Such cycles of activity in amoebae during a 24 – hour period may possibly be related also to observed sequential changes in form.[44]

Synthesis of DNA, as traced in the macronucleous of *Paramecium aurelia* with the scanning microspectrophotometer during logarithmic growth, starts about midway between fissions and is continued throughout the rest of the interdivisional period.[266] These findings agree fairly well with another report for *P. aurelia*.[514] In *P. caudatum* synthesis of DNA has doubled quickly toward the end of interphase, while in *T. pyriformis* DNA was found to increase almost linearly between fissions.[490] In an amicronucleate strain of *T. pyriformis*, on the other hand, the synthesis of DNA occurred mostly in the first half of the interdivisional period and apparently ended about 80 minutes before onset of the next fission.[312] By tracing the incorporation of $C^{14}$-methionine and tritium-thymidine in synchronized cultures of the same species, Prescott[366] also found that synthesis of DNA is limited to the first half of the interdivisional period. The synthesis of RNA, on the other hand, was low in the first half of the period and high in the second half. Other observations on synchronized *T. pyriformis* have indicated that the synthesis of DNA is almost linear during treatment for synchronization.[422] In *Trypanosoma mega* the synthesis of DNA occurs in approximately a seven-hour period preceding duplication of chromosomes.[461]

## Protozoan Populations

In many investigations on Protozoa, data are accumulated as measurements of population growth, either by counting organisms in samples of the cultures or, less directly, by measuring optical density of cultures or determining total nitrogen of the population. Such new tools as the "Coulter Counter" for recording both number and size of microorganisms may prove to be extremely useful in following growth of protozoan populations. In any case, such data make possible objective comparison of initial densities of population with those reached after incubation of cultures; measurements at suitable intervals may be used for tracing growth curves. With allowance for differences in tempo, curves which trace growth of protozoan populations in axenic cultures are similar in general features to those for bacteria and yeasts. Such populations are conventionally traced through several successive phases: lag phase (including an initial stationary phase, if any); a phase of logarithmic growth (exponential growth) during which the population increases at a maximal rate characteristic of the species and environmental conditions; a phase of negative growth acceleration as the population nears the maximum; a maximal stationary phase, in which the population remains at a maximum and essentially constant for a certain period; and phases of death, during which the density of population decreases, the negative slope and form of the curve varying with the species and environmental conditions.

A reasonable familiarity with growth of populations in a species under investigation is essential in tracing effects of various factors on growth. Terminal observations, at the beginning and the end of a selected incubation period, are satisfactory for some purposes but such observations can lead to inaccurate or erroneous interpretations. A population in an experimental medium might grow more rapidly or more slowly than the control and yet reach the same maximal density. Similarly, populations in different media could have almost identical densities after a short period of incubation and then show marked differences after longer incubation. Such dissimilarities and similarities might be overlooked in terminal observations after a specific period of incubation.

The overall feature of the lag phase is a gradual increase in rate of population growth as the logarithmic phase is approached. Theoretically, introduction of healthy organisms into a completely satisfactory fresh medium should not retard growth. This assumption seems to be in accord with many observations. However, a lag is sometimes observed and has stimulated a few investigations and speculations on the factors responsible. For example, the physiological condition of the organisms was one of the first factors to be considered important. Phelps,[354] for example, found that in populations of *Tetrahymena pyriformis* the occurrence of lag in a peptone medium was related to age of the inoculum. Inocula from logarithmic-phase cultures showed no lag at all and there seemed to be no relation between the number of ciliates inoculated and the occurrence or the length of lag. In analogous cases, *T. pyriformis* has shown a lag only when the inocula were taken from cultures more than 12 hours old.[214, 363] However, the situation may vary with the species and the type of culture medium. Corbett[90] noted that *Euglena gracilis*, transferred from a stock culture to fresh medium, showed an increase in volume attributed to uptake of food followed by an increased absorption of water. The degree of expansion varied with size of the inoculum, apparently suggesting that there may be an optimal range of initial population densities favoring the most rapid uptake of food in a given medium.

Although mere size of the inoculum may or may not influence the occurrence of a lag in particular media, the observations of Phelps and others clearly imply that members of older populations are less fitted for rapid reproduction than are organisms in relatively young populations. In the case of *T. pyriformis*, average size of the ciliates decreases in older cultures,[91] and a drop in reproductive potential might be attributable to a "microstarvation" involving such substances as vitamins present only in traces in the original medium. Organisms reaching a state of trace-factor starvation could need a little time for regenerating enzyme systems after transfer to a fresh medium. Such a situation apparently has been illustrated in *Euglena gracilis* grown in a defined medium with a low $B_{12}$ content ($0.001$ m$\mu$g/ml). Upon transfer to a $B_{12}$-supplemented medium, the length of lag was found to decrease from 27 to 13 hours with increasing concentration of $B_{12}$ ($0.02$–$20.0$ m$\mu$g/ml) and presumably was directly related to the time depleted flagellates needed for replenishing their supply of this vitamin.[89]

Transfer to a new type of medium also might require the synthesis of adaptive enzymes before the new diet could be used to full advantage. For example, *Polytoma uvella*, grown in an acetate medium, develops appropriate adaptive enzymes upon transfer to a butyrate medium[72, 73] and, in addition, undergoes a long-term adaptation covering several generations and leading to a shortened generation time.[74] An apparently comparable adaptation of *Tritrichomonas gallinae* to galactose also has been reported.[382] In addition, it is possible that in a medium containing a rapidly consumable substrate an old population might have exhausted the supply and the appropriate enzymes could have undergone significant regression. Upon transfer to fresh medium containing the particular substrate, the concentration of specific enzymes might have to reach par again before the rate of reproduction could approach that of the logarithmic phase. Even a deficiency in $CO_2$ has increased the length of lag in cultures of *Chilomonas paramecium*.[241] Another suggestion is that the length of lag depends largely upon the time required for nuclear growth to bring the "daughter cell volume" up to the usual prophase volume.[468]

That certain types of enzymatic activity may be characteristic of lag is indicated by the marked phosphatase activity in cultures of *Tetrahymena pyriformis*, with inorganic phosphate being liberated into the medium during this growth phase, whereas uptake of phosphate occurs during logarithmic growth.[144] In media containing complex foods which must be digested before assimilation, the resumption of rapid growth might depend upon at least a minimal amount of preliminary digestion. Another suggested possibility is that "senility" of populations involves accumulation in the organisms of inhibitory substances which must be eliminated before normal reproductive activities can be resumed in a fresh medium.[328]

Nutritionally poor (or minimal) media could involve another mechanism in production of a lag. Inoculation of the medium might be followed by an environmental selection: only the variants with a certain genetic equipment would have the ability to grow, while the remaining organisms would perish. The result would be a recognizable delay in growth of the population.

The logarithmic phase is characterized by a growth rate which is constant and maximal for the particular species in its specific environment. This rate may vary considerably with such environmental conditions as temperature, as in *T. pyriformis*, different strains of which show different thermal optima.[362] The average size also may tend to remain constant during exponential growth at a level characteristic of the species, as in *T. pyriformis*.[349] Scherbaum[419] has noted, in a different strain of *T. pyriformis*, that the average size decreased as maximal density was approached. In any species the average size probably may vary with a particular environmental factor. Thus, in *T. pyriformis*, the average volume decreased with increasing temperature of incubation within the limits, 10–30°C,[244] presumably reflecting an inverse relationship between average volume of the organisms and rate of fission. Although it has often been assumed that metabolic efficiency decreases as a culture grows older, Hull and Morrissey[214] have shown that the ability of *T. pyriformis* to metabolize such substrates as acetate and pyruvate is not affected appreciably by age of the culture within the limits of 12–196 hours of incubation. The utilization of glucose, however, is maximal during logarithmic growth, during which the ciliates consume about 80 per cent of the total sugar available.[271]

Length of the logarithmic phase probably depends primarily upon such factors as the concentration of essential growth-factors and minerals unless the particular medium approaches a starvation diet with respect to substrates.

Media may be so constructed that a single vitamin or a trace metal can be the critical limiting factor. In particular cases it has been possible to extend the logarithmic phase by addition of extra thiamine[92] or a single metal such as Mg.[187] Within certain limits of concentration, there is a more or less linear growth response to increments of the limiting factor in such cases. Growth-limiting media, prepared with a single known deficiency, have been applied especially to the assay of vitamins.

If the exponential growth phase is not ended by a dietary deficiency, changes produced by the organisms may slow down reproduction sooner or later. Such changes include shifts in pH or oxidation-reduction potential of the medium to unfavorable levels and, in some cases, possibly the accumulation of specific waste products which retard growth. Such adverse changes are illustrated, during growth of *Chilomonas paramecium* in an acetate and ammonium-N medium, by the sharp rise in pH which checks growth of the population soon after the medium becomes distinctly alkaline. However, if a little acid—either a substrate (acetic, lactic) or a metabolically useless acid such as hydrochloric—is added at intervals, the ultimate population may be 2–4 times as great as that in the usual medium.[220]

Sooner or later the rate of reproduction begins to drop as the population approaches maximal density. During this period, a decrease in oxygen uptake has been noted in cultures of *Chilomonas paramecium*,[219] *Tetrahymena pyriformis*[351] and *Trypanosoma cruzi*.[50] In *T. cruzi* the change in oxygen consumption was believed to be correlated with a shift from predominantly carbohydrate metabolism to the use of proteins.

The density of population at the maximum may be limited primarily by those factors which control length of the logarithmic phase—i.e., quantity of available substrate, the supply of vitamins or trace metals, or adverse changes in properties of the medium. Duration of the phase of maximal density presumably depends upon much the same factors as those controlling the density reached by the population.

The final portion of the growth curve traces the decline of the population as a culture grows old. In some cases, such as *Paramecium bursaria* in a peptone medium,[293] this phase of death has followed a smooth curve with a gradual negative slope. *Tetrahymena pyriformis*, on the other hand, in another type of peptone medium, has shown interruption of the decline by a second "stationary phase" lasting two or three weeks.[190] In a different peptone medium, however, this portion of the curve for *T. pyriformis* has been more nearly comparable to that for *P. bursaria*. After the population of such organisms as *T. pyriformis* drops to a low level there may be little additional change for periods of six months or more in suitable media. In the writer's experience with cultures of *T. pyriformis*, certain amicronnucleate and micronucleate strains have remained viable for well over a year in firmly closed screw-cap tubes. One of the more important factors influencing longevity of this ciliate seems to be the supply of thiamine. Sterilized filtrates of very old peptone cultures permit survival of freshly inoculated *T. pyriformis* for only a few days, even when supplied with several vitamins. However, when thiamine is included in the vitamin supplement, the filtrates support moderate growth and the ciliates may remain alive for at least nine months.[189]

## Physico-chemical Factors Influencing Growth

It is obvious that growth of protozoan populations is dependent upon suitable physico-chemical factors. Oxidation-reduction and pH of the medium, temperature of incubation, oxygen tension, carbon dioxide tension and intensity of illumination all may affect protozoan activities important in growth and survival of the species. Two of these factors, pH of the medium and temperature, have attracted more attention from investigators than have the others. Interactions of two (e.g., temperature, pH of the medium) or more (e.g., temperature, oxygen tension, carbon dioxide tension, pH of the medium) environmental factors are generally recognized as important but the experimental consideration of variations in combined effects is another matter. Often, data which have been accumulated by varying a single environmental factor actually reflect the composite effect of changing several interrelated factors. For example, changing the pH of the medium would affect oxidation-reduction potential, oxygen tension and carbon dioxide tension of the medium, and also might modify effects of a particular temperature on the Protozoa under investigation.

### pH OF THE MEDIUM

Growth of protozoan populations is influenced by pH of the medium, at least to the extent that growth of a given species in a particular medium is restricted to a certain pH range. In addition, there is good evidence that for at least a few species growth occurs more rapidly at one pH level than at another. For various species, cited elsewhere,[186] the range permitting growth falls within the range, pH 2.2–9.2, approximately. However, only a few species such as *Euglena gracilis* var. *bacillaris* and *Polytomella caeca* are known to grow throughout most of this potential range. Survival, for several days at least, may be possible at levels below or above the general range—e.g., *Euglena mutabilis* at pH 1.4,[101] *E. gracilis* at pH 11.0.[13]

A pH optimum has been reported for a number of species. Such reports have often been based mainly upon terminal observations of populations after certain periods of incubation and the recorded optima vary with the species and the type of medium. In some cases, growth has shown a bimodal relationship to initial pH of the medium, as in several strains of *Tetrahymena pyriformis* grown in certain peptone media[131, 132, 506] and also in *Chilomonas paramecium* in a peptone medium.[292] It is interesting that the rate of swimming in *Euglena gracilis* var. *bacillaris* shows an analogous bimodal relationship to pH of the medium, although only a single optimum was

13 RP

observed in *Chilomonas paramecium* under similar conditions.[282] In many other cases, a single "optimum" has been reported for growth of protozoan populations.

It is uncertain just what combination of factors is responsible for such a pH optimum, but the relations of pH to solubility and uptake of substrates may be assumed. The uptake of phosphate in *Tetrahymena pyriformis* apparently involves an active transport mechanism for the undissociated phosphate molecule, and there is experimental evidence for its relation to the pH of the suspending medium, the optimum being about pH 6.5.[82] Similarly, with certain substrates the higher rates of respiration of *Euglena gracilis* at pH levels below 7.0 have favored the view that the flagellates are more permeable to the free acids tested than to their corresponding ions.[103] Differential effects of varied pH on growth and respiration have been compared in *Euglena gracilis* var. *bacillaris*.[504] With succinate, pH 7.0 was optimal for growth but slightly inhibitory for respiration. With acetate as the substrate, pH 5.0 was inhibitory for growth but not for respiration, and a similar relationship was observed for malate at pH 3.5. The data suggested operation of a transport mechanism for the succinate ion, and indicated also that the rate of growth is somewhat more sensitive than the rate of respiration to changes in pH of the medium. In *Astasia longa*, analogous relationships between uptake of substrate and pH of the medium have been observed for intermediates of the TCA cycle.[216]

In addition to probable effects on uptake of substrates, any extracellular enzyme activity presumably would be influenced by pH of the medium. Pseudopodial activity in *Amoeba proteus*[359] and rate of food vacuole formation in *Paramecium*[281] also are influenced by pH of the medium. Hence, it seems likely that the so-called pH optimum for growth is the resultant of at least several effects of pH upon activities of the organism and properties of the medium.

In terms of population growth, the significance of such an optimum might be a little clearer if more of the reported data had been based upon growth curves rather than on terminal observations. Much published information fails to exclude the possibility that limited variation of the pH above or below the apparent optimum may merely retard growth without greatly modifying the maximal density of population. This point is illustrated in observations on *Astasia longa*[425] and *Tritrichomonas suis*.[352] In *A. longa* closely similar growth rates were observed for the first few days in media ranging from about pH 3.0 to 8.8. After this preliminary period, marked divergence occurred—at pH 3.0–3.1, little or no additional growth; at 3.5–3.7, essentially no growth for 3–4 weeks, and then moderately rapid growth to an almost normal level; at pH 6.1–6.4, continued rapid growth without interruption until maximal density was approached; at pH 8.8, steady growth toward a normal maximum but at a somewhat lower rate than at pH 6.1.

## TEMPERATURE

The temperature range within which growth is possible varies with the species of Protozoa and also with the individual strain in such species as *T. pyriformis*. For example, strain HS of *T. pyriformis* in peptone medium has shown an optimum of 32.5° and a lethal T. of 36.6–38.0°. For strain GL, the comparable temperatures are 29° and 34.6–35.4°.[362] Holz,[203] in testing 45 mating type strains of *T. pyriformis*, found that all mating types in varieties 1, 2, 3 and 5, and also mating type 3 of variety 4 grew well at 35°, even after previous incubation at 20–25°. Mating types 1 and 2 of variety 4 and all other mating types tested failed to grow at 35° when transferred from incubators set at 20–25°. Gradual adaptation apparently helped the ciliates, since mating types of variety 6 survived transfer stepwise but were killed by direct transfer from 20–25° to 41°. Several of the older strains (GF-J, PR, F, HS, Y, YE), mostly amicronucleate, could be grown at temperatures above 35°.

In addition to its relation to growth of populations, incubation temperature is known to influence such things as average size of *T. pyriformis*,[244] the rate at which DNA is lost during starvation of *Urostyla*,[356] the elimination or retention of cellular K and Na,[16] or in the case of heat shock to arrest temporarily both mitosis and differentiation of feeding organelles during fission of *T. pyriformis*,[208] and to induce bleaching in susceptible strains of *Euglena gracilis*.[29, 369, 388]

Ecological data for *T. pyriformis*[142] indicate that there is no necessarily strict correlation between natural habitat and tolerance of high temperatures. For example, mating type 5 of variety 2, discovered in a cold mountain stream, grew well at 35°, while mating type 2 of variety 9, from a warm habitat, failed to survive at 35°C. However, the occurrence of certain Protozoa, listed elsewhere,[186] in the waters of hot springs at temperatures up to 50–54° suggests that there are at least a few naturally thermophilic Protozoa.

Such differences in thermal ranges and optima suggest that factors under genetic control influence the limits of the biothermal range for particular strains. On the other hand, there are experimental data which indicate that the thermal limits for growth of a given species may, within genetic potentialities, depend to some extent upon such external factors as concentrations of dissolved oxygen and carbon dioxide in the medium, the pH and the nutrient components of the medium. In at least one case, there is clear evidence that composition of the culture medium influences the optimum for growth. *Euglena gracilis*, in a peptone medium, has shown an optimum at 10° for growth in darkness. Upon addition of acetate to the medium, the optimum was shifted to 23°, which is approximately the optimum for incubation in light in the unsupplemented peptone medium used.[240] This species also is known to be most tolerant of high temperatures in a peptone medium at about pH 5.0.[239]

13*

Although adaptation to temperatures somewhat beyond the usual limits has been observed, as reported for *Tetrahymena pyriformis*,[203] *E. gracilis*[29] and *Ochromonas malhamensis*,[225] relatively little is known about this phase of biothermal relationship in Protozoa. In the case of *O. malhamensis*, growth at temperatures above 35° necessitated increasing the amounts of thiamine, cyanocobalamin and several metals (Fe, Mg, Mn, Zn) and also adding to the medium several amino acids not required for growth at lower temperatures. Some of the increases in requirements were striking—e.g., in a shift from 34 to 38°, the $B_{12}$ requirement was increased about 3000 times. In another procedure which also illustrates the increased metabolic stress imposed by high environmental temperature, it has been shown that *Escherichia coli*, after inactivation at high temperatures (60, 72°), could be revitalized by treatment with such metabolites as lactate, citrate and malate in particular, although less marked effects were obtained with oxalacetate, succinate, $\alpha$-ketoglutarate and fumarate, while a mixture of 11 metabolites was much more effective than any single one.[197] The meager data for Protozoa indicate in general that growth at high temperatures is apt to be accompanied by a need for exogenous supplies of materials which an organism can synthesize in adequate amounts at lower temperatures. However, some of the apparent requirements for more amino acids may reflect in part a need for additional $CO_2$ at high temperatures, as demonstrated in *Lactobacillus arabinosus*.[42]

Resistance to low temperatures may be a little more common in Protozoa than resistance to high temperatures, as indicated by survival times reported for various species at temperatures below 0°C. Early observations on malarial parasites[80, 324, 325, 512] indicated that these organisms could survive low temperatures (e.g., $-65$ to $-78$°C. for avian malaria parasites) for periods of several months. These methods, with later improvements, were extended to human malaria,[245] to become part of the routine technique for preserving strains of clinical and experimental value. Similar methods have been used for freezing and storage of the enigmatic *Toxoplasma gondii*.[149] Aside from the obvious saving in laboratory assistance and experimental animals, low temperature storage is less likely than animal passage to modify strains of parasites. Both sporozoites[247] and trophozoites[245] of human malaria parasites survive such treatment. The addition of glycerol, at a relatively high concentration (16.6%), to citrated whole blood before freezing is distinctly beneficial for the avian (*Plasmodium gallinaceum*) and mammalian parasites (*P. berghei*) which have been tested thoroughly.[246]

Early tests with *Trypanosoma equiperdum* showed that this parasite can be preserved for months by freezing the flagellates in whole blood.[465] Trichomonad flagellates also survive freezing, or at least slow freezing, with glycerol (5–10%) added to the medium,[286] and the procedure has been applied to the preservation of stock strains.[313] Survival time is influenced by growth phase of the culture at the time of freezing[285] and also by the temperature of freezing.[284] Survival of *Tritrichomonas foetus* is better at − 95 than at − 28°C.; at the lower temperature the density of population may remain approximately constant for as long as 256 days.[284] In addition to these flagellates, *Entamoeba histolytica* can be preserved in glycerolized medium.[163]

## OSMOTIC RELATIONSHIPS

Little is known about the effect of osmotic relationships on growth of Protozoa although, as expected, changes in appropriate properties of the medium are known to modify population growth in certain species. Fission rate of *Astasia klebsii*, for example, has been modified by addition of certain solutes to a basal medium. The fission-rate depressions noted with various concentrations of the added solutes were similar with all five substances tested; fission was inhibited in media showing a freezing point depression of − 0.8°C. At this limit, however, the continuation of individual growth and nuclear division resulted in multinucleate giants incapable of undergoing fission even after return to the unmodified basal medium.[102] In a similar investigation on *Tetrahymena pyriformis*, growth of populations was retarded at first by moderate concentrations of sucrose (0.1–0.2 M) but the subsequent period of rapid fission was extended well past that in the basal medium, thus producing larger populations. Higher concentrations of sucrose (0.3–0.4 M) reduced both growth rate and maximal density.[57] An unusual Australian strain of *T. pyriformis*, which grows equally well in media prepared with fresh or salt water,[139] appears to be much less sensitive than the strain investigated by Browning.[57]

Several investigations on osmotic relationships have been concerned primarily with adaptability of particular species to progressive changes in osmotic pressure.[45, 155, 211, 294] In axenic cultures adaptability to increasing salinity has varied with the species (*Chlorogonium euchlorum⟩ Astasia longa⟩ Euglena gracilis*) and with the strain of *T. pyriformis* (strain H⟩ strain GP); the most adaptable of all, strain H, became adjusted to a salinity higher than that of seawater.[294] *Amoeba lacerata* also has undergone gradual adaptation from fresh water to seawater.[211] A marine amoeba, *Flabellula mira*, has undergone the reverse adaptation and its fresh-water phase shows a contractile vacuole while the marine phase does not.[45] However, available data support the assumption that the majority of Protozoa are more limited in their adaptability to unaccustomed osmotic pressures.

## REFERENCES †

1. AARONSON, S. (1960) Mode of action of 3-amino-1,2,4-triazole on photosynthetic microorganisms. *J. Protozool.* **7**, 289–294.
2. AARONSON, S., and BAKER, H. (1959) A comparative biochemical study of two species of *Ochromonas. J. Protozool.* **6**, 282–284.
3. AARONSON, S., and BAKER, H. (1961) Lipid and sterol content of some Protozoa. *J. Protozool.* **8**, 274–277.
4. AARONSON, S., and BENSKY, B. (1962) O-methylthreonine, a new bleaching agent for *Euglena gracilis. J. Gen. Microbiol.* **27**, 75–88.
5. AARONSON, S., and BENSKY, B. (1962) Study of the cellular action of drugs with Protozoa. I. Effect of 1-aminocyclohexane-1-carboxylic acid on the phytoflagellate *Ochromonas danica. Biochem. Pharmacol.* **11**, 983–986.
6. AARONSON, S., BENSKY, B., SHIFRINE, M., and BAKER, H. (1962) Effect of hypocholesteremic agents on Protozoa. *Proc. Soc. Exper. Biol. Med.* **109**, 130–132.
7. AARONSON, S., and NATHAN, H. (1954) Utilization of imidazole counterparts of purines in microbial systems. *Biochim. Biophys. Acta* **15**, 306–307.
8. AARONSON, S., and SCHER, S. (1960) Effect of aminotriazole and streptomycin on multiplication and pigment production of photosynthetic microorganisms. *J. Protozool.* **7**, 156–158.
9. ABBOTT, B. C., and BALLANTINE, D. (1957) The toxin from *Gymnodinium veneficum* Ballantine. *J. Mar. Biol. Assoc. U.K.* **36**, 169–189.
10. ADAM, K. M. G. (1959) The growth of *Acanthamoeba* sp. in a chemically defined medium. *J. Gen. Microbiol.* **21**, 519–529.
11. AGOSIN, M., and WEINBACH, E. C. (1956) Partial purification and characterization of the isocitric dehydrogenase from *Trypanosoma cruzi. Biochim. Biophys. Acta* **21**, 117–126.
12. ALDRICH, D. V. (1962) Photoautotrophy in *Gymnodinium breve* Davis. *Science* **137**, 988–990.
13. ALEXANDER, G. (1931) The significance of hydrogen ion concentration in the biology of *Euglena gracilis* Klebs. *Biol. Bull.* **61**, 165–184.
14. ALLEN, B. M. (1956) Excretion of organic compounds by *Chlamydomonas. Arch. Mikrobiol.* **24**, 163–168.
14a. ALLEN, J. R., HUTNER, S. H., GOLDSTONE, E., LEE, J. J., and SUSSMAN, M. (1963) Culture of the acrasian *Polysphondylium pallidum* ws-320 in defined media. *J. Protozool.* **10**, (Suppl.), 13.
15. ANDRESEN, N., and HOLTER, H. (1949) The genera of Amoebae. *Science* **110**, 114–115.
16. ANDRUS, W. DEW., and GIESE, A. C. (1963) Mechanisms of sodium and potassium regulation in *Tetrahymena pyriformis* strain W. *J. Cell. Comp. Physiol.* **61**, 17–30.
17. ASAMI, K., NODAKE, Y., and UENO, T. (1955) Cultivation of *Trichomonas vaginalis* on solid medium. *Exper. Parasitol.* **4**, 34–39.
18. BAERNSTEIN, H. D. (1953) The enzyme systems of the culture form of *Trypanosoma cruzi. Ann. N.Y. Acad. Sci.* **56**, 982–994.
19. BAERNSTEIN, H. D. (1955) Aldolase in *Trichomonas vaginalis. Exper. Parasitol.* **4**, 323–334.
20. BAERNSTEIN, H. D. (1959) Lactic dehydrogenase in *Trichomonas vaginalis. J. Parasitol.* **45**, 491–498.

† Several fairly recent reviews are concerned, at least in part, with protozoan nutrition: Protozoa in general[250]; flagellates[214a, 230, 392, 393]; amoebae[30a]; ciliates[214a, 458, 508]. In addition, volume 3 of Biochemistry and Physiology of Protozoa, which appeared after this manuscript was completed, contains chapters reviewing nutrition of ciliates and trichomonad and trypanosomid flagellates.

21. BAERNSTEIN, H. D., and REES, C. W. (1952) Aldolase in the culture form of *Trypanosoma cruzi. Exper. Parasitol.* 1, 215–228.
22. BAKER, H., FRANK, O., HUTNER, S. H., AARONSON, S., ZIFFER, H., and SOBOTKA, H. (1962) Lesions in folic acid metabolism induced by primidone. *Experientia* 18, 224–229.
23. BAKER, H., FRANK, O., MATOVITCH, V. B., PASHER, I., AARONSON, S., HUTNER, S. H., and SOBOTKA, H. (1962) A new assay for biotin in blood, serum, urine and tissues. *Anal. Biochem.* 3, 31–39.
24. BAKER, H., FRANK, O., PASHER, I., DINNERSTEIN, A., and SOBOTKA, H. (1960) An assay for pantothenic acid in biologic fluids. *Clinical Chem.* 6, 36–42.
25. BAKER, H., FRANK, O., PASHER, I., HUTNER, S. H., HERBERT, V., and SOBOTKA, H. (1959) Mono-substituted Vit. $B_{12}$ amides. I. A microbiological study. *Proc. Soc. Exper. Biol. Med.* 100, 825–827.
26. BAKER, H., FRANK, O., PASHER, I., HUTNER, S. H., and SOBOTKA, H. (1960) Nicotinic acid assay in blood and urine. *Clinical Chem.* 6, 572–577.
27. BAKER, H., FRANK, O., PASHER, I., HUTNER, S. H., and SOBOTKA, H. (1960) Mono-substituted Vit. $B_{12}$ amides. II. Further inhibition study. *Proc. Soc. Exper. Biol. Med.* 104, 33–35.
28. BAKER, H., FRANK, O., PASHER, I., and SOBOTKA, H. (1960) Vitamin $B_{12}$ in human blood and serum. I. Comparison of microbiological assays using normal subjects. *Clinical Chem.* 6, 578–581.
29. BAKER, H., HUTNER, S. H., and SOBOTKA, H. (1955) Nutritional factors in thermophily: a comparative study of bacilli and *Euglena. Ann. N.Y. Acad. Sci.* 62, 349–376.
30. BAKER, H., PASHER, I., FRANK, O., HUTNER, S. H., AARONSON, S., and SOBOTKA, H. (1959) Assay of thiamine in biologic fluids. *Clinical Chem.* 5, 13–17.
30a. BALAMUTH, W., and THOMPSON, P. E. (1955) Comparative studies on amoebae and amoebicides, in HUTNER, S. H., and LWOFF, A., *Biochemistry and Physiology of Protozoa*, Academic Press, New York, 277–345.
31. BAND, R. N. (1959) Nutritional and related biological studies on the free-living soil amoeba, *Hartmannella rhysodes. J. Gen. Microbiol.* 21, 80–95.
32. BAND, R. N. (1962) The amino acid requirements of the soil amoeba, *Hartmannella rhysodes. J. Protozool.* 9, 377–379.
33. BARBER, F. W., BAILE, D. L., TROESCHER, C. B., and HUHTANEN, C. N. (1953) Preliminary studies of the response of a chrysomonad to vitamin $B_{12}$ and related substances. *Ann. N.Y. Acad. Sci.* 56, 863–869.
34. BARKER, S. A., and BOURNE, E. J. (1955) Composition and synthesis of the starch of *Polytomella caeca*, in HUTNER, S. H., and LWOFF, A., *Biochemistry and Physiology of Protozoa*, Academic Press, New York, 45–56.
35. BARRY, S.-N. C. (1962) Utilization of glucose by *Astasia longa. J. Protozool.* 9, 395–400.
36. BEBBINGTON, A. E., BOURNE, E. J., and WILKINSON, I. A. (1952) The conversion of amylose into amylopectin by the Q enzyme of *Polytomella caeca. J. Chem. Soc., London* 1952, 246–253.
37. BELSKY, M. M., and SCHULTZ, J. (1962) Partial characterization of hexokinase from *Euglena gracilis* var. *bacillaris. J. Protozool.* 9, 195–200.
38. BIAGI, F. F., ROBDELO, E., SERVIN, H., and MARTUSCELLI, A. (1962) The effect of cholesterol on the pathogenicity of *Entamoeba histolytica. Amer. J. Trop. Med. Hyg.* 11, 333–340.
39. BIRDSEY, E. C., and LYNCH, V. H. (1962) Utilization of nitrogen compounds by unicellular algae. *Science* 137, 763–764.
40. BLUM, J. J., PODOLSKY, B., and HUTCHENS, J. P. (1951) Heat production in *Chilomonas. J. Cell. Comp. Physiol.* 37, 403–426.
41. BONÉ, G. J., and PARENT, G. (1963) Stearic acid, an essential growth-factor for *Trypanosoma cruzi. J. Gen. Microbiol.* 31, 261–266.

42. BOREK, E., and WAELSCH, H. (1951) The effect of temperature on the nutritional requirement of microorganisms. *J. Biol. Chem.* **190**, 191–196.
43. BOURNE, E. J., STACEY, M., and WILKENSON, I. A. (1950) The composition of the polysaccharide synthesized by *Polytomella caeca*. *J. Chem. Soc., London* 1950, 2694–2698.
44. BOVEE, E. C. (1949) Some observations on *Trichamoeba osseosaccus* Schaeffer. *Trans. Amer. Micr. Soc.* **70**, 47–56.
45. BOVEE, E. C. (1953) Presence of the contractile vacuole in *Flabellula mira* Schaeffer in fresh water. Proc. Soc. Protozool. **4**, 15.
46. BOVEE, E. C. (1960) Studies of feeding behavior of amoebas. I. Ingestion of thecate rhizopods and flagellates by verrucosid amoebas, particularly *Thecamoeba sphaeronucleolus*. *J. Protozool.* **7**, 55–60.
47. BOWMAN, I. B. R., BRAND, T. VON, and TOBIE, E. J. (1960) The cultivation and metabolism of trypanosomes in the presence of trehalose with observations on trehalose in blood serum. *Exper. Parasitol.* **10**, 274–283.
48. BRAND, T. VON (1951) Metabolism of Trypanosomidae and Bodonidae, in LWOFF, A., *The Biochemistry and Physiology of Protozoa*, Academic Press, New York, 177–234.
49. BRAND, T. VON (1960) The metabolism of trypanosomes with special reference to *Trypanosoma cruzi*. An. Congr. Intern. Doenca de Chagas, 24 pp.
50. BRAND, T. VON, JOHNSON, E. M., and REES, C. W. (1947) Observations on the respiration of *Trypanosoma cruzi* in cultures. *J. Gen. Physiol.* **30**, 163–175.
51. BRAND, T. VON, MCMAHON, O., TOBIE, E. J., THOMPSON, M. J., and MOSETTIG, E. (1959) Chemical composition of the culture form of *Trypanosoma cruzi*. *Exper. Parasitol.* **8**, 171–181.
52. BRAND, T. VON, and TOBIE, E. J. (1959) Observations on the culture forms of *Trypanosoma congolense*. *J. Parasitol.* **45**, 204–208.
53. BRANDT, P. W. (1958) A study of the mechanism of pinocytosis. *Exper. Cell Res.* **15**, 300–313.
54. BRANDT, P. W., and PAPPAS, G. D. (1960) An electron microscope study of pinocytosis in *Amoeba*. *J. Biophys. Biochem. Cytol.* **8**, 675–687.
55. BROQUIST, H. P., and ALBRECHT, A. M. (1955) Pteridines and nutrition of the protozoon *Crithidia fasciculata*. Proc. Soc. Exper. Biol. Med. **89**, 178–180.
56. BROWN, H. P., and JENKINS, M. M. (1962) A protozoon (*Dileptus*: Ciliata) predatory upon Metazoa. *Science* **136**, 710.
57. BROWNING, I. (1949) Relation between ion action and osmotic pressure on a ciliated protozoon. *J. Exper. Zool.* **110**, 441–460.
58. BROWNING, I., VARNEDOE, N. B., and SWINFORD, L. R. (1952) Time of nuclear, cytoplasmic and cortical division of the ciliated protozoon *Tetrahymena geleii*. *J. Cell. Comp. Physiol.* **39**, 371–381.
59. BUETOW, D. E., and LEVEDAHL, B. H. (1961) The activity of testosterone at the cell level. Testosterone stimulation of the respiration of *Euglena gracilis*. *Arch. Biochem. Biophys.* **94**, 358–363.
60. BUETOW, D. E., and PADILLA, G. M. (1963) Growth of *Astasia longa* on ethanol. I. Effects of ethanol on generation time, population density and biochemical profile. *J. Protozool.* **10**, 121–123.
61. BURBANCK, W. D. (1942) Physiology of the ciliate *Colpidium colpoda*. I. The effect of various bacteria as food on the division rate of *Colpidium colpoda*. *Physiol. Zool.* **15**, 342–362.
62. BURBANCK, W. D., and EISEN, J. D. (1960) The inadequacy of monobacterially fed *Paramecium aurelia* as food for *Didinium nasutum*. *J. Protozool.* **7**, 201–206.
63. BURKE, J. M., MARCHISOTTO, J., MCLAUGHLIN, J. J. A., and PROVASOLI, L. (1960) Analysis of the toxin produced by *Gonyaulax catenella* in axenic culture. *Ann. N.Y. Ac. Sci.* **90**, 837–842.

64. CAILLEAU, R. (1937) La nutrition des flagellés Tetramitidés. Les stérols, facteurs de croissance pour les trichomonades. *Ann. Inst. Pasteur* **59**, 137–293.
65. CAMERON, I. L., and PRESCOTT, D. M. (1961) Relations between cell growth and cell division. V. Cell and macronuclear volumes of *Tetrahymena pyriformis* HSM during the cell life cycle. *Exper. Cell Res.* **23**, 354–360.
66. CANELLA, M. F. (1957) Studi e recerche sui Tentaculiferi nel quadro della biologia generale. Ann. Univ. Ferrara, III, **1**, 259–716.
67. CARLSTRÖM, D., and MØLLER, M. (1961) Further observations on the native and recrystallized crystals of the amoeba *Amoeba proteus*. *Exper. Cell Res.* **24**, 393–404.
68. CHADWICK, A. (1961) The fate of radioactively labelled glycine introduced into *Amoeba proteus* and *Stentor coeruleus*. *Exper. Cell Res.* **25**, 131–148.
69. CHANG, S. L. (1958) Cultural, cytological and ecological observations on the amoeba stage of *Naegleria gruberi*. *J. Gen. Microbiol.* **18**, 565–578.
70. CHAPMAN-ADRESEN, C., and NILSSON, J. R. (1960) Electron micrographs of pinocytosis channels in *Amoeba proteus*. *Exper. Cell Res.* **19**, 631–633.
71. CIRILLO, V. P. (1951) The utilization of various organic nitrogen compounds for the growth of *Chilomonas paramecium*. *Proc. Amer. Soc. Protozool.* **2**, 19.
72. CIRILLO, V. P. (1955) Induction and inhibition of adaptive enzyme synthesis in a phytoflagellate. *Proc. Soc. Exper. Biol. Med.* **88**, 352–354.
73. CIRILLO, V. P. (1956) Induced enzyme synthesis in the phytoflagellate *Polytoma*. *J. Protozool.* **3**, 69–74.
74. CIRILLO, V. P. (1957) Long-term adaptation to fatty acids by the phytoflagellate, *Polytoma uvella*. *J. Protozool.* **4**, 60–62.
75. CIRILLO, V. P. (1961) Sugar transport in microorganisms. *Ann. Rev. Microbiol.* **15**, 197–218.
76. CIRILLO, V. P. (1962) Mechanism of arabinose transport in *Tetrahymena pyriformis*. *J. Bact.* **84**, 754–758.
77. CIRILLO, V. P., and DANFORTH, W. (1951) The chemical purity and the effects of autoclaving asparagine, glutamine, and ornithine and their influence on the growth of *Chilomonas paramecium*. *Proc. Amer. Soc. Protozool.* **2**, 19–20.
78. CLAFF, C. L., DEWEY, V. C., and KIDDER, G. W. (1941) Feeding mechanisms and nutrition in three species of *Bresslaua*. *Biol. Bull.* **81**, 221–234.
79. CLAUSEN, J. K. (1955) Observations on the carbohydrate metabolism of the flagellate *Strigomonas oncopelti*. *J. Gen. Microbiol.* **12**, 496–502.
80. COGGESHALL, L. T. (1939) Preservation of viable malaria parasites in the frozen state. *Proc. Soc. Exper. Biol. Med.* **42**, 499–501.
81. CONNER, R. L. (1959) Inhibition of growth of *Tetrahymena pyriformis* by certain steroids. *J. Gen. Microbiol.* **21**, 180–185
82. CONNER, R. L., GOLDBERG, R., and KORNACKER, M. S. (1961) The influence of hydrogen ion concentration and 2:4-dinitrophenol on orthophosphate accumulation in *Tetrahymena pyriformis*. *J. Gen. Microbiol.* **24**, 239–246.
83. CONNER, R. L., KORNACKER, M. S., and GOLDBERG, R. (1961) Influence of certain sterols and 2:4-dinitrophenol on phosphate accumulation and distribution in *Tetrahymena pyriformis*. *J. Gen. Microbiol.* **26**, 437–442.
84. CONNER, R. L., and NAKATANI, M. (1958) Stigmasterol antagonism of certain growth inhibitors for *Tetrahymena pyriformis*. *Arch. Biochem. Biophys.* **74**, 175–181.
85. CONNER, R. L., and WAGTENDONK, J. W. VAN (1955) Steroid requirements of *Paramecium aurelia*. *J. Gen. Microbiol.* **12**, 31–36.
86. CONNER, R. L., and WAGTENDONK, W. J. VAN, and MILLER, C. A. (1953) The isolation from lemon juice of a growth factor of steroid nature required for the growth of a strain of *Paramecium aurelia*. *J. Gen. Microbiol.* **9**, 434–439.

87. COOK, L., GRANT, P. T., and KERMACK, W. O. (1961) Proteolytic enzymes of the erythrocytic forms of rodent and simian species of malarial parasites. *Exper. Parasitol.* **11**, 372–379.

88. CORBETT, J. J. (1954) Formation of thiamine by *Chilomonas paramecium*. *J. Protozool.* **1**, (Suppl.), 12.

89. CORBETT, J. J. (1956) Occurrence of lag phase due to vitamin depletion of *Euglena gracilis*. *J. Protozool.* **3**, Suppl., 12.

90. CORBETT, J. J. (1957) Volume expansion of *Euglena gracilis* in fresh culture medium. *J. Protozool.* **4**, 71–74.

91. CORBETT, J. J. (1958) Factors influencing substrate utilization by *Tetrahymena pyriformis*. Exper. Cell Res. **15**, 512–521.

92. COSGROVE, W. B. (1950) Studies on the question of chemoautotrophy in *Chilomonas paramecium*. *Physiol. Zool.* **23**, 73–84.

93. COSGROVE, W. B. (1954) Acid production in cultures of *Crithidia fasciculata*. *J. Protozool.* **1**, Suppl., 1–2.

94. COSGROVE, W. B. (1959) Utilization of carbohydrates by the mosquito flagellate, *Crithidia fasciculata*. *Canad. J. Microbiol.* **5**, 573–578.

95. COSGROVE, W. B., and COLLINS, D. C. (1962) Sorbitol oxidation by *Crithidia fasciculata*. *J. Protozool.* **9**, Suppl., 9.

96. COSGROVE, W. B., and HANSON, W. L. (1962) Partial characterization of a polysaccharide from the trypanosomid flagellate, *Crithidia fasciculata*. *Amer. Zool.* **2**, 401.

97. COSGROVE, W. B., and SWANSON, B. K. (1952) Growth of *Chilomonas paramecium* in simple inorganic media. *Physiol. Zool.* **25**, 287–292.

98. COWPERTHWAITE, J., WEBER, M. M., PACKER, L., and HUTNER, S. H. (1953) Nutrition of *Herpetomonas* (*Strigonomas*) *culicidarum*. *Ann. N.Y. Acad. Sci.* **56**, 972–981.

99. CRAMER, M., and MYERS, J. (1952) Growth and photosynthetic characteristics of *Euglena gracilis*. *Arch. Mikrobiol.* **17**, 384–402.

100. CUNNINGHAM, B., and KIRK, P. L. (1941) The chemical metabolism of *Paramecium caudatum*. *J. Cell. Comp. Physiol.* **18**, 299–316.

101. DACH, H. VON (1943) The effect of pH on pure cultures of *Euglena mutabilis*. *Ohio J. Sci.* **43**, 47–48.

102. DACH, H. VON (1950) Effect of high osmotic pressures on growth and respiration of a fresh-water flagellate, *Astasia klebsii*. *J. Exper. Zool.* **115**, 1–16.

103. DANFORTH, W. (1953) Oxidative metabolism of *Euglena*. *Arch. Biochem. Biophys.* **46**, 164–173.

104. DANFORTH, W. (1961) Oxidative assimilation of acetate by *Euglena*. Carbon balance and effects of ethanol. *J. Protozool.* **8**, 152–158.

105. DANFORTH, W., and WILSON, B. W. (1957) Adaptive changes in the acetate metabolism of *Euglena*. *J. Protozool.* **4**, 52–55.

106. DANFORTH, W., and WILSON, B. W. (1961) The endogenous metabolism of *Euglena gracilis*. *J. Gen. Microbiol.* **24**, 95–105.

107. DANIEL, J. W., and RUSCH, H. P. (1961) The pure culture of *Physarum polycephalum* on a partially defined soluble medium. *J. Gen. Microbiol.* **25**, 47–59.

108. DETERRA, N., and RUSTAD, R. C. (1959) The dependence of pinocytosis on temperature and aerobic respiration. *Exper. Cell Res.* **17**, 191–195.

109. DEWEY, V. C., HEINRICH, M. R., and KIDDER, G. W. (1957) Evidence for the absence of the urea cycle in *Tetrahymena*. *J. Protozool.* **4**, 211–219.

110. DEWEY, V. C., HEINRICH, M. R., MARKEES, D. G., and KIDDER, G. W. (1960) Multiple inhibition by 6-methylpurine. *Biochem. Pharmacol.* **3**, 173–180.

111. DEWEY, V. C., and KIDDER, G. W. (1958) Amino acid antagonisms in *Tetrahymena*. *Arch. Biochem. Biophys.* **73**, 29–37.

112. DEWEY, V. C., and KIDDER, G. W. (1960) The influence of folic acid, threonine and glycine on serine synthesis in *Tetrahymena*. *J. Gen. Microbiol.* **22**, 72–78.

113. DEWEY, V. C., and KIDDER, G. W. (1960) Serine synthesis in *Tetrahymena* from non-amino acid sources; compounds derived from serine. *J. Gen. Microbiol.* **22**, 79–92.

114. DEWEY, V. C., KIDDER, G. W., and MARKEES, D. G. (1959) Purine antagonists and growth of *Tetrahymena. Proc. Soc. Exper. Biol. Med.* **102**, 306–308.

115. DIAMOND, L. (1957) The establishment of various trichomonads of animals and man in axenic cultures. *J. Parasitol.* **43**, 488–490.

116. DIAMOND, L. (1960) The axenic cultivation of two reptilian parasites, *Entamoeba terrapinae* Sanders and Cleveland, 1930, and *Entamoeba invadens* Rodhain, 1934. *J. Parasitol.* **46**, 484.

117. DIAMOND, L. (1961) Axenic cultivation of *Entamoeba histolytica. Science* **134**, 336–337.

118. DIAMOND, L. (1962) Axenic cultivation of *Trichomonas tenax*, the oral flagellate of man. I. Establishment of cultures. *J. Protozool.* **9**, 442–444.

119. DORAN, D. J. (1957) Studies on trichomonads. I. The metabolism of *Tritrichomonas foetus* and trichomonads from the nasal cavity and cecum of swine. *J. Protozool.* **4**, 182–190.

120. DORAN, D. J. (1958) Studies on trichomonads. II. The metabolism of a *Tritrichomonas batrachorum*-type flagellate from the cecum of swine. *J. Protozool.* **5**, 89–93.

121. DORAN, D. J. (1959) Studies on trichomonads. III. Inhibitors, acid production, and substrate utilization by 4 strains of *Tritrichomonas foetus. J. Protozool.* **6**, 177–182.

122. DOYLE, W. L., and PATTERSON, E. K. (1942) Origin of dipeptidase in a protozoon. *Science* **95**, 206.

123. DROOP, M. R. (1954) A note on the isolation of small marine algae and flagellates in pure cultures. *J. Mar. Biol. Assoc. U.K.* **33**, 511–514.

124. DROOP, M. R. (1959) Water-soluble factors in the nutrition of *Oxyrrhis marina. J. Mar. Biol. Assoc. U.K.* **38**, 605–620.

125. DROOP, M. R. (1961) Vitamin $B_{12}$ and marine ecology: the response of *Monochrysis lutheri. J. Mar. Biol. Assoc. U.K.* **41**, 69–76.

126. DUNN, M. S., and ROCKLAND, L. B. (1947) Biological value of proteins determined with *Tetrahymena geleii* H. *Proc. Soc. Exper. Biol. Med.* **64**, 377–379.

127. DUSI, H. (1932) L'assimilation des acides aminés par quelques Eugléniens. *C. R. Soc. Biol.* **107**, 1232–1234.

128. EBRINGER, L. (1962) Erythromycin-induced bleaching of *Euglena gracilis. J. Protozool.* **9**, 373–374.

129. EICHEL, H. J. (1954) Studies on the oxidation of succinic acid by cell-free homogenates of *Tetrahymena pyriformis* S and W. *J. Biol. Chem.* **206**, 159–169.

130. EICHEL, H. J. (1956) Purine-metabolising enzymes of *Tetrahymena pyriformis. J. Biol. Chem.* **220**, 209–220.

131. ELLIOTT, A. M. (1933) Isolation of *Colpidium striatum* Stokes in bacteria-free cultures and the relation of growth to pH of the medium. *Biol. Bull.* **65**, 45–56.

132. ELLIOTT, A. M. (1935) The influence of pantothenic acid on growth of Protozoa. *Biol. Bull.* **68**, 82–92.

133. ELLIOTT, A. M. (1935) Effects of certain organic acids and protein derivatives on the growth of *Colpidium. Arch. Protistenk.* **84**, 472–494.

134. ELLIOTT, A. M. (1935) Effects of carbohydrates on growth of *Colpidium. Arch. Protistenk.* **84**, 156–174.

135. ELLIOTT, A. M. (1949) The amino acid requirements of *Tetrahymena geleii* (E). *Physiol. Zool.* **22**, 337–345.

136. ELLIOTT, A. M. (1950) The growth factor requirements of *T. geleii* E. *Physiol. Zool.* **23**, 85–91.

137. ELLIOTT, A. M., BROWNELL, L. E., and GROSS, J. A. (1954) The use of *Tetrahymena* to evaluate the effects of gamma radiation on essential nutrilites. *J. Protozool.* **1**, 193–199.

138. ELLIOTT, A. M., and BYRD, J. R. (1959) Serotypes in eight varieties of *Tetrahymena pyriformis*. *J. Protozool.* **6**, Suppl., 19.
139. ELLIOTT, A. M., CAREY, S. E., and STUDIER, M. A. (1962) *Tetrahymena pyriformis* from several Pacific islands. *J. Protozool.* **9**, Suppl., 25.
140. ELLIOTT, A. M., and CLARK, G. M. (1958) Genetic studies of the pyridoxine mutant in variety two of *Tetrahymena pyriformis*. *J. Protozool.* **5**, 235–240.
141. ELLIOTT, A. M., and CLARK, G. M. (1958) Genetic studies of the serine mutant in variety two of *Tetrahymena pyriformis*. *J. Protozool.* **5**, 240–246.
142. ELLIOTT, A. M., and HAYES, R. E. (1955) *Tetrahymena* from Mexico, Panama, and Colombia, with special reference to sexuality. *J. Protozool.* **2**, 75–80.
143. ELLIOTT, A. M., and HOGG, J. F. (1952) Culture variations in *Tetrahymena*. *Physiol. Zool.* **25**, 318–323.
144. ELLIOTT, A. M., and HUNTER, R. L. (1951) Phosphatase activity in *Tetrahymena*. *Biol. Bull.* **100**, 165–172.
145. ELLIOTT, A. M., KENNEDY, J. R., JR., and BAK, I. J. (1962) Macronuclear events in synchronously dividing *Tetrahymena pyriformis*. *J. Cell Biol.* **12**, 515–531.
146. EPSTEIN, S. S., WEISS, J. B., CAUSELEY, D., and BUSH, P. (1962) Influence of vitamin $B_{12}$ on the size and growth of *Euglena gracilis*. *J. Protozool.* **9**, 336–339.
147. ERWIN, J. A., and HOLZ, G. G., JR. (1962) Production of a vitamin $B_{12}$ compound by tetrahymenids. *J. Protozool.* **9**, 211–214.
148. EVERSOLE, R. A. (1956) Biochemical mutants of *Chlamydomonas reinhardi*. *Amer. J. Bot.* **43**, 404–407.
149. EYLES, D. E., COLEMAN, N., and CAVANAUGH, D. J. (1956) Preservation of *Toxoplasma gondii* by freezing. *J. Parasitol.* **42**, 408–413.
150. FAURÉ-FREMIET, E. (1950) Écologie des ciliés psammophiles littoraux. *Bull. Biol. Fr. Belg.* **84**, 36–75.
151. FELLIG, J. (1960) Laminarase of *Euglena gracilis*. *Science* **131**, 832.
152. FERNANDES, J. F., and CASTELLANI, O. (1958) Nucleotide and polynucleotide synthesis in *Trypanosoma cruzi*. I. Precursors of purine compounds. *Exper. Parasitol.* **7**, 224–235.
153. FERNELL, W. R., and ROSEN, G. D. (1956) Microbiological evaluation of protein quality with *Tetrahymena pyriformis* W. I. Characteristics of growth of the organism and determination of relative nutritive values of intact proteins. *Brit. J. Nutrition* **10**, 143–156.
154. FILADORO, F., and ORSI, N. (1958) Cultivation of *Trichomonas vaginalis* on a solid medium and its application to the assay of trichomycin potency. *Antibiot. and Chemother.* **8**, 561–563.
155. FINLEY, H. E. (1930) Toleration of fresh water Protozoa to increased salinity. *Ecology* **11**, 337–347.
156. FLAVIN, M., and GRAFF, S. (1951) Utilization of guanine for nucleic acid biosynthesis by *Tetrahymena geleii*. *J. Biol. Chem.* **191**, 55–61.
157. FLAVIN, M., and GRAFF, S. (1951) The utilization of adenine for nucleic acid biosynthesis by *Tetrahymena geleii*. *J. Biol. Chem.* **192**, 485–488.
158. FORD, J. E. (1953) The microbiological assay of vitamin $B_{12}$. The specificity of the requirement of *Ochromonas malhamensis* for cyanocobalamin. *Brit. J. Nutrition* **7**, 299–306.
159. FORD, J. E. (1958) $B_{12}$ vitamins and growth of the flagellate *Ochromonas malhamensis*. *J. Gen. Microbiol.* **19**, 161–172.
160. FORD, J. E., and GOULDEN, J. D. S. (1959) The influence of vitamin $B_{122}$ on growth rate and cell composition of the flagellate *Ochromonas malhamensis*. *J. Gen. Microbiol.* **20**, 267–276.
161. FRANK, O., BAKER, H., ZIFFER, H., AARONSON, S., HUTNER, S. H., and LEVY, C. M. (1963) Metabolic deficiences in Protozoa induced by thalidomide. *Science* **139**, 110–111.

162. FREUDENTHAL, H. D. (1962) *Symbiodinium* gen. nov. and *Symbiodinium micro-adriaticum* sp. nov., a zooxanthella: taxonomy, life cycle and morphology. *J. Proto-zool.* **9**, 45–52.

163. FULTON, J. D., and SMITH, A. U. (1953) Preservation of *Entamoeba histolytica* at −79°C. in the presence of glycerol. *Ann. Trop. Med. Parasitol.* **47**, 240–246.

164. FULTON, J. D., and SPOONER, D. F. (1956) Inhibition of the respiration of *Trypano-soma rhodesiense* by thiols. *Biochem. J.* **63**, 475–481.

165. FULTON, J. D., and STEVENS, T. S. (1945) The glucose metabolism *in vitro* of *Try-panosoma rhodesiense*. *Biochem. J.* **39**, 317–320.

166. FUNK, H. B., and NATHAN, H. A. (1958) Inhibition of growth of microorganisms by benzimidazole. *Proc. Soc. Exper. Biol. Med.* **99**, 394–397.

167. GILL, J. W., and VOGEL, H. J. (1962) Lysine synthesis and phylogeny: biochemical evidence for a bacterial-type endosymbiote in the protozoon *Herpetomonas (Strigo-monas) oncopelti*. *Biochim. Biophys. Acta* **56**, 200–201.

168. GILL, J. N., and VOGEL, H. J. (1963) A bacterial endosymbiote in *Crithidia (Strigo-monas) oncopelti*: biochemical and morphological aspects. *J. Protozool.* **10**, 148–152.

169. GOBLE, F., and BOYD, J. L. (1959) Action of certain tetrapyrrole derivatives in experimental *Trypanosoma congolense* infections. *Proc. Soc. Exper. Biol. Med.* **100**, 745–750.

170. GOREAU, T., and GOREAU, N. I. (1959) The physiology of skeleton formation in corals. II. Calcium deposition by hermatypic corals under various conditions in the reef. *Biol. Bull.* **117**, 239–250.

171. GOREAU, T., and GOREAU, N. I. (1960) Distribution of labeled carbon in reef-building corals with and without zooxanthellae. *Science* **131**, 668–669.

172. GRANT, P. T., and FULTON, J. D. (1957) The catabolism of glucose by strains of *Trypanosoma rhodesiense*. *Biochem. J.* **66**, 242–250.

173. GRANT, P. T., and SARGENT, J. R. (1960) Properties of L-α-glycerophosphate oxidase and its role in the respiration of *Trypanosoma rhodesiense*. *Biochem. J.* **76**, 229–237.

174. GRANT, P. T., and SARGENT, J. R. (1961) L-α-glycerophosphate dehydrogenase, a component of an oxidase system in *Trypanosoma rhodesiense*. *Biochem. J.* **81**, 206–214.

175. GRANT, P. T., SARGENT, J. R., and RYLEY, J. F. (1961) Respiratory systems in the Trypanosomidae. *Biochem. J.* **81**, 200–206.

176. GREENBLATT, C. L., and SHARPLESS, N. E. (1949) Effects of some metabolic inhibitors on the pigments of *Euglena gracilis* in an acidic medium. *J. Protozool.* **6**, 241–248.

177. GROSS, D., and TARNER, H. (1955) Studies on ethionine. V. The incorporation of ethionine into the proteins of *Tetrahymena*. *J. Biol. Chem.* **217**, 169–182.

178. GROSS, J. A., and JAHN, T. L. (1962) Cellular responses to thermal and photo stress. I. *Euglena* and *Chlamydomonas*. *J. Protozool.* **9**, 340–346.

179. GROSS, J. A., JAHN, T. L., and BERNSTEIN, E. (1955) The effect of antihistamines on the pigments of green protista. *J. Protozool.* **2**, 71–75.

180. GUTTMAN, R., and BACK, A. (1958) Effects of kinetin on cell division in *Paramecium caudatum*. *Nature* **181**, 852.

181. GUTTMAN, R., and BACK, A. (1960) Effect of kinetin on *Paramecium caudatum* under varying culture conditions. *Science* **131**, 986–987.

182. HAINES, T. H., AARONSON, S., GELLERMAN, L., and SCHLENK, H. (1962) Occurrence of arachidonic and related acids in the protozoon *Ochromonas danica*. *Nature* **194**, 1282–1283.

183. HAINES, T. H., and BLOCK, R. J. (1962) Sulfur metabolism in algae. Synthesis of metabolically inert chloroform-soluble sulfate esters by two chrysomonads and *Chlorella pyrenoidosa*. *J. Protozool.* **9**, 33–38.

184. HALEVY, S. (1963) Lipid composition and metabolism of *Trichomonas foetus*. *Proc. Soc. Exper. Biol. Med.* **113**, 47–48.

185. HALL, R. P. (1937) Certain culture reactions of several species of Euglenidae. *Trans. Amer. Micro. Soc.* **56**, 285–287.
186. HALL, R. P. (1953) Protozoology, Prentice-Hall, New York.
187. HALL, R. P. (1954) Effects of certain metal ions on growth of *Tetrahymena pyriformis*. *J. Protozool.* **1**, 74–79.
188. HALL, R. P. (1954) Data on the metal requirements of *Tetrahymena pyriformis*. *Trans. N.Y. Acad. Sci.* **16**, 418–419.
189. HALL, R. P., and COSGROVE, W. B. (1947) An exogenous limiting factor in the longevity of bacteria-free ciliate populations. *Anat. Rec.* **99**, 130–131.
190. HALL, R. P., and SHOTTENFELD, A. (1941) Maximal density and phases of death in populations of *Glaucoma piriformis*. *Physiol. Zool.* **14**, 384–393.
191. HAMILTON, L. (1953) Utilization of purines for nucleic acid synthesis in chrysomonads and other organisms. *Ann. N.Y. Acad. Sci.* **56**, 961–968.
192. HAMILTON, L., HUTNER, S. H., and PROVASOLI, L. (1952) The use of Protozoa in analysis. *The Analyst* **77**, 618–628.
193. HARTMANN, R. T. (1960) Algae and metabolites of natural waters. In TRYON, C. A., JR. and HARTMANN, R. T., *The ecology of algae. Pymatuning Symposia in Ecology*, Univ. Pittsburgh. 38–55.
194. HARVEY, S. C. (1949) The carbohydrate metabolism of *Trypanosoma hippicum*. *J. Biol. Chem.* **179**, 435–453.
195. HAWKINS, S. E., and DANIELLI, J. F. (1961) Investigation of free amino acid differences in amoebae. *Exper. Cell Res.* **23**, 504–509.
196. HEFTMANN, E., WRIGHT, B. E., and LIDDELL, G. U. (1960) The isolation of $\Delta^{22}$-stigmasten-3$\beta$-ol from *Dictyostelium discoideum*. *Arch. Biochem. Biophys.* **91**, 266–270.
197. HEINMETZ, W., TAYLOR, W. W., and LEHMAN, J. J. (1954) The use of metabolites in the restoration of the viability of heat and chemically inactivated *Escherichia coli*. *J. Bact.* **67**, 5–12.
198. HEINRICH, M. R., DEWEY, V. C., and KIDDER, G. W. (1957) The origin of thymine and cytosine in *Tetrahymena*. *Biochim. Biophys. Acta* **25**, 199–200.
199. HOGG, J. F., and ELLIOTT, A. M. (1951) Comparative amino acid metabolism of *Tetrahymena geleii*. *J. Biol. Chem.* **192**, 131–139.
200. HOLTER, H. (1959) Problems of pinocytosis, with special reference to amoebae. *Ann. N.Y. Acad. Sci.* **78**, 524–537.
201. HOLTER, H., and DOYLE, W. H. (1938) Studies on enzymatic histochemistry. xxviii. Enzymatic studies on Protozoa. *J. Cell. Comp. Physiol.* **12**, 295–308.
202. HOLZ, G. G., JR. (1954) The oxidative metabolism of a cryptomonad flagellate, *Chilomonas paramecium*. *J. Protozool.* **1**, 114–120.
203. HOLZ, G. G., JR. (1957) Thermophily in ciliated Protozoa. *Anat. Rec.* **128**, 566–567.
204. HOLZ, G. G., JR. (1960) Structural and functional changes in a generation in *Tetrahymena*. *Biol. Bull.* **118**, 84–95.
205. HOLZ, G. G., JR., ERWIN, J., ROSENBAUM, N., and AARONSON, S. (1962) Triparanol inhibition of *Tetrahymena* and its prevention by lipids. *Arch. Biochem. Biophys.* **98**, 312–322.
206. HOLZ, G. G., JR., ERWIN, J., and WAGNER, B. (1961) The sterol requirements of *Tetrahymena paravorax* RP. *J. Protozool.* **8**, 297–300.
207. HOLZ, G. G., JR., ERWIN, J., WAGNER, B., and ROSENBAUM, N. (1962) The nutrition of *Tetrahymena setifera* HZ-1; sterol and alcohol requirements. *J. Protozool.* **9**, 359–363.
208. HOLZ, G. G., JR., SCHERBAUM, O. H., and WILLIAMS, N. (1957) The arrest of mitosis and stomatogenesis during temperature-induction of synchronous division in *Tetrahymena pyriformis*, mating type 1, variety 1. *Exper. Cell Res.* **13**, 618–621.
209. HOLZ, G. G., JR., WAGNER, B., ERWIN, J., BRITT, J. J., and BLOCH, K. (1961) Sterol requirements of a ciliate, *Tetrahymena corlissi* Th-X. *Comp. Biochem. Physiol.* **2**, 202–217.

210. HOLZ, G.G., JR., WAGNER, B., ERWIN, J., and KESSLER, D. (1961) The nutrition of *Glaucoma chattoni* A. *J. Protozool.* **8**, 192–199.

211. HOPKINS, D. L. (1946) The contractile vacuole and the adjustment to changing concentration in freshwater amoebae. *Biol. Bull.* **90**, 158–176.

212. HULL, R. W. (1961) Studies on suctorian protozoa: The mechanism of prey adherence. *J. Protozool.* **8**, 343–350.

213. HULL, R. W. (1961) Studies on suctorian protozoa: The mechanism of ingestion of prey cytoplasm. *J. Protozool.* **8**, 351–359.

214. HULL, R. W., and MORRISEY, J. E. (1960) Metabolic efficiency of *Tetrahymena pyriformis*, strain W, as related to culture age. *Trans. Amer. Micr. Soc.* **79**, 127–135.

214a. HUNGATE, R. E. (1955) Mutualistic intestinal Protozoa, in HUTNER, S. H. and LWOFF, *Biochemistry and Physiology of Protozoa*, Academic Press, New York, 159–199.

215. HUNTER, F. R. (1960) Aerobic metabolism of *Crithidia fasciculata. Exper. Parasitol.* **9**, 271–280.

216. HUNTER, F. R., and LEE, J. W. (1962) On the metabolism of *Astasia longa* (Jahn). *J. Protozool.* **9**, 74–78.

217. HURLBERT, R. E., and RITTENBERG, S. C. (1962) Glucose metabolism in *Euglena gracilis* var. *bacillaris*; growth and enzymatic studies. *J. Protozool.* **9**, 170–182.

218. HUTCHENS, J. O. (1940) The need of *Chilomonas paramecium* for iron. *J. Cell. Comp. Physiol.* **16**, 265–267.

219. HUTCHENS, J. O. (1941) The effect of age of the culture on the rate of oxygen consumption and the respiratory quotient of *Chilomonas paramecium. J. Cell. Comp. Physiol.* **17**, 321–332.

220. HUTCHENS, J. O. (1948) Growth of *Chilomonas paramecium* in mass cultures. *J. Cell. Comp. Physiol.* **32**, 105–116.

221. HUTCHENS, J. O., JANDORF, B. J., and HASTINGS, A. B. (1941) Synthesis of diphosphopyridine nucleotide by *Chilomonas paramecium. J. Biol. Chem.* **138**, 321–325.

222. HUTNER, S. H. (1961) The environment and growth: protozoan origins of metazoan responsivities. *Symp. Soc. Gen. Microbiol.* **XI**, 1–18.

223. HUTNER, S. H., AARONSON, S., NATHAN, H. A., SCHER, S., and CURY, A. (1958) Trace elements in microorganisms: the temperature factor approach, in LAMB, C. A., BENTLEY, O. G. and BEATTIE, J. M., *Trace Elements*, Academic Press, New York, 47–65.

224. HUTNER, S. H., BACH, M. K., and ROSS, G. I. M. (1956) A sugar-containing basal medium for vitamin $B_{12}$-assay with *Euglena*; application to body fluids. *J. Protozool.* **3**, 101–112.

225. HUTNER, S. H., BAKER, H., AARONSON, S., NATHAN, H. A., RODRIGUEZ, E., LOCKWOOD, S., SANDERS, M., and PETERSEN, R. A. (1957) Growing *Ochromonas malhamensis* above 35°C. *J. Protozool.* **4**, 259–269.

226. HUTNER, S. H., CURY, A., and BAKER, H. (1958) Microbiological assays. *Anal. Chem.* **30**, 849–886.

227. HUTNER, S. H., and HOLZ, G. G., JR. (1962) Lipid requirements of microorganisms. *Ann. Rev. Microbiol.* **16**, 189–204.

228. HUTNER, S. H., NATHAN, H. A., AARONSON, S., BAKER, H., and SCHER, S. (1958) General considerations in the use of microorganisms in screening anti-tumor agents. *Ann. N.Y. Acad. Sci.* **76**, 457–468.

229. HUTNER, S. H., and PROVASOLI, L. (1951) The phytoflagellates, in LWOFF, A., *Biochemistry and Physiology of Protozoa*, Academic Press, New York, 28–128.

230. HUTNER, S. H. (1955) Comparative biochemistry of flagellates, in HUTNER, S. H., and LWOFF, A., *Biochemistry and Physiology of Protozoa*, Academic Press, New York, 17–43.

231. HUTNER, S. H., PROVASOLI, L., and BAKER, H. (1961) Development of microbiological assays for biochemical, oceanographic and clinical use. *Microchem. J.* **1**, 95–113.

232. HUTNER, S. H., PROVASOLI, L., and FILFUS, J. (1953) Nutrition of some phagotrophic fresh-water chrysomonads. *Ann. N.Y. Acad. Sci.* **56**, 852–862.

233. HUTNER, S. H., PROVASOLI, L., SCHATZ, A., and HASKINS, C. P. (1950) Some approaches to the study of the role of metals in the metabolism of microorganisms. *Proc. Amer. Phil. Soc.* **94**, 152–170.

234. HUTNER, S. H., PROVASOLI, L., STOKSTAD, E. L. R., HOFFMAN, C. C., BELT, M., FRANKLIN, A. L., and JUKES, T. H. (1949) Assay of the anti-pernicious anemia factor with *Euglena. Proc. Soc. Exper. Biol. Med.* **70**, 118–120.

235. HUZISIGE, H., and SATOH, K. (1960) Biochemical studies on the photochemical nitrite reduction systems of green plants. I. Photochemical nitrite reduction by *Euglena* cells. *Biol. J. Okayama Univ.* **6**, 71–82.

236. ISENBERG, H. D., BERKMAN, J. I., and SUNDHEIM, L. H. (1962) The response of *Poteriochromonas stipitata* to urethan and related compounds. *J. Protozool.* **9**, 40–44.

237. ISENBERG, H. D., SEIFTER, E., BERKMAN, J. I., MUELLER, A., and HENSON, E. (1962) Suppression of urethan-induced growth inhibition of *Poteriochromonas spitata. J. Protozool.* **9**, 262–264.

238. IVEY, M. H. (1961) Growth characteristics of clones of *Trichomonas vaginalis* in solid medium. *J. Parasitol.* **47**, 539–544.

239. JAHN, T. L. (1933) Studies on the physiology of the euglenoid flagellates. IV. The thermal death time of *Euglena gracilis* Klebs. *Arch. Protistenk.* **79**, 249–262.

240. JAHN, T. L. (1935) Studies on the physiology of the euglenoid flagellates. VI. The effect of temperature and of acetate on *Euglena gracilis* cultures in the dark. *Arch. Protistenk.* **86**, 251–257.

241. JAHN, T. L. (1936) Effect of aeration and lack of $CO_2$ on growth of bacteria-free cultures of Protozoa. *Proc. Soc. Exper. Biol. Med.* **33**, 494–498.

242. JAHN, T. L., and DANFORTH, W. (1952) Inhibition of growth of a green flagellate by the antihistamine, $\beta$-dimethylaminoethyl benzhydryl ether (Benadryl). *Proc. Soc. Exper. Biol. Med.* **80**, 13–15.

243. JAMES, T. W. (1959) Synchronization of cell division in amoebae. *Ann. N.Y. Acad. Sci.* **78**, 501–514.

244. JAMES, T. W., and READ, C. P. (1957) The effect of incubation temperature on the cell size of *Tetrahymena pyriformis. Exper. Cell Res.* **13**, 510–513.

245. JEFFERY, G. M. (1957) Extended low temperature preservation of human malaria parasites. *J. Parasitol.* **43**, 488.

246. JEFFERY, G. M. (1962) Survival of trophozoites of *Plasmodium berghei* and *Plasmodium gallinaceum* in glyzerolized whole blood at low temperatures. *J. Parasitol.* **48**, 601–606.

247. JEFFERY, G. M., and RENDTDORFF, R. C. (1955) Preservation of viable malaria sporozoites by low temperature freezing. *Exper. Parasitol.* **4**, 445–454.

248. JOHNSON, D. F., WRIGHT, B. E., and HEFTMANN, E. (1962) Biogenesis of $\Delta^{22}$-stigmasten-3$\beta$-ol in *Dictyostelium discoideum. Arch. Biochem. Biophys.* **97**, 232–235.

249. JOHNSON, W. H. (1952) Further studies on the sterile culture of *Paramecium. Physiol. Zool.* **25**, 10–15.

250. JOHNSON, W. H. (1956) Nutrition of Protozoa. *Ann. Rev. Microbiol.* **10**, 193–212.

251. JOHNSON, W. H., and MILLER, C. A. (1956) A further analysis of the nutrition of *Paramecium. J. Protozool.* **3**, 221–226.

252. JOHNSON, W. H., and MILLER, C. A. (1957) The nitrogen requirements of *Paramecium multimicronucleatum. Physiol. Zool.* **30**, 106–113.

253. JOHNSON, W. H., and MILLER, C. A. (1957) A purine and pyrimidine requirement for *Paramecium multimicronucleatum. J. Protozool.* **4**, 200–204.

254. JONES, A. S., and THOMPSON, T. N. (1963) The deoxyribonucleic acids of some Protozoa and a mold. *J. Protozool.* **10**, 91–93.

255. JONES, R. F., and LEWIN, R. A. (1960) The chemical nature of the flagella of *Chlamydomonas moewusii. Exper. Cell Res.* **19**, 408–410.

256. JONES, R. F., and LEWIN, R. A. (1961) Nucleotides, amino acids and peptides in perchloric acid extracts of *Chlamydomonas moewusii. Exper. Cell Res.* **22**, 86–92.

257. JURAND, A. (1961) An electron microscope study of food vacuoles in *Paramecium aurelia. J. Protozool.* **8**, 125–130.

257a. KARAKSHIAN, S. J. (1963) Growth of *Paramecium bursaria* as influenced by the presence of algal symbiotes. *Physiol. Zool.* **36**, 52–68.

258. KIDDER, G. W., and DEWEY, V. C. (1942) The biosynthesis of thiamine by normally athiaminogenic microorganism. *Growth* **6**, 405–418.

259. KIDDER, G. W., and DEWEY, V. C. (1944) Thiamine and *Tetrahymena. Biol. Bull.* **87**, 121–133.

260. KIDDER, G. W., and DEWEY, V. C. (1945) Studies on the biochemistry of *Tetrahymena.* IV. Amino acids and their relation to the biosynthesis of thiamine. *Biol. Bull.* **89**, 131–143.

261. KIDDER, G. W., and DEWEY, V. C. (1945) Studies on the biochemistry of *Tetrahymena.* VII. Riboflavin, pantothen, biotin, niacin and pyridoxine in the growth of *T. geleii* W. *Biol. Bull.* **89**, 229–241.

262. KIDDER, G. W., and DEWEY, V. C. (1951) The biochemistry of ciliates. In LWOFF, A., *Biochemistry and Physiology of Protozoa*, Academic Press, New York, 323–400.

262a. KIDDER, G. W., and DEWEY, V. C. (1955) The purine and pyrimidine requirements of *Glaucoma scintillans. Arch. Biochem. Biophys.* **55**, 126–129.

263. KIDDER, G. W., and DEWEY, V. C. (1957) Deazapurines as growth inhibitors. *Arch. Biochem. Biophys.* **66**, 486–492.

264. KIDDER, G. W., DEWEY, V. C., and FULLER, R. C. (1954) Nitrogen requirements of *Glaucoma scintillans* and *Colpidium campylum. Proc. Soc. Exper. Biol. Med.* **86**, 685–689.

265. KIDDER, G. W., and DUTTA, B. N. (1958) The growth and nutrition of *Crithidia fasciculata. J. Gen. Microbiol.* **18**, 621–638.

266. KIMBALL, R. F., and BARKA, T. (1959) Quantitative cytochemical studies on *Paramecium aurelia.* II. Feulgen microspectrophotometry of the macronucleus during exponential growth. *Exper. Cell Res.* **17**, 173–182.

267. KIMBALL, R. F., CASPERSSON, T. O., SVENSSON, G., and CARLSON, L. (1959) Quantitative cytochemical studies on *Paramecium aurelia.* I. Growth in total dry weight measured by the scanning interference microscope and X-ray diffraction methods. *Exper. Cell Res.* **17**, 160–172.

268. KIMBALL, R. F., and PRESCOTT, D. M. (1962) Deoxyribonucleic acid synthesis and distribution during growth and amitosis of the macronucleus of *Euplotes. J. Protozool.* **9**, 88–92.

269. KIMBALL, R. F., and VOGT-KÖHNE, L. (1961) Quantitative cytochemical studies on *Paramecium aurelia.* IV. The effect of limited food and starvation on the macronucleus. *Exper. Cell Res.* **23**, 479–487.

270. KITCHING, J. A. (1960) Responses of the heliozoon *Actinophrys sol* to prey, to mechanical stimulation, and to solutions of proteins and certain other chemical substances. *J. Exper. Biol.* **37**, 407–416.

271. KLAMER, B., and FENNELL, R. A. (1963) Acid phosphatase activity during growth and synchronous division of *Tetrahymena pyriformis* W. *Exper. Cell Res.* **29**, 166–175.

272. KLEIN, R. L. (1961) Homeostatic mechanisms for cation regulation in *Acanthamoeba* sp. *Exper. Cell Res.* **25**, 571–584.

273. KUNITAKE, G., STILL, C., and SALTMAN, P. (1962) Terminal respiration in *Trichomonas vaginalis. J. Protozool.* **9**, 371–373.

274. KUPFERBERG, A. B., and JOHNSON, G. (1941) Physiology of bacteria-free culture of *Trichomonas vaginalis.* VI. Effect of female sex hormones on population. *Proc. Soc. Exper. Biol. Med.* **48**, 516–518.

275. LAWRIE, N. R. (1935) Studies in the metabolism of Protozoa. II. Some biochemical reactions occuring in the presence of washed cells of *Glaucoma piriformis. Biochem. J.* **29**, 2297–2302.

276. LAWRIE, N. R. (1937) Studies in the metabolism of Protozoa. III. Some properties of a proteolytic extract obtained from *Glaucoma piriformis*. *Biochem. J.* **31**, 789–798.

277. LAZO, W. R. (1961) Obtaining the slime mold *Fuligo septica* in pure culture. *J. Protozool.* **8**, 97.

278. LEE, J. J., and PIERCE, S. (1960) *Hypotrichomonas acosta* from reptiles. II. Physiology. *J. Protozool.* **7**, 402–409.

279. LEE, J. J., PIERCE, S., HUTNER, S. H., SMITH, B. J., and GURSKI, D. (1962) Trichomonads from poikilotherms: nutritional and physiological notes. *J. Protozool.* **9**, 445–450.

280. LEE, J. J., PIERCE, S., TENTCHOFF, M., and McLAUGHLIN, J. J. A. (1961) Growth and physiology of foraminifera in the laboratory: Part 1—Collection and maintenance. *Micropaleontol.* **7**, 461–466.

281. LEE, J. W. (1942) The effect of pH on food-vacuole formation in *Paramecium*. *Physiol. Zool.* **15**, 459–465.

282. LEE, J. W. (1954) The effect of pH on forward swimming in *Euglena* and *Chilomonas*. *Physiol. Zool.* **27**, 272–275.

283. LEHMANN, D. E., and SORSOLI, W. A. (1962) The cultural forms of *Trypanosoma ranarum* (Lankester, 1871). I. Relation between cyclic development of culture forms, oxygen consumption in the presence of glucose, and malonate inhibition. *J. Protozool.* **9**. 58–60.

284. LEVINE, N. D., ANDERSON, F. L., LOSCH, M. B., NOTZOLD, R. A., and MEHRA, K. N. (1962) Survival of *Tritrichomonas foetus* stored at −28 and −95°C. after freezing in the presence of glycerol. *J. Protozool.* **9**, 347–350.

285. LEVINE, N. D., McCAUL, W. E., and MIZELL, M. (1959) The relation of the stage of the population growth curve to the survival of *Tritrichomonas foetus* upon freezing in the presence of glycerol. *J. Protozool.* **6**, 116–120.

286. LEVINE, N. D., and MARQUARDT, W. C. (1955) The effect of glycerol and related compounds on survival of *Tritrichomonas foetus*. *J. Protozool.* **2**, 100–107.

287. LEWIN, R. A. (1952) Ultraviolet-induced mutuations in *Chlamydomonas moewusii* Gerloff. *J. Gen. Microbiol.* **6**, 233–248.

288. LEWIN, R. A. (1954) The utilization of acetate by wild-type and mutant *Chlamydomonas dysmosos*. *J. Gen. Microbiol.* **11**, 459–471.

289. LEWIN, R. A. (1956) Extracellular polysaccharides of green algae. *Canad. J. Microbiol.* **2**, 665–672.

290. LILLY, D. M., and KLOSEK, R. C. (1961) A protein factor in the nutrition of *Paramedium caudatum*. *J. Gen. Microbiol.* **24**, 327–334.

291. LINDBLOM, G. P. (1961) Carbohydrate metabolism of trichomonads: growth, respiration and enzymatic activity in four species. *J. Protozool.* **8**, 139–150.

292. LOEFER, J. B. (1935) Relation of hydrogen-ion concentration to growth of *Chilomonas* and *Chlorogonium*. *Arch. Protistenk.* **85**, 209–223.

293. LOEFER, J. B. (1936) Bacteria-free culture of *Paramecium bursaria* and concentration of the medium as a factor in growth. *J. Exper. Zool.* **72**, 387–407.

294. LOEFER, J. B. (1939) Acclimatization of freshwater ciliates and flagellates to media of higher osmotic pressure. *Physiol. Zool.* **12**, 161–172.

295. LOEFER, J. B., and McDANIEL, M. R. (1950) Acid formation by different strains of *Tetrahymena*. *Proc. Amer. Soc. Protozool.* **1**, 7.

296. LOEFER, J. B., and OWEN, R. D. (1961) Characterization and distribution of "H" serotypes in 25°C cultures of *Tetrahymena pyriformis*, variety 1. *J. Protozool.* **8**, 387–391.

297. LOEFER, J. B., OWEN, R. D., CHRISTENSEN, E. (1958) Serological types among thirty-one strains of the ciliated protozoan *Tetrahymena pyriformis*. *J. Protozool.* **5**, 209–217.

298. LOEFER, J. B., and SCHERBAUM, O. H. (1961) Amino acid composition of Protozoa. Comparative studies on *Tetrahymena*. *J. Protozool.* **8**, 184–192.

299. LUND, P. G., and SHORB, M. S. (1962) Steroid requirements of trichomonads. *J. Protozool.* **9**, 151–154.

300. LWOFF, A. (1932) Recherches biochimiques sur la nutrition des Protozoaires. Monogr. Inst. Pasteur (Paris).

301. LWOFF, A. (1947) Some aspects of the problem of growth-factors for Protozoa. *Ann. Rev. Microbiol.* **1**, 101–114.

302. LWOFF, A., and DUSI, H. (1937) La pyrimidine et le thiazol, facteurs de croissance pour le flagellé *Polytomella caeca*. *C.R. Acad. Sci.* **205**, 630–632.

303. LWOFF, A., and DUSI, H. (1937) Le thiazol, facteur de croissance pour les flagellés *Polytoma caudatum* et *Chilomonas paramecium*. *C.R. Acad. Sci.* **205**, 756–758.

304. LWOFF, A., and DUSI, H. (1937) Le thiazol, facteur de croissance pour *Polytoma ocellatum* (Chlamydomonadine). Importance des constituants de l'aneurine pour les flagellés leucophytes. *C.R. Acad. Sci.* **205**, 882–883.

305. LWOFF, A., and DUSI, H. (1938) Culture de divers Flagellés leucophytes en milieu synthétique. *C.R. Soc. Biol.* **127**, 53–56.

306. LWOFF, A., and DUSI, H. (1941) Recherches sur la nutrition des flagellés. 1. *Polytoma uvella* et *Polytoma obtusum*: nécessité du fer, nutrition azotée. *Ann. Inst. Pasteur* **67**, 229–239.

307. LWOFF, A., and LWOFF, M. (1937) L'aneurine, facteur de croissance pour le cilié *Glaucoma piriformis*. *C.R. Soc. Biol.* **126**, 644–646.

308. LWOFF, M. (1951) The nutrition of parasitic flagellates (Trypanosomidae, Trichomonadinae), in LWOFF, A., *Biochemistry and Physiology of Protozoa*, Academic Press, New York, 129–176.

309. LYNCH, V. H., and CALVIN, M. (1952) Carbon dioxide fixation by microorganisms. *J. Bact.* **63**, 525–531.

310. LYNCH, V. H., and CALVIN, M. (1953) $CO_2$ fixation by *Euglena*. *Ann. N.Y. Acad. Sci.* **56**, 890–900.

311. McCASHLAND, B.W., and STEINACHER, R. H. (1962) Metabolism changes in *Tetrahymena pyriformis* W adapted to potassium cyanide. *Proc. Soc. Exper. Biol. Med.* **111**, 789–793.

312. MacDONALD, B. B. (1958) Quantitative aspects of deoxyribose nucleic acid (DNA) metabolism in an amicronucleate strain of *Tetrahymena*. *Biol. Bull.* **114**, 71–94.

313. McENTEGART, H. G. (1954) The maintenance of stock strains of trichomonads by freezing. *J. Hyg.* **52**, 545–550.

314. McLAUGHLIN, J. J. A. (1958) Euryhaline chrysomonads: Nutrition and toxigenesis in *Prymnesium parvum*, with notes on *Isochrysis galbana* and *Monochrysis lutheri*. *J. Protozool.* **5**, 75–81.

315. McLAUGHLIN, J. J. A., and ZAHL, P. A. (1957) Studies in marine biology. II. *In vitro* culture of zooxanthellae. *Proc. Soc. Exper. Biol. Med.* **95**, 115–120.

316. McLAUGHLIN, J. J. A., and ZAHL, P. A. (1959). Axenic zooxanthellae from various invertebrate hosts. *Ann. N.Y. Acad. Sci.* **77**, 55–72.

317. McLAUGHLIN, J. J. A., and ZAHL, P. A. (1961) *In vitro* culture of *Pyrodinium*. *Science* **134**, 1878.

318. McLAUGHLIN, J. J. A., and ZAHL, P. A. (1962) Axenic cultivation of the dinoflagellate symbiont from the coral *Cladocora*. *Arch. Mikrobiol.* **42**, 40–41.

319. McLAUGHLIN, J. J. A., ZAHL, P. A., NOWAK, A., MARCHISOTTO, J., and PRAGER, J. (1960) Mass cultivation of some phytoplanktons. *Ann. N.Y. Acad. Sci.* **90**, 856–865.

320. McMANUS, M. A., and SULLIVAN, K. (1961) Effects of kinetin and indole-3-acetic acid on multiplication rates of *Paramecium*. *Nature* **191**, 619–620.

321. MAINX, F. (1928) Beiträge zur Morphologie und Physiologie der Eugleninen. *Arch. Protistenk.* **60**, 305–414.

322. MANNERS, D. J., and RYLEY, J. R. (1952) Studies on the metabolism of the Protozoa. 2. The glycogen of the ciliate *Tetrahymena pyriformis* (*Glaucoma pyriformis*). *Biochem. J.* **52**, 480–482.

323. MANNERS, D. J., and RYLEY, J. R. (1955) Studies on the metabolism of the Proto-zoa. 6. The glycogens of the parasitic flagellates *Trichomonas foetus* and *Trichomonas gallinae*. *Biochem. J.* **59**, 369–372.

324. MANWELL, R. D. (1943) The low-temperature freezing of malaria parasites. *Amer. J. Trop. Med.* **23**, 123–131.

325. MANWELL, R. D., and JEFFERY, G. H. (1942) Preservation of avian malaria parasites by low temperature freezing. *Proc. Soc. Exper. Biol. Med.* **50**, 222–224.

326. MARSHALL, J. W., JR., SCHUMAKER, V. N., and BRANDT, P. W. (1959) Pinocytosis in amoebae. *Ann. N.Y. Acad. Sci.* **78**, 515–523.

327. MAST, S. O., and DOYLE, N. L. (1934) Ingestion of fluid by amoeba. *Protoplasma* **20**, 555–560.

328. MAST, S. O., and PACE, D. M. (1938) The effect of substances produced by *Chilomonas paramecium* on the rate of reproduction. *Physiol. Zool.* **11**, 359–382.

329. MICHAELS, R. M., and TREICK, R. W. (1962) The mode of action of certain 3 and 5 nitropyridines and pyrimidines. III. Biochemical lesions in *T. vaginalis*. *Exper. Parasit.* **12**, 401–417.

330. MILLER, C. A., and JOHNSON, W. H. (1957) A purine and pyrimidine requirement for *Paramecium multimicronucleatum*. *J. Protozool.* **4**, 200–204.

331. MILLER, C. A., and JOHNSON, W. H. (1960) Nutrition of *Paramecium*: a fatty acid requirement. *J. Protozool.* **7**, 297–301.

332. MILLER, C. A., and WAGTENDONK, W. J. VAN (1956) The essential metabolites of a strain of *Paramecium aurelia* (stock 47–8) and a comparison of the growth rate of different strains of *Paramecium aurelia* in axenic culture. *J. Gen. Microbiol.* **15**, 280–291.

333. MOULDER, J. W., and EVANS, E. A., JR. (1946) The biochemistry of the malaria para-site. VI. Studies on the nitrogen metabolism of the malaria parasite. *J. Biol. Chem.* **164**, 145–157.

334. MYERS, J., and GRAHAM, J. R. (1956) The role of photosynthesis in the physiology of *Ochromonas*. *J. Cell. Comp. Physiol.* **47**, 397–414.

335. NAKAMURA, M. (1957) Methylthioadenosine, a growth factor for *Endamoeba histo-lytica*. *Exper. Cell Res.* **12**, 200–201.

336. NARDONE, R. M., and WILBER, C. G. (1950) Nitrogenous excretion in *Colpidium campylum*. *Proc. Soc. Exper. Biol. Med.* **75**, 559–561.

337. NATHAN, H. A. (1958) Purine biosynthesis by the trypanosomid flagellate, *Strigo-monas oncopelti*. *J. Protozool.* **5**, 194–195.

338. NATHAN, H. A., BAKER, H., and FRANK, O. (1960) Influence of pteridines on the production of vitamin $B_{12}$ by trypanosomid flagellates. *Nature* **188**, 35–37.

339. NATHAN, H. A., and COWPERTHWAITE, J. (1954) Use of the trypanosomid flagellate, *Critihidia fasciculata*, for evaluating antimalarials. *Proc. Soc. Exper. Biol. Med.* **85**, 117–119.

340. NATHAN, H. A., and COWPERTHWAITE, J. (1955) "Crithidia factor"—a new member of the folic acid group of vitamins. *J. Protozool.* **2**, 37–42.

341. NATHAN, H. A., and FRIEDMAN, W. A. (1962) Chlorpromazine affects permeability of resting cells of *Tetrahymena pyriformis*. *Science* **135**, 793–794.

342. NATHAN, H. A., and FUNK, H. B. (1959) Relationship between pteridines and other heterocycles (purines, riboflavin, and vitamin $B_{12}$). *Amer. J. Clin. Nutr.* **7**, 375–384.

343. NATHAN, H. A., HUTNER, S. H., and LEVIN, H. L. (1956) Independent requirements for "Crithidia Factor" and folic acid in a trypanosomid flagellate. *Nature* **178**, 741–742.

344. NATHAN, H. A., HUTNER, S. H., and LEVIN, H. L. (1958) Assay of pteridines with *Crithidia fasciculata*. *J. Protozool.* **5**, 134–138.

345. NEFF, R. J. (1958) Mechanisms of purifying amoebae by migration on agar surfaces. *J. Protozool.* **5**, 226–231.

346. NEFF, R. J., and BENTON, W. F. (1962) Localization of cellulose in the cysts of *Acanthamoeba* sp. *J. Protozool.* **9**, Suppl., 11.

347. NEWTON, B. A. (1957) Nutritional requirements and biosynthetic capabilities of the parasitic flagellate *Strigomonas oncopelti*. *J. Gen. Microbiol.* **17**, 708–717.

348. OLIVE, L., DUTTA, S. K., and STOIANOVITCH, C. (1961) Variation in the cellular slime mold *Acrasis rosea*. *J. Protozool.* **8**, 467–472.

349. ORMSBEE, R. A. (1942) Growth and respiration of *Tetrahymena geleii*. *Biol. Bull.* **82**, 423–437.

350. OXFORD, A. E. (1951) The conversion of certain soluble sugars to a glucosan by holotrich ciliates in the rumen of sheep. *J. Gen. Microbiol.* **5**, 83.

351. PACE, D. M., and LYMAN, E. D. (1947) Oxygen consumption and carbon dioxide elimination in *Tetrahymena geleii* Furgason. *Biol. Bull.* **92**, 210–216.

352. PALMQUIST, D., and BUTTERY, B. W. (1960) The relation of hydrogen-ion concentration to growth and size of a porcine trichomonad from the caecum. *Proc. S. Dakota Acad. Sci.* **39**, 109–116.

353. PARNESS, I., REICH, K., and BERGMANN, F. (1962) Photoinactivation of ichthyotoxin from axenic cultures of *Prymnesium parvum* Carter. *Applied Microbiol.* **10**, 237–239.

354. PHELPS, A. (1935) Growth of Protozoa in pure culture. I. Effect upon the growth curve of the age of the inoculum and of the amount of the inoculum. *J. Exper. Zool.* **70**, 109–130.

355. PHILLIPS, B. P. (1953) Studies on the cultivation of *Endamoeba histolytica* with *Trypanosoma cruzi*. *Ann. N.Y. Acad. Sci.* **56**, 1028–1032.

356. PIGÓN, A., and EDSTROM, J. E. (1959) Nucleic acid changes during starvation and encystment in a ciliate (*Urostyla*). *Exper. Cell Res.* **16**, 648–656.

357. PILCHER, H. L., and WILLIAMS, H. H. (1954) Microbiological evalution of protein quality. II. Studies of the responses of *Tetrahymena pyriformis* W to intact proteins. *J. Nutr.* **53**, 589–599.

358. PITELKA, D. R. (1961) Observations on the kinetoplast-mitochondrion and the cytostome of *Bodo*. *Exper. Cell Res.* **25**, 87–93.

359. PITTS, R. F., and MAST, S. O. (1934) The relation between inorganic salt concentration, hydrogen ion concentration and physiological processes in *Amoeba proteus*. *J. Cell. Comp. Physiol.* **4**, 237–256.

359a. PRAGER, J. C., and MAHONEY, J. P. (1963) Isolation and culture of luminscent *Gonyaulax scrippsae*. *J. Protozool.* **10**, (Suppl.), 10.

360. PRESCOTT, D. M. (1955) Relations between cell growth and cell division. I. Reduced weight, cell volume, protein content, and nuclear volume of *Amoeba proteus* from division to division. *Exper. Cell Res.* **9**, 328–337.

361. PRESCOTT, D. M. (1956) Relation between cell growth and cell division. II. The effect of cell size on cell growth rate and generation time in *Amoeba proteus*. III. Changes in nuclear volume and growth rate and prevention of cell division in *Amoeba proteus* resulting from cytoplasmic amputations. *Exper. Cell Res.* **11**, 86–98.

362. PRESCOTT, D. M. (1957) Relation between multiplication rate and temperature in *Tetrahymena pyriformis*, strains HS and GL. *J. Protozool.* **4**, 252–256.

363. PRESCOTT, D. M. (1957) Changes in the physiological state of a cell population as a function of culture growth and age. *Exper. Cell Res.* **12**, 126–134.

364. PRESCOTT, D. M. (1957) The nucleus and ribonucleic acid synthesis in *Amoeba*. *Exper. Cell. Res.* **12**, 196–198.

365. PRESCOTT, D. M. (1960) The nuclear dependence of RNA synthesis in *Acanthamoeba* sp. *Exper. Cell Res.* **19**, 29–34.

366. PRESCOTT, D. M. (1960) Relation between cell growth and cell division. IV. The synthesis of DNA, RNA and protein from division to division in *Tetrahymena*. *Exper. Cell Res.* **19**, 228–238.

367. PRESCOTT, G. W. (1960) Biological disturbances resulting from algal populations in standing waters, in TRYON, C. A. and HARTMANN, R. T., *The ecology of algae, Pymatuning Symposia in Ecology*, University of Pittsburgh, 32–37.

368. PRINGSHEIM, E. G. (1952) On the nutrition of *Ochromonas*. *Quart. J. Micro. Sci.* **93**, 71–96.

369. PRINGSHEIM, E. G., and PRINGSHEIM, O. (1952) Experimental elimination of chromatophores and eye-spot in *Euglena gracilis*. *New Phytol.* **51**, 65–76.

370. PROCTOR, V. W. (1957) Studies of algal antibiosis using *Haematococcus* and *Clamydomonas*. *Limnol. and Oceanogr.* **2**, 125–139.

371. PROVASOLI, L. (1938) Studii sulla nutrizione dei protozoi. *Boll. Zool. Agr. Bachicol.* **9**, 1–124.

372. PROVASOLI, L. (1958) Nutrition and ecology of Protozoa and algae. *Ann. Rev. Microbiol.* **12**, 279–308.

373. PROVASOLI, L. (1958) Growth factors in unicellular algae. *In* BUZZATI-TRAVERSO, A. A., *Perspectives in marine biology*, Univ. Calif. Press, Berkeley, 385–403.

374. PROVASOLI, L. (1958) A catalogue of laboratory strains of free living and parasitic protozoa (with sources from which they may be obtained and directions for their maintenance). *J. Protozool.* **5**, 1–38.

375. PROVASOLI, L., HUTNER, S. H., and PINTNER, I. J. (1951) Destruction of chloroplasts by streptomycin. *Cold Spr. Harbor Symp. Quant. Biol.* **16**, 113–120.

376. PROVASOLI, L., HUTNER, S. H., and SCHATZ, A. (1948) Streptomycin-induced chlorophyll-less races of *Euglena*. *Proc. Soc. Exper. Biol. Med.* **69**, 279–282.

377. PROVASOLI, L., and MCLAUGHLIN, J. J. A. (1963) Limited heterotrophy of some photosynthetic dinoflagellates, in OPPENHEIM, C. H., *Symposium on Marine Microbiology*, Thomas, Springfield, 105–113.

378. PROVASOLI, L., HUTNER, S. H., and DROOP, M. R. (1957) The development of artifical media for marine algae. *Arch. Mikrobiol.* **25**, 392–428.

379. PROVASOLI, L., and PINTNER, I. J. (1953) Ecological implications of *in vitro* nutritional requirements of algal flagellates. *Ann. N.Y. Acad. Sci.* **56**, 839–851.

380. PROVASOLI, L., and PINTNER, I. J. (1960) Artificial media for fresh-water algae. *In* TRYON, C. A., and HARTMANN, R. T., *The ecology of algae, Pymatuning Symposia in Ecology*, University of Pittsburgh, 84–96.

381. RAHAT, M., and REICH, K. (1963) The $B_{12}$ vitamins and methionine in the metabolism of *Prymnesium parvum*. *J. Gen. Microbiol.* **31**, 203–209.

382. READ, C. P. (1957) Comparative studies on the physiology of trichomonad Protozoa. *J. Parasit.* **43**, 385–394.

383. REICH, K., and PARNAS, I. (1962) Effect of illumination on ichthyotoxin in an axenic culture of *Prymnesium parvum*. *J. Protozool.* **9**, 38–40.

384. REICH, K., and ROTBERG, M. (1958) Some factors influencing the formation of toxin poisonous to fish in bacteria-free cultures of *Prymnesium*. *Bull. Res. Council Israel, Sect. B*, **7**B, 199–202.

384a. REILLY, SR., M., and LILLY, D. M. (1963) A chemically defined medium for *Paramecium caudatum*. *J. Protozool.* **10**, (Suppl.), 12.

385. REY, L., and FERNANDES, J. F. (1962) Nucleotide and polynucleotide synthesis in *Trypanosoma cruzi*. *Exper. Parasit.* **12**, 55–60.

386. REYNOLDS, H., and WRAGG, J. B. (1962) Effect of type of carbohydrate on growth and synthesis by *Tetrahymena pyriformis*. *J. Protozool.* **9**, 214–222.

387. RINALDI, R. A. (1959) The induction of pinocytosis in *Amoeba proteus* by ultraviolet radiation. *Exper. Cell Res.* **18**, 70–75.

388. ROBBINS, W. J., HERVEY, A., and STEBBINS, H. E. (1953) *Euglena* and vitamin $B_{12}$. *Ann. N.Y. Acad. Sci.* **56**, 818–830.

389. RON, A., and GUTTMAN, R. (1961) The effect of kinetin on synchronous cell division in *Tetrahymena pyriformis*. *Exper. Cell Res.* **25**, 176–178.

390. RONKIN, R. R. (1959) Motility and power dissipation in flagellated cells, especially *Chlamydomonas. Biol. Bull.* **116**, 285–293.
391. ROSE, I. A., and SCHWEIGERT, B. S. (1953) Incorporation of $C^{14}$ totally labeled nucleosides into nucleic acids. *J. Biol. Chem.* **202**, 635–645.
392. ROSEN, W. G., and GAWLIK, S. R. (1961) Effect of streptomycin on chlorophyll accumulation in *Euglena gracilis. J. Protozool.* **8**, 90–96.
393. ROSS, G. I. M. (1952) Vitamin $B_{12}$ assay in body fluids using *Euglena gracilis. J. Clin. Pathol.* **5**, 250–256.
394. ROTH, L. E. (1960) Electron microscopy of pinocytosis and food vacuoles in *Pelomyxa. J. Protozool.* **7**, 176–185.
395. ROTH, J. S. (1962) Biochemical studies on irradiated Protozoa. I. Effect of metabolites on the respiration of X-irradiated *Tetrahymena pyriformis. J. Protozool.* **9**, 142–146.
396. ROTH, J. S., and EICHEL, H. J. (1961) Studies on the metabolism of L-phenylalanine by *Tetrahymena pyriformis* W. *J. Protozool.* **8**, 69–71.
397. ROTH, J. S., EICHEL, H. J., and GINTNER, E. (1954) The oxidation of amino acids by *Tetrahymena pyriformis* W. *Arch. Biochem. Biophys.* **48**, 112–119.
398. RUDZINSKA, M. A. (1962) The role of the tentacle in the feeding mechanism of *Tokophrya infusionum. J. Protozool.* **9**, Suppl., 7.
399. RUDZINSKA, M. A., and GRANICK, S. (1953) Protoporphyrin production of *Tetrahymena geleii. Proc. Soc. Exp. Biol. Med.* **83**, 525–526.
400. RUDZINSKA, M. A., and TRAGER, W. (1957) Intracellular phagotrophy by malarial parasites: an electron microscope study of *Plasmodium lophurae. J. Protozool.* **4**, 190–199.
401. RUDZINSKA, M. A., and TRAGER, W. (1959) Phagotrophy and two new structures in the malaria parasite *Plasmodium berghei. J. Biophys. Biochem. Cytol.* **6**, 103–112.
402. RUDZINSKA, M. A., and TRAGER, W. (1962) Intracellular phagotrophy in *Babesia rodhaini* as revealed by electron microscopy. *J. Protozool.* **9**, 279–288.
403. RYLEY, J. F. (1951) Studies on the metabolism of the Protozoa. 1. Metabolism of the parasitic flagellate, *Trypanosoma lewisi. Biochem. J.* **49**, 577–585.
404. RYLEY, J. F. (1952) Studies on the metabolism of the Protozoa. 3. Metabolism of the ciliate *Tetrahymena pyriformis* (*Glaucoma piriformis*). *Biochem. J.* **52**, 483–492.
405. RYLEY, J. F. (1955) Studies on the metabolism of the protozoa. 4. Metabolism of the parasitic flagellate *Strigomonas oncopelti. Biochem. J.* **59**, 353–361.
406. RYLEY, J. F. (1955) Studies on the metabolism of the protozoa. 5. Metabolism of the parasitic flagellate *Trichomonas foetus. Biochem. J.* **59**, 361–369.
407. RYLEY, J. F. (1956) Studies on the metabolism of the protozoa. 7. Comparative carbohydrate metabolism of eleven species of trypanosomes. *Biochem. J.* **62**, 215–222.
408. RYLEY, J. F. (1962) Studies on the metabolism of the protozoa. 9. Comparative metabolism of blood-stream and culture forms of *Trypanosoma rhodesiense. Biochem. J.* **85**, 211–223.
409. RYTHER, J. H. (1960) Organic production by plankton algae, and its environmental control, in TRYON, C. A., and HARTMANN, R. T., *The ecology of algae, Pymatuning Symposia in Ecology*, Univ. Pittsburgh, 72–83.
410. SAGER, R., and GRANICK, S. (1953) Nutritional studies with *Chlamydomonas reinhardi. Ann. N.Y. Acad. Sci.* **56**, 831–838.
411. SALLE, A. J., and SCHMIDT, C. L. A. (1928) The metabolism of *Leishmania tropica. J. Inf. Dis.* **43**, 378–384.
412. SALT, G. W. (1961) Feeding activity by *Amoeba proteus. Exper. Cell Res.* **24**, 618–620.
413. SAMUELS, R. (1962) Agar techniques for colonizing and cloning trichomonads. *J. Protozool.* **9**, 103–107.
414. SAMUELS, R., and BREIL, E. A. (1962) Serum-free medium for axenic culture of trichomonads. *J. Protozool.* **9**, Suppl., 19.

415. SAMUELS, R., and STOUDER, D. J. (1962) Disc testing against plated *Trichomonas vaginalis. J. Protozool.* **9**, 249–254.
416. SANDERS, F., and SEAMAN, G. R. (1959) Purification of the vitamin $B_{12}$-active material from the haemoflagellate, *Crithidia fasciculata. Biochem. J.* **73**, 580–582.
417. SANDERS, M. (1957) Replacement of serum for *in vitro* cultivation of *Trichomonas foetus. J. Protozool.* **4**, 118–119.
418. SANDERS, M., and NATHAN, H. A. (1959) Protozoa as pharmacological tools: the antihistamines. *J. Gen. Microbiol.* **21**, 264–270.
419. SCHERBAUM, O. (1956) Cell growth in normal and synchronously dividing mass cultures of *Tetrahymena pyriformis. Exper. Cell Res.* **11**, 464–476.
420. SCHERBAUM, O. (1960) Synchronous division of microorganisms. *Ann. Rev. Microbiol.* **14**, 283–310.
421. SCHERBAUM, O., JAMES, T. W., and JAHN, T. L. (1959) The amino acid composition in relation to cell growth and cell division in synchronized cultures of *Tetrahymena pyriformis. J. Cell. Comp. Physiol.* **53**, 119–137.
422. SCHERBAUM, O., LOUDERBACK, A. L., and JAHN, T. L. (1959) DNA synthesis, phosphate content and growth in mass and volume in synchronously dividing cells. *Exper. Cell Res.* **18**, 150–166.
423. SCHERBAUM, O., and ZEUTHEN, E. (1954) Induction of synchronous cell division in mass cultures of *Tetrahymena pyriformis. Exper. Cell Res.* **6**, 221–227.
424. SCHOENBORN, H. W. (1946) Studies on the nutrition of colorless euglenoid flagellates. II. Growth of *Astasia* in an inorganic medium. *Physiol. Zool.* **19**, 430–442.
425. SCHOENBORN, H. W. (1949) Growth of *Astasia longa* in relation to hydrogen ion concentration. *J. Exper. Zool.* **111**, 437–447.
426. SCHOENBORN, H. W. (1952) Studies on the nutrition of colorless euglenoid flagellates. III. *Astasia longa, A. klebsii* and *Khawkinea quartana. Physiol. Zool.* **25**, 15–19.
427. SCHOENBORN, H. W. (1954) Mutations in *Astasia longa* induced by radiation. *J. Protozool.* **1**, 170–173.
427a. SCHOENBORN, H. W. (1964) Studies on the nutrition of colorless euglenoid flagellates. IV. *Astasia longa. Physiol. Zool.* **37**, 240–244.
428. SCHUMAKER, V. N. (1958) Uptake of protein from solution by *Amoeba proteus. Exper. Cell Res.* **15**, 314–331.
429. SEAMAN, G. R. (1951) Enzyme systems in *Tetrahymena geleii* S. *J. Biol. Chem.* **191**, 439–446.
430. SEAMAN, G. R. (1952) Replacement of protogen by lipoic acid in the growth of *Tetrahymena. Proc. Soc. Exper. Biol. Med.* **79**, 158–159.
431. SEAMAN, G. R. (1953) Synthesis of B vitamins by *Tetrahymena geleii* S. *Physiol. Zool.* **26**, 22–28.
432. SEAMAN, G. R. (1953) The metabolism of protogen in *Tetrahymena. Ann. N.Y. Acad. Sci.* **56**, 921–928.
433. SEAMAN, G. R. (1953) Enzyme systems in *Tetrahymena.* V. Comparison of succinic oxidase activity in different strains. *Arch. Biochem. Biophys.* **48**, 424–430.
434. SEAMAN, G. R. (1953) Inhibition of the succinic dehydrogenase of parasitic protozoans by an arsono and a phosphono analog of succinic acid. *Exper. Parasit.* **2**, 366–373.
435. SEAMAN, G. R. (1953) The succinic dehydrogenase of *Trypanosoma cruzi. Exper. Parasit.* **2**, 236–241.
436. SEAMAN, G. R. (1954) Enzyme systems in *Tetrahymena pyriformis.* VI. Urea formation and breakdown. *J. Protozool.* **1**, 207–210.
437. SEAMAN, G. R. (1954) Pyruvate oxidation by extracts of *Tetrahymena pyriformis. J. Gen. Microbiol.* **11**, 300–306.
438. SEAMAN, G. R. (1955) Metabolism of free-living ciliates, in HUTNER, S. H., and LWOFF, A., *Biochemistry and Physiology of Protozoa*, Academic Press, New York, 91–158.

439. SEAMAN, G. R. (1959) Cytochemical evidence for urease activity in *Tetrahymena*. *J. Protozool.* **6**, 331–333.

440. SEAMAN, G. R. (1961) Some aspects of phagotrophy in *Tetrahymena*. *J. Protozool.* **8**, 204–212.

441. SEAMAN, G. R. (1961) Acid phosphatase activity associated with phagotrophy in the ciliate *Tetrahymena*. *J. Biophys. Biochem. Cytol.* **9**, 243–245.

442. SEAMAN, G. R. (1963) Metabolism of purines by extracts of *Tetrahymena*. *J. Protozool.* **10**, 87–91.

443. SEARLE, D. S., and REINER, L. (1941) The role of carbon dioxide in the glucose metabolism of *Trypanosoma lewisi*. *J. Biol. Chem.* **141**, 563–572.

444. SHERMAN, I. W. (1962) Heterogeneity of lactic dehydrogenase in intra-erythrocytic parasites. *Trans. N.Y. Acad. Sci., Ser. II*, **24**, 944–953.

445. SHERMAN, I. W., and HULL, R. W. (1906) The pigment (hemozoin) and proteins of the avian malaria parasite *Plasmodium lophurae*. *J. Protozool.* **7**, 409–416.

446. SHILO, M., and ROSENBERGER, R. F. (1960) Studies on the toxic principle formed by the chrysomonad *Pyrmnesium parvum* Carter. *Ann. N.Y. Acad. Sci.* **90**, 866–876.

447. SHORB, M. S., and LUND, P. G. (1959) Requirement of trichomonads for unidentified growth factors, saturated and unsaturated fatty acids. *J. Protozool.* **6**, 122–130.

448. SINGER, S. (1961) Some amino acid-folic interrelationships in *Tetrahymena pyriformis* H. *J. Protozool.* **8**, 265–271.

449. SINGH, B. N. (1959) Effect of cholesterol on the virulence of *Entamoeba histolytica* in rats. *J. Sci. Ind. Res.* **18**C, 166–169.

450. SLATER, J. V. (1952) The magnesium requirement of *Tetrahymena*. *Physiol. Zool.* **25**, 283–287.

451. SLATER, J. V. (1952) The influence of cobalt on the growth of the protozoon *Tetrahymena*. *Physiol. Zool.* **25**, 323–332.

452. SLATER, J. V. (1957) Radiocobalt accumulation in *Tetrahymena*. *Biol. Bull.* **112**, 390–399.

453. SLATER, J. V. (1957) Radioactive phosphorus uptake during conjugation in *Tetrahymena*. *J. Protozool.* **4**, Suppl., 11.

454. SOLDO, A. T. (1955) Vitamin $B_{12}$ and nucleic acid production in *Euglena*. *Arch. Biochem. Biophys.* **55**, 71–76.

455. SOLDO, A. T. (1960) Cultivation of two strains of killer *Paramecium aurelia* in axenic medium. *Proc. Soc. Exper. Biol. Med.* **105**, 612–615.

456. SOLDO, A. T., and WAGTENDONK, W. J. VAN (1961) Nitrogen metabolism in *Paramecium aurelia*. *J. Protozool.* **8**, 41–55.

457. SPEK, J. F., and EVANS, E. A., JR. (1945) The biochemistry of the malaria parasite. III. Glycolysis in cell-free preparations of the malaria parasite. *J. Biol. Chem.* **159**, 71–81.

458. SPEK, J. F., MOULDER, J. W., and EVANS, E. A., JR. (1946) The biochemistry of the malaria parasite. V. Mechanisms of pyruvate oxidation in the malaria parasite. *J. Biol. Chem.* **164**, 119–144.

459. STEEL, W. J., and GURIN, S. (1960) Biosynthesis of β-carotene in *Euglena gracilis*. *J. Biol. Chem.* **235**, 2778–2785.

460. STEINERT, M., and NOVIKOFF, A. B. (1960) The existence of a cytostome and the occurrence of pinocytosis in the trypanosome, *Trypanosoma mega*. *J. Biophys. Biochem. Cytol.* **8**, 563–569.

461. STEINERT, M., and STEINERT, G. (1962) La synthèse de l'acide désoxyribonucléique au cours du cycle de division de *Trypanosoma mega*. *J. Protozool.* **9**, 203–211.

462. STERN, A. I., SCHIFF, J. A., and KLEIN, H. P. (1960) Isolation of ergosterol from *Euglena gracilis*; distribution among mutant strains. *J. Protozool.* **7**, 52–55.

463. STOKSTAD, E. L. R., HOFFMAN, C. E., REGAN, M. A., FORDHAM, D., and JUKES, T. H. (1949) An unknown growth-factor essential for *Tetrahymena geleii*. *Arch. Biochem.* **20**, 75–82.

464. STOKSTAD, E. L. R., SEAMAN, G. R., DAVIS, R. J., and HUTNER, S. H. (1956) Assay of thioctic acid, in GLICK, D., *Methods in Biochemical Analysis*, v. 3, Interscience Publ., New York, 23–47.

465. STONE, W. S., and THOMPSON, A. T. (1940) A method for preserving *Trypanosoma equiperdum*. *Science* 91, 344.

466. STORM, J., and HUTNER, S. H. (1953) Nutrition of *Peranema*. *Ann. N.Y. Acad. Sci.* 56, 901–909.

467. SULLIVAN, B. J. (1950) Protein and carbohydrate synthesis in *Chilomonas paramecium*. *J. Exper. Zool.* 114, 227–237.

468. SUMMERS, L., BERNSTEIN, E., and JAMES, T. W. (1957) A correlation between nuclear activity and the growth phase in cultures of protozoan cells. *Exper. Cell Res.* 13, 436–437.

469. SUSSMAN, M. (1961) Cultivation and serial transfer of the slime mold, *Dictyostelium discoideum*, in a liquid medium. *J. Gen. Microbiol.* 25, 375–378.

470. TARENTOLA, V. A., and WAGTENDONK, W. J. VAN (1959) Further nutritional requirements of *Paramecium aurelia*. *J. Protozool.* 6, 189–195.

471. TARTAR, V. (1957) Reactions of *Stentor coeruleus* to certain substances added to the medium. *Exper. Cell Res.* 13, 317–322.

472. THOMAS, J. O. (1943) The anaerobic carbohydrate metabolism of *Tetrahymena geleii*. Thesis, Stanford University.

473. THURSTON, J. P. (1958) The oxygen uptake of *Trypanosoma lewisi* and *Trypanosoma equiperdum*, with special reference to oxygen consumption in the presence of amino-acids. *Parasitol.* 48, 149–164.

474. TRAGER, W. (1954) Coenzyme A and the malaria parasite *Plasmodium lophurae*. *J. Protozool.* 1, 231–237.

475. TRAGER, W. (1957) Nutrition of a haemoflagellate (*Leishmania tarentolae*) having an interchangable requirement for choline or pyridoxal. *J. Protozool.* 4, 269–276.

476. TRAGER, W. (1959) Development of *Trypanosoma vivax* to the infective stage in tsetse fly tissue culture. *Nature* 184, 30–31.

477. TRAGER, W. (1959) Tsetse-fly tissue culture and the development of trypanosomes to the infective stage. *Ann. Trop. Med. Parasit.* 53, 473–491.

478. TUZET, O., and LOUBATIÈRES, R. (1946) Notes sur Monocystidées. I. Monocystides parasites de l'*Allobophora gigas* des environs de Montpellier. *Arch. Zool. Exper. Gén.* 84, N. et R., 132–149.

479. VARMA, T. N., ABRAHAM, A., and HANSEN, I. A. (1961) Accumulation of $Co^{58}$-vitamin $B_{12}$ by *Euglena gracilis*. *J. Protozool.* 8, 212–216.

480. VÁVRA, J. (1957) The action of streptomycin on chloroplasts of the flagellate *Euglena gracilis* Klebs. *Folia Biologia* 3, 108–113.

481. VISHNIAC, H. S. (1955) The nutritional requirements of isolates of *Labyrinthula* spp. *J. Gen. Microbiol.* 12, 455–463.

482. VISHNIAC, H. S. (1955) The activity of steroids as growth factors for a *Labyrinthula* sp. *J. Gen. Microbiol.* 12, 464–472.

483. VISHNIAC, H. S., and WATSON, S. W. (1953) The steroid requirements of *Labyrinthula vitellina* var. *pacifica*. *J. Gen. Microbiol.* 8, 248–255.

484. VISWANATHA, T., and LIENER, I. E. (1955) Utilization of native and denatured proteins by *Tetrahymena pyriformis*. *Arch. Biochem. Biophys.* 56, 222–229.

485. VISWANATHA, T., and LIENER, I. E. (1956) Isolation and properties of a proteinase from *Tetrahymena pyriformis* W. *Arch. Biochem. Biophys.* 61, 410–421.

486. VOGEL, H. J. (1959) Lysine biosynthesis in *Chlorella* and *Euglena*: phylogenetic significance. *Biochem. Biophys. Acta* 34, 282–283.

487. VOGEL, H. J. (1959) Lysine formation in higher plants. *Proc. Nat. Acad. Sci.* 45, 1717–1721.

488. WAGTENDONK, W. J. VAN (1955) The nutrition of ciliates, in HUTNER, S. H., and LWOFF, A., *Biochemistry and Physiology of Protozoa*, Academic Press, New York, 57–84.

489. WAGTENDONK, W. J. VAN, CONNER, R. L., MILLER, C. A., and RAO, M. R. R. (1953) Growth requirements of *Paramecium aurelia* var. 4, stock 51.7 sensitives and killers in axenic medium. *Ann. N.Y. Acad. Sci.* **56**, 929–937.

490. WALKER, P. M. B., and MITCHISON, J. M. (1957) DNA synthesis in two ciliates. *Exper. Cell Res.* **13**, 167–170.

491. WARNOCK, L. G., and EYS, J. VAN (1962) Normal carbohydrate metabolism in *Tetrahymena pyriformis*. *J. Cell. Comp. Physiol.* **60**, 53–60.

492. WARNOCK, L. G., and EYS, J. VAN (1963) Inhibition of growth of *Tetrahymena pyriformis* by oxamic acid. *J. Bact.* **85**, 1179–1181.

493. WATSON, M. R., HOPKINS, J. M., and RANDALL, J. T. (1961) Isolated cilia from *Tetrahymena pyriformis*. *Exper. Cell Res.* **23**, 629–631.

494. WEINMAN, D. (1957) Cultivation of trypanosomes. *Trans. Roy. Soc. Trop. Med. Hyg.* **51**, 560–561.

495. WELLERSON, R., DOSCHER, G., and KUPFERBERG, A. (1959) Metabolic studies on *Trichomonas vaginalis*. *Ann. N.Y. Acad. Sci.* **83**, 253–258.

496. WELLERSON, R., DOSCHER, G., and KUPFERBERG, A. (1960) Carbon dioxide fixation in *Trichomonas vaginalis*. *Biochem. J.* **75**, 562–565.

497. WELLERSON, R., and KUPFERBERG, A. B. (1962) On glycolysis in *Trichomonas vaginalis*. *J. Protozool.* **9**, 418–424.

498. WELLS, C. (1960) Identification of free and bound amino acids in three strains of *Tetrahymena pyriformis* using paper chromatography. *J. Protozool.* **7**, 7–10.

499. WENDEL, W. B., and KIMBALL, S. (1942) Formation of lactic and pyruvic acid in blood containing *Plasmodium knowlesi*. *J. Biol. Chem.* **145**, 343–344.

500. WERTLIEB, D. M., and GUTTMAN, H. N. (1963) Catalase in insect Trypanosomatids. *J. Protozool.* **10**, 109–112.

501. WEST, R. A., JR., BARBERA, P. W., KOLAR, J. R., and MURELL, C. B. (1962) The agar layer method for determining the activity of diverse materials against selected Protozoa. *J. Protozool.* **9**, 65–73.

502. WILLIAMS, N. E. (1962) Synchrony and the "Thormar effect" in *Tetrahymena vorax*. *J. Protozool.* **9**, Suppl., 14–15.

503. WILLIAMS, N. E., and SCHERBAUM, O. H. (1959) Morphogenetic events in normal and synchronously dividing *Tetrahymena*. *J. Embryol. Exper. Morphol.* **7**, 241–256.

504. WILSON, B. W., BUETOW, D. E., JAHN, T. L., and LEVEDAHL, B. H. (1959) A differential effect of pH on cell growth and respiration. *Exper. Cell Res.* **18**, 454–465.

505. WILSON, B. W., and DANFORTH, W. F. (1958) The extent of acetate and ethanol oxidation by *Euglena gracilis*. *J. Gen. Microbiol.* **18**, 535–542.

506. WINGO, W. J., and ANDERSON, N. L. (1951) Effect of pH of medium upon the growth rate of *Tetrahymena geleii*. *J. Exper. Zool.* **116**, 571–575.

507. WIRTSCHAFTER, S. K. (1954) Evidence for the existence of the enzymes hexokinase and aldolase in the protozoan parasite *Trichomonas vaginalis*. *J. Parasit.* **40**, 360–362.

508. WIRTSCHAFTER, S. K., and JAHN, T. L. (1956) The metabolism of *Trichomonas vaginalis*, the glycolytic pathway. *J. Protozool.* **3**, 83–85.

509. WIRTSCHAFTER, S. K., SALTMAN, P., and JAHN, T. L. (1956) The metabolism of *Trichomonas vaginalis*: the oxidative pathway. *J. Protozool.* **3**, 86–88.

510. WISE, D. L. (1955) Carbon sources for *Polytomella caeca*. *J. Protozool.* **2**, 156–158.

511. WISE, D. L. (1959) Carbon nutrition and metabolism of *Polytomella caeca*. *J. Protozool.* **6**, 19–23.

512. WOLFSON, F. (1945) Effect of preservation by freezing upon the virulence of *Plasmodium* for ducks. *Amer. J. Hyg.* **42**, 155–166.

513. WOLKEN, J. J. (1961) *Euglena*, an experimental organism for biochemical and biophysical studies, Rutgers University, xii + 173 pp.

514. WOODWARD, J., GELBER, B., and SWIFT, H. (1961) Nucleoprotein changes during the mitotic cycle in *Paramecium aurelia*. *Exper. Cell. Res.* **23**, 258–264.
515. WU, C., and HOGG, J. F. (1952) The amino acid composition and nitrogen metabolism of *Tetrahymena geleii*. *J. Biol. Chem.* **198**, 753–764.
516. WU, C., and HOGG, J. F. (1956) Free and non-protein amino acids of *Tetrahymena pyriformis*. *Arch. Biochem. Biophys.* **62**, 70–77.
517. WYSS, W., KRADOLFE, F., and MEIER, R. (1960) Lipophilic growth factors for *Trichomonas*. *Exper. Parasit.* **10**, 66–71.
518. YAEGER, R. G., and MILLER, O. N. (1906) Effects of malnutrition on susceptibility of rats to *Trypanosoma cruzi*. I. Thiamine deficiency. *Exper. Parasit.* **9**, 215–222.
519. YAEGER, R. G., and MILLER, O. N. (1960) Effect of malnutrition on susceptibility of rats to *Trypanosoma cruzi*. II. Riboflavin deficiency. *Exper. Parasit.* **10**, 227–231.
520. YAEGER, R. G., and MILLER, O. N. (1960) Effect of malnutrition on susceptibility of rats to *Trypanosoma cruzi*. III. Pantothenate deficiency. *Exper. Parasit.* **10**, 232–237.
521. YAEGER, R. G., and MILLER, O. N. (1960) Effect of malnutrition on susceptibility of rats to *Trypanosoma cruzi*. IV. Pyridoxine deficiency. *Exper. Parasit.* **10**, 238–244.
522. YARIV, J., and HESTRIN, S. (1961) Toxicity of the extracellular phase of *Prymnesium parvum* cultures. *J. Gen. Microbiol.* **24**, 165–175.
523. ZAHL, P. A., and MCLAUGHLIN, J. J. A. (1959) Studies in marine biology. IV. On the role of algal cells in the tissues of marine invertebrates. *J. Protozool.* **6**, 343–352.

# INDEX OF SCIENTIFIC NAMES

# SUBJECT INDEX

# CONTENTS OF VOLUME 2

*Volumes 3 and 4 in preparation*